Fire Department Occupational Health and Safety Standards Handbook

Fire Department Occupational Health and Safety Standards Handbook

FIRST EDITION

EDITED BY

Stephen N. Foley
Senior Fire Service Specialist

With the complete text of NFPA 1500, *Standard on Fire Department Occupational Safety and Health Program* (1997); NFPA 1521, *Standard for Fire Department Safety Officer* (1997); NFPA 1561, *Standard on Fire Department Incident Management System* (1995); NFPA 1581, *Standard on Fire Department Infection Control Program* (1995); and NFPA 1582, *Standard on Medical Requirements for Fire Fighters* (1997)

National Fire Protection Association, Quincy, Massachusetts

Product Manager: Lauren MacCarthy and Jim L. Linville
Developmental Editor: Pamela A. Powell
Project Editor: Joyce Grandy
Copy Editor: Marilyn Morrison
Text Processing: Louise Grant and Kathy Barber
Composition: Argosy
Art Coordinator: Nancy Maria
Illustrations: George Nichols/Todd Bowman
Interior Design Coordinator: Cathy Ray
Cover Design: Groppi Associates
Manufacturing Buyer: Ellen Glisker
Printer: World Color, Taunton, MA

Notice Concerning Liability: Publication of this handbook is for the purpose of circulating information and opinion among those concerned for fire and electrical safety and related subjects. While every effort has been made to achieve a work of high quality, neither the NFPA nor the contributors to this handbook guarantee the accuracy or completeness of or assume any liability in connection with the information and opinions contained in this handbook. The NFPA and the contributors shall in no event be liable for any personal injury, property, or other damages of any nature whatsoever, whether special, indirect, consequential, or compensatory, directly or indirectly resulting from the publication, use of, or reliance upon this handbook.

This handbook is published with the understanding that the NFPA and the contributors to this handbook are supplying information and opinion but are not attempting to render engineering or other professional services. If such services are required, the assistance of an appropriate professional should be sought.

Notice Concerning Code Interpretations: This first edition of *Fire Department Occupational Health and Safety Standards Handbook* is based on NFPA 1500, *Standard on Fire Department Occupational Safety and Health Program* (1997); NFPA 1521, *Standard for Fire Department Safety Officer* (1997); NFPA 1561, *Standard on Fire Department Incident Management System* (1995); NFPA 1581, *Standard on Fire Department Infection Control Program* (1995); and NFPA 1582, *Standard on Medical Requirements for Fire Fighters* (1997). All NFPA codes, standards, recommended practices, and guides are developed in accordance with the published procedures of the NFPA technical committees comprised of volunteers drawn from a broad array of relevant interests. The handbook contains the complete text of NFPA 1500, 1521, 1561, 1581, 1582 and any applicable Formal Interpretations issued by the Association. These documents are accompanied by explanatory commentary and other supplementary materials.

The commentary and supplementary materials in this handbook are not a part of the standards and do not constitute Formal Interpretations of the NFPA (which can be obtained only through requests processed through the responsible technical committee in accordance with the published procedures of the NFPA). The commentary and supplementary materials, therefore, solely reflect the personal opinions of the editor or other contributors and do not necessarily represent the official position of the NFPA or its technical committees.

ISBN: 0-87765-413-1
Library of Congress Card Catalog No.: 98-065472

Printed in the United States of America
01 00 99 98 5 4 3 2 1

This book is dedicated to all my brother and sister fire fighters, who taught me that this profession puts a human face on the term public service.

Contents

Appendices

PART TWO

NFPA 1521, *Standard for Fire Department Safety Officer,* and Commentary 103

Appendices

PART THREE

NFPA 1561, *Standard on Fire Department Incident Management Systems,* and Commentary 141

Appendices

PART SIX

Preface

The topic of health and safety elicits strong comments from career and volunteer fire fighters alike. The issues surrounding this topic are varied and include deployment, staffing, apparatus, equipment, response, types and levels of service, as well as a host of others. Often, there are no single correct answers to questions of fire fighter occupational safety and health, but instead a myriad of entwined issues that influence fire service operations.

The foundation of a fire department occupational safety and health program should be NFPA 1500, *Standard on Fire Department Occupational Safety and Health Program.* Prior to the development of this document in 1987, there was no standard for an occupational safety and health program for the fire service. As with each of the previous editions, the 1997 edition of NFPA 1500 provides the basic framework for developing a comprehensive safety and health program and establishes the means for its implementation and management. From its inception, this standard was intended to serve as a "safety umbrella," with a series of companion documents providing more specific details on various components and aspects of the program.

In addition to the complete text of NFPA 1500, this handbook contains the text of the four companion documents that have been developed to date:

- NFPA 1521, *Fire Department Safety Officer*, expands on the requirements for a fire department safety officer found in Chapter 2 of NFPA 1500.
- NFPA 1561, *Fire Department Incident Management System,* provides detailed coverage of the incident management system required by Chapter 6 of NFPA 1500.
- NFPA 1581, *Fire Department Infection Control Program,* which is expanded from Chapter 8 in NFPA 1500, covers the use of personal protective clothing, cleaning and disinfecting procedures, exposure reporting, inoculations, and cleanliness.
- NFPA 1582, *Medical Requirements for Fire Fighters,* is also rooted in Chapter 8 of NFPA 1500 and provides in-depth information on a number of topics essential to the health and fitness of fire service personnel.

When planning this handbook, the goal of the project team was to develop a user-friendly, "how to" guide for fire department use. The format provides a toolbox concept to occupational safety and health. Whether a department is planning a new program, expanding an existing program, or attempting to evaluate its current approach to occupational safety and health, this handbook makes the appropriate tools readily available.

This toolbox approach is similar to that used in incident command. Incident commanders/users have available a set of resources/tools to manage an incident. In our case, the handbook user has numerous resources available, such as a separate part for each of the five standards in NFPA's occupational safety and health series. A sixth part contains supplementary materials in the form of informational documents and sample forms that can be adapted or used as is by the authority having jurisdiction.

Just like a toolbox, this handbook is meant to be used. Readers are encouraged to take from each chapter or section the tools needed to develop, implement, or refine an occupational safety and health program for fire fighters. Fire fighter safety and health is increasing and will continue to do so only as long as we remember that "Health and Safety" are requirements, not options.

Acknowledgments

NFPA's fire fighter occupational safety and health projects are the work of many people. NFPA technical committee members, both past and present, began that work when they stepped to the forefront of the sometimes difficult issues surrounding fire fighter occupational safety and health. Their ability to take a stand on issues paramount to America's noblest profession has produced standards that today influence all aspects of the fire service, and their lasting contributions to reducing fire fighter fatalities and injuries will long be remembered by the fire service. Now, fire department members can look forward to a healthy life and lifestyle long after they are too old to respond. I believe we have truly turned the corner on fire service occupational safety and health, thanks to the dedicated efforts of the NFPA technical committee members over the years.

Like the standards, this handbook is the result of the combined efforts of many people. The handbook's content authors—M. S. Bogucki, Margaret Dimmick, Jonathan D. Kipp, Murrey E. Loflin, and Gordon M. Sachs—have been able to translate their experiences in the field into a "how to" for the user. I'm fortunate to have known these authors, both as peer professionals and as friends. Their commitment to fire fighter safety and health is unparalleled, and my many thanks go to them.

A tip of the hat and kudos to project manager Jim Linville for his ability to pick up the ball and run with it; to Sylvia Dovner and the NFPA editorial and production staff members for their devotion to this project; to Pam Powell who served as a "first down" reviewer and editor; and to the staff of the Public Fire Protection Division, especially my administrative assistant DianeMarie Collins. Extra thanks go to Public Fire Protection Division Director Gary O. Tokle for his guidance and support on this project. I am also grateful to the folks in NFPA's Fire Data and Analysis Division—Dr. John Hall, Rita Fahey, Paul LeBlanc, Ken Tremblay, Arthur Washburn, Steve Badger, Gary Stein, and other members of the staff—who bring unparalleled dedication to their work and who always seemed to have the answers whenever I needed them.

On a more personal level, I need to pause and thank those who have had a positive impact, both personally and professionally. Professionally, my thanks go to the late Chief Edward F. Brock and his son Daniel (now fire chief in Wrentham, Massachusetts), who were there when I started in the fire service; to retired Assistant Chief Jack Peltier and Lt. Fred Quinn (the commissioner) from Southborough, Massachusetts, who encouraged me to become a fire instructor and pursue career advancement; and to retired Captain Bruce Whitney, his wife, Maggie, and sons, Brian and Kevin, who were my first fire-fighting family.

For their more recent contributions, I thank Chief Alan Brunacini, who championed the cause of fire fighter safety and is the original "safety zealot"; Bruce W. Teele, of the NFPA staff, a true believer in fire fighter health and safety and the first staff liaison for the occupational safety and health committee; Captain Murrey E. Loflin, bless his heart, who is a great friend and has shared many experiences. Thanks to the following friends and professionals for permission to use their photographs: Battalion Chief Michael W. Wade and Master FF James M. Milligan of the Virginia Beach, Virginia, Fire Department; Battalion Chief Glenn P. Benarick of the Fairfax County,Virginia, Fire and Rescue Department; Timothy J. O'Neill, President, and Dawn S. Wicklund, Communication Manager, of Greenwood Fire Apparatus; Jack Jordan, Media Specialist, of the Phoenix Fire Department; Don Aldrich and Lisa Szwec of Lion Apparel Uniform Company; and Captain Eric Madison of the Longmeadow, Massachusetts, Fire Department.

Personally, I offer my thanks and love to my late father, William T. Foley, Jr., who taught me that family and hard work went in that order; to my wife Judy, wonderful partner and best friend, who has been a rock these past twenty-two plus years in allowing me to pursue my varied passions in the fire service; and last, but certainly not least, to my three children, Timothy, Kaitlin (Kate), and Meghan (Meg).

You have all helped make fire fighting safer.

Stephen N. Foley
April 1998

PART ONE

NFPA 1500

Standard on Fire Department Occupational Safety and Health Program and Commentary

Part One of this handbook includes the complete text of the 1997 edition of NFPA 1500, *Standard on Fire Department Occupational Safety and Health Program.* The first edition of NFPA 1500 was developed in 1987 to address growing concerns about fire fighter line-of-duty deaths and injuries and to raise the awareness level of the fire service on how to address the safety and health concerns of the profession. This third edition contains new and expanded text on many significant topics, including risk management, accountability, incident management, rehabilitation, and fire department operations that involve civil disturbances and/or terrorism, to name a few.

The mandatory provisions found in Chapters 1 through 11 of the NFPA 1500 were prepared by the Technical Committee on Fire Service Occupational Safety within the framework of NFPA's consensus codes- and standards-making system. Because these provisions are designed to be suitable for adoption into law or for reference by other codes and standards, the text is concise, without extended explanation.

The material found in Appendix A of NFPA 1500 was also developed by the Technical Committee on Fire Service Occupational Safety within NFPA's codes- and standards-making system to assist users in understanding and interpreting the mandatory provisions of the standard. Appendix A is not considered part of the requirements of the standard; it is advisory or informational. An asterisk (*) following a paragraph number in the standard indicates that advisory appendix material pertaining to that paragraph appears in Appendix A. For the reader's convenience, in this handbook, Appendix A material has been repositioned to appear immediately following its base paragraph in the body of the standard. The text of the standard and the Appendix A material are printed in black in this handbook.

Explanatory commentary, which was prepared by the handbook editor, Stephen N. Foley, immediately follows the standard text it discusses and is printed in blue for easy identification. The commentary is intended to provide the reader with a deeper understanding of the standard and to serve as a resource and reference for implementing its provisions. It is not a substitute for the actual wording of the standard or the text of any code or standard that may be incorporated by reference.

Foley is NFPA's senior fire service specialist and staff liaison to several of NFPA's technical committees. He serves as executive secretary of NFPA's Fire Service Section and is a member of the National Emergency Training Center staff. Foley has helped develop courses at the National Fire Academy, the Emergency Management Institute, and the Federal Law Enforcement Training Center, where he also served as lead instructor. Foley, who has 23 years of fire protection experience, speaks extensively on such topics as fire fighter health and safety, incident management, fire service and EMS deployment and organization, and hazardous materials and disaster management. He is a co-author of the second edition of the *Fire Chief's Handbook* and contributing author to the NFPA *Fire Protection Handbook*, 18th edition.

Foley received his Bachelor of Science Degree in Fire Science Administration from the State University of New York, has completed course work toward a master's degree in management, and has graduated from the Executive Fire Officer Program at the National Fire Academy. Prior to joining the staff of NFPA, Foley served as Fire Chief of the Longmeadow, Massachusetts, Fire Department.

CHAPTER 1

Administration

1-1 Scope

1-1.1

This standard contains minimum requirements for a fire-service-related occupational safety and health program.

According to 1-1.1, NFPA 1500 establishes minimum requirements. Users are permitted and encouraged to exceed the requirements of this standard. Like all other NFPA documents, NFPA 1500 establishes *minimum* requirements.

1-1.2

These requirements are applicable to public, governmental, military, private, and industrial fire department organizations providing rescue, fire suppression, emergency medical services, hazardous materials mitigation, special operations, and other emergency services.

1-1.3

This standard does not apply to industrial fire brigades or industrial fire departments meeting the requirements of NFPA 600, *Standard on Industrial Fire Brigades*. Industrial fire brigades or fire departments shall also be permitted to be known as emergency brigades, emergency response teams, fire teams, plant emergency organizations, or mine emergency response teams.

Paragraph 1-1.3 establishes that NFPA 1500 does not apply to industrial fire brigades.

Many facilities in the private sector have established some level of emergency response team (ERT) to assist with mitigating a specific hazard. These teams may or may not have specific training in fire suppression, technical rescue, hazardous materials, or other emergency training. NFPA 600, *Standard on Industrial Fire Brigades* (1996), addresses those concerns.

1-2 Purpose

1-2.1

The purpose of this standard is to specify the minimum requirements for an occupational safety and health program for a fire department and to specify safety guidelines for those members involved in rescue, fire suppression, emergency medical services, hazardous materials operations, special operations, and related activities.

1-2.2*

Many of the performance objectives of this standard shall be permitted to be achieved in a variety of ways. The achievement of these objectives is intended to help prevent accidents, injuries, and exposures and to reduce the severity of those accidents, injuries, and exposures that do occur. They will also help to prevent exposure to hazardous materials and contagious diseases and to reduce the probability of occupational fatalities, illnesses, and disabilities affecting fire service personnel.

A-1-2.2 It is possible that an existing program or policy can satisfy the requirements of this standard; if so, it can be adopted in whole or in part in order to comply with this standard. Examples of such existing programs and policies can be a mandatory SCBA rule, seat belt rule, corporate safety program, or municipal employee assistance program.

Paragraph 1-2.2 makes a basic point: There is no "one" way to meet the requirements of this standard. The authority having jurisdiction (AHJ) will determine how to meet the requirements of NFPA 1500.

1-2.3

Nothing herein shall be intended to restrict any jurisdiction from exceeding these minimum requirements.

1-3 Implementation

1-3.1*

When this standard is adopted by a jurisdiction, the authority having jurisdiction shall set a date or dates for achieving compliance with the requirements of this standard and shall be permitted to establish a phase-in schedule for compliance with specific requirements of this standard.

On August 10, 1989, a Formal Interpretation concerning Section 1-5 in the 1987 edition was issued by the Standards Council. In the 1997 edition Section 1-5 has been renumbered as paragraph 1-3.1. That Formal Interpretation is still valid and is reproduced here for the reader's convenience.

Formal Interpretation

Reference: 1-5

F.I. No.: 87-2

Question: If no jurisdiction having regulatory authority over a fire department has formally and legally adopted NFPA 1500 as a standard, can that fire department be considered as the authority having jurisdiction if they adopt 1500 as their own policy/program?

Answer: Yes.

Issue Edition: 1987

Reference: 1-5

Issue Date: July 21, 1989

Effective Date: August 10, 1989

A-1-3.1 The specific determination of the authority having jurisdiction depends on the mechanism under which this standard is adopted and enforced. Where the standard is adopted voluntarily by a particular fire department for its own use, the authority having jurisdiction should be the fire chief or the political entity that is responsible for the operation of the fire department. Where the standard is legally adopted and enforced by a body having regulatory authority over a fire department, such as federal, state, or local government or political subdivision, this body is responsible for making those determinations as the authority having jurisdiction. The plan should take into account the services the fire department is required to provide, the financial resources available to the fire department, the availability of personnel, the availability of trainers, and such other factors as will affect the fire department's ability to achieve compliance.

The worksheet that appeared in Appendix B of NFPA 1500 and is reproduced as Form S12-3 of Supplement 12 in Part Six of this handbook provides a template for developing a safety and health program. The checklist may also be used to track progress, at least annually, toward department implementation. Many users of this checklist also find it useful for both yearly budget purposes and long-range capital budget planning

1-3.2*

The fire department shall adopt a risk management plan as specified in Section 2-2 of this standard. This risk management plan shall include a written plan for compliance with this standard.

A-1-3.2 For a fire department to evaluate its compliance with the standard, it must develop some type of logical process. The worksheet in Appendix B of this document illustrates one way that an action plan can be developed to determine code compliance.

This standard is intended to be implemented in a logical sequence, based upon a balanced evaluation of economic as well as public safety and personnel safety factors. The compliance schedule request assures that risk is objectively assessed and reasonable priorities set toward reaching compliance. Interim compensatory measures are intended to assure that safety action that can be taken until full compliance is reached is comprehensively examined and formally adopted into the fire department organization's policies and procedures. This can include, but is not limited to, increased inspections, testing, temporary suspension or restriction of use of specific equipment, specialized training, and administrative controls.

Paragraph 1-3.2 links two important elements: the implementation of a fire department occupational safety and health program with the department's overall risk management plan. The fire department's risk management plan may be part of an overall community risk management plan. Chapter 3 of NFPA 1500 covers the development of a risk management plan. Agencies have either developed their risk management plan independently or used a community risk management consultant to assist in developing their plan. EDITOR'S NOTE: In 1996, the NFPA Standards Council appointed a Technical Committee to develop a proposed NFPA 1250, *Standard on Emergency Services Administrative Risk Management*.

1-4 Equivalency

1-4.1

The authority having jurisdiction shall be permitted to approve an equivalent level of qualifications for the requirements specified in 3-1.6, 3-3.2, 3-3.3, 3-3.4, and 3-3.5 of this standard, provided that the fire department has technical documentation to demonstrate equivalency.

1-4.2

The approved equivalent levels shall provide as nearly equivalent training, education, competency, and safety as possible and shall require that training, education, and competency be commensurate with those functions that the members are expected to perform as specified in the organizational statement in accordance with 2-1.1 and also in accordance with 3-1.3 and 3-1.4 of this standard. In no case shall the equivalency afford less competency of members or safety to members than that which, in the judgment of the authority having jurisdiction, would be provided by compliance with the provisions of the specified paragraphs.

Paragraph 1-4.2 deals with equivalent qualifications and training, which is sometimes confused with *certification.* Only agencies that participate in an accreditation program may offer certification. As a result, many users of NFPA 1500 will provide training without offering certification. In any event, paragraph 1-4.2 does not require certification. However, it is paramount that the training is documented and meets the requirements of NFPA 1500 Chapter 3, *Training and Education.*

1-5 Definitions

Definitions in an NFPA document provide uniform terms that the document's users and enforcers accept. Standardizing terminology helps provide a consistent pattern of interpretation of the intent of the standard.

Advanced Life Support (ALS). Emergency medical treatment beyond basic life support level as defined by the medical authority having jurisdiction.

Aerial Device. An aerial ladder, elevating platform, aerial ladder platform, or water tower that is designed to position personnel, handle materials, provide egress, and discharge water.

Aircraft Rescue and Fire Fighting. The fire-fighting actions taken to rescue persons and to control or extinguish fire involving or adjacent to aircraft on the ground. Such rescue and fire-fighting actions are performed both inside and outside of the aircraft.

Approach Fire Fighting. Limited, specialized exterior fire-fighting operations at incidents involving fires producing very high levels of conductive, convective, and radiant heat, such as bulk flammable gas and bulk flammable liquid fires. Specialized thermal protection from exposure to high levels of radiant heat is necessary for the persons involved in such operations due to the limited scope of these operations and the greater distance from the fire at which these operations are conducted. Approach fire fighting is not entry, proximity, or structural fire fighting. See also Entry Fire Fighting, Proximity Fire Fighting, and Structural Fire Fighting.

Approved.* Acceptable to the authority having jurisdiction.

A-1-5 Approved. The National Fire Protection Association does not approve, inspect, or certify any installations, procedures, equipment, or materials; nor does it approve or evaluate testing laboratories. In determining the acceptability of installations, procedures, equipment, or materials, the authority having jurisdiction may base acceptance on compliance with NFPA or other appropriate standards. In the absence of such standards, said authority may require evidence of proper installation, procedure, or use. The authority having jurisdiction may also refer to the listings or labeling practices of an organization that is concerned with product evaluations and is thus in a position to determine compliance with appropriate standards for the current production of listed items.

Authority Having Jurisdiction.* The organization, office, or individual responsible for approving equipment, an installation, or a procedure.

A-1-5 Authority Having Jurisdiction. The phrase "authority having jurisdiction" is used in NFPA documents in a broad manner, since jurisdictions and approval agencies vary, as do their responsibilities. Where public safety is primary, the authority having jurisdiction may be a federal, state, local, or other regional department or individual such as a fire chief; fire marshal; chief of a fire prevention bureau, labor department, or health department; building official; electrical inspector; or others having statutory authority. For insurance purposes, an insurance inspection department, rating bureau, or other insurance company representative may be the authority having jurisdiction. In many circumstances, the property owner or his or her designated agent assumes the role of the authority having jurisdiction; at government installations, the commanding officer or departmental official may be the authority having jurisdiction.

Basic Life Support (BLS). Emergency medical treatment at a level as defined by the medical authority having jurisdiction.

Belt. A system component; material configured as a device that fastens around the waist only and is designated as a ladder belt, an escape belt, or a ladder/escape belt.

Escape Belt. A belt that is certified as compliant with the applicable requirements of this standard and is intended for use only by the wearer as an emergency self-rescue device.

Ladder Belt. A belt that is certified as compliant with the applicable requirements of this standard and is intended for use as a positioning device for a person on a ladder.

Ladder/Escape Belt. A belt that is certified as compliant with the applicable requirements of this standard for both a ladder belt and an escape belt and that is intended for use as a positioning device for a person on a ladder as well as for use only by the wearer as an emergency self-rescue device.

Candidate.* A person who has submitted an application to become a member of the fire department.

A-1-5 Candidate. In an employment context, the Americans With Disabilities Act (discussed in further detail in Appendix D of NFPA 1582, *Standard on Medical Requirements for Fire Fighters*) requires that any medical examination to be conducted take place after an offer of employment is made and prior to the commencement of duties. Therefore, in the employment context, the definition of "candidate" should be applied so as to be consistent with that requirement. Volunteer fire fighters have been deemed to be "employees" in some states or jurisdictions. Volunteer fire departments should seek legal counsel as to their legal responsibilities in these matters.

Closed-Circuit Self-Contained Breathing Apparatus (SCBA). A recirculation-type SCBA in which the exhaled gas is rebreathed by the wearer after the carbon dioxide has been removed from the exhalation gas and the oxygen content within the system has been restored from sources such as compressed breathing air, chemical oxygen, and liquid oxygen, or compressed gaseous oxygen.

Communicable Disease. A disease that can be transmitted from one person to another. Also known as contagious disease.

Company. A group of members having the following characteristics:

(a) Under the direct supervision of an officer or leader
(b) Trained and equipped to perform assigned tasks
(c) Usually organized and identified as engine companies, ladder companies, rescue companies, or squad companies
(d) Usually operating with one piece of fire apparatus (e.g., quint, pumper, ladder truck, elevating platform, rescue, squad, or ambulance)
(e) Arriving at the incident scene on fire apparatus or assembling at the scene prior to assignment

Confined Space. An area large enough and so configured that a member can bodily enter and perform assigned work. An area with limited or restricted means for entry and exit. An area that is not designed for continuous human occupancy. Additionally, a confined space is further defined as having one or more of the following characteristics:

(a) The area contains or has a potential to contain a hazardous atmosphere, including an oxygen-deficient atmosphere.
(b) The area contains a material with a potential to engulf a member.
(c) The area has an internal configuration such that a member could be trapped by inwardly converging walls or a floor that slopes downward and tapers to a small cross section.
(d) The area contains any other recognized serious hazard.

Contaminant. A harmful, irritating, or nuisance material foreign to the normal atmosphere.

Debilitating Illness or Injury. A condition that temporarily or permanently prevents a member of the fire department from engaging in normal duties and activities as a result of illness or injury.

Defensive Operations. Actions that are intended to control a fire by limiting its spread to a defined area, avoiding the commitment of personnel and equipment to dangerous areas. Defensive operations are generally performed from the exterior of structures and are based on a determination that the risk to personnel exceeds the potential benefits of offensive actions.

Drug. Any substance, chemical, over-the-counter medication, or prescribed medication that can affect the performance of the fire fighter.

Emergency Incident. A specific emergency operation.

Emergency Medical Services. The provision of treatment—such as first aid, cardiopulmonary resuscitation, basic life support, advanced life support, and other pre-hospital procedures including ambulance transportation—to patients.

Emergency Operations. Activities of the fire department relating to rescue, fire suppression, emergency medical care, and special operations, including response to the scene of the incident and all functions performed at the scene.

Entry Fire Fighting. Extraordinarily specialized firefighting operations that can include the activities of rescue, fire suppression, and property conservation at incidents involving fires producing very high levels of conductive, convective, and radiant heat, such as aircraft fires, bulk flammable gas fires, and bulk flammable liquid fires. Highly specialized thermal protection from exposure to extreme levels of conductive, convective, and radiant heat is necessary for persons involved in such extraordinarily specialized operations due to the scope of these operations and because direct entry into flames is made. Usually these operations are exterior operations. Entry fire fighting is not structural fire fighting. See also Approach Fire Fighting, Proximity Fire Fighting, and Structural Fire Fighting.

Facility. See Fire Department Facility.

Fire Apparatus. Any vehicle—including those used for rescue, fire suppression, emergency medical services, hazardous materials operations, wildland, or other functions—operated by a fire department member.

Fire Chief. The highest ranking officer in charge of a fire department.

Fire Department. An organization providing rescue, fire suppression, and related activities. It can also provide emergency medical services, hazardous materials operations, and special operations. The term "fire department" shall include any public, governmental, private, industrial, or military organization engaging in this type of activity.

Fire Department Facility. Any building or area owned, operated, occupied, or used by a fire department on a routine basis. This does not include locations where a fire department can be summoned to perform emergency operations or other duties, unless such premises are normally under the control of the fire department.

Fire Department Member. See Member.

Fire Shelter. A personal protection item carried by fire fighters that, when deployed, unfolds to form a shelter of heat-reflective materials.

Fire Suppression. The activities involved in controlling and extinguishing fires. Fire suppression shall include all activities performed at the scene of a fire incident or training exercise that expose fire department members to the dangers of heat, flame, smoke, and other products of combustion, explosion, or structural collapse.

Flame Resistance. The property of a material whereby the application of a flaming or nonflaming source of ignition and the subsequent removal of the ignition source results in the termination of combustion. Flame resistance can be an inherent property of the material, or it can be imparted by specific treatment.

Fully Enclosed Area. A cab or passenger compartment of fire apparatus providing total enclosure equipped with positive latching doors for entry and exit.

Gloves. An element of the protective ensemble designed to provide minimum protection to the fingers, thumb, hand, and wrist.

Guideline. A written indication or outline of department policy that allows flexibility in application.

Hazard. The potential for harm or damage to people, property, or the environment. Hazards include the characteristics of facilities, equipment systems, property, hardware, or other objects and the actions and inactions of people that create such hazards.

Hazardous Area. The area where members might be exposed to a hazardous atmosphere. A particular substance, device, event, circumstance, or condition that presents a danger to members of the fire department.

Hazardous Atmosphere. Any atmosphere that is oxygen deficient or that contains a toxic or disease-producing contaminant. A hazardous atmosphere can be immediately dangerous to life and health.

Hazardous Material. A substance that presents an unusual danger to persons due to properties of toxicity, chemical reactivity or decomposition, corrosivity, explosion or detonation, etiological hazards, or similar properties.

Hazardous Materials Operations. All activities performed at the scene of a hazardous materials incident that expose fire department members to the dangers of hazardous materials.

Health and Fitness Coordinator. The person who, under the supervision of the fire department physician, has been designated by the department to coordinate and be responsible for the health and fitness programs of the department.

Health and Safety Officer. The member of the fire department assigned and authorized by the fire chief as the manager of the safety and health program and who performs the duties and responsibilities specified in this standard. This individual can be the incident safety officer or that can also be a separate function.

Health Data Base. A compilation of records and data that relates to the health experience of a group of individuals and is maintained in a manner such that it is retrievable for study and analysis over a period of time.

Health Promotion. Preventive health activities that identify real and potential health risks in the work environment and that inform, motivate, and otherwise help people to adopt and maintain healthy practices and lifestyles.

Hot Zone. The area immediately surrounding a hazardous material incident that extends far enough to prevent adverse effects from the release of hazardous materials to personnel outside the zone. This zone is also referred to as the "exclusion zone" or "restricted zone" in other documents.

Immediately Dangerous to Life or Health (IDLH). Any atmosphere that poses an immediate hazard to life or produces immediate irreversible debilitating effects on health.

Incident Action Plan. The objectives reflecting the overall incident strategy, tactics, risk management, and member safety that are developed by the incident commander. Incident action plans are updated throughout the incident.

Incident Commander. The fire department member in overall command of an emergency incident.

Incident Management System (IMS). An organized system of roles, responsibilities, and standard operating procedures used to manage emergency operations. Such systems are often referred to as incident command systems (ICS).

Incident Safety Officer. An individual appointed to respond or assigned at an incident scene by the incident commander to perform the duties and responsibilities specified in this standard. This individual can be the incident safety officer or can be a separate individual, appointed by the incident commander, or a predesignated individual.

Industrial Fire Department.* An organization providing rescue, fire suppression, and related activities. It can also provide emergency medical services, hazardous material operations, or other activities. These activities can occur at a single facility or facilities under the same management, whether for profit, not for profit, or government owned or operated, including occupancies such as industrial, commercial, mercantile, warehouse, and institutional. The industrial fire department is generally trained and equipped for specialized operation based on site-specific hazards present at the facilities.

Groups or teams that are organized to perform specialized rescue services but that do not perform fire suppression activities are not considered as industrial fire departments.

A-1-5 Industrial Fire Department. The vast majority of industrial fire brigades are not industrial fire departments. Industrial fire departments are those few brigades that resemble and function as municipal fire departments. These are generally found only at large industrial facilities and at industrial facilities that also perform municipal fire fighting, usually where the plant is located far from municipalities with organized fire departments. Industrial fire departments are organized and equipped for interior structural fire fighting similar to municipal fire departments. Their apparatus is similar to that used by municipal fire departments.

Industrial fire brigades that provide rescue services are industrial fire departments. Industrial facilities can have separate organizations, covered by separate organizational statements, operating as industrial fire brigades and operating as rescue teams providing rescue not related to fire incidents. Membership in these two organizations can overlap.

Infection Control Program. The fire department's formal policy and implementation of procedures relating to the control of infectious and communicable disease hazards where employees, patients, or the general public could be exposed to blood, body fluids, or other potentially infectious materials in the fire department work environment.

Infectious Disease. An illness or disease resulting from invasion of a host by disease-producing organisms such as bacteria, viruses, fungi, or parasites.

Interface Area. An area of the body where the protective garments, helmet, gloves, footwear, or SCBA facepiece meet (i.e., the protective coat/helmet/SCBA facepiece area, the protective coat/protective trouser area, the protective coat/glove area, and the protective trouser/footwear area).

Interface Components. Elements of the protective ensemble that are designed to provide limited protection to interface areas.

Life Safety Harness System Components. The following are utilized for fall arrest and rappelling operations:

Class I Life Safety Harness. Harness that fastens around waist and around thighs or under buttocks and designed to be used for emergency escape with one-person loads (300 pounds).

Class II Life Safety Harness. Harness that fastens around waist and around thighs or under buttocks and designed for rescue where two-person loads can be encountered (600 pounds).

Class III Life Safety Harness. Harness that fastens around waist, around thighs or under buttocks, and over shoulders and designed for rescue where two-person loads can be encountered (600 pounds) and where inverting might occur. Class III life safety harnesses shall be permitted to consist of one or more parts.

Medical Evaluation. The analysis of information for the purpose of making a determination of medical certification. Medical evaluation can include a medical examination.

Member. A person involved in performing the duties and responsibilities of a fire department, under the auspices of the organization. A fire department member can be a full-time or part-time employee or a paid or unpaid volunteer, can occupy any position or rank within the fire department, and can engage in emergency operations.

Member Assistance Program (MAP). A generic term used to describe the various methods used in the fire department for the control of alcohol and other substance abuse, stress, and personal problems that adversely affect member performance.

Member Organization. An organization formed to represent the collective and individual rights and interests of the members of the fire department, such as a labor union or fire fighters' association. This definition includes any organization authorized to represent the interests of its members in dealing with the fire department management.

Occasionally Assigned. The infrequent fire-fighting responsibility in a given jurisdiction, district, or area. Fire-fighting situations that are less likely to occur or that occur on an infrequent basis within the response area.

Occupational Illness. An illness or disease contracted through or aggravated by the performance of the duties, responsibilities, and functions of a fire department member.

Occupational Injury. An injury sustained during the performance of the duties, responsibilities, and functions of a fire department member.

Offensive Operations. Actions that involve a direct attack on a fire to directly control and extinguish the fire, generally performed in the interior of involved structures.

Open-Circuit SCBA. An SCBA in which exhalation is vented to the atmosphere and not rebreathed. There are two types of open-circuit SCBA: negative-pressure or demand type and positive-pressure or pressure-demand type.

Oxygen-Deficient Atmosphere. Air atmospheres containing less than 19.5 percent oxygen by volume at one standard atmosphere pressure.

Personnel Accountability System. A system that readily identifies both the location and function of all members operating at an incident scene.

Positive-Pressure SCBA. An SCBA in which the pressure inside the facepiece, in relation to the pressure surrounding the outside of the facepiece, is positive during both inhalation and exhalation when tested by NIOSH in accordance with 42 CFR 84, Subpart H.

Pressure-Demand SCBA. See Positive-Pressure SCBA.

Primarily Assigned. The principal fire-fighting responsibility in a given jurisdiction, district, or area. Fire-fighting situations that are most likely to occur within the response area.

Procedure. An organizational directive issued by the authority having jurisdiction or by the department that establishes a specific policy that must be followed.

Property Conservation. Those activities directed at stopping or minimizing the dollar loss to buildings and property from the effects of fire and fire suppression activities or other emergency situations and the mitigation of those emergencies.

Protective Clothing Ensemble. Multiple elements of clothing and equipment designed to provide a degree of protection for fire fighters from adverse exposures to the inherent risks of structural fire-fighting operations and certain other emergency operations. The elements of the protective ensemble are coats, trousers, coveralls, helmets, gloves, footwear, and interface components.

Protective Uniform. A unit of textile apparel configured as a shirt, pant, or coverall and designed to be both the thermal barrier or a portion of the thermal barrier of a garment element of the protective ensemble and an apparel unit(s) of a station/work uniform.

Proximity Fire Fighting. Specialized fire-fighting operations that can include the activities of rescue, fire suppression, and property conservation at incidents involving fires producing very high levels of conductive, convective, and radiant heat such as aircraft fires, bulk flammable gas fires, and bulk flammable liquid fires. Specialized thermal protection from exposure to high levels of radiant heat, as well as thermal protection from conductive and convective heat, is necessary for persons involved in such operations due to the scope of these operations and the close distance to the fire at which these operations are conducted, although direct entry into flame is *not* made. These operations usually are exterior operations but might be combined with interior operations. Proximity fire fighting is not structural fire fighting but might be combined with structural fire-fighting operations. Proximity fire fighting also is not entry fire fighting. See also Approach Fire Fighting, Entry Fire Fighting, and Structural Fire Fighting.

Qualified Person. A person who, by possession of a recognized degree, certificate, professional standing, or skill, and who, by knowledge, training, and experience, has demonstrated the ability to deal with problems related to the subject matter, the work, or the project.

Related Activities. Any and all functions that fire department members can be called upon to perform in the execution of their duties.

Rescue. Those activities directed at locating endangered persons at an emergency incident, removing those persons from danger, treating the injured, and providing for transport to an appropriate health care facility.

Rescue Incident. An emergency incident that primarily involves the rescue of persons subject to physical danger and that can include the provision of emergency medical services.

Risk. A measure of the probability and severity of adverse effects. These adverse effects result from an exposure to a hazard.

Risk Management. Identification and analysis of exposure to hazards, selection of appropriate risk management techniques to handle exposures, implementation of chosen techniques, and monitoring of results, with respect to the health and safety of members.

Rope. A compact but flexible, torsionally balanced, continuous structure of fibers produced from strands that are twisted, plaited, or braided together and that serve primarily to support a load or transmit a force from the point of origin to the point of application.

Life Safety Rope. Rope dedicated solely for the purpose of supporting people during rescue, fire fighting, other emergency operations, or during training evaluations. See also Personal Escape Rope.

One-Person Rope. Life safety rope designed to support a one-person load when in use; also can be used to support a two-person load when used in systems where two ropes are used as separate and equal members.

Two-Person Rope. Life safety rope designed to support a two-person load when in use.

Personal Escape Rope. A system component; a single-purpose, one-person, one-time use, emergency self-escape (self-rescue) rope; not classified as a life safety rope. See also Life Safety Rope.

SCBA. See Self-Contained Breathing Apparatus.

Seat Belt. A two-point lap belt, a three-point lap/shoulder belt, or a four-point lap/shoulder harness for vehicle occupants designed to limit their movement in the event of an accident, rapid acceleration, or rapid deceleration by securing individuals safely to a vehicle in a seated position. See also Vehicle Safety Harness.

Self-Contained Breathing Apparatus (SCBA). A respirator worn by the user that supplies a respirable atmosphere that is either carried in or generated by the apparatus and is independent of the ambient environment.

Service Testing. The regular, periodic inspection and testing of apparatus and equipment, according to an established schedule and guideline, to ensure that they are in safe and functional operating condition.

Shall. Indicates a mandatory requirement.

Should. Indicates a recommendation or that which is advised but not required.

Special Operations. Those emergency incidents to which the fire department responds that require specific and advanced training and specialized tools and equipment. Special operations include water rescue, extrication, hazardous materials, confined space entry, high-angle rescue, aircraft rescue and fire fighting, and other operations requiring specialized training.

Standard Operating Guideline.* An organizational directive that establishes a course of action.

A-1-5 Standard Operating Guideline. An organizational directive sometimes referred to as a standard operating guideline (SOG) that outlines a course of action that allows flexibility in application.

Structural Fire Fighting. The activities of rescue, fire suppression, and property conservation in buildings, enclosed structures, aircraft interiors, vehicles, vessels, or like properties that are involved in a fire or emergency situation.

Tactical Level Management Unit. A management unit identified in the incident management system commonly known as "division," "group," or "sector."

Vehicle Safety Harness. A restraint device for vehicle occupants designed to limit their movement in the event of an accident, rapid acceleration, or rapid deceleration by securing individuals safely to a vehicle either in a seated position or tethered to the vehicle. See also Seat Belt.

Wildland Fire Fighting. The activities of fire suppression and property conservation in vegetation that is not within structures but is involved in a fire situation.

Working Structural Fire. Any fire that requires the use of a $1^1/_2$-in. (3.8-cm) or larger fire attack hose line and that also requires the use of self-contained breathing apparatus for members entering the hazardous area.

CHAPTER 2

Organization

2-1 Fire Department Organizational Statement

2-1.1*

The fire department shall prepare and maintain a written statement or policy that establishes the existence of the fire department, the services the fire department is authorized and expected to perform, and the basic organizational structure.

A-2-1.1 The organizational statement is a very important basis for many of the provisions of this standard. The statement sets forth the legal basis for operating a fire department, the organizational structure of the fire department, number of members, training requirements, expected functions, and authorities and responsibilities of various members or defined positions.

A key point is to clearly set out the specific services the fire department is authorized and expected to perform. Most fire departments are responsible to a governing body. The governing body has the right and should assert its authority to set the specific services and the limits of the services the fire department will provide and has the responsibility to furnish the necessary resources for delivery of the designated services. The fire department should provide its governing body with a specific description of each service with options or alternatives and with an accurate analysis of the costs and resources needed for each service.

Such services might include structural fire fighting, wildland fire fighting, airport/aircraft fire fighting, emergency medical services, hazardous materials response, high-angle rescue, heavy rescue, and others.

Spelling out the specific parameters of services to be provided allows the fire department to plan, staff, equip, train, and deploy members to perform these duties. It also gives the governing body an accounting of the costs of services and allows it to select those services they can afford to provide. Likewise, the governing body should identify services it cannot afford to provide and cannot authorize the fire department to deliver, or it should assign those services to another agency.

The fire department should be no different from any other government agency that has the parameters of its authority and services clearly defined by the governing body.

Legal counsel should be used to assure that any statutory services and responsibilities are being met.

The majority of public fire departments are established under the charter provisions of their governing body or through the adoption of statutes. These acts define the legal basis for operating a fire department, the mission of the organization, the duties that are authorized and expected to be performed, and the authority and responsibilities that are assigned to certain individuals to direct the operations of the fire department.

The documents that officially establish the fire department as an identifiable organization are necessary to determine specific responsibilities and to determine the parties responsible for compliance with the provisions of this standard.

In many cases, these documents could be a part of state laws, a municipal charter, or an annual budget. In such cases, it would be appropriate to make these existing documents part of the organizational statement, if applicable.

In cases other than governmentally operated public fire departments, there is a need to formally establish the existence of the organization through the adoption of a charter, the approval of a constitution or articles of incorporation, or through some equivalent official action of an authorized body. A fire department that operates entirely within the private sector, such as an industrial fire department, could legally establish and operate a fire protection organization by the adoption of a corporate policy as described in the organizational statement.

In addition to specifically defining the organization that is expected to comply with this standard, 2-1.1 requires that the organizational structure, membership, expected functions, and training requirements be contained in documents that are accessible for examination. These requirements are intended to reinforce the fact that the fire department is an identifiable organization that operates with known and specific expectations.

Where a fire department functions as a unit of a larger entity, such as one of several municipal departments or a particular unit of a private corporation, the larger organization is often able to provide some of the same elements that are required to be provided by the fire department. This would satisfy the requirements for the fire department to provide those elements.

The fire department organizational statement required by paragraph 2-1.1 outlines the fire department's existence, types and levels of service the fire department performs, and the department organization. The description of organization includes not only the simple rank structure, but also reporting authority and divisional responsibilities, for example, code enforcement. The organizational statement will also specify whether the department is a privately held corporation or a municipal fire department, either career, volunteer, or combination. *(See Figures 1500-2.1, 1500-2.2, and 1500-2.3.)*

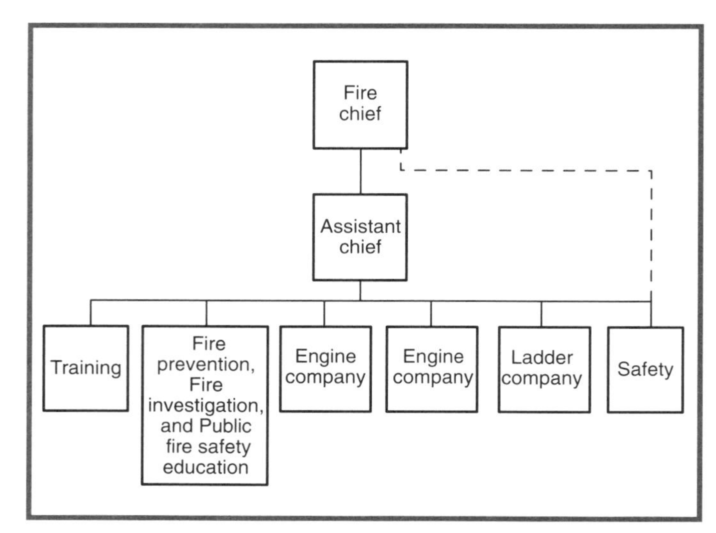

Figure 1500-2.1 Organizational chart for a typical small-size fire department. [Figure A-5-4.1(a) from NFPA 1201, 1994]

2-1.2*

The fire department shall prepare and maintain written policies and standard operating procedures that document the organization structure, membership, roles and responsibilities, expected functions, and training requirements, including the following:

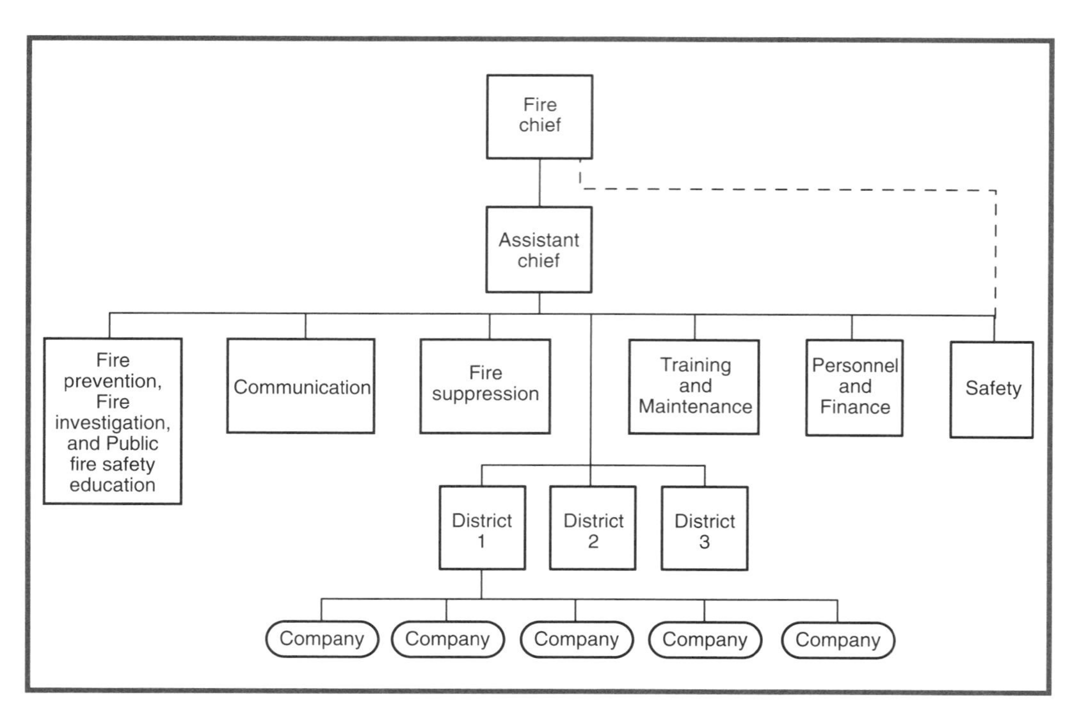

Figure 1500-2.2 *Organizational chart for a typical medium-size fire department. [Figure A-5-4.1(b) from NFPA 1201, 1994]*

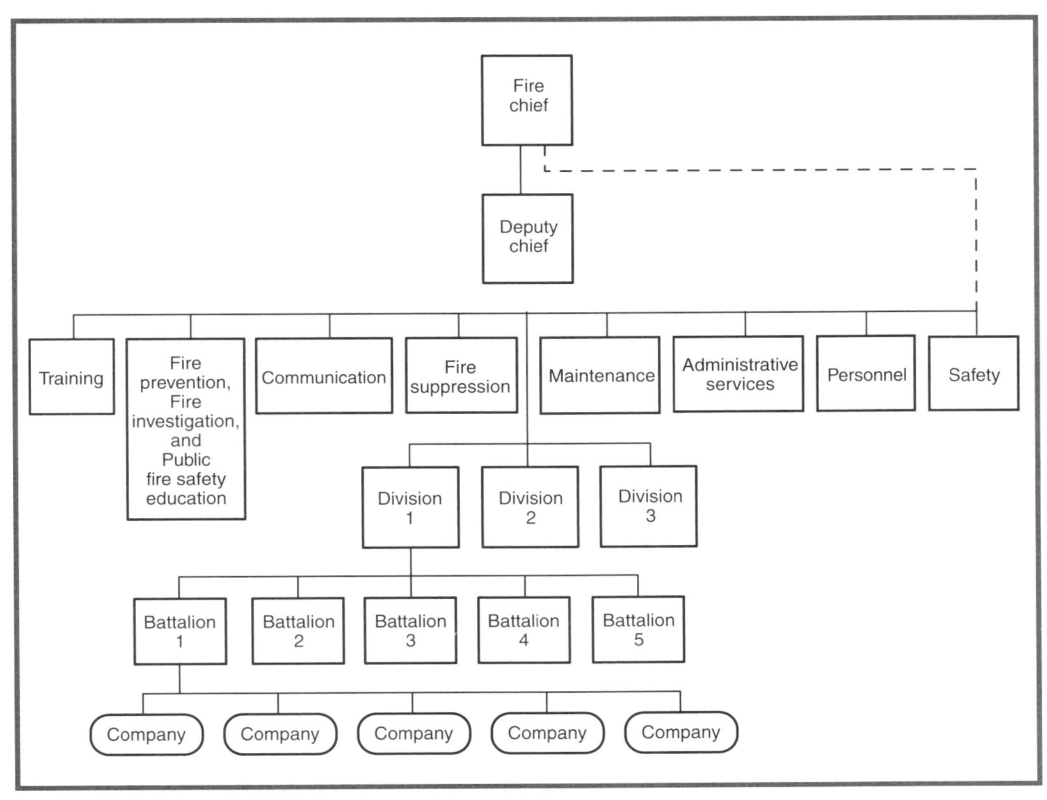

Figure 1500-2.3 Organizational chart for a typical large-size fire department. [Figure A-5-4.1(c) from NFPA 1201, 1994]

(a) The types of standard evolutions that are expected to be performed and the evolutions that must be performed simultaneously or in sequence for different types of situations
(b) The minimum number of members who are required to perform each function or evolution and the manner in which the function is to be performed
(c) The number and types of apparatus and the number of personnel that will be dispatched to different types of incidents
(d) The procedures that will be employed to initiate and manage operations at the scene of an emergency incident

A-2-1.2 Additional information on fire department organization and operations can be found in Section 10 of the NFPA *Fire Protection Handbook*, 18th edition; and Chapter 5 of *Managing Fire Services*, 2nd edition, published by the International City Management Association.

The written policies and procedures required by 2-1.2 outline the crux of fire department operations: the who, what, when, where, and how. In these policies and procedures, the fire department outlines the types and level of services provided to the community and the risks associated with this level of service. These policies and procedures, then, are a primary component of a fire department's risk management plan.

2-1.3

The organizational statement and procedures shall be available for inspection by members or their designated representative.

Written policies and procedures enable members to understand and follow department policies and procedures. As one fire chief said, "If it isn't written down, it doesn't exist."

2-2 Risk Management Plan

2-2.1*

The fire department shall develop and adopt a comprehensive written risk management plan. The risk management plan shall consider all fire department policies and procedures, and it shall include goals and objectives to ensure that the risks associated with the operations of the fire department are identified and effectively managed.

Some communities have an overall community risk management plan that includes all agencies or departments. A community-wide risk management plan does not absolve the fire department from developing its own plan, as required by paragraph 2-2.1. The fire department's risk management plan must dovetail with the community plan.

A-2-2.1 Sample Risk Management Plan.

ANYTOWN FIRE DEPARTMENT
RISK MANAGEMENT PLAN

PURPOSE:

The Anytown Fire Department has developed and implemented a risk management plan. The goals and objectives of the plan are the following:

(a) To limit the exposure of the fire department to situations and occurrences that could have harmful or undesirable consequences on the department or its members
(b) To provide the safest possible work environment for the members of the fire department, while recognizing the risks inherent to the fire department's mission

SCOPE:

The risk management plan is intended to comply with the requirements of NFPA 1500, *Standard on Fire Department Occupational Safety and Health Program,* specifically Section 2-2.

METHODOLOGY:

The risk management plan uses a variety of strategies and approaches to address different objectives. The specific objectives are identified from the following sources of information:

(a) Records and reports on the frequency and severity of accidents and injuries in the Anytown Fire Department
(b) Reports received from the Anytown's insurance carriers
(c) Specific occurrences that identify the need for risk management
(d) National trends and reports that are applicable to Anytown
(e) Knowledge of the inherent risks that are encountered by fire departments and specific situations that are identified in Anytown
(f) Any additional areas identified by fire department staff and personnel

RESPONSIBILITIES:

The fire chief has responsibility for the implementation and operation of the department's risk management plan. The department's health and safety officer has the responsibility to develop, manage, and annually revise the risk management plan. The health and safety officer also has the responsibility to modify the risk management plan when it is warranted by changing exposures, occurrences, and activities.

All members of the Anytown Fire Department have responsibility for ensuring their own health and safety based upon the requirements of the risk management plan and the department's safety and health program.

PLAN ORGANIZATION:

The risk management plan includes the following:

(a) Identification of the risks that members of the fire department could actually or potentially encounter, both emergency and nonemergency
   1. Emergency risks include those presented at emergency incidents, both fire and nonfire (e.g., hazardous materials), Emergency Medical Services incidents, and emergency response.
   2. Nonemergency risks include those encountered while performing the following functions: training, physical fitness, nonemergency vehicle operation, and station activities (e.g., vehicle maintenance, station maintenance, daily office functions).
(b) Evaluation of the identified risks based upon the frequency and severity factors
(c) Development and implementation of an action plan for controlling each of the risks, in order of priority
(d) Provisions for monitoring the effectiveness of the controls implemented
(e) A periodic review of the plan with modifications made as needed

RISK MANAGEMENT PLAN MONITORING:

(a) The Anytown Fire Department's risk management program will be monitored annually, in January, by the health and safety officer.
(b) Recommendations and revisions will be made based on the following criteria:
   1. Annual accident and injury data for the preceding year
   2. Significant incidents that have occurred during the past year
   3. Information and suggestions from department staff and personnel
(c) Every 3 years, the risk management program will be evaluated by an independent source. Recommendations will be sent to the fire chief, the health and safety officer, and the occupational safety and health committee.

(See Table A-2-2.1.)

2-2.2

The risk management plan shall at least cover the risks associated with the following:

(a) Administration
(b) Facilities
(c) Training

Table A-2-2.1 Anytown Fire Department Control Measures

Identification	Frequency/ Severity	Priority			Summary of Control Measures
Strains and sprains	High/medium	High	1.	O	Periodic awareness training for all members
			2.	O	Evaluate function areas to determine location and frequency of occurrence
			3.	O	Based upon outcome of evaluation, conduct a task analysis of identified problems
Stress	Low/high	High	1.	O	Continue health maintenance program
			2.	O	Member participation in physical fitness program
Exposure to fire products	Low/high	Medium	1.	A	Re-evaluate department's philosophy on mandatory SCBA usage
			2.	O	Revise department policy and procedures on mandatory usage
			3.	A	Retraining and education of personnel on chronic effects of inhalation of by-products of combustion
			4.	A	Provide monitoring process of carbon monoxide (CO) levels at fire scenes, especially during overhaul
Vehicle-related incidents	Medium/high	High	1.	O	Compliance of department with state motor vehicle laws relating to emergency response
			2.	O	Mandatory department-wide EVOC
			3.	O	Monitor individual member's driving record
Terrorism and the workplace	Low/high	Low	1.	O	Provide awareness training for all personnel
			2.	O	Develop policy and procedures as indicated by need
Incident scene safety	Medium/high	High	1.	O	Revise and implement department incident-management system
			2.	O	Revise current policy on mandatory use of full personal protective equipment including SCBA
			3.	O	Evaluate effectiveness of the department's personal accountability system and make needed adjustments
			4.	A	Train all officers in NFA Incident Safety Officer course
Equipment loss	Low/medium	Medium	1.	O	Review annual accident/loss statistics and implement loss-reduction procedures
			2.	A	Develop procedures for review and recommendation for loss prevention based upon significant loss ($1000+)
			3.	O	Maintain department equipment inventory
Facilities and property	Low/high	Medium	1.	A	Review insurance coverage of contents and facilities for adequate coverage due to catastrophe
			2.	O	All new and renovated facilities incorporate life safety and health designs.
			3.	O	Conduct routine safety and health inspections of facilities

NOTE: O = Ongoing; A = Action required

(d) Vehicle operations, both emergency and nonemergency
(e) Protective clothing and equipment
(f) Operations at emergency incidents
(g) Operations at nonemergency incidents
(h) Other related activities

2-2.3*

The risk management plan shall include at least the following components:

(a) *Risk Identification.* Actual and potential hazards
(b) *Risk Evaluation.* Likelihood of occurrence of a given hazard and severity of its consequences
(c) *Risk Control Techniques.* Solutions for elimination or mitigation of potential hazards; implementation of best solution
(d) *Risk Management Monitoring.* Evaluation of effectiveness of risk control techniques

A-2-2.3 Essentially, a risk management plan serves as documentation that risks have been identified and evaluated and that a reasonable control plan has been implemented and followed.

The following are some factors to consider for each step of the process:

(a) *Risk Identification.* For every aspect of the operation of the fire department, list potential problems. The following are examples of sources of information that might be useful in the process:

1. A list of the risks to which members are or can be exposed
2. Records of previous accidents, illnesses, and injuries, both locally and nationally
3. Facility and apparatus surveys, inspections, and so forth

(b) *Risk Evaluation.* Evaluate each item listed in the risk identification process using the following two questions:

1. What is the potential frequency of occurrence?
2. What is the potential severity and expense of its occurrence?

This will help to set priorities in the control plan.

Some sources of information that could be useful are the following:

1. Safety audits and inspection reports
2. Prior accident, illness, and injury statistics
3. Application of national data to the local circumstances
4. Professional judgment in evaluating risks unique to the jurisdiction

(c) *Risk Control.* Once risks are identified and evaluated, a control for each should be implemented and documented. The two primary methods of controlling risk, in order of preference, are as follows:

1. Wherever possible, totally eliminate/avoid the risk or the activity that presents the risk. For example, if the risk is falling on the ice, then do not allow members to go outside when icy conditions are present.
2. Where it is not possible or practical to avoid or eliminate the risk, steps should be taken to control it. In the example above, some methods of control would be sand/salt procedures, the wearing of proper footwear, and so forth.

(d) Other methods of control to consider are the following:

1. Safety program development, adoption, and enforcement
2. Standard operating procedures development, dissemination, and enforcement
3. Training
4. Inspections

(e) *Risk Management Monitoring and Follow-Up.* As with any program, it is important to evaluate whether the plan is working. Periodic evaluations should be made, and, if the program elements are not working satisfactorily, then modifications should be made.

2-3 Policy

2-3.1*

The fire department shall adopt an official written departmental occupational safety and health policy that identifies specific goals and objectives for the prevention and elimination of accidents and occupational injuries, exposures to communicable disease, illnesses, and fatalities. It shall be the policy of the fire department to seek and to provide an occupational safety and health program that complies with this standard for its members.

A-2-3.1 Example of a safety policy statement:

> It is the policy of the fire department to provide and to operate with the highest possible levels of safety and health for all members. The prevention and reduction of accidents, injuries, and occupational illnesses are goals of the fire department and shall be primary considerations at all times. This concern for safety and health applies to all members of the fire department and to any other persons who might be involved in fire department activities.

The safety policy statement required by paragraph 2-3.1 provides fire department members with a written commitment of the fire department's concern for their occupational safety and health. There are many federal mandates that fire departments are required to follow (such as OSHA-required training for hazardous materials covered under 29 *CFR* 1910.120 and EPA regulations), but this policy statement includes those mandates. The fire department occupational safety and health policy should include all applicable sections of NFPA 1500.

2-3.2*

The fire department shall evaluate the effectiveness of the occupational safety and health program at least once every three years. An audit report of the findings shall be submitted to the fire chief and to the members of the occupational safety and health committee.

A-2-3.2 Experience has shown that there is often a significant difference between a written occupational safety and health program and the actual program that has been implemented. Periodic evaluations are one method the fire chief can use to measure how the program is being conducted. This evaluation should be conducted by a qualified individual from outside of the fire department, as outside evaluators provide a different perspective, which can be constructive. Outside evaluators could include municipal risk managers, safety directors, consultants, insurance carrier representatives, fire chiefs, safety officers, or others having knowledge of fire department operations and occupational safety and health program implementation.

The intent of paragraph 2-3.2 is to make the fire department occupational safety and health program a "living" program, allowing the department and its members to track progress toward compliance. A safety audit every three years provides both management and members alike a process to monitor compliance. Many departments conduct an annual safety audit and use the resulting information for budgetary purposes. Departments may also find the information from the safety audit to be a valuable asset in updating their data base of occupational safety and health incidents on a yearly basis. The NFPA 1500 Fire Department Occupational Safety and Health Worksheet that appeared as Appendix B to the standard and that is reproduced as Form S12-3 in Supplement 12 of Part Six of this handbook is a convenient checklist format for monitoring progress toward compliance.

2-4 Roles and Responsibilities

2-4.1

It shall be the responsibility of the fire department to research, develop, implement, and enforce an occupational safety and health program that recognizes and reduces the inherent risks involved in the operations of a fire department.

Paragraph 2-4.1 calls for significant research before other occupational safety and health program activities can begin. Most fire departments do not have the resources of personnel, time, or money to conduct this level of research. However, fire departments have access to existing work by federal agencies such as the Occupational Safety and Health Administration (OSHA), labor organizations such as the International Association of Fire Fighters, management organizations such as the International Association of Fire Chiefs, or other organizations such as the National Institutes of Occupational Safety and Health, the Centers for Disease Control and Prevention, or the Learning Resource Center at the National Emergency Training Center. The NFPA Fire Data and Analysis Division has been tracking fire fighter fatalities and injuries for over twenty years. *(See Figure 1500-2.4.)*

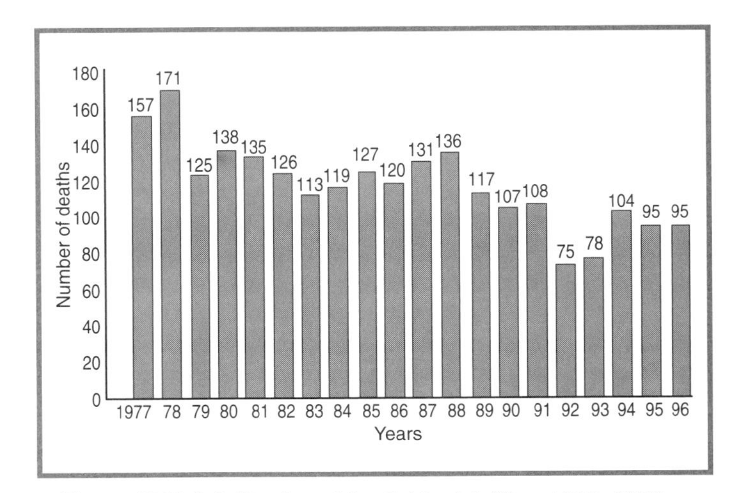

Figure 1500-2.4 *Number of fire fighter fatalities, 1977–1996. (NFPA FIDO data)*

National Fire Incident Reporting System data from the United States Fire Administration may also assist in meeting the requirements of this section. Supplement 1 in Part six of this handbook contains NFPA's 1996 Fire Fighter Fatality Report and figures that summarize the most recently available information on fire fighter fatalities. *(See also Figure 1500-2.5.)*

2-4.1.1 The fire department shall be responsible for compliance with all applicable laws and legal requirements with respect to member safety and health.

The many enforcement powers—whether provided by legislation or by reference—of agencies including the Centers for Disease Prevention and Control, the EPA, NIOSH, and OSHA may require the fire department to comply with paragraph 2-4.1.1, regardless of

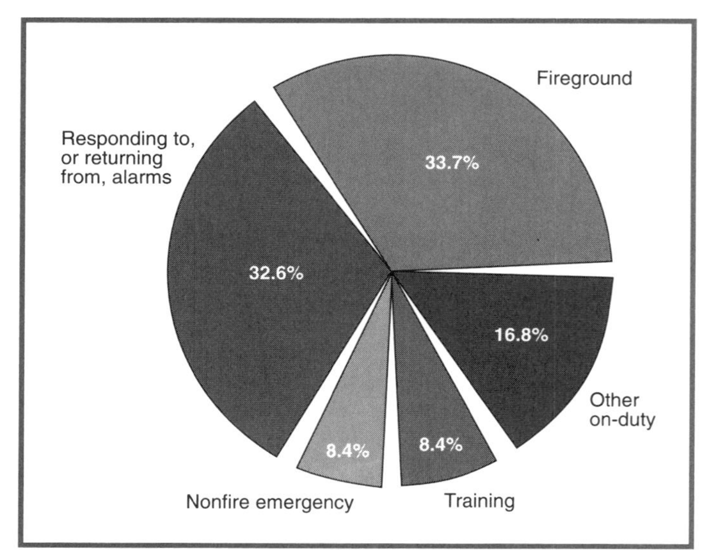

Figure 1500-2.5 Number of fire fighter fatalities by type of duty in 1996. The 1996 figures are very similar to those of the last 5 years where the larger percentages occur either on the fireground or in responding to or returning from alarms.

the adoption of NFPA 1500. Fire department managers need to know which statutory regulations they are required to meet. As in other areas, ignorance of the law in occupational safety and health is no excuse for failing to follow the law.

2-4.1.2* The fire department shall establish and enforce rules, regulations, and standard operating procedures to reach the objectives of this standard.

A-2-4.1.2 The responsibility for establishing and enforcing safety rules and regulations rests with the management of the fire department. Enforcement implies that appropriate action, including disciplinary measures if necessary, will be taken to ensure compliance. A standard approach to enforcement should address both sanctions and rewards. All fire department members should recognize and support the need for a standard regulatory approach to safety and health. In addition to the management responsibilities, an effective safety program requires commitment and support from all members and member organizations.

2-4.2

The fire department shall be responsible for developing and implementing an accident investigation procedure.

2-4.2.1* All accidents, injuries, fatalities, illnesses, and exposures involving members shall be investigated.

A-2-4.2.1 See A-2-4.1.2.

2-4.2.2 All accidents involving fire department vehicles, equipment, or fire department facilities shall be investigated.

In addition to "lessons learned," accident investigation provides a process for tracking injuries, exposures, accidents, and so forth. Such information becomes part of the department's occupational safety and health data base. The data base not only provides a history of what occurs within the department, but can also be used to track the department's experience against national trends. *(See also Section 2-7, Records.)*

The investigation of accidents and near misses provides an opportunity for members to benefit from lessons learned. Accidents, injuries, and fatalities may be investigated by an outside agency(s) with appropriate training and expertise. An external investigator provides more objectivity than is possible for internal fire department investigators, who are likely to know the people involved in an accident or near miss. Outside investigation services may be provided by private or public sector teams. Many states or other AHJs use commercial accident reconstruction teams. In the Commonwealth of Massachusetts, the investigation of fatal accidents is performed by the Massachusetts State Police.

2-4.2.3 The fire department shall take whatever appropriate corrective action that is necessary to avoid repetitive occurrences of accidents and exposure to communicable diseases.

2-4.2.4 Records of such investigations shall be kept in accordance with the applicable provisions of Section 2-7 of this chapter.

2-4.3

Each individual member of the fire department shall cooperate, participate, and comply with the provisions of the occupational safety and health program.

The total occupational safety and health program specified in NFPA 1500 needs member input to be successful. For example, structural fire-fighting gloves are researched, tested, and purchased with input from the members; any hand injuries that ensue are then analyzed. Answers to questions from the members, such as, "Were the members wearing the gloves?" "Were the gloves worn properly?" "Are the gloves fitted correctly?" and "Were the gloves being used for their intended purpose?" should lead the health and safety committee in the right direction to solve the problem.

As paragraph 2-4.3 points out, compliance with the department's occupational safety and health program is not an option. Members must understand that their protection depends on complying with the *total* program.

2-4.3.1 It shall be the right of each member to be protected by an effective occupational safety and health program and to participate or be represented in the research, development, implementation, evaluation, and enforcement of the program.

2-4.4

The member organization, where such an organization exists, shall cooperate with the fire department by representing the interests and the welfare of the members in the research, development, implementation, and evaluation of the occupational safety and health program.

2-4.4.1 The member organization shall have the right to represent the individual and collective rights of its members in the occupational safety and health program.

NFPA 1500 applies to all fire department members, whether or not they are represented by a labor organization: The labor organization is represented on the occupational safety and health committee. Members have the right to be represented by a member organization or outside counsel in order to be protected by this program.

2-5 Health and Safety Officer

The requirements of Section 2-5 are covered in depth by Chapter 3 of NFPA 1521, *Standard for Fire Department Safety Officer (1997). (See Part Two of this handbook.)* Figure 1500-2.6 shows a sample description of the safety officer position. This description can serve as a guide for departments in creating or reevaluating the health and safety officer's function.

There is currently no national professional qualifications standard for the fire department health and safety officer. However, the position is included on the command staff in the incident command system. The National Wildfire Coordinating Group's Safety Officer I and Safety Officer II curriculum outlines position requirements. *(See Figure 1500-2.6.)*

2-5.1

The fire chief shall appoint a designated fire department health and safety officer. This position shall comply with the requirements of NFPA 1521, *Standard for Fire Department Safety Officer.*

2-5.2

The fire department health and safety officer shall be responsible for the management of the occupational safety and health program.

Safety Officer

The safety officer, a member of the command staff, is responsible for monitoring and assessing hazardous and unsafe situations and developing measures for assuring personnel safety. Although the safety officer may exercise emergency authority to stop or prevent unsafe acts when immediate action is required, the officer will generally correct unsafe acts or conditions through the regular line of authority. The officer maintains awareness of active and developing situations, approves the Medical Plan (ICS Form 206), and includes safety messages in each Incident Action Plan.

- Obtain briefing from incident commander.
- Identify hazardous situations associated with the incident.
- Participate in planning meetings.
- Review Incident Action Plans.
- Identify potentially unsafe situations.
- Exercise emergency authority to stop and prevent unsafe acts.
- Investigate accidents that have occurred within incident areas.
- Review and approve Medical Plan (ICS Form 206).
- Maintain Unit Log (ICS Form 214).

Figure 1500-2.6 *Position description for incident safety officer. The safety officer's position is part of the command staff and functions as the eyes and ears for safety for the incident commander. (From the Field Operations Guide, ICS-420-1, August 1983; available from Fire Protection Publications, Oklahoma State University, Stillwater, OK)*

2-5.3

The fire chief shall assign or make available in accordance with Chapter 2 of NFPA 1521, *Standard for Fire Department Safety Officer,* such additional assistant safety officers and resources as required to fulfill the requirements of the occupational safety and health program.

2-6 Occupational Safety and Health Committee

The occupational safety and health committee should assist with research and development and with implementation of safety programs and policies. In addition, the committee serves the fire chief in an advisory role. In some departments, the occupational safety and health committee assists with writing specifications, developing plans, and writing SOPs.

The makeup of the committee allows all areas of the department to be represented, providing a "quality circle" approach and process for employee input at each level. This "buy-in" approach has worked successfully in many jurisdictions.

2-6.1*

An occupational safety and health committee shall be established and shall serve in an advisory capacity to the fire chief. The committee shall include the designated fire department health and safety officer, representatives of fire department management, and individual members or representatives of member organizations. The committee shall also be permitted to include other persons. Representatives of member organizations shall be selected by their respective organizations, but other committee members shall be appointed to the safety committee by the fire chief.

A-2-6.1 One of the most important provisions for improving the safety and health of the fire service is through an official organizational structure that has the support of the members and the fire department management. Without official recognition and support, safety and health committees might be ineffective showpieces, lack authority, or be dominated by particular interests. To avoid such situations, it is recommended that a safety and health committee be composed of equal numbers of fire department management representatives and member representatives. Specific areas of responsibility of the joint safety and health committee should be outlined in detail through written procedures or contractual negotiation.

2-6.2

The purpose of this committee shall be to conduct research, develop recommendations, and study and review matters pertaining to occupational safety and health within the fire department.

2-6.3*

The committee shall hold regularly scheduled meetings and shall be permitted to hold special meetings whenever necessary. Regular meetings shall be held at least once every six months. Written minutes of each meeting shall be retained and shall be made available to all members.

A-2-6.3 The requirement for one regularly scheduled meeting every six months is intended as a minimum. Committee meetings should be held as often as necessary to deal with the issues confronting the group. The written minutes of each meeting should be distributed and posted in a conspicuous place in each fire station so that all members can be aware of issues under discussion and actions that have been taken.

2-7 Records

The data collection system required by Section 2-7 provides a factual data base for use by the occupational safety and health committee and risk managers. This data base includes confidential personnel health records, as well as documentation of exposures to hazards, training and investigation, and equipment maintenance and repair records. Any information in the data base may be requested for civil or criminal action. In some cases, jurisdictions are required to maintain the data base for as long as thirty years after an employee is deceased.

2-7.1*

The fire department shall establish a data collection system and maintain permanent records of all accidents, injuries, illnesses, exposures to infectious agents and communicable diseases, or deaths that are or might be job related.

A-2-7.1 The data collection system for accidents, injuries, illnesses, exposures, and deaths should provide both incident-specific information for future reference and information that can be processed in studies of morbidity, mortality, and causation. The use of standard coding as provided by NFPA 901, *Standard Classifications for Incident Reporting and Fire Protection Data*, will allow compatibility with national and regional reporting systems.

2-7.2

The data collection system shall also maintain individual records of any occupational exposure to known or suspected toxic products or infectious or communicable diseases.

2-7.3

The fire department shall assure that a confidential health record for each member and a health data base is maintained as specified in Chapter 8 of this standard.

2-7.4*

The fire department shall maintain training records for each member indicating dates, subjects covered, satisfactory completion, and, if any, certifications achieved.

A-2-7.4 See NFPA 1401, *Recommended Practice for Fire Service Training Reports and Records,* for further information and guidance.

2-7.5

The fire department shall assure that inspection, maintenance, repair, and service records are maintained for all vehicles and equipment used for emergency operations and training.

CHAPTER 3

Training and Education

3-1 General Requirements

3-1.1

The fire department shall establish and maintain a training and education program with a goal of preventing occupational accidents, deaths, injuries, and illnesses.

As paragraph 3-1.1 suggests, training and education are key to an effective occupational safety and health program. *(See Figure 1500-3.1.)* It is critical that members are trained before they perform certain tasks. Safety is paramount in fire department operations. There is only one way to do a task: safely. *(See Figure 1500-3.2.)*

3-1.2

The training and education provided to members shall address all of the applicable provisions of this standard.

Figure 1500-3.1 *A well-equipped training division office has the necessary tools to track and document fire department training. (Photo courtesy of Virginia Beach Fire Department)*

Figure 1500-3.2 *Driver/operator training is an important safety consideration and is a key component in a department's training program. Driver/operators should be trained to meet the requirements of NFPA 1002 (1993). (Photo courtesy of Virginia Beach Fire Department)*

3-1.2.1 Equivalent levels of training shall be permitted as specified in Section 1-4 of this document.

Paragraph 3-1.2.1 permits equivalent training but adheres to the requirement in Section 1-4 for technical documentation of the equivalent training. Certification is not required.

3-1.3*

The fire department shall provide training and education for all fire department members commensurate with the duties and functions that they are expected to perform. Members shall be provided with training and education appropriate for their duties and responsibilities before being permitted to engage in emergency operations.

A-3-1.3 Members who have not met the specific qualifications listed in 3-3.2 through 3-3.6 should not perform the listed duties in actual emergency incidents. These members might, however, be utilized under structured supervision to perform functions for which they have been trained.

3-1.4

The fire department shall provide training and education for all members to assure that they are able to perform their assigned duties in a safe manner that does not pose a hazard to themselves or to other members.

3-1.5*

All training and education shall be provided by qualified persons.

A-3-1.5 A particular training class or session might be conducted by an individual who has special expertise or abilities in the subject area, whether or not the instructor is a member of the fire department or a qualified fire service instructor.

According to paragraph A-3-1.5, trainers must be qualified, but need not be members of the fire service. Training in fire department administration, management, special operations, and other areas must be conducted by the most qualified person. When the fire department does not have a qualified trainer for a specific subject, outside trainers may be used. For example, physicians may provide EMS training, personnel from the Appalachian Mountain Club could teach high-angle rescue, and businesspeople could instruct in management.

3-1.6

Fire department training officers shall at least meet the qualifications for Instructor I as specified in NFPA 1041, *Standard for Fire Service Instructor Professional Qualifications.*

3-1.7

The training program for all members engaged in emergency operations shall include procedures for the safe exit of members from the dangerous area in the event of equipment failure or sudden changes in conditions.

Procedures for safe exit, as introduced in 3-1.7, are integral to a fire department's incident management system [described further in NFPA 1561, *Standard on Fire Department Incident Management System* (1995) in Part Three of this handbook]. Members will be able to recognize the evacuation signal. The need for training in safe exit procedures not only applies to special operations, but is critical to routine fire suppression operations as well. In both structural and wildland fire-fighting operations, fire fighters must know when and how to evacuate in an emergency.

3-1.8

Training in emergency operations shall be based on standard operating procedures. These procedures shall be maintained in written form (in conjunction with the fire department risk management plan) and shall address anticipated emergency scene operations.

3-1.9

Training exercises shall be conducted in accordance with the established standard operating procedures and shall be supervised by qualified instructors.

Paragraph 3-1.9 and the late football coach Vince Lombardi make the same point: "Practice like you are going to play." Training based on standard operating procedures, especially if linked to an incident command system, safely prepares members at all levels to respond to actual incidents.

3-1.10

All members who are likely to be involved in emergency operations shall be trained in the incident management system used by the fire department as specified in 6-1.2 of this standard.

Using an incident management system only for "the big one" will not work. As paragraph 3-1.10 requires, members need to be trained at every level and position to which they may be assigned. An IMS focuses on safety by providing a system to properly deploy personnel to operate in a safe and healthy work environment. As a result, a focus on safety will drive training in the incident management system.

Paragraph 3-1.10 requires the basic training in IMS and how the department utilizes its system. Participation in the National Fire Academy's 12-hour course on Incident Command Systems is one way to acquire the training required in this section. *(See also Chapter 6, "Emergency Operations.")*

3-2 Training Requirements

Section 3-2 sets forth the minimum requirements, based on NFPA professional qualification standards, that personnel should have before being assigned or promoted to a rank or position. *(See Figure 1500-3.3.)* These standards, based on measurable job performance requirements developed by peer professionals, may also provide a logical progression for promotion although they were not developed with that intent.

Figure 1500-3.3 Utilizing different positions within the incident command system at training exercises proves to be a valuable tool in training new personnel. It also reinforces the use of the incident management system at training exercises. (Photo courtesy of Virginia Beach Fire Department)

3-2.1*

All members who engage in structural fire fighting shall at least meet the requirements of Fire Fighter I as specified in NFPA 1001, *Standard on Fire Fighter Professional Qualifications*.

A-3-2.1 In order to ensure compliance with the minimum requirements of NFPA 1001, *Standard on Fire Fighter Professional Qualifications*, fire department training programs should be certified through a recognized accreditation system. Members who have not completed the training requirements for Fire Fighter I should not participate in interior structural fire fighting but might perform other support functions at emergency incidents.

3-2.2

Any training involving live fire-fighting exercises shall be conducted in compliance with NFPA 1403, *Standard on Live Fire Training Evolutions*.

The need for paragraph 3-2.2 grew from fire fighter fatalities and injuries during live fire training operations. NFPA 1403 was developed by NFPA's Training Committee after fire fighter fatalities occurred at Boulder, Colorado. All fire department training, especially when live fire is involved, should be conducted in the safest environment possible.

3-2.3

All fire apparatus drivers/operators shall meet the applicable requirements specified in NFPA 1002, *Standard for Fire Department Vehicle Driver/Operator Professional Qualifications*.

3-2.4

All members who are primarily assigned to aircraft rescue and fire fighting shall meet the requirements specified in NFPA 1003, *Standard for Airport Fire Fighter Professional Qualifications*.

3-2.5

All fire officers shall at least meet the requirements for Fire Officer I as specified in NFPA 1021, *Standard for Fire Officer Professional Qualifications*.

3-2.6

All members who engage in wildland fire fighting shall meet the requirements for wildland fire fighters as specified in NFPA 1051, *Standard for Wildland Fire Fighter Professional Qualifications*.

Input from the U.S. Forest Service resulted in the addition of paragraph 3-2.6 to the 1997 edition of NFPA 1500. The wildland environment requires a different set of skills and training than does structural fire fighting. Fire fighters who operate within the wildland/urban interface must be trained in wildland fire fighting. A wildland fire incident on Long Island in 1996 demonstrated the need for structural fire fighters to be trained and equipped for wildland fire fighting. The fire fighters were not trained in wildland/grass fire-fighting procedures, their incident management structure was incapable of handling an incident of that size, and the fire fighters lacked the proper protective clothing.

3-2.7

All members who engage in emergency medical services shall meet the requirements of the authority having jurisdiction.

Today's fire services that provide emergency medical service find that such services make up 60 percent to 80 percent of their responses. The level of service determined by the AHJ could range from first responder to advanced life support (ALS) and may or may not include patient transport. Paragraph 3-2.7 requires the AHJ to set requirements for emergency medical service providers; those requirements should be commensurate with the level of service provided.

3-2.8

All members shall meet the training requirements for infectious disease control as specified in NFPA 1581, *Standard on Fire Department Infection Control Program.*

The requirements of this section are further explained in Chapter 2 of NFPA 1581, *Standard on Fire Department Infection Control Programs* (1995). (See Part Four of this handbook.) Note that fire departments that do not provide emergency medical services must comply with NFPA 1581, since incidents such as auto extrication expose members to possible hazards.

3-2.9*

All members who respond to incidents involving the release or potential release of hazardous substances shall meet at least the requirements for First Responder Operations Level as specified in NFPA 472, *Standard for Professional Competence of Responders to Hazardous Materials Incidents.*

A-3-2.9 In the United States, federal regulations require a minimum amount of training for fire service personnel who respond to hazardous materials incidents. These requirements can be found in 29 CFR 1910.120 (OSHA) and in 40 CFR 311 (EPA). These regulations affect all fire departments in the United States whether full-time career, part-time, combination career and volunteer, or fully volunteer. These regulations apply in all states, and not just in those states with federally approved state OSHA programs.

In the U.S. federal regulations, First Responder Operations Level is defined as follows:

> First responders at the operations level are individuals who respond to releases or potential releases of hazardous substances as part of the initial response to the site for the purpose of protecting nearby persons, property, or the environment from the effects of the release. They are trained to respond in a defensive fashion without actually trying to stop the release. Their function is to contain the release from a safe distance, keep it from spreading, and prevent exposure. First responders at the operational level shall have received at least 8 hr of training or have had sufficient experience to objectively demonstrate competency in the following areas in addition to those listed in the awareness level and the employer shall so certify:
>
> (a) Knowledge of the basic hazard and risk assessment techniques;
> (b) Know how to properly select and use proper personal protective equipment provided to the First Responder Operations Level;
> (c) An understanding of basic hazardous materials terms;
> (d) Know how to perform basic control, confinement, and/or confinement operations within the capabilities of the resources and personal protective equipment available with their unit;
> (e) Know how to implement basic decontamination procedures;
> (f) An understanding of the relevant standard operating procedures and termination procedures.

The First Responder Operations Level in both the U.S. federal regulations and NFPA 472, *Standard for Professional Competence of Responders to Hazardous Materials Incidents*, is similar. Whereas the U.S. federal regulations (29 CFR 1910.120 or 40 CFR 311) govern the fire service in every state in the United States, the minimum level of training for all fire fighters must be the First Responder Operations Level.

Requirements for the First Responder Operations Level of NFPA 472 are the same as in OSHA regulations 29 *CFR* 1910.120, as described in paragraph A-3-2.9.

3-2.10

All members who respond to marine vessel fires from land-based companies shall be trained to meet the requirements of NFPA 1405, *Guide for Land-Based Fire Fighters Who Respond to Marine Vessel Fires.*

3-2.11

All members who engage in emergency operations shall be trained commensurate with their duties and responsibilities. Training shall be as frequent as necessary to ensure that members can perform their assigned duties in a safe and competent manner but shall not be less frequent than specified in this section.

3-2.11.1* The fire department shall assure that all members who engage in fire-fighting operations are aware of the flammability and thermal stability characteristics of various types of fabrics used in clothing.

A-3-2.11.1 Clothing that is made from 100 percent natural fibers or blends that are principally natural fibers should be selected over other fabrics that have poor thermal stability or ignite easily.

The very fact that persons are fire fighters indicates that all clothing that they wear should be flame resistant (as children's sleepwear is required to be) to give a degree of safety if unanticipated happenings occur that expose the clothing to flame, flash, sparks, or hot substances. *(See also 5-1.7.)*

Fire fighters wear many types of garments under their protective clothing ensemble; this clothing may not meet NFPA 1975, *Standard on Station/Work Uniforms for*

Fire Fighters (1994). It is possible for a protective ensemble to remain fully intact while the clothing underneath fails, causing severe burns. Consequently, members need to know about a fabric's flammability and thermal stability and how that fabric performs under fire-fighting conditions.

Paragraph 3-2.11.1 applies to career personnel and may be even more applicable to those volunteers, paid-call personnel, and career personnel who respond off duty.

3-2.12

Members who use respiratory protection equipment at emergency incidents or in hazardous or potentially hazardous atmospheres shall be qualified to use respiratory protection. Members shall be trained for each type and model of respiratory protection they are required to use.

The language of 3-2.12 is consistent with the OSHA regulation 29 *CFR* 1910.134, *Standard on Respiratory Protection.*

3-2.13

The officers in charge of fire prevention, maintenance, communications, and other specialized bureaus shall be responsible for special training needed by the personnel assigned to their particular staff function. They shall coordinate this special training with other programs of the department and with the training officer.

3-2.14

Where the fire department is responsible for nonstructural fire-fighting operations, including but not limited to wildland or other exterior fires, the fire department shall provide training in such fire-fighting operations in compliance with NFPA 1403, *Standard on Live Fire Training Evolutions.*

3-2.15

These training sessions shall be in addition to the training required in 3-3.3 of this chapter for members who are also assigned to structural fire-fighting duties.

3-2.16*

Smoke-generating devices that produce a hazardous atmosphere shall not be used in training exercises.

A-3-2.16 Several accidents have occurred where smoke bombs or other smoke-generating devices that produce a toxic atmosphere have been used for training exercises. Where training exercises are intended to simulate emergency conditions, smoke-generating devices that do not create a hazard are required.

3-3 Frequency

3-3.1

Training shall be provided for all members as often as necessary to meet the applicable requirements of this chapter, but not less than twice each year.

3-3.2

Whenever changes in standard operating procedures or technology are introduced, or new hazards are identified in the work environment, appropriate training and education shall be provided for all affected members.

Quite simply, paragraph 3-3.2 means no on-the-job training. When members are assigned or reassigned specific tasks or provide a new or different level of service, they must be trained *before* the new work begins.

3-3.3

Where the fire department is responsible for structural fire-fighting operations, the fire department shall provide structural fire-fighting training at least monthly.

3-3.4

Members who engage in structural fire fighting shall attend a minimum of 10 monthly structural fire-fighting training sessions. Members shall participate in at least 24 hours of structural fire-fighting training annually.

3-3.5

Members who are primarily assigned to nonstructural fire-fighting operations shall attend nonstructural fire-fighting training sessions consisting of at least 24 hours of training annually.

3-3.6

Members who occasionally are assigned to nonstructural fire-fighting operations shall attend nonstructural fire-fighting training sessions consisting of at least nine hours annually.

Paragraphs 3-3.3 through 3-3.6 are based on the fact that fire department members who are not assigned to suppression need training in their specific job function. Training for those who engage in structural fire fighting from time to time is a matter of safety.

3-4 Special Operations

Fire departments provide many special services beyond structural fire fighting and emergency medical services. These special operations may include high-angle rescue, swift-water rescue, urban search and rescue, trench cave-in rescue, and hazardous materials response and training beyond the operations level specified in NFPA 472, *Standard for Professional Competence of Responders to Hazardous Materials Incidents* (1997). According to Chapter 2 of NFPA 1500, these levels of service should be outlined in the department's organizational statement. The organizational statement should also be a primary component of the department's risk management plan.

The necessary equipment, time, training, and costs of special operations need to be evaluated at every level. The consensus may be that special operations services are provided regionally, through another agency, or by mutual aid. The operational and organizational complexity may make special operations cost prohibitive for some departments; for other departments, the need may not exist.

3-4.1

Specific and advanced training and education shall be provided to members who engage in special operations.

3-4.2

The fire department shall develop written standard operating procedures that describe the actions to be taken in situations involving special operations and shall include these standard operating procedures in the advanced training and education program.

3-4.3

All members who are likely to be involved in hazardous materials mitigation shall be trained to the appropriate level above First Responder Operations in accordance with NFPA 472, *Standard for Professional Competence of Responders to Hazardous Materials Incidents.*

Paragraph 3-4.3 requires the same level of hazardous material training required by OSHA 29 *CFR* 1910.120.

CHAPTER 4

Vehicles, Equipment, and Drivers

4-1 Fire Department Vehicles

4-1.1*

The fire department shall consider safety and health as primary concerns in the specification, design, construction, acquisition, operation, maintenance, inspection, and repair of all fire department vehicles.

A-4-1.1 Information regarding ambulance specifications can be found in the current U.S. Federal Government General Services Administration's Federal Specification KKK-A-1822D for Ambulances.

4-1.2

All new fire apparatus, including but not limited to pumpers, initial fire attack, mobile water supply, ladder and elevating platforms, and special service apparatus, shall be specified and ordered to meet the applicable requirements of NFPA 1901, *Standard for Automotive Fire Apparatus.*

According to paragraph 4-1.2, the 1996 edition of NFPA 1901, *Standard for Automotive Fire Apparatus,* contains all requirements for all types of fire apparatus (except wildland apparatus). This provision enables the user of the document to specify particular components of the type of apparatus by citing individual chapters of NFPA 1901 (for example, chapters dealing with drive train, chassis, or electrical systems) and then providing the particular requirements for pumpers, aerials, or special duty apparatus. *(See Figures 1500-4.1 and 1500-4.2.)*

4-1.3

All new wildland fire apparatus shall be specified and ordered to meet the requirements of NFPA 1906, *Standard for Wildland Fire Apparatus.*

4-1.4

Where tools, equipment, or respiratory protection are carried within enclosed seating areas of fire department vehicles, such items shall be secured by either a positive mechanical means of holding the item in its stowed position or in a compartment with a positive latching door. The means of holding the item in place or the compartment shall be designed to minimize injury to persons in the enclosed area of the vehicle caused by loose equipment during travel and in the event of an accident, a rapid deceleration, or a rapid acceleration.

Paragraph 4-1.4 concentrates on preventing injury by requiring loose equipment on fire apparatus to be secured. NFPA 1901 (1996) requires SCBA mounting brackets to meet a 10-gravity deceleration test. In addition to SCBA, many fire department vehicles carry map books, lights, assorted tools, and other equipment in the riding areas of apparatus. When the apparatus is required to stop or start suddenly, these loose items become missiles and can potentially injure or kill fire fighters. The hazards of loose items are further compounded when the apparatus is involved in a collision or accident.

4-2 Drivers/Operators of Fire Department Apparatus

4-2.1*

Fire department vehicles shall be operated only by members who have successfully completed an approved driver training program or by student drivers who are under the supervision of a qualified driver. Driver/operators of fire apparatus shall meet the requirements specified in Chapter 3 of this standard.

Figure 1500-4.1 Design criteria for apparatus include the safety of the personnel who will respond on and operate that apparatus. (Photo courtesy of Greenwood Fire Apparatus)

Figure 1500-4.2 Using NFPA 1901 (1996) as a base foundation for the design and specification of new apparatus will assist the department in providing the safest vehicle possible. (Photo courtesy of Greenwood Fire Apparatus)

A-4-2.1 NFPA 1451, *Standard for a Fire Service Vehicle Operations Training Program,* can be used to meet the requirements of an "approved driver training program."

According to data provided by NFPA's Fire Analysis and Research Division, 31 fire fighters have died in apparatus accidents since 1977. *(See Figure 1500-2.4 in Chapter 2.)* These apparatus accidents, all too often, involve vehicles driven by untrained or unqualified operators. For a 10-year analysis of fire fighter fatality data, see Supplement 1 in Part Six of this handbook.

4-2.2*

Drivers of fire department vehicles shall have valid driver's licenses. Vehicles shall be operated in compliance with all traffic laws, including sections pertaining to emergency vehicles, and any requirements of the authority having jurisdiction.

Paragraph 4-2.2 requires a valid driver's license and other mandates of the AHJ. In addition to a driver's license, many municipalities, states, provinces, territories, and jurisdictions require a special classification of driver's license to operate fire apparatus. This is usually based on the GVW (gross vehicle weight) of the apparatus. U.S. Department of Labor requirements specify that operators have a commercial driver's license (CDL) to operate apparatus. Departments should check with their city attorney or local law enforcement agency to see which parts of the Department of Labor regulations apply to them.

A-4-2.2 When members respond to incidents or to the fire station in their own vehicles, the operation of these vehicles is governed by all applicable traffic laws and codes as enacted by the authority having jurisdiction. The fire department should enact specific rules and regulations pertaining to the use of private vehicles for emergency response. These rules and regulations should be at least equal to the provisions regulating the operation of fire department vehicles.

The determination of driver's license requirements is a function of a particular authority in each location. This agency can be a state or provincial Department of Transportation or an equivalent agency. Other authorities, such as military branches, have the authority to issue permits to operate their vehicles. It is a responsibility of the fire department to determine the requirements that apply in each situation and for each class of vehicle.

On August 10, 1989, a Formal Interpretation concerning paragraph 4-2.2 was issued by the Standards Council. That Formal Interpretation is still valid and is reproduced here for the reader's convenience.

Formal Interpretation

Reference: 4-2.2

F.I. No.: 87-4

Question: Is the intent of 4-2.2 to require members of a fire department who drive fire apparatus be licensed as required by the motor vehicle laws of the state in which that department is located?

Answer: Yes.

Issue Edition: 1987

Reference: 4-2.2

Issue Date: July 21, 1989

Effective Date: August 10, 1989

4-2.3*

Drivers of fire department vehicles shall be directly responsible for the safe and prudent operation of the vehicles under all conditions. When the driver is under the direct supervision of an officer, that officer shall also assume responsibility for the actions of the driver.

The officer, or person in the right front seat, is responsible for the driving actions of the vehicle operator. If members and apparatus do not arrive on-scene safely and quickly, the outcomes of the incident are drastically changed.

A-4-2.3 The driver of any vehicle has legal responsibility for its safe and prudent operation at all times. While the driver is responsible for the operation of the vehicle, the officer is responsible for the actions of the driver.

4-2.4

Drivers shall not move fire department vehicles until all persons on the vehicle are seated and secured with seat belts in approved riding positions, other than as specifically allowed in 4-3.1.1 of this chapter.

The requirement of paragraph 4-2.4 has been in NFPA 1500 since the 1987 edition. As a result, today's designs for fire apparatus require the department to specify how many members will be riding on the apparatus and that personnel be seated and belted before the apparatus moves. Standing up in apparatus, even when totally enclosed, yields a false sense of security. Fire fighters who are not seated and belted risk falling out of the doors of the apparatus as it is responding. *(See Supplement 1, "1996 Fire Fighter Fatalities," in Part Six of this handbook.)*

4-2.5

During nonemergency travel, drivers of fire department vehicles shall obey all traffic control signals and signs and all laws and rules of the road of the jurisdiction for the operation of motor vehicles.

4-2.6*

The fire department shall develop standard operating procedures for safely driving fire department vehicles during nonemergency travel and emergency response and shall include specific criteria for vehicle speed, crossing intersections, traversing railroad grade crossings, and the use of emergency warning devices. Such procedures for emergency response shall emphasize that the safe arrival of fire department vehicles at the emergency scene is the first priority.

A-4-2.6 The development, implementation, and periodic review of standard operating procedures for driving any fire department vehicle is an important element in clearly identifying the fire department's policy on what is expected of drivers. Safe arrival is of prime importance. Standard operating procedures should include a "challenge and response" dialogue between the vehicle driver on an emergency response and the officer or other member in the driver compartment. The "challenge and response" dialogue should be instituted to determine the driver's intentions when approaching any perceived or identified hazard on the response route to remind the driver of the presence of the hazard and the planned procedures for managing the hazard, and to ensure that the driver is coping with stressors encountered during the response and not focusing only on arriving at the site of the emergency.

The specific inclusion of railroad grade crossing is based upon recommendations made by the National Transportation Safety Board (NTSB) to NFPA following the 1989 investigation of a collision between a fire department pumper and a passenger train. The NTSB report states that "planning how to safely traverse grade crossing encountered en route is a necessary part of any fire company's response plan."

NTSB recommends that the following be considered when developing the plans:

> If it is not practical to plan an emergency response route that avoids grade crossings, selection of crossings that are equipped with automatic warning devices is preferable to selection of those that are not. All planning should include identification of the location at the crossing from which a driver or other observer assigned to the apparatus can see the maximum available distance down the track(s) on both sides.
>
> At crossings over a single straight track with no nearby obstructions, briefly stopping or slowing the apparatus to allow a proper scan both left and right may be sufficient. If the tracks are curved, vision is obstructed, or the crossing has more than one set of tracks where the presence of one train may hide the approach of another, sight distance may be optimized by having one or more members cross the tracks on foot and look for approaching trains.

4-2.7*

During emergency response, drivers of fire department vehicles shall bring the vehicle to a complete stop under any of the following circumstances:

(a) When directed by a law enforcement officer
(b) Red traffic lights
(c) Stop signs
(d) Negative right-of-way intersections
(e) Blind intersections
(f) When the driver cannot account for all lanes of traffic in an intersection
(g) When other intersection hazards are present
(h) When encountering a stopped school bus with flashing warning lights

A-4-2.7 Accidents at intersections contribute to both civilian and fire fighter deaths and injuries while fire department vehicles are responding to or returning from an emergency incident. Coming to a complete stop when there are any intersection hazards and proceeding only when the driver can do so safely will reduce accidents and the risk of injury or death. It is recommended that intersection control devices be installed that allow emergency vehicles to control traffic lights at intersections.

Many insurance carriers, including Volunteer Fireman's Insurance Services and Travelers Insurance Company, provide or require emergency vehicle operator training. *(See Figure 1500-4.3.)*

4-2.7.1 Drivers shall proceed through intersections only when the driver can account for all lanes of traffic in the intersection.

Emergency Vehicle Driver Training (Instructor)

This 16-hour seminar is targeted to the Training Officers and Instructors who are responsible for training emergency vehicle operators. Recently redesigned and updated, the program incorporates the major elements of a comprehensive driver training program—classroom instruction, competency course, and testing. The intent of the emergency vehicle driver training course is to train instructors to teach the students to use their own thought processes and to make them aware of the tragedy, financial loss, the legal and moral responsibilities that they have when operating emergency vehicles.

***Figure 1500-4.3** Course description for an emergency vehicle driver training program.*

4-2.8*

During emergency response or nonemergency travel, drivers of fire department vehicles shall come to a complete stop at all unguarded railroad grade crossings. Drivers shall assure that it is safe to proceed before crossing the railroad track(s). Drivers shall also use caution when approaching and crossing any guarded grade railroad crossing.

A-4-2.8 Vehicle accidents at railroad crossings have resulted in a number of deaths and injuries to fire department members. A National Transportation Safety Board (NTSB) study concluded that a train's warning horn becomes an ineffective device for warning large vehicles or trucks unless the vehicle driver stops; idles the engine; turns off all radios, fans, wipers, and other noise-producing equipment in the cab; lowers the window; and listens for a train's horn before entering a grade crossing.

Paragraph 4-2.8 was added to NFPA 1500 after numerous fire apparatus accidents that resulted in fire fighter fatalities. The March 1991 National Transportation Safety Board (NTSB) Special Investigation Report, "Emergency Fire Apparatus" (PB91-917001), recommended specific training and safety requirements for apparatus. Supplement 2 in Part Six of this handbook includes that report.

4-2.9

The fire department shall include in the driver training program information on the potential hazards of retarders, such as engine, transmission, and driveline retarders, and shall develop written procedures pertaining to the use of such retarders.

4-2.10

The fire department shall develop written procedures requiring drivers to discontinue the use of manual brake limiting valves, frequently labeled as a "wet road/dry road" switch, and requiring that the valve/switch remains in the "dry road" position.

The requirements in paragraphs 4-2.9 and 4-2.10 were included first in the 1992 edition. Apparatus accidents have been attributed to the use of these devices, along with inadequate vehicle operator training in their use.

4-3 Persons Riding in Fire Apparatus

4-3.1*

All persons riding in fire apparatus shall be seated and belted securely by seat belts in approved riding positions and at any time the vehicle is in motion other than as allowed in 4-3.1.1, 4-3.1.2, and 4-3.1.3 of this section. Standing or riding on tail steps, sidesteps, running boards, or in any other exposed position shall be specifically prohibited. Seatbelts shall not be released or loosened for any purpose while the vehicle is in motion, including the donning of respiratory protection equipment or protective clothing.

A-4-3.1 It is intended for the requirements of 4-3.1 to apply to all situations when persons or members are riding on fire apparatus other than for the specific variances in 4-3.1.1, 4-3.1.2, and 4-3.1.3. Included in the "seated and belted" requirement are any times the fire apparatus is traveling to, participating in, or returning from any funeral, parade, or public relations/education event. Fire fighters cannot be allowed to ride on the outside of apparatus in order to fight wildland fires. The Fire Line Safety Committee (FLSC) of the National Wildfire Coordinating Group (NWCG) represents the U.S. Forest Service, Bureau of Land Management, Bureau of Indian Affairs, Fish and Wildlife Agency, National Park Service, and the National Association of State Foresters. Their position is that the practice of fire fighters riding on the outside of vehicles and fighting wildland fires from these positions is very dangerous, and they strongly recommend this not be allowed. One issue is the exposure to personnel in unprotected positions. Persons have been killed while performing this operation. Also, the vehicle driver's vision is impaired. The second issue is that this is not an effective way to extinguish the fire, as it can allow the vehicle to pass over or by areas not completely extinguished. Fire can then flare up underneath or behind the vehicle and could cut off escape routes. The FLSC and the NWCG strongly recommend that two fire fighters, each with a hose line, walk ahead and aside of the vehicle's path, both fire fighters on the same side of the vehicle (not one on each side), in clear view of the driver, with the vehicle being driven in uninvolved terrain. This allows the fire fighters to operate in an unhurried manner, with a clear view of fire conditions and the success of the extinguishment. Areas not extinguished should not be bypassed unless follow-up crews are operating behind the lead unit and there is no danger to escape routes or to personnel.

Since the 1987 edition, NFPA 1500 has required approved riding positions for personnel so that they are seated, belted, and enclosed. These positions, designated in the apparatus specification, provide the safest position from the elements. *(See Figure 1500-4.4; see commentary following paragraph 4-2.4.)*

4-3.1.1* Members actively performing necessary emergency medical care while the vehicle is in motion shall be secured to the vehicle by a seat belt, or by a safety harness designed for occupant restraint, to the extent consistent with the effective provision of such emergency medical care. All other persons in the vehicle shall be seated and belted in approved riding positions while the vehicle is in motion.

A-4-3.1.1 There are instances in which members must provide emergency medical care while the vehicle is in motion.

Figure 1500-4.4 Note the enclosed cab on this fire apparatus. (Photo courtesy of Greenwood Fire Apparatus)

In some situations, the provision of such medical care would not allow the members to remain seated and secured to the vehicle. Such situations, while they occur infrequently, might include performing chest compressions during CPR. If a vehicle accident were to occur while an unsecured member was performing necessary emergency medical care, there would be substantial risk of injury to the member.

Ambulance manufacturers were made aware of the requirements of paragraph 4-3.1.1 in the 1992 edition. Since that time, manufacturers have developed ways to assist EMS providers in being tethered inside the vehicle. Providing definitive EMS care at the ALS level requires the provider to move rapidly about the patient. Both driver/operators and care providers must understand potential dangers to providers and patients alike while en route to a medical facility.

4-3.1.2* Fire departments permitting hose loading operations while the vehicle is in motion shall develop written standard operating procedures addressing all safety aspects.

A-4-3.1.2

(a) Hose loading procedures should be specified in a written standard operating procedure that includes at least these safety conditions. All members involved in the hose loading should have been trained in these procedures.

(b) There should be a member, other than those members loading hose, assigned as a safety observer. The safety observer should have an unobstructed view of the hose loading operation and be in visual and voice contact with the apparatus operator.

(c) Non-fire department vehicular traffic should be excluded from the area or should be under the control of authorized traffic control persons.

(d) The fire apparatus can be driven only in a forward direction at a speed of 5 mph (8 kph) or less.

(e) No members can be allowed to stand on the tailstep, sidesteps, running boards, or any other location on the apparatus while the apparatus is in motion.

(f) Members can be permitted to be in the hose bed, but should not stand while the apparatus is in motion.

(g) Prior to the beginning of each hose loading operation, the situation should be evaluated to ensure compliance with all the provisions of the written procedures. If the written procedures cannot be complied with, or if there is any question as to the safety of the operation for the specific situation, then the hose should not be loaded on moving fire apparatus.

4-3.1.3* Fire departments permitting tiller training, where both the instructor and the trainee are at the tiller position, shall develop written standard operating procedures addressing all safety aspects.

A-4-3.1.3

(a) Tiller training procedures should be specified in a written standard operating procedures that includes at least these safety conditions. All members involved in tiller training should have been trained in these procedures.

(b) The aerial apparatus should be equipped with seating positions for both the tiller instructor and the tiller trainee. Both seating positions should be equipped with seat belts for each individual. The tiller instructor should be permitted to take a position alongside the tiller trainee.

(c) The tiller instructor's seat should be permitted to be detachable. Where the instructor's seat is detachable, the detachable seat assembly should be structurally sufficient to support and secure the instructor. The detachable seat assembly should be attached and positioned in a safe manner immediately adjacent to the regular tiller seat. The detachable seat assembly should be equipped with a seat belt or vehicle safety harness. The detachable seat assembly should be attached and used only for training purposes.

(d) Both the tiller instructor and the tiller trainee should be seated and belted.

(e) The instructor and trainee should wear and use both helmet and eye protection if not seated in an enclosed area.

(f) In the event the aerial apparatus is needed for an emergency response during a tiller training session, the training session should be terminated, and all members should be seated and belted in the approved riding positions. There should be only one person at the tiller position. During the emergency response, the apparatus should be operated by qualified driver/operators.

The requirements of 4-3.1.2 and 4-3.1.3 were more stringent in the 1992 edition of NFPA 1500, calling for additional safety requirements that may have been prohibitive. In the 1997 edition, these requirements have been moved to Appendix A to provide guidance for users.

4-3.2*

Helmets and eye protection shall be provided for and used by persons riding in cabs or tiller seats that are not enclosed on at least three sides and the top.

A-4-3.2 Helmets and eye protection (goggles, safety glasses, or faceshield) should be worn by all members riding in positions that do not provide the protection of an enclosed cab. Helmets are also recommended for members riding in enclosed areas where seats are not designed to provide head and neck protection in a collision. Properly designed seats, with head and neck protection, alleviate the need for helmets, and, in some cases, helmets would compromise the safety provided by the seats.

4-3.3

On existing fire apparatus where there is an insufficient number of seats available for the number of members assigned to or expected to ride on that piece of apparatus, alternate means of transportation that provide seating positions shall be used. Such alternate means of transportation shall include, but not be limited to, other fire apparatus, automobiles, or vans.

Paragraph 4-3.3 opens the door for the use of personal vehicles by members at the emergency scene. The fire department should develop a plan for the safe and efficient response of personnel to an incident scene. Past incidents, such as the LaBianca plane crash on Long Island, show the need for a plan for personal vehicle response. In this incident, personal vehicles had to be towed to allow the entry and egress of emergency response apparatus. The insurance policies of some departments require that members respond on fire department-owned vehicles. Other departments allow personal vehicle use and have developed specific response SOPs, parking locations that do not impede emergency vehicle traffic, and specific staging locations for arriving personnel.

4-3.4*

All new fire apparatus shall be specified and ordered in accordance with the appropriate fire apparatus standard specified in Section 4-1 of this chapter with a sufficient number of seats in a fully enclosed personnel area for the maximum number of persons expected to ride on the vehicle at any time. The fully enclosed personnel area shall consist of a roof, a floor, and four sides, with positive latching doors that provide total enclosure.

A-4-3.4 The minimum requirement for new fire apparatus provides seats in fully enclosed areas for all members who ride on fire apparatus at any time. It is generally agreed that fully enclosed driver compartments and passenger compartments provide a higher level of safety in collisions and rollovers, protection from flying objects, noise reduction, and protection from inclement weather; therefore, fully enclosed cabs are required for new apparatus purchases and strongly recommended for renovation of existing apparatus where possible. It is extremely important that all members remain seated and secured by seat belts, in the seats provided, at all times when the vehicle is in motion.

4-4 Inspection, Maintenance, and Repair of Fire Apparatus

4-4.1*

All fire department vehicles shall be inspected at least weekly, within 24 hours after any use or repair, and prior to being placed in service or used for emergency purposes to identify and correct unsafe conditions.

A-4-4.1 and A-4-5.5 The purpose of these paragraphs is to assure that all vehicles are inspected on a regular basis and checked for the proper operation of all safety features. This inspection should include tires, brakes, warning lights and devices, headlights and clearance lights, windshield wipers, and mirrors. The apparatus should be started and the operation of pumps and other equipment should be verified. Fluid levels should also be checked regularly.

Where apparatus is in regular daily use, these checks should be performed on a daily basis. Apparatus stored in unattended stations that might not be used for extended periods should be checked weekly. Any time such a vehicle is used, it should be checked before being placed back in service. The 24-hour reference provides for situations in which a vehicle can be used within the period preceding a scheduled inspection, although any deficiencies noted in use should be corrected without delay.

The safety equipment carried on fire department vehicles should be inspected in conjunction with the inspection of the vehicle.

4-4.2

A preventive maintenance program shall be established, and records shall be maintained as specified in 2-7.5 of this standard. Maintenance, inspections, and repairs shall be performed by qualified persons in accordance with manufacturer's instructions. Manufacturer's instructions shall be considered as minimum criteria for the maintenance, inspection, and repair of equipment.

The proper care, inspection, and maintenance of fire apparatus are crucial to its safe arrival and subsequent use by fire fighters. The addition of computers and other technology into apparatus makes it imperative that apparatus inspection, maintenance, and repair be done by qualified personnel. The National Association of Emergency Vehicle Technicians (NAEVT) has developed certification programs for personnel who repair apparatus. [Information can be obtained from NAEVT, PO Box 97, Lynnfield, MA 01940-0097 (800-446-2388).] Along the same lines, NFPA's Technical Committee 1071 is developing a proposed *Standard on Professional Qualifications for Apparatus Technician,* which is in the 1999 meeting cycle.

4-4.3*

The fire department shall establish a list of major defects to be utilized to evaluate when a vehicle shall be declared unsafe. Any fire department vehicle found to be unsafe shall be placed out of service until repaired.

A-4-4.3 Applicable federal and state regulations, standards, or guidelines should be used as a basis for creating the list to evaluate whether or not a vehicle is safe.

4-4.4

All repairs to fire department apparatus shall be made by qualified persons experienced with the type of vehicle or the type of work to be performed in accordance with the vehicle manufacturer's instructions.

Paragraph 4-4.4 addresses the need for special qualifications to repair specialized vehicles such as fire apparatus. Many fire department apparatus bid specifications include the location, staffing, and qualifications of the closest authorized apparatus repair facility. Departments have, in some cases, included specific language and a service contract similar to those within the automobile industry. *(See Figure 1500-4.5 for a sample maintenance checklist.)* Proposed NFPA 1071,

Chassis Checklist

- ☐ Lubricate chassis component
- ☐ Change motor oil and filter(s)
- ☐ Change fuel filter(s)
- ☐ Change coolant filter and check coolant PH rating
- ☐ Change transmission filter (external only)
- ☐ Check and fill miscellaneous fluids to capacity (1 gallon limit)
- ☐ Lubricate cab and compartment door latches
- ☐ Inspect the following:
  - ☐ Alternator output
  - ☐ Batteries and clean terminals
  - ☐ Engine belts and hoses
  - ☐ All lights
  - ☐ Correct tire pressure
  - ☐ Rear differential

Pumper Service Checklist

- ☐ Change pump transfer fluid
- ☐ Pressurize pump with air and check for leaks
- ☐ Lubricate relief valve and check operation
- ☐ Vacuum test for proper primer operation
- ☐ Lubricate ball valves and check operations
- ☐ Adjust pump packing
- ☐ Inspect the following:
  - ☐ Pump shift operation
  - ☐ Auto lube and fill
  - ☐ Inspect pump input/output shaft seals

Figure 1500-4.5 *Sample maintenance checklist for firefighting apparatus. This is a partial list of the items that would be included in a routine maintenance check. (Courtesy of Greenwood Fire Apparatus)*

Standard for Emergency Vehicle Technician Professional Qualifications, addresses the qualifications for apparatus technician/mechanic.

4-4.5

Fire pumps on apparatus shall be service tested in accordance with the applicable requirements of NFPA 1911, *Standard for Service Tests of Pumps on Fire Department Apparatus.*

4-4.6

All aerial devices shall be inspected and service tested in accordance with the applicable requirements of NFPA 1914, *Standard for Testing Fire Department Aerial Devices.*

Inspection and testing of aerial devices, as outlined in paragraph 4-4.6, are directly related to fire department occupational safety and health. The number of aerial failures—and subsequent fire fighter injury or death—is attributable to lack of operator training, use of the aerial for purposes not designed for, and the lack of annual inspection by qualified personnel. *(See Figure 1500-4.6.)*

4-4.7

All fire department apparatus shall be cleaned and disinfected after responding to an emergency medical services incident where the potential for contamination from exposure to communicable diseases could have occurred. Cleaning and disinfecting shall be in accordance with NFPA 1581, *Standard on Fire Department Infection Control Program.*

Paragraph 4-4.7 applies to all fire apparatus, not just ambulances. In today's tiered response systems, many fire apparatus are on-scene and providing some level of patient care before the transport vehicle arrives. In this situation, the fire apparatus shall be properly cleaned and disinfected before being placed back in service.

4-5 Tools and Equipment

4-5.1

The fire department shall consider safety and health as primary concerns in the specification, design, construction, acquisition, operation, maintenance, inspection, and repair of all tools and equipment.

Figure 1500-4.6 *According to NFPA 1500, an aerial apparatus shall be tested annually to certify that it meets the requirements of NFPA 1914 (1997). This testing can be done by outside vendors and is typically done on a regional basis for cost purposes. (Photo courtesy of Greenwood Fire Apparatus)*

4-5.1.1 The hearing conservation objectives of Section 5-11 of this standard shall be taken into account in the acquisition of new power tools and power equipment.

When the department purchases new tools and equipment, part of the specifications should relate to what the noise or decibel level is. These specifications then become part of the department's hearing conservation program.

Hearing loss is an occupational hazard of the fire service. As paragraph 4-5.1.1 suggests, preventing hearing loss includes preventing exposure to noise from power tools and equipment. Chapter 8 of NFPA 1500 and NFPA 1582, *Standard on Medical Requirements for Fire Fighters* (1997) (Part Five of this handbook), address this issue. In addition, the health and safety committee should address hearing conservation programs as new tools and equipment are specified and purchased.

4-5.2

All new fire department ground ladders shall be specified and ordered to meet the applicable requirements of NFPA 1931, *Standard on Design of and Design Verification Tests for Fire Department Ground Ladders.*

4-5.3

All new fire hose shall be specified and ordered to meet the applicable requirements of NFPA 1961, *Standard on Fire Hose.*

4-5.4

All new fire department spray nozzles shall be specified and ordered to meet the applicable requirements of NFPA 1964, *Standard for Spray Nozzles (Shutoff and Tip).*

4-5.5*

All equipment carried on fire apparatus or designated for training shall be inspected at least weekly and within 24 hours after any use. Inventory records shall be maintained for the equipment carried on each vehicle. Records shall also be maintained for equipment designated for training.

A-4-5.5 See A-4-4.1.

4-5.6

All equipment carried on fire apparatus or designated for training shall be tested at least annually in accordance with manufacturer's instructions and applicable standards.

4-5.7

Fire-fighting equipment found to be defective or in unserviceable condition shall be removed from service and repaired or replaced.

A process should be in place to identify and mark out-of-service equipment so that it will not be placed back on the apparatus. A record-keeping system is needed to record the date(s) when removed from service, by whom, the reason, by whom or where repaired, and when returned to service after testing. *(See Figure 1500-4.7.)*

Warranty Information

E-One Vehicle	1 year* *2nd year applies if purchased separately
E-One Cab and Body Structure	10 years
E-One Paint and Corrosion	4 years
Booster/Foam Tank	Lifetime for original owner
Hale Pump	2 years or 20,000 hours
Detroit Diesel Engine	5 years or 50,000 miles
Cummins Diesel Engine	5 years or 100,000 miles
Allison Transmission	
Allison MD Series	2 years
Allison HT-740	2 years/50,000 miles pro-rated
Allison HD Series	5 years 100%
Rockwell Axles	3 years
Emergency Lights	Vary by manufacturer. Whelen also warrants strobe bulbs for 1 year if lenses are unbroken.
All Tires (E-One & Commercial Chassis)	Warranted against design and defects, pro-rated, will repair or replace in station.
Goodyear Tires (Commercial Chassis)	Warranted against design and defects, pro-rated.
Neihoff Alternators (Detroit Engine)	1 year
Leece-Neville Alternators (All engines)	1 year

Figure 1500-4.7 Typical warranty information for fire-fighting apparatus. When an apparatus is specified and ordered, this is a typical list of the items warranted. (Courtesy of Greenwood Fire Apparatus)

4-5.8

All fire department equipment and tools shall be cleaned and disinfected after responding to an emergency medical services incident where the potential for contamination from exposure to communicable diseases might have occurred. Cleaning and disinfecting shall be in accordance with NFPA 1581, *Standard on Fire Department Infection Control Program.*

Paragraph 4-4.7 covered cleaning and disinfecting of fire department apparatus; paragraph 4-5.8 applies the same requirement to equipment and tools. The need to clean and disinfect EMS equipment is well known and practiced by providers. The department must follow the same regimen for other tools and equipment used by personnel.

4-5.9

All ground ladders shall be inspected and service tested in accordance with the applicable requirements of NFPA 1932, *Standard on Use, Maintenance, and Service Testing of Fire Department Ground Ladders.*

4-5.10

All fire hose shall be inspected and service tested in accordance with the applicable requirements of NFPA 1962, *Standard for the Care, Use, and Service Testing of Fire Hose Including Couplings and Nozzles.*

4-5.11

All fire extinguishers shall be inspected and tested in accordance with the applicable requirements of NFPA 10, *Standard for Portable Fire Extinguishers.*

CHAPTER 5

Protective Clothing and Protective Equipment

The many roles and services of today's fire department demand particular types and levels of protective clothing and equipment. The Technical Correlating Committee, which oversees the protective clothing and equipment project, has developed requirements that will afford the wearer a maximum degree of protection. The health and safety of members who are required to wear protective clothing depend on an ongoing educational process. As outlined in Chapter 3 of NFPA 1500, members must be trained in the use of the protective clothing and, most importantly, its limitations. The protective clothing fire fighters wear is specified, built, and certified to NFPA standards. These are minimum standards, and fire fighters should not have a false sense of security by thinking protective clothing will protect them against every hazard. Data provided by NFPA's Fire Analysis and Research Division include reports of injured fire fighters who were not wearing the protective clothing and equipment provided. Nowhere is this more evident than in smoke-inhalation injuries.

By providing and requiring the use of protective clothing and equipment that meet the standards, fire departments also provide themselves a layer of protection. Injuries due to the failure to wear or a supervisor's failure to enforce the wearing of protective clothing and equipment may have severe, long-term financial implications to the department. These costs may include medical and health care expenses, time lost from duty, full-time unemployment or litigation costs, and possible increased insurance premiums.

5-1 General

5-1.1*

The fire department shall provide each member with the appropriate protective clothing and protective equipment to provide protection from the hazards to which the member is or is likely to be exposed. Such protective clothing and protective equipment shall be suitable for the tasks that the member is expected to perform.

A-5-1.1 The provision and use of protective clothing and equipment should include safety shoes, gloves, goggles, safety glasses, and any other items appropriate to the members' activities. This applies to all activities members are expected to perform, including nonemergency activities. The applicable regulations pertaining to industrial worker safety should be consulted to determine the need for protective equipment in nonemergency activities.

5-1.2*

Protective clothing and protective equipment shall be used whenever the member is exposed or potentially exposed to the hazards for which it is provided.

A-5-1.2 The fire department should provide body armor for all members who operate in areas where a potential for violence or civil unrest exists.

5-1.3

Members shall be fully trained in the care, use, inspection, maintenance, and limitations of the protective clothing and protective equipment assigned to them or available for their use.

5-1.4*

Structural fire-fighting protective clothing shall be periodically cleaned at least every 6 months as specified in NFPA 1581, *Standard on Fire Department Infection Control Program.*

A-5-1.4 Inspection of protective coats and protective trousers should be conducted on a frequent basis by members to assure the protective clothing's continued suitability for use.

The fire department should inspect all protective clothing at least annually. The inspection should include the following:

(a) All materials should be free from tears, embrittlement, and fraying.
(b) Seams should be intact and show no signs of excessive wear.
(c) Reflective trim should show no signs of abrasion or loss of reflectivity due to heat exposure.
(d) All pockets, knee pads, and other accessory items should be firmly attached to the garment and show no signs of excessive wear.
(e) Sleeve and pant cuffs should show no signs of fraying.
(f) The entire garment should be free from excessive dirt and stains.
(g) Where a fabric color change is noted, a condition that could be caused by high heat exposure or ultraviolet exposure, the entire area should be checked for loss of tear strength.

5-1.5*

Cleaning processes for protective clothing ensembles shall be appropriate for the types of contaminants and for the materials that are to be cleaned.

A-5-1.5 Protective clothing ensembles can be contaminated by bodily fluids or other contaminants encountered while providing medical care, or by smoke, soot, hydrocarbons, asbestos, chemicals, or other substances encountered during fire fighting and other operations.

5-1.6*

Where station/work uniforms are worn by members, such station/work uniforms shall meet the requirements of NFPA 1975, *Standard on Station/Work Uniforms for Fire Fighters.*

A-5-1.6 Station/work uniforms are required to meet NFPA 1975, *Standard on Station/Work Uniforms for Fire Fighters. (See 5-1.6.)*

Because it is impossible to ensure that every member—whether a volunteer, call, or off-duty career member—will respond to an incident in a station/work uniform or will change into station/work uniform clothing before donning protective garments, it is very important that members understand the hazards of some fabrics that more easily melt, drip, burn, shrink, or transmit heat rapidly and cause burns to the wearer.

Clothing that is made from 100 percent natural fibers or blends that are principally natural fibers should be selected over other fabrics that have poor thermal stability or ignite easily.

The very fact that persons are fire fighters indicates that all clothing that they wear should be flame resistant (as children's sleepwear is required to be) to give a degree of safety if unanticipated happenings occur that expose the clothing to flame, flash, sparks, or hot substances.

5-1.7

While on duty, members shall not wear any clothing that is unsafe due to poor thermal stability or poor flame-resistant characteristics of the fabric(s).

Paragraph 5-1.7 is part of NFPA 1500 because the clothing worn by members under their structural fire-fighting protective ensemble may fail, even though the structural integrity of their protective clothing is intact. Training about the potential hazards of wearing unsafe clothing is imperative, as outlined in Chapter 3 of NFPA 1500.

5-1.8*

The fire department shall provide for the cleaning of protective clothing and station/work uniforms. Such cleaning shall be performed either by a cleaning service that is familiar with the proper procedures and equipped to handle contaminated clothing or by a fire department facility that is equipped to handle contaminated clothing.

A-5-1.8 The fire department should establish procedures for cleaning contaminated protective clothing (i.e., turnout gear) and station work uniforms. This decontamination and cleaning can be done if the proper washers are available.

Commercial washers are available for the fire service that allow the cleaning of fire department contaminated protective clothing and station/work uniforms and noncontaminated items such as bed linens, dish towels, and truck towels.

The proper components of this process include a commercial washer that is front loading, has a stainless steel tub, has a water temperature is greater than 130°F (54°C), and has a programmed cycle to decontaminate the tub after the cleaning of contaminated protective clothing and station work uniforms.

Top-loading residential washers with enamel tubs do not meet the requirements nor do commercial washers that the public has access to such as in laundromats. If residential washers are going to be utilized for cleaning of station work uniforms that are contaminated or potentially contaminated, separate washers must be utilized. Residential washers cannot be utilized for cleaning turnout gear. For proper procedures for cleaning protective clothing and station work uniforms, refer to the manufacturer's instructions and NFPA 1971, *Standard on Protective Ensemble for Structural Fire Fighting,* and NFPA 1581, *Standard on Fire Department Infection Control Program.*

To effectively implement paragraph 5-1.8, fire departments must include in their SOPs procedures for the proper cleaning of protective clothing. Many departments contract with an outside party for laundry services, as they do not have the funding or physical space to clean the members' protective clothing. To avoid contaminating their personal vehicles or exposing their families to contaminated garments, members should not take contaminated clothing home or wash it in their appliances at home.

5-1.8.1 Where such cleaning is conducted in fire stations, the fire department shall provide at least one washing machine for this purpose in the designated cleaning area specified in NFPA 1581, *Standard on Fire Department Infection Control Program*.

Protective clothing is not regular laundry, but requires special care for infection control and other purposes. *(See Figure 1500-5.1.)* Before any cleaning of fire-fighting garments, the manufacturer's instructions must be studied. The manufacturer's specific cleaning instructions must be followed since failure to maintain the garment may reduce its protective qualities or void warranties.

Figure 1500-5.1 *This front-loading machine affords the opportunity to properly clean protective clothing. (Photo courtesy of Virginia Beach Fire Department)*

Structural fire-fighting protective garments should be cleaned periodically to remove foreign and flammable contaminants. Periodic cleaning should prolong the life and maintain the performance of the protective garments. NFPA 1500 requires that clothing be cleaned at least every six months by the fire department by utilizing either a cleaning service or a fire department facility that is equipped to handle contaminated clothing. (See paragraph 5-1.4.)

Even inherently flame-resistant fabrics can have their flame resistance compromised by improper care and use. Examples of improper care or use include leaving the garment exposed to direct sunlight (destroying the fabric), using bleach when the manufacturer cautions against its use, or using an improper thread or stitching when making repairs. The amount of soil, cleaning procedures, and chemicals utilized can adversely affect a fabric's performance. Protective garments are composed of a combination of materials, each with its own unique characteristics, capabilities, and weaknesses. Thus, cleaning procedures must protect the weakest of the materials. Historically, fabric suppliers' care recommendations failed to consider other materials in the garment. Many recommendations, while appropriate for the fabric supplier's own material, adversely impact the other components, thus destroying the garment's protection.

5-2 Protective Clothing for Structural Fire Fighting

5-2.1

Members who engage in or are exposed to the hazards of structural fire fighting shall be provided with and shall use a protective ensemble that shall meet the applicable requirements of NFPA 1971, *Standard on Protective Ensemble for Structural Fire Fighting*.

5-2.1.1 There shall be at least a 2-in. (5.08-cm) overlap of all layers of the protective coat and the protective trousers so there is no gaping of the total thermal protection when the protective garments are worn. The minimum overlap shall be determined by measuring the garments on the wearer, without SCBA, in both of the following positions:

Position A. Standing, hands together reaching overhead as high as possible

Position B. Standing, hands together reaching overhead, with body bent forward, to the side, and to the back as much as possible

Paragraph 5-2.1.1 specifies requirements for overlap between protective coat and trousers. *(See Figure 1500-5.2.)* Overlap is a key component of fit, and fit is a key component of protection. Proper fit of protective garments has a direct relationship to fire fighter safety. Before manufacturing the garments, the protective garment manufacturer should measure the individuals to assure a proper fit of the protective garments. Fit is important since an overlap of at least 2 inches of all the required layers of the coat and trousers prevents any gaping of total thermal protection. To assure proper overlap protection, each fire fighter must be measured in two positions while wearing the protective coat and protective trousers without any belt, waist strap, or SCBA. The first position requires the wearer to stand erect, with hands together and reaching overhead as far as possible. In the second position, the wearer bends forward, to each side, and to the back as much as possible, while standing with hands together reaching as far overhead as possible. The 2-inch overlap must be maintained in each position.

Sizing of protective garments can be done through several methods. One is the system used in standard clothing, where numerical sizes are based on chest measurements, such as 36, 38, and 40. Numerical sizing is the most popular sizing system because it provides effective fit in many situations and at moderate cost. Another method uses S/M/L/XL/XXL notation, in which each size combines a larger increment of chest measurements. For example, a size medium fits 42 through 45. The S/M/L/XL/XXL system is the most economical but least accurate sizing method. The third method is known as custom sizing, in which the individual fire fighter is measured by the manufacturer's representative (or according to the manufacturer's instructions); a specific garment is produced to these measurements. The custom sizing allows for superior fit, especially for fire fighters who are shorter or taller than average or who have shorter- or longer-than-average arms or torsos.

Fire fighters with longer- or shorter-than-average upper or lower torsos or fire fighters with longer- or shorter-than-average arm lengths merit particular attention when fitting for protective clothing. The numeric and S/M/L/XL/XXXL sizing methods probably will not allow for the proper fitting of these per-

Figure 1500-5.2 *An overlap of at least 2 inches for all the required layers of the coat and trousers prevents any gaping of thermal protection.*

sons, as a good chest fit does not provide for other than the average arm or torso length. Waist size does not provide for other than the average lower torso length. Custom sizing is the most desirable method.

5-2.1.2 Single piece protective coveralls shall not be required to have an overlap of all layers provided there is continuous composite protection.

5-2.1.3 Fire departments that provide protective coats with protective resilient wristlets secured through a thumb opening shall be permitted to provide gloves of the gauntlet type for use with these protective coats. Fire departments that do not provide such wristlets attached to all protective coats shall provide gloves of the wristlet type for use with these protective coats.

5-2.1.4* Protective clothing and protective equipment shall be used and maintained in accordance with manufacturer's instructions. The fire department shall establish a maintenance and inspection program for protective clothing and protective equipment. Specific responsibilities shall be assigned for inspection and maintenance.

A-5-2.1.4 Properly fitting protective clothing is important for the safety of the fire fighter. It is important to understand that all protective clothing should be correctly sized to allow for freedom of movement. Protective garments that are too small or too large and protective trouser legs that are too long or too short are safety hazards and should be avoided. Protective coat sleeves should be of sufficient length and design to protect the coat/glove interface area when reaching overhead or to the side. For proper fitting of a fire fighter, the protective clothing manufacturer should be contacted to provide sizing instructions.

5-2.1.5 The fire department shall require all members to wear all the protective ensemble as specified in 5-2.1, 5-2.1.3, and 5-2.1.4.

5-3 Respiratory Protection

5-3.1*

The fire department shall adopt and maintain a respiratory protection program that addresses the selection, inspection, safe use, and maintenance of respiratory protection equipment, training in its use, and the assurance of air quality testing. Members shall be tested and certified at least annually in the safe and proper use of respiratory protection equipment that they are authorized to use.

A-5-3.1 Selection of SCBA is an important function, particularly when resources are limited and SCBA have to be used for different applications and with different equipment. Confined space, haz-mat, and other operations can require different cylinders, umbilical connections, and features that are easier to ascertain and coordinate with a selection stage.

5-3.1.1 The respiratory protection program shall meet the requirements of NFPA 1404, *Standard for a Fire Department Self-Contained Breathing Apparatus Program.*

5-3.2*

The fire department shall have written standard operating procedures to address the safe use of respiratory protection in hazardous atmospheres that can be encountered in normal operations and in emergencies.

A-5-3.2 The required use of SCBA means that the user must have the facepiece in place, breathing air from the SCBA only. Wearing SCBA without the facepiece in place does not satisfy this requirement and should be permitted only under conditions in which the immediate safety of the atmosphere is assured. All members working in proximity to areas where SCBA use is required should have SCBA on their backs or immediately available for donning.

Areas where the atmosphere can rapidly become hazardous could include rooftop areas during ventilation operations and areas where an explosion or container rupture could be anticipated.

A hazardous atmosphere would be suspected in overhaul areas and above the fire floor in a building. Members working in these areas are required to use their SCBA unless the safety of the atmosphere is established by testing and maintained by effective ventilation. With effective ventilation in operation, facepieces could be removed, under direct supervision, but SCBA should continue to be worn or immediately available.

5-3.3*

The fire department shall provide to all members and require all members to use SCBA that meets NFPA 1981, *Standard on Open-Circuit Self-Contained Breathing Apparatus for Fire Fighters*, when engaged in any operations where they might encounter atmospheres that are immediately dangerous to life or health (IDLH) or potentially IDLH or where the atmosphere is unknown.

A-5-3.3 Hazardous atmospheres requiring SCBA can be found in (but are not limited to) the following operations: structural fire fighting, aircraft fire fighting, shipboard fire fighting, confined space rescue, and any incident involving hazardous materials.

All SCBA are classified as either positive pressure (also called pressure demand) or demand. U.S. OSHA regulations require use of only positive-pressure SCBA for structural fire-fighting operations and do not permit use of demand SCBA. The OSHA language is as follows:

> (2) Positive-pressure breathing apparatus. (i) The employer shall assure that self-contained breathing apparatus ordered or purchased after July 1, 1981, for use by fire brigade members performing interior structural fire-fighting operations, are of the pressure-demand or other positive-pressure type. Effective July 1, 1983, only pressure-demand or other positive-pressure self-contained breathing apparatus shall be worn by fire brigade members performing interior structural fire fighting.
>
> (ii) This paragraph does not prohibit the use of a self-contained breathing apparatus where the apparatus can be switched from a demand to a positive-pressure mode. However, such apparatus shall be in the positive-pressure mode when fire brigade members are performing interior structural fire-fighting operations.

(See 29 *CFR* 1910.157.)

The widespread use of positive-pressure SCBA in the U.S. fire service only began in the early to middle 1980s. During normal use, a positive pressure within the facepiece (i.e., higher than ambient atmospheric pressure) reduces the potential for inward leakage of a contaminated atmosphere around the perimeter of the facepiece. However, the positive-pressure feature does not take the place of proper facepiece fitting and fit testing for each user. The positive-pressure feature cannot and will not compensate for any interference (such as from beards or other facial hair or from eyeglass temple bows or straps) with the facepiece-to-face seal. A positive-pressure SCBA will use little, if any, more air than a demand SCBA, if properly fitted. A poorly fitting or improperly adjusted facepiece can allow outward leakage, thus seriously reducing the rated service life and endangering the user by allowing inward leakage of the contaminated atmosphere.

Demand SCBA permits airflow to the user only during inhalation. Demand SCBA requires negative pressure to initiate and maintain breathing air flow during inhalation. The danger of the contaminated atmosphere's being drawn into the SCBA facepiece is significant and accounts for the OSHA prohibition against demand SCBA.

Tests by the Los Alamos National Laboratory in 1995–1996 revealed substantial inward leakage of toxic materials within facepieces of demand SCBA. Quantitative tests revealed the respiratory protection provided by demand SCBA to be far below levels considered safe for emergency operations in toxic and radioactive atmospheres. Positive-pressure SCBA, however, provided adequate levels of protection for such environments.

The adoption of positive-pressure SCBA has been one of the most important actions taken by fire departments to increase respiratory protection.

5-3.4*

Closed-circuit SCBA shall be permitted when SCBA is required. Closed-circuit SCBA shall be NIOSH certified with a minimum service duration of at least 30 minutes and shall operate in the positive-pressure mode only.

A-5-3.4 The use of long-duration SCBA should be restricted to operations in tunnels and underground structures, on board ships, and in other situations where the need for this capability is demonstrated.

Weight and stress reduction should be an objective in the acquisition of new SCBA and when upgrading currently used SCBA. Weight and other stress factors are major contributions to fire fighter fatigue and injury, and SCBA should be chosen accordingly.

5-3.5*

Members using SCBA shall not compromise the protective integrity of the SCBA for any reason when operating in a hazardous atmosphere, or in an atmosphere where the quality of air is unknown, by removing the facepiece or disconnecting any portion of the SCBA that would allow the ambient atmosphere to be breathed.

A-5-3.5 Manufacturers of fire service SCBA that are NIOSH certified and that also meet requirements of NFPA 1981, *Standard on Open-Circuit Self-Contained Breathing Apparatus for Fire Fighters,* provide SCBA with a reasonable level of dependability, if correctly used and maintained.

In those cases where there is a reported failure of SCBA, a before-use check, a more thorough user inspection program, or a preventive maintenance program most likely would have eliminated the failure.

Fire fighters should be thoroughly trained in emergency procedures that can reverse problems encountered with their SCBA. Use of the regulator bypass valve, corrective action for facepiece and breathing tube damage, and breathing directly from the regulator (where applicable) are basic emergency procedures that should be taught to, and practiced by, the individual user. Fundamental to all emergency procedure training is the principle of not compromising the integrity of the user's SCBA, with particular emphasis on not removing the facepiece for any reason. The danger of compromising the integrity of the SCBA by removing the facepiece in atmospheres where the quality of air is unknown must be reinforced throughout the SCBA training program.

It is natural that this same philosophy be adopted when dealing with the subject of "buddy breathing." The "buddy breathing" addressed herein is a procedure that requires compromising the rescuer's SCBA by either removal of the facepiece or disconnection of the breathing tube, as these actions place the rescuer in grave danger.

The subject of "buddy breathing" is always a highly emotional one. Training must stress that fire fighters must not remove the facepiece of the SCBA in a hazardous atmosphere to assist a civilian fire victim, thereby exposing themselves to the toxic atmosphere, but instead rely on a rapid removal of the victim to a safe atmosphere or to a place of refuge where the rescuer can obtain further assistance in removing the victim to fresh air and treatment. However, when a fire fighter becomes the victim due to exhaustion of the breathing air supply or other impairment, some fire departments or fire service personnel insist upon engaging in procedures that are extremely difficult at best, even with consistent training in relatively ideal conditions. Virtually all "buddy breathing" procedures require compromising the rescuer's SCBA and, for this reason, cannot be condoned. Positive-pressure SCBA has made certain methods of "buddy breathing" more complicated, if not impossible.

A key disadvantage in "buddy breathing" is that it is extremely difficult for two people to leave the hazardous atmosphere quickly while engaged in "buddy breathing," simultaneously consuming air at a faster rate. The risk that both individuals will inhale sufficient products of combustion to cause impairment or death is a very distinct possibility.

It is difficult to understand why "buddy breathing" advocates believe that an atmosphere that is deadly for one fire fighter, and causes that fire fighter to become a victim, can safely be breathed by another fire fighter (the would-be rescuer) while using a "buddy breathing" procedure.

A scenario involving two fire fighters working at a warehouse fire provides a graphic example of how "buddy breathing" can be more hazardous than beneficial to both the rescuer and the victim. While working in an interior operation at a warehouse fire, one fire fighter suffered depletion of his breathing air supply. The other fire fighter commenced "buddy breathing" while both attempted to move out of the building. Unable to make sufficient progress as the first fire fighter was being overcome, the rescuer left the victim and attempted to leave the area for help. But because the rescuer had inhaled sufficient products of combustion during the attempted "buddy breathing" operation, he collapsed before he could exit the building. He was rescued by other fire fighters and removed to a hospital before he could relate the circumstances regarding the first fire fighter. The first fire fighter was found dead some time later.

If the fire fighter had been trained to remove the victim completely from the building or from immediate physical danger if possible, a number of things would have been accomplished without endangering the rescuer's life and with less risk to the victim fire fighter. If the rescuer had not compromised his SCBA, he would not have been affected by the products of combustion, he would have retained a greater air supply, and he would have either removed the victim fire fighter by himself or exited the area for additional assistance and alerted medical help.

The risk of both victim and rescuer exhausting their air supplies is another scenario associated with "buddy breathing." In this case, what starts out as a rescuer-victim relationship ends up a victim-victim relationship, as the shared air supply is exhausted before exiting is possible.

The one scenario that does not allow exiting is that in which two or more persons are trapped and share air supplies by "buddy breathing." In this case, survival is based upon the time it takes those outside to realize that persons are trapped, initiate rescue operations, and accomplish rescue. Unfortunately "buddy breathing" might only provide a simultaneous ending of multiple lives.

SCBA emergency procedures should be an integral part of any respiratory protection SCBA program, with written policies for the removal of victims, both civilian and fire service, from hazardous atmospheres without compromising the rescuer's respiratory protection SCBA for any reason.

Factors that can limit the need for "buddy breathing" include the following:

(a) A strong, well-administered respiratory protection SCBA program
(b) Emphasis on user testing and inspection of respiratory protection SCBA
(c) Required before-use and after-use testing and maintenance
(d) Functional preventive maintenance program
(e) Fire ground management based upon safe operations with knowledge of fire development, building construction, and coordinated fire-fighting operations
(f) Quality breathing air
(g) Personal alert safety system (PASS devices) and portable radios for interior fire-fighting teams
(h) Thorough training in survival techniques, controlled breathing, and stress management
(i) Accountability for interior fire-fighting crews
(j) Physical fitness of fire fighters
(k) Use of positive-pressure SCBA that are NIOSH approved and that meet the requirements of NFPA 1981, *Standard on Open-Circuit Self-Contained Breathing Apparatus for Fire Fighters*

NFPA, ANSI, IAFF, and most SCBA manufacturers do not recommend "buddy breathing" since it compromises one or more SCBA and can result in the needless impairment or death of either the rescuer or the victim, or both. The use of at least one five-minute emergency escape self-contained breathing apparatus (ESCBA), carried by a member of a fire-fighting team, is recommended for victim rescue (both civilian and fire fighter).

5-3.6

Compressed gaseous breathing air for SCBA cylinders shall meet the requirements of ANSI/CGA G7.1, *Commodity Specification for Air*, with a minimum air quality of Grade D, and shall have a dew point level of –65°F (–54°C) or dryer (24 ppm v/v or less) and a maximum particulate level of 5 mg/m^3 air.

5-3.7

When the fire department purchases compressed breathing air in a vendor-supplied SCBA cylinder, the fire department shall require the vendor to provide documentation that a sample of the breathing air obtained directly at the point of transfer from the vendor's filling system to the SCBA cylinder has been tested at least quarterly and that it meets the requirements of 5-3.6 of this section.

5-3.7.1 When a fire department manufactures its own breathing air, the fire department shall be required to provide documentation that a sample of the breathing air obtained directly from the point of transfer from the filling system to the SCBA cylinders has been tested at least quarterly and that it meets the requirements of 5-3.6 of this section.

5-3.7.2 When the fire department obtains compressed breathing air from a supplier and transfers it to other storage cylinders, cascade system cylinders, storage receivers, and other such storage equipment used for filling SCBA, the supplier shall be required to provide documentation that a sample of the breathing air obtained directly at the point of transfer from the filling system to the storage cylinders, cascade system cylinders, storage receivers, and other such storage equipment has been tested at least quarterly and that it meets the requirements of 5-3.6 of this section. In addition, the fire department itself shall obtain documentation that a sample of the breathing air obtained directly at the point of transfer to the SCBA cylinders from the storage cylinders, cascade system cylinders, storage receivers, and other such storage equipment used for filling SCBA has been tested at least quarterly and that it meets the requirements of 5-3.6 of this section.

Paragraph 5-3.7.2, dealing with compressed breathing air, was completely rewritten for the 1997 edition; in addition two Tentative Interim Amendments (TIAs) on compressed breathing air were processed. Concerns about air quality arose when a department refilled its cylinders from a mutual-aid department or refilled from a vendor. *(See Figures 1500-5.3 and 1500-5.4.)* Fire fighters should check documentation provided by the air supplier (whether the fire department or a private vendor) to be assured that the air in their SCBA cylinders meets the requirements in paragraph 5-3.6. Documentation and testing are emphasized in each paragraph of this section.

Figure 1500-5.3 *Air quality for self-contained breathing apparatus (SCBA) is a critical issue. It is the fire department's responsibility to ensure that the air quality meets the requirements of 5-3.6 of NFPA 1500. (Photo courtesy of Virginia Beach Fire Department)*

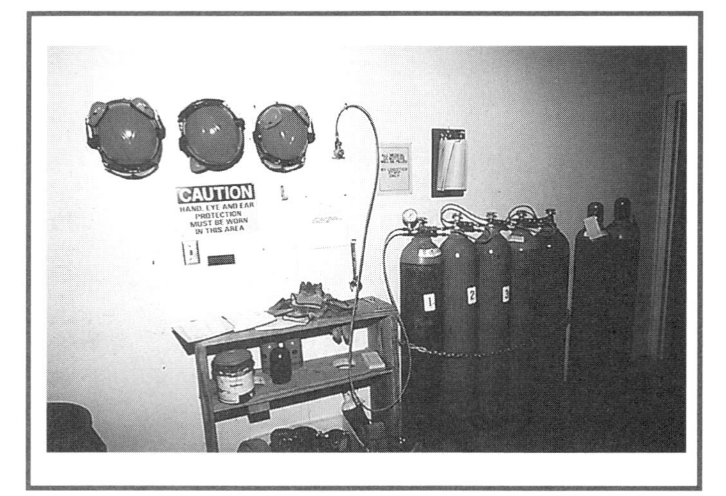

Figure 1500-5.4 *Whether the fire department manufactures its own breathing air, purchases it from a private vendor, or uses another fire department as its supplier, it is the fire department's responsibility to ensure that the air quality meets the requirements of 5-3.6 of NFPA 1500. (Photo courtesy of Virginia Beach Fire Department)*

5-3.8

SCBA cylinders shall be hydrostatically tested within the periods specified by the manufacturers and the applicable governmental agencies.

The U.S. Department of Transportation (DOT) regulates hydrostatic testing of SCBA cylinders in the U.S. According to DOT regulations, hydrostatic tests must be conducted at least every five years for steel or aluminum cylinders and every three years for composite-aluminum-wrapped cylinders. Damage to the cylinder or substantial cleaning of its interior or exterior may require inspection and hydrostatic testing of the cylinder.

An internal inspection is required at the time of hydrostatic testing. The purpose of the internal inspection is to determine any conditions that may contribute to the deterioration of the cylinder or possibly cause malfunction of the SCBA and injury to personnel. The object of the internal inspection is to check for rust, corrosion, moisture, and other damage, and traces or evidence of oil and/or hydrocarbon contamination. Initial corrosion may take the form of a light powder or flaking around cylinder walls, which can be easily removed by rolling or spinning small balls around the inside of the cylinder. Extensive corrosion can cause pitting and eventual weakening of cylinder walls.

5-3.9*

The facepiece seal capability of each member qualified to use SCBA shall be verified by qualitative fit testing on an annual basis and whenever new types of SCBA or facepieces are issued. Each new member shall be tested before being permitted to use SCBA in a hazardous atmosphere. Only members with a properly fitting facepiece shall be permitted by the fire department to function in a hazardous atmosphere with SCBA.

A-5-3.9 The procedures for qualitative fit testing are included in ANSI Z88.5, *Practices for Respiratory Protection for the Fire Service.* Quantitative fit testing is considered to be more precise than qualitative fit testing, but is not considered to be necessary where positive-pressure SCBA are used. If qualitative fit testing does not provide satisfactory results, the fire department should refer to ANSI Z88.5 for further information on quantitative fit testing. If necessary, the fire department should provide a facepiece of larger or smaller size to provide an adequate seal for an individual, and such individuals shall use only the facepiece provided. An effective face-to-facepiece seal is extremely important when using respiratory protection SCBA. Even a minor leakage can allow contaminants to enter the facepiece, even with positive-pressure respiratory protection SCBA. Any outward leakage will increase the rate of air consumption, reducing the time available for use and safe exit. The facepiece should seal tightly against the skin, without penetration or interference by any protective clothing or other equipment.

5-3.10*

Members who have a beard or facial hair at any point where the SCBA facepiece is designed to seal with the face, or hair that could interfere with the operation of the unit, shall not be permitted to use respiratory protection at emergency incidents or in hazardous or potentially hazardous atmospheres. These restrictions shall apply regardless of the specific fit test measurement that can be obtained under test conditions.

A-5-3.10 The following ruling regarding facial hair and SCBA or respirator use was issued in February 1990 by the Directorate of Compliance Programs, Occupational Safety and Health Administration, U.S. Department of Labor:

> With respect to regulating the use of respiratory protection self-contained breathing apparatus (SCBA) for protecting employees with beards, 29 *CFR* 1910.134(e)(5)(i) contains the statement, "Respirators shall not be worn when conditions prevent a good face seal." This prohibition applies to any negative or positive-pressure personal respiratory protection device of a design relying on the principle of forming a face seal to perform at maximum effectiveness.
>
> A beard growing on the face at points where the seal with the respirator is to occur is a condition that has been shown to prevent a good face seal. Thus an employer using SCBA to protect an employee with a growth of beard at points where the SCBA facepiece is designed to seal with the face, is violating 29 *CFR* 1910.134(e)(5)(i). This is so regardless of what fit test measurement can be obtained. If the beard is styled so no hair underlies the points where the SCBA facepiece is designed to seal with the face, then the employer may use the SCBA to protect the employee, however.

Paragraph 5-3.10 addresses the sometimes controversial relationship between beards, facial hair, and the seal of SCBA facepieces. Can fire fighters have beards or facial hair? If members are required to wear SCBA and could potentially be in an IDLH atmosphere, the answer is no. There is no way to maintain a proper facepiece seal with a beard, as emphasized in the OSHA ruling of February 1990. *(See Figure 1500-5.5.)*

5-3.11

When a member must wear spectacles while using a full facepiece respiratory protection, the respiratory protection full facepiece shall be fitted with spectacles in such a manner that it shall not interfere with the facepiece-to-face seal.

5-3.11.1 Spectacles with any strap or temple bars that pass through the facepiece-to-face seal area shall be prohibited.

5-3.11.2* Use of contact lenses shall be permitted during full facepiece respiratory protection use, provided that the member has previously demonstrated successful long-term contact lens use.

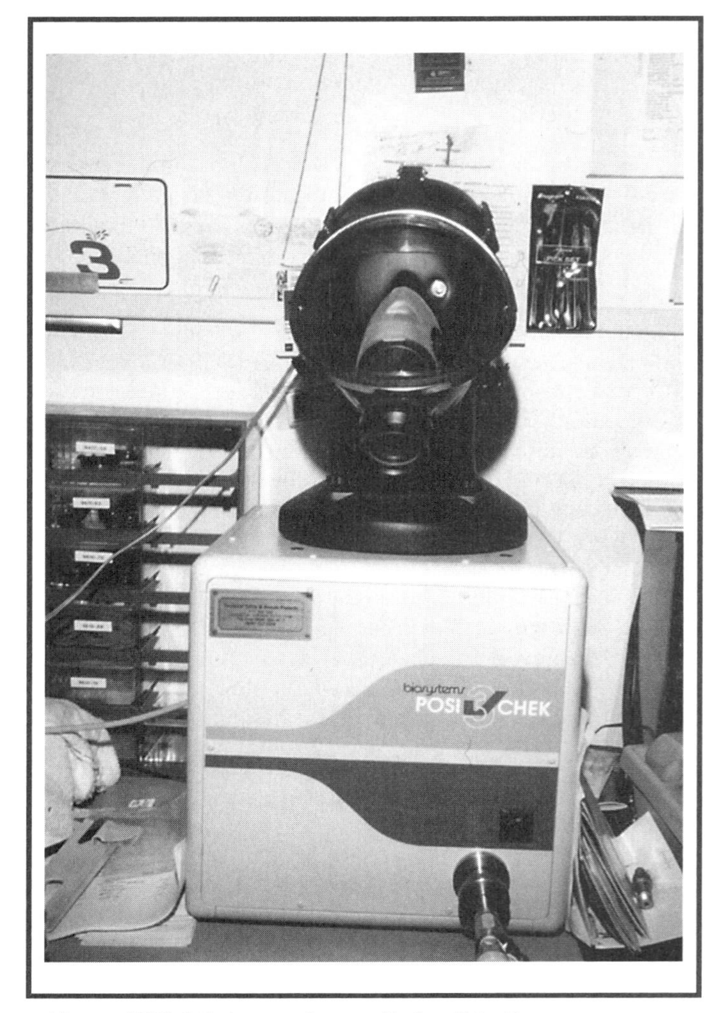

Figure 1500-5.5 An ongoing qualitative fit testing process should be in place to ensure that members have properly fitting facepieces for their SCBA. (Photo courtesy of Virginia Beach Fire Department)

A-5-3.11.2 The user should be able to demonstrate the successful use of an SCBA with the contact lenses in a nonhazardous training environment before being allowed to use them in an incident. Successful long-term soft contact lens use should be measured by the ability to wear soft contact lenses for at least six months without any problems.

The use of either hard or soft contact lenses is allowed with the successful demonstration of their use during training exercises.

5-3.12

Nothing shall be allowed to enter or pass through the area where the respiratory protection facepiece is designed to seal with the face, regardless of the specific fit test measurement that can be obtained.

5-3.12.1 Any head covering that passes between the sealing surface of the respiratory protection facepiece and the member's face shall be prohibited.

5-3.12.2 The respiratory protection facepiece and head harness with straps shall be worn under the protective hoods specified in 5-2.1.5 and 5-4.5 of this chapter.

5-3.12.3 The respiratory protection facepiece and head harness with straps shall be worn under the head protection of any hazardous chemical protective clothing specified in Section 5-6 of this standard.

5-3.12.4 Helmets shall not interfere with the respiratory protection facepiece-to-face seal.

5-4 Protective Clothing for Proximity Fire-Fighting Operations

Section 5-4 addresses protective clothing for proximity fire-fighting operations, which include aircraft rescue and fire fighting, bulk flammable liquids fire fighting, flammable gas fire fighting, and similar situations releasing high levels of radiant heat. Proximity protective garments are designed to protect fire fighters against the hazards associated with these special operations. On the other hand, proximity protective garments are not designed to provide protection from hazardous materials emergencies or act as an entry protective garment.

The performance requirements for proximity protective garments were not intended to limit the fire fighter's working environment, but to establish material performance requirements based on empirical field data and laboratory testing. While performing proximity fire fighting, users must be aware that the feeling of continually increasing heat indicates that injury may be imminent.

Definitions have been developed to differentiate between the specialized fire-fighting operations for which structural fire fighting protective clothing and equipment is not suitable and special protective clothing and equipment must be used. (See definitions in 1-5 of NFPA 1500.)

On January 20, 1997, a Formal Interpretation concerning Section 5-4 was issued by the Standards Council. That Formal Interpretation is still valid and is reproduced here for the reader's convenience.

Formal Interpretation

Reference: 5-4

F.I. No.: 1500-92-2

Question 1: Given the definition of "proximity fire fighting" in Section 1-5, is it the intent of Section 5-4 to require that all members who engage in or are exposed to the hazards of aircraft fire fighting operations be protected by proximity protective clothing and equipment that is compliant with the requirements of Section 5-4?

Answer: Yes. It is the intent of the Technical Committee to require members who are routinely engaged in aircraft incidents where burning fuel creates a potential for high radiant heat levels to wear proximity personal protective equipment.

Issue Edition: 1992

Reference: 5-4

Issue Date: December 31, 1996

Effective Date: January 20, 1997

5-4.1

Members who engage in or are exposed to the hazards of proximity fire fighting shall be provided with and shall use both proximity protective coats and proximity protective trousers, or a proximity protective coverall, for limb/torso protection. The proximity protective coat and proximity protective trousers, or the proximity protective coverall, shall meet the applicable requirements of NFPA 1976, *Standard on Protective Clothing for Proximity Fire Fighting.*

5-4.1.1 There shall be at least a 2-in. (5.08-cm) overlap of all layers of the proximity protective coat and proximity protective trousers so there is no gaping of the total thermal and radiant heat protection when the protective garments are worn. The minimum overlap shall be determined by measuring the garments on the wearer, without SCBA, in both of the following positions:

Position A. Standing, hands together reaching overhead as high as possible

Position B. Standing, hands together reaching overhead, with body bent forward, to the side, and to the back as much as possible

5-4.1.2 Single piece proximity protective coveralls shall not be required to have an overlap of all layers, provided there is continuous full thermal and radiant heat protection.

5-4.2

Members who engage in or are exposed to the hazards of proximity fire fighting shall be provided with and shall use helmets that meet the applicable requirements of NFPA 1971, *Standard on Protective Ensemble for Structural Fire Fighting*, and additional radiant reflective criteria that are approved for the expected proximity fire-fighting exposures where the helmet will be used.

5-4.3

Members who engage in or are exposed to the hazards of proximity fire fighting shall be provided with and shall use gloves that meet the applicable requirements of NFPA 1971, *Standard on Protective Ensemble for Structural Fire Fighting*, and additional radiant reflective criteria that are approved for the expected proximity fire-fighting exposures where the gloves will be used.

5-4.4

Members who engage in or are exposed to the hazards of proximity fire fighting shall be provided with and shall use footwear that meets the applicable requirements of NFPA 1971, *Standard on Protective Ensemble for Structural Fire Fighting*, and additional radiant reflective criteria that are approved for the expected proximity fire-fighting exposures where the footwear will be used.

5-4.5

Members who engage in or are exposed to the hazards of proximity fire fighting shall be provided with and shall use protective hoods that meet the applicable requirements of NFPA 1971, *Standard on Protective Ensemble for Structural Fire Fighting*, and additional radiant reflective criteria that are approved for the expected proximity fire-fighting exposures where the hood will be used.

5-4.6

Where SCBA is worn over or outside the proximity protective garment, the fire department shall inform the member of the potential high levels of radiant heat that can result in the failure of the SCBA. The fire department shall require additional approved radiant reflective criteria, including but not limited to a protective cover, for the expected proximity fire-fighting exposures when the SCBA is worn over or outside the proximity protective garment.

Paragraph 5-4.6 covers the use of SCBA with proximity protective clothing. NFPA 1500 requires the use of self-contained breathing apparatus whenever fire fighters are exposed or may be exposed to the products of combustion or oxygen-deficient or toxic atmospheres.

Since this requirement covers most, if not all, proximity fire-fighting situations, SCBA shall be used with proximity protective clothing.

SCBA that is worn over or outside of the proximity garments is unprotected and will be exposed to the high radiant levels. Therefore, SCBA is required to have proximity protective covers to protect the SCBA cylinder, regulator, hoses, and straps from the radiant heat. Specialized face shields (such as gold-coated reflective face shields) that mitigate the effects of high levels of radiant energy to the face and the SCBA facepiece should be worn during proximity operations. SCBA can be worn under the proximity protective coat only if the protective coat is designed to allow access to the apparatus and the controls and sufficient room for movement without binding or hindering the wearer.

5-5* Protective Clothing for Emergency Medical Operations

A-5-5 Fire department personnel involved in emergency medical operations must be protected against potential medical hazards. These hazards include exposure to blood or other body fluids contaminated with infectious agents such as hepatitis and human immunodeficiency viruses. The purpose of emergency medical protective clothing is to shield individuals from these medical hazards and conversely protect patients from potential hazards from the emergency responder. Emergency medical gloves are to be used for all patient care. Emergency medical garments and face protection devices are to be used for any situation where the potential for contact with blood or other body fluids is high.

NFPA 1999, *Standard on Protective Clothing for Emergency Medical Operations*, covers garments, gloves, and face protection devices that are designed to prevent exposure to blood or other body fluids for those individuals engaged in emergency medical patient care and similar operations. The standard specifies a series of requirements for each type of protective clothing. Garments can be full body clothing or clothing items such as coveralls, aprons, or sleeve protectors. For the intended areas of body protection, the garment must allow no penetration of virus, offer "liquid-tight" integrity, and have limited physical durability and hazard resistance. Gloves must allow no penetration of virus, offer "liquid-tight" integrity, and meet other requirements for tear resistance, puncture resistance, heat aging, alcohol resistance, sizing, and dexterity. Face protection devices can be masks, hoods, visors, safety glasses, or goggles. Any combination of items can be used to provide protection to the wearer's face, principally the eyes, nose, and mouth. For the intended areas of face protection, these devices must allow no penetration of virus, offer "liquid-tight" integrity, and provide adequate visibility for those portions of the device covering the wearer's eyes.

Emergency medical services represent a large portion of the fire department workload. It is estimated that from 60 to 80 percent of the fire department responses for departments that provide EMS are for EMS calls.

5-5.1

Members who perform emergency medical care or are otherwise likely to be exposed to blood or other body fluids shall be provided with emergency medical garments, emergency medical face protection devices, and emergency medical gloves that meet the applicable requirements of NFPA 1999, *Standard on Protective Clothing for Emergency Medical Operations.*

5-5.2*

Members shall wear emergency medical gloves when providing emergency medical care. Patient care shall not be initiated before the gloves are in place.

A-5-5.2 In order to avoid all potential exposure to infectious diseases, it is important that all members use gloves when providing patient care. All members who might come in contact with the patient should use gloves.

The Centers for Disease Control and Prevention (CDC) *Guidelines for Public Safety Workers* discusses the selection and use of appropriate clothing and equipment during medical emergencies. CDC recommends that all personnel wear disposable gloves before beginning any emergency patient care tasks involving exposure to blood or body fluids. Extra pairs of gloves should always be available. When treating multiple victims, fire fighters should change gloves between patient contacts. *(See Figures 1500-5.6 and 1500-5.7.)*

Figure 1500-5.6 *At any level of emergency medical care members who may be exposed to airborne infectious diseases must be trained in the care and use of the appropriate protective equipment. (Photo courtesy of Fairfax County, Virginia, Fire and Rescue Department)*

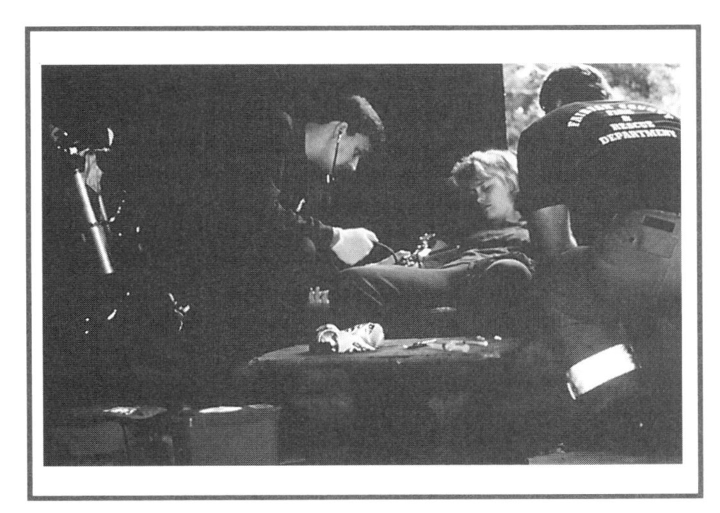

Figure 1500-5.7 While members provide patient care, the number of members who may be potentially exposed should be limited. Those members should afford themselves the necessary protection from bloodborne and airborne pathogens. (Photo courtesy of Fairfax County, Virginia, Fire and Rescue Department)

While wearing gloves, members should avoid handling personal items, such as combs and pens, that could become contaminated. Gloves contaminated with blood or other body fluids to which universal precautions apply should be removed as soon as possible, taking care to avoid skin contact with the exterior surface; the term "universal precautions" applies to face and eye protection, gowns, respiratory protection, and handwashing, in addition to gloves.

The use of gloves does not eliminate the need to wash hands after emergency medical incidents. Handwashing is one of the most important elements of infection control!

5-5.2.1* The fire department shall provide all fire fighters who perform emergency medical care or are likely to be exposed to airborne infectious disease with NIOSH-approved Type C respirators certified to meet 42 *CFR* 84.

A-5-5.2.1 For additional information refer to Federal Register, Vol. 60, No. 110; 29 *CFR* 1910.134, Respiratory Protection; OSHA Enforcement Policy and Procedures for Occupational Exposure to Tuberculosis; Center for Disease Control and Prevention, "Guidelines for Preventing the Transmission of *Mycobacterium Tuberculosis* in Health-Care Facilities," 1994.

The use of Type C respirators, as required by paragraph 5-5.2.1, is designed to protect against tuberculosis and other respiratory infectious diseases, which have increased over the past five years. Just as fire fighters wear SCBA in potentially dangerous atmospheres, fire fighters need respiratory protection when providing emergency medical care.

5-5.3

Each member shall use emergency medical garments and emergency medical face protection devices prior to any patient care during which large splashes of body fluids can occur, such as situations involving spurting blood or childbirth.

5-5.4

Contaminated emergency medical garments, emergency medical face protection devices, and emergency medical gloves shall be cleaned and disinfected or disposed of in accordance with NFPA 1581, *Standard on Fire Department Infection Control Program.*

Each fire department must have procedures for the decontamination of specific items of clothing and equipment. Cleaning, disinfecting, and disposal criteria are included in NFPA 1581, *Standard on Fire Department Infection Control Program* (1995) (Part Four of this handbook), and are required to be utilized by 5-5.4. The CDC *Public Safety Worker Guidelines* also has recommendations for these procedures. *(See Figure 1500-5.8.)*

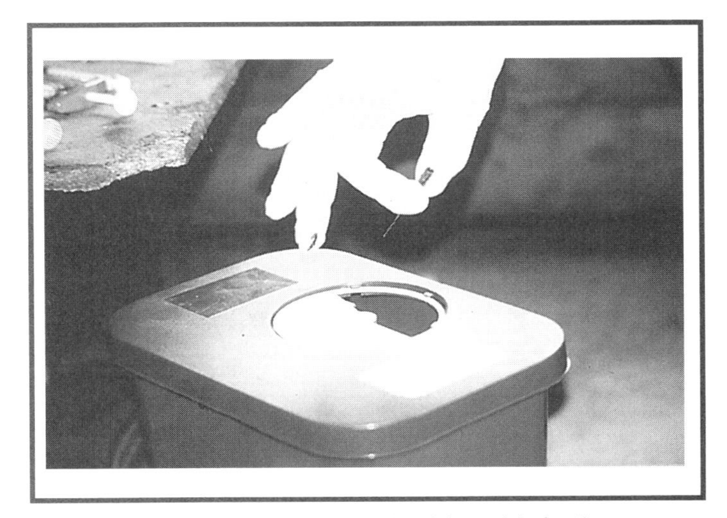

Figure 1500-5.8 Departments should provide for the proper care and disposal of a contaminated emergency medical equipment. This Sharps needlebox is being used at the scene. (Photo courtesy of Fairfax County, Virginia, Fire and Rescue Department)

The CDC *Public Safety Worker Guidelines* recommend and U.S. OSHA requires employers to routinely make laundry facilities or services available. Protective clothing and station/work uniforms should be washed and dried according to manufacturers' recommendations. Also, boots and leather goods can be scrubbed with soap and hot water to remove contamination. The OSHA bloodborne pathogen regulation, 29 *CFR* 1910.1030, also has specific laundering requirements.

Care also must be taken in the use of disinfectants. Disinfectants used for decontaminating equipment should be EPA-registered hospital disinfectant chemical germicides that have been documented as effective against *Mycobacterium tuberculosis*. Members should be aware of the flammability and reactivity of disinfectants and should follow manufacturer's instructions (e.g., contact time and temperature) for use. Disinfectants should only be used with adequate ventilation and while wearing appropriate garments and equipment, including eye protection, gloves, and aprons. It also is important to check with the germicide's manufacturer to determine compatibility of the protective clothing and the disinfectant.

Information on specific label claims of commercial germicides can be obtained by contacting the Disinfectants Branch, Office of Pesticides, EPA, 401 M St., SW, Washington, DC 20460.

5-5.5

The fire department shall provide gloves that meet the requirements of NFPA 1971, *Standard on Protective Ensemble for Structural Fire Fighting*, during operations where sharp or rough edges are likely to be encountered during emergency medical care operations.

5-6* Chemical-Protective Clothing for Hazardous Chemical Emergency Operations

A-5-6 Fire department personnel involved in a hazardous materials incident must be protected against potential chemical hazards. The purpose of chemical-protective clothing and equipment is to shield or isolate individuals from the chemical hazards that can be encountered during hazardous materials responses. Adequate chemical-protective clothing must be carefully selected and used to protect the respiratory system, skin, eyes, face, hands, feet, head, body, and hearing.

Structural fire-fighting protective clothing and equipment should not be used for hazardous materials incidents. Even where certified to the appropriate NFPA standards for structural fire fighting, these clothing and equipment items provide little or no protection against hazardous chemicals. Use of this clothing for hazardous materials emergency response can result in serious injury or death for the following reasons:

(a) Structural fire-fighting protective clothing materials are easily permeated or penetrated by most hazardous chemicals. Some parts of structural fire-fighting clothing can actually absorb chemical liquids or vapors, increasing the likelihood of serious exposure.

(b) Many hardware items will fail or lose function when contacted by chemicals (e.g., etching of visors, deterioration of straps, corrosion of hooks or other metal items).

(c) Contamination of structural fire-fighting protective clothing might not be effectively removed by laundering. Reuse of contaminated clothing can cause chronic exposure and accelerate physiological effects produced by contact with the chemical.

Fire fighters must realize that no single combination of protective equipment and clothing is capable of protecting them against all hazards. Therefore, chemical-protective clothing should be used in conjunction with other protective methods. The use of such clothing can itself create significant wearer hazards, such as heat stress, and physical and psychological stress, as well as impaired vision, mobility, and communication. In general, the greater the level of chemical clothing protection, the greater are the associated risks. For any given situation, equipment and clothing should be selected that provide an adequate level of protection. Overprotection as well as underprotection can be hazardous and should be avoided.

The approach to selecting personal protective clothing and equipment must encompass an "ensemble" of clothing and equipment items that are easily integrated to provide both an appropriate level of protection and the ability to carry out emergency response activities. The following is a checklist of components that can form the chemical-protective ensemble:

(a) Protective clothing (i.e., suit, coveralls, hoods, gloves, boots)
(b) Respiratory equipment (i.e., SCBA, combination SCBA/SAR)
(c) Cooling system (i.e., ice vest, air circulation, water circulation)
(d) Communications device
(e) Head protection
(f) Ear protection
(g) Inner garments
(h) Outer protection (i.e., overgloves, overboots, flash-covers)

The United States Environmental Protection Agency (EPA) has outlined four levels of protection: A, B, C, and D. The EPA defined these levels of protection primarily for workers at hazardous waste sites, where emergency conditions do not usually exist. These levels of protection are commonly and often inappropriately utilized by the fire service. They are inadequate and do not correctly define the chemical-protective clothing with respect to the intended use based on the hazard and the required performance the selected clothing or equipment must offer.

EPA levels of protection should be used only as the starting point for ensemble creation; however, each ensemble must be tailored to the specific situation in order to provide the most appropriate level of protection. For example, if the emergency response activity involves a highly contaminated area or the potential of contamination is high, it might be advisable to wear a disposable covering such as coveralls or splash suits over the protective ensemble.

It is important to realize that selecting items by their design or configuration alone is not sufficient to ensure adequate protection. In other words, just having the right components to form an ensemble is not enough. Again, the EPA levels of protection do not define what performance the selected clothing or equipment must offer.

For emergency response, the only acceptable types of protective clothing include fully or totally encapsulating suits and nonencapsulating or "splash" suits combined with accessory clothing items such as chemical-resistant gloves and boots. These descriptions apply to how the clothing is designed, not to its performance. The NFPA has classified chemical-protective suits by their performance in the following three standards:

(a) Vapor-protective suits (NFPA 1991, *Standard on Vapor-Protective Suits for Hazardous Chemical Emergencies)*
(b) Liquid splash-protective suits (NFPA 1992, *Standard on Liquid Splash-Protective Suits for Hazardous Chemical Emergencies)*
(c) Support function protective suits (NFPA 1993, *Standard on Support Function Protective Clothing for Hazardous Chemical Operations)*

Protective clothing should completely cover both the wearer and the wearer's breathing apparatus. Wearing SCBA or other respiratory equipment outside the suit subjects this equipment to the chemically contaminated environment. The SCBA used for hazardous materials emergency response are generally the same as those used in structural fire fighting. Respiratory protective equipment is not designed to resist chemical contamination and should be protected from these environments. NFPA 1991 vapor-protective suits require that respiratory protection SCBA be worn on the inside. NFPA 1992 liquid splash-protective suits can be configured with the SCBA on either the inside or the outside. However, it is strongly recommended that respiratory equipment be worn inside the ensemble to prevent its failure and to reduce decontamination problems.

There are a variety of accessories available for chemical-protective ensembles. As with protective clothing and respirators, it is important that these components integrate easily into an ensemble without a decrease in the protective integrity offered by any one component. For the most part, the protective suit is the main integrating ensemble component, since it must accommodate all other equipment while completely covering the wearer. Nevertheless, selection of an ensemble configuration must consider all items simultaneously.

Fire departments are faced with selecting a number of available chemical-protective garments and sorting through the variety of information provided by the manufacturer. What follows are some guidelines that can be used in selecting chemical-protective suits.

(a) It must be determined if the clothing item is intended to provide vapor or liquid splash protection. Vapor-protective suits also provide liquid splash protection. Both vapor- and liquid splash-protective suits also provide protection against solid chemicals and particles. Many garments can be labeled as totally encapsulating but do not provide gas-tight integrity due to inadequate seams or closures. Splash suits must still cover the entire body when combined with the respirator, gloves, and boots. Applying duct tape to a splash suit does not enable it to protect against vapors. Gas-tight integrity can only be determined by performing a pressure or inflation test of the respective protective suit. ASTM F 1052, *Standard Practice for Pressure Testing of Gas-Tight Totally Encapsulating Chemical Protective Suits*, offers a procedure for conducting this test. This test involves the following:

1. Closing off suit exhalation valves
2. Inflating the suit to a prespecified pressure
3. Observing whether the suit holds the above pressure for a designated period of time

Liquid splash-protective suits must provide "liquid-tight" integrity. Liquid-tight integrity is best evaluated by determining how the chemical-protective suit and other clothing prevent sprayed liquid from contacting the wearer. ASTM F 1359, *Practice for Evaluating the Liquid-Tight Integrity of Chemical Protective Suits and Ensembles Under Static Conditions*, offers procedures for conducting this test involving the placement of the suit and other clothing over a mannequin that is dressed in a water-absorptive garment. Surfactant-treated water is sprayed at the suited mannequin from several different directions. Observations of water penetration on the water-absorptive garment indicate a lack of liquid-tight integrity. In particular, seam, closure, and clothing item interface areas should be examined closely for water-tight integrity.

(b) It must be determined if the clothing item provides full-body protection. A vapor-protective or totally encapsulating suit will meet this requirement by passing gas-tight integrity tests. Liquid splash-protective suits can have separate parts. Missing clothing items must be obtained separately and match or exceed the performance of the garment. Buying a polyvinyl chloride (PVC) glove for a PVC splash suit does not mean that the same level of protection is obtained. This determination must be made by comparing chemical resistance data.

Component parts of the liquid splash-protective suit must also integrate and provide liquid-tight integrity as described previously.

(c) The manufacturer's chemical resistance data provided with the garment must be evaluated. Technical data packages are required to be supplied by the manufacturers of protective suits that are certified to NFPA 1991, *Standard on Vapor-Protective Suits for Hazardous Chemical Emergencies*, or NFPA 1992, *Standard on Liquid Splash-Protective Suits for Hazardous Chemical Emergencies*. Manufacturers of vapor-protective suits must provide permeation resistance data for their products, while penetration resistance data must accompany liquid splash-protective garments. Data must be provided for every primary material in the suit, including the garment, visor, gloves, and boots.

Permeation data should include a citation that testing was conducted in accordance with ASTM F 739, *Test Method for Resistance of Protective Clothing Materials to Permeation by Liquids or Gases*, and the following:

1. Chemical name
2. Breakthrough time (indicates how soon the chemical permeates)
3. Permeation rate (indicates the rate at which the chemical permeates)
4. System sensitivity (allows comparison of test results from different laboratories)

If no data is provided or if the data lacks any of the information above, the manufacturer should be asked to supply the missing data, or the product will not be considered. Manufacturers that provide only numerical or qualitative ratings must support their recommendations with complete test data.

Penetration data should include a pass or fail determination for each chemical listed and a citation that testing was conducted in accordance with ASTM F 903, *Standard Test Method for Resistance of Protective Clothing Materials to Penetration by Liquids*. Protective suits that are certified to NFPA 1991 or NFPA 1992 should meet all of the above requirements.

Suit materials that show no breakthrough or no penetration in response to a large number of chemicals are likely to have a broad range of chemical resistance. (Breakthrough times greater than one hour are usually considered to be an indication of acceptable performance.) If there are specific chemicals within a response area that have not been tested, the manufacturer should be consulted for test data on these chemicals.

(d) The manufacturer's instruction manual should be obtained and examined.

This manual should document all the features of the suit and describe those materials that are used in its construction. It should cite specific limitations for the suit and the restrictions that apply to its use. Procedures and recommendations should be supplied for at least the following:

1. Donning and doffing
2. Inspection, maintenance, and storage
3. Decontamination
4. Use

The manufacturer's instructions should be thorough enough to allow trained fire department members to wear and use the suit without a large number of questions.

(e) Sample garments should be obtained and inspected.

An examination of the quality of suit construction and other features that will impact its wearing should be made. If possible, representative garments should be obtained in advance, inspected prior to purchase, and reviewed with an individual who has experience in their use. It is also helpful to "try out" representative garments prior to purchase by having personnel run through exercises to simulate response activities while wearing the garments.

Despite the fact that a fire department has gone through a very careful selection process, a number of situations will arise where no information is available to judge whether the protective clothing chosen will provide adequate protection. These situations include the following:

1. Chemicals that have not been tested with the garment materials
2. Mixtures of two or more different chemicals
3. Chemicals that cannot be readily identified
4. Extreme environmental conditions (hot temperatures)
5. Lack of data in all suit components (e.g., gloves, visors)

Testing material specimens using newly developed field test kits can offer one means for making on-site clothing selection. A portable test kit has been developed by the EPA using a simple weight loss method that allows field qualification of protective clothing materials within one hour. Use of this kit can compensate for the absence of data and provide additional criteria for clothing selection.

Selection of chemical-protective clothing is a complex task and should be performed by personnel with both extensive training and experience. Under all conditions, clothing should be selected by evaluating its performance characteristics against the requirements and limitations imposed by the response activity.

Anyone involved in a hazardous materials incident must be protected against potential hazards. The purpose of personal protective clothing and equipment is to shield or isolate individuals from the chemical, physical, and biological hazards that may be encountered during hazardous materials responses. Adequate chemical-protective clothing must be carefully selected and used to protect the respiratory system, skin, eyes, face, hands, feet, head, body, and hearing.

Structural fire-fighting protective clothing and equipment should not be used for hazardous materials incidents. Even when certified to the appropriate NFPA standards, structural fire-fighting protective clothing and equipment provide little or no protection against hazardous chemicals. Use of structural protective elements for hazardous materials emergency response may result in serious injury or death for the following reasons:

- Most hazardous chemicals easily permeate or penetrate structural fire-fighting protective clothing. Some parts of structural fire-fighting clothing elements may actually absorb chemical liquids or vapors, increasing the likelihood of serious exposure.
- Many hardware items will fail or lose function when contacted by chemicals (e.g., etching of visors, deterioration of straps, corrosion of hooks or other metal items).
- Laundering may not be effective in decontamination of structural fire-fighting protective clothing. Reuse of contaminated clothing may cause chronic exposure and accelerate physiological effects produced by contact with the chemical.

No single combination of protective clothing and equipment is capable of protecting fire fighters against all hazards. Therefore, chemical-protective clothing should be used in conjunction with other protective methods. The use of chemical-protective clothing can itself create significant wearer hazards, such as heat stress, physical and psychological stress, impaired vision, impaired mobility, and impaired communications. In general, the greater the level of chemical clothing protection, the greater are the associated risks. For any given situation, protective clothing and equipment should be selected that provide an adequate level of protection. Overprotection and underprotection can be hazardous and should be avoided.

An ensemble of clothing and equipment items is easily integrated to provide both an appropriate level of protection and the ability to carry out emergency response. The following list of components may form the chemical-protective ensemble:

- Protective clothing (suit, coveralls, hoods, gloves, boots)
- Respiratory equipment (SCBA, combination SCBA/SAR)
- Cooling system (ice vest, air circulation, water circulation)
- Communications device
- Head protection
- Ear protection
- Inner garments
- Outer protection (overgloves, overboots, flashcovers)

5-6.1* Vapor-Protective Garments.

A-5-6.1 NFPA 1991, *Standard on Vapor-Protective Suits for Hazardous Chemical Emergencies*, covers vapor-protective suits that are designed to provide "gas-tight" integrity and are intended for response situations where no chemical contact is permissible. This type of suit is equivalent to the clothing required in EPA's Level A. The standard specifies a battery of 17 chemicals, which were selected because they are representative of the classes of chemicals that are encountered during hazardous materials emergencies. Vapor-protective suits must resist permeation by the chemicals present during a response. Permeation occurs when chemical molecules "diffuse" through the material, often without any evidence of chemical attack. Permeation resistance is measured in terms of breakthrough time. An acceptable material is one where the breakthrough time exceeds the expected period of garment use. Chemical permeation resistance for one hour or more against each chemical in the NFPA battery is required for primary suit materials (garment, visor, gloves, and boots). To be certified for any additional chemicals or specific chemical mixtures, a suit must meet the same permeation performance requirements.

Other performance requirements are included in NFPA 1991 in order to reflect simulated emergency hazardous materials response use conditions. To determine adequate suit component performance in hazardous chemical environments, the following tests are required:

(a) A suit pressurization test to check the air-tight integrity of each protective suit
(b) An overall suit water penetration test designed to ensure the suit provides full body protection against liquid splashes
(c) Penetration resistance testing of closures
(d) Leak and creaking pressure tests for exhaust valves

To ensure that the materials used for vapor-protective suits will afford adequate protection in the environment where they will be used, material testing for burst strength, tear resistance, abrasion resistance, flammability resistance, cold temperature performance, and flexural fatigue are also required.

5-6.1.1 Members who engage in operations during hazardous chemical emergencies that will expose them to known chemicals in vapor form or to unknown chemicals shall be provided with and shall use vapor-protective suits. Vapor-protective suits shall meet the applicable requirements of

NFPA 1991, *Standard on Vapor-Protective Suits for Hazardous Chemical Emergencies.*

NFPA 1991, *Standard on Vapor-Protective Suits for Hazardous Chemical Emergencies* (1994), covers vapor-protective suits that are designed to provide gas-tight integrity and are intended for response situations where no chemical contact is permissible or where the exposure is unknown. This type of suit is equivalent to the clothing required in EPA's Level A. To determine adequate suit component performance in hazardous chemical environments, the following performance tests are required.

Permeation resistance testing specifies a battery of 21 chemicals and gases, selected because they are representative of the classes of chemicals that are encountered during hazardous materials emergencies. Vapor-protective suits must resist permeation by the chemicals present during a response. Permeation occurs when chemical molecules diffuse through the material, often without any evidence of chemical attack. Permeation resistance is measured in terms of breakthrough time. An acceptable material is one where the breakthrough time exceeds the expected period of garment use. A chemical permeation resistance time of at least one hour or more must be met for each chemical specified in ASTM F 1001, *Standard Guide for Chemicals to Evaluate Protective Clothing Materials,* and is required for primary suit materials (garment, visor, gloves, and boots). Any additional chemicals or specific chemical mixtures for which the manufacturer is certifying the suit must meet the same permeation performance requirements.

Gas-tight integrity testing evaluates the suit for air leakage using a pressurization test to check *each* protective suit. The suit must maintain at least 1.6-in. water gauge pressure.

Liquid-tight integrity testing evaluates the suit for water leakage using an overall suit liquid penetration test. No liquid penetration of the suit can occur.

Overall suit function and integrity testing evaluates the entire suit for ability to function and retain gas-tight integrity while a test subject performs exercises while wearing the suit. The suit must maintain at least 1.6 in. water gauge pressure.

Suit ventilation rate testing evaluates the suit's ability to vent internal overpressure without compromising the suit or the gas tight criteria

Physical durability testing for the materials used for vapor-protective suits evaluates the material's ability to perform and resist chemical breakthrough for at least one hour after being subjected to abrasion and flexing, and also tests for burst strength, puncture propagation, flammability resistance, and cold temperature performance.

5-6.1.2 Prior to use, the incident commander shall consult the technical data package, manufacturer's instructions, and manufacturer's recommendations as provided and required by Chapters 2 and 3 of NFPA 1991, *Standard on Vapor-Protective Suits for Hazardous Chemical Emergencies,* to assure that the garment is appropriate for the specific hazardous chemical emergency.

5-6.1.3 All members who engage in operations during hazardous chemical emergencies that will expose them to known chemicals in vapor form or to unknown chemicals shall be provided with and shall use SCBA that meet the applicable requirements of Section 5-3 of this chapter. Additional outside air supplies shall be permitted to be utilized in conjunction with SCBA, provided such systems are positive pressure and have been certified by NIOSH under 42 *CFR* 84.

5-6.1.4* Vapor-protective suits shall not be used alone for any fire-fighting applications or for protection from radiological, biological, or cryogenic agents, or in flammable or explosive atmospheres.

A-5-6.1.4 Materials used in vapor-protective suits are tested for limited thermal resistance; however, this testing only prevents the use of inherently flammable materials. There are no performance criteria provided in NFPA 1991, *Standard on Vapor-Protective Suits for Hazardous Chemical Emergencies,* to demonstrate protection of NFPA 1991-compliant vapor-protective suits during fire-fighting operations. There are no test requirements or performance criteria in NFPA 1991 addressing protection from radiological, biological, or cryogenic hazards.

5-6.1.5 Vapor-protective suits shall be permitted to be used for protection from liquid splashes or solid chemicals and particulates.

5-6.2* Liquid Splash-Protective Garments.

A-5-6.2 NFPA 1992, *Standard on Liquid Splash-Protective Suits for Hazardous Chemical Emergencies*, covers liquid splash-protective suits, which are designed to protect emergency responders against liquid chemicals in the form of splashes, but not against continuous liquid contact or chemical vapors and gases. Liquid splash-protective suits can be acceptable for some chemicals that do not present vapor hazards. Essentially, this type of clothing meets EPA Level B needs. It is important to note, however, that wearing liquid splash-protective clothing does not protect the wearer from exposure to chemical vapors and gases, since this clothing does not offer gas-tight performance, even if duct tape is used to seal clothing interfaces. Therefore, where the environment is unknown or not quantified through monitoring, where exposures include carcinogens, where the chemicals have a high vapor pressure, or where the splash-protective suit has not been certified for the chemical exposure, an NFPA 1991-compliant garment should be utilized.

NFPA 1992 specifies a battery of nine chemicals, including liquid chemicals with low vapor pressures with no known skin absorption toxicity, that are representative of the classes of chemicals likely to be encountered during hazardous materials emergencies. Chemical penetration resistance against the NFPA battery of test chemicals is required. Any additional chemicals or specific chemical mixtures for which the manufacturer is certifying the suit must meet the same penetration performance requirements.

Other NFPA 1992 performance requirements include an overall suit water penetration test to ensure the suit provides full body splash protection. As in NFPA 1991, *Standard on Vapor-Protective Suits for Hazardous Chemical Emergencies,* this standard contains performance criteria to ensure that the materials used for liquid-splash suits afford adequate protection in the environment where they will be used. These test requirements include material testing for burst strength, tear resistance, flammability resistance, abrasion resistance, cold temperature performance, and flexural fatigue testing.

NFPA 1992, *Standard on Liquid Splash-Protective Suits for Hazardous Chemical Emergencies* (1994), covers liquid splash-protective suits that are designed to protect emergency responders against liquid chemicals in the form of splashes, but not against continuous liquid contact or chemical vapors and gases. Liquid splash-protective suits may be acceptable with some chemicals that do not present vapor hazards. Essentially, this type of clothing meets EPA Level B needs. It is important to note, however, that *by wearing liquid splash-protective clothing, the wearer accepts exposure to chemical vapors and gases.* Materials that prevent liquid penetration can still allow chemical permeation since this clothing does not offer gas-tight performance even if duct tape is used to seal clothing interfaces.

NFPA 1992 specifies a battery of seven liquid chemicals that are representative of the classes of chemicals likely to be encountered during hazardous materials emergencies. Any additional chemicals or specific chemical mixtures for which the manufacturer is certifying the suit must meet the same penetration performance requirements.

Liquid splash-protective suits are for use only for protection from liquids with low vapor pressures and with no known skin absorption toxicity. Liquid splash-protective suits cannot be used for known or suspected carcinogens. The following performance tests are required.

Penetration resistance testing specifies a battery of seven chemicals that were selected because they are representative of the classes of chemicals that are encountered during hazardous materials emergencies. Penetration resistance is measured in terms of penetration resistance time. An acceptable material is one where the resistance to liquid transfer time exceeds the expected period of garment use. A chemical penetration resistance time of at least one hour or more must be met for each of the seven chemicals specified and is required for primary suit materials (garment, visor, gloves, and boots). Any additional chemicals or specific chemical mixtures for which the manufacturer is certifying the suit must meet the same penetration performance requirements.

Overall suit function and integrity testing evaluates the entire suit for ability to function and retain liquid-tight integrity while a test subject performs exercises while wearing the suit. The suit shall not allow any liquid penetration.

Liquid-tight integrity testing evaluates the suit for water leakage using an overall suit liquid penetration test. No liquid penetration of the suit can occur.

Physical durability testing for the materials used for liquid-protective suits evaluates the material's ability to perform and resist chemical penetration for at least one hour after being subjected to abrasion and flexing, and also tests for burst strength, puncture propagation, flammability resistance, and cold temperature performance.

5-6.2.1 Members who engage in operations during hazardous chemical emergencies that will expose them to known chemicals in liquid-splash form shall be provided with and shall use liquid splash-protective suits. Liquid splash-protective suits shall meet the applicable requirements of NFPA 1992, *Standard on Liquid Splash-Protective Suits for Hazardous Chemical Emergencies.*

5-6.2.2 Prior to use of the garment, the incident commander shall consult the technical data package, manufacturer's instructions, and manufacturer's recommendations as provided and required by Chapters 2 and 3 of NFPA 1992, *Standard on Liquid Splash-Protective Suits for Hazardous Chemical Emergencies,* to assure that the garment is appropriate for the specific hazardous chemical emergency.

5-6.2.3 All members who engage in operations during hazardous chemical emergencies that will expose them to known chemicals in liquid-splash form shall be provided with and shall use either SCBA that meet the applicable requirements of Section 5-3 of this chapter or respiratory protective devices that are NIOSH certified under 42 *CFR* 84 as suitable for the specific chemical environment. Additional outside air supplies shall be permitted to be utilized in conjunction with SCBA, provided such systems are positive pressure and have been certified by NIOSH under 42 *CFR* 84.

5-6.2.4 Liquid splash-protective suits shall not be used for protection from chemicals in vapor form, or from unknown liquid chemicals or chemical mixtures. Only vapor-protective suits specified in 5-6.1 of this chapter and SCBA specified in Section 5-3 of this chapter shall be considered for use.

5-6.2.5 Liquid splash-protective suits shall not be used for protection from chemicals or specific chemical mixtures with known or suspected carcinogenicity as indicated by any one of the following documents:

(a) N. Irving Sax, *Dangerous Properties of Industrial Chemicals*
(b) NIOSH *Pocket Guide to Chemical Hazards*
(c) U.S. Coast Guard *Chemical Hazard Response Information System (CHRIS)*, Volumes 1–3, "Hazardous Chemical Data"

5-6.2.6 Liquid splash-protective suits shall not be used for protection from chemicals or specific chemical mixtures with skin toxicity notations as indicated by the American Conference of Governmental Industrial Hygienists, *Threshold Limit Values and Biological Exposure Indices for 1996–1997.*

5-6.2.7* Liquid splash-protective suits shall not be used alone for any fire-fighting applications or for protection from radiological, biological, or cryogenic agents; from flammable or explosive atmospheres; or from hazardous chemical vapor atmospheres.

A-5-6.2.7 Materials used in liquid splash-protective suits are tested for limited thermal resistance; however, this testing only prevents the use of inherently flammable materials. There are no performance criteria provided in NFPA 1992, *Standard on Liquid Splash-Protective Suits for Hazardous Chemical Emergencies*, to demonstrate protection of NFPA 1992-compliant liquid splash-protective suits during fire-fighting operations. There are no test requirements or performance criteria in NFPA 1992 addressing protection from radiological, biological, or cryogenic hazards.

5-6.2.8 Liquid splash-protective suits shall be permitted to be used for protection from solid chemicals and particulates.

5-6.3* Support Function Protective Garments.

A-5-6.3 NFPA 1993, *Standard on Support Function Protective Clothing for Hazardous Chemical Operations,* covers support function suits that provide liquid splash protection as required in NFPA 1992, *Standard on Liquid Splash-Protective Suits for Hazardous Chemical Emergencies,* but offer limited physical protection. These garments can be made without the construction requirements for reuse of the garments. They can be designed by the manufacturer for a single use or a limited use expectancy. These garments can comprise several separate protective clothing components (i.e., coveralls, hoods, gloves, and boots). They are intended for use in nonemergency, nonflammable situations where the chemical hazards have been completely characterized. Examples of support functions include decontamination, hazardous waste cleanup, and training. Support function protective garments should not be used during emergency response outside of support functions and should never be utilized for protection in a hot zone.

NFPA 1993, *Standard on Support Function Protective Clothing for Hazardous Chemical Operations* (1994), covers support function protective clothing that provides liquid splash protection but offers limited physical protection. These garments can be constructed without the rigid construction requirements for garments that are intended for reuse. They can be designed by the manufacturer for a single use or a limited use expectancy.

These garments may comprise several separate protective clothing components (i.e., coveralls, hoods, gloves, and boots). They are intended for use in nonemergency, nonflammable, controlled situations where the chemical hazards have been completely characterized. Examples of support functions include decontamination, hazardous waste cleanup, and training. *Support function protective garments must not be used during emergency response outside of support functions.* The following performance tests are required.

Penetration resistance testing specifies a battery of seven chemicals that were selected because they are representative of the classes of chemicals that are encountered during hazardous materials emergencies. Penetration resistance is measured in terms of penetration resistance time. An acceptable material is one where the resistance to liquid transfer time exceeds the expected period of garment use. A chemical penetration resistance time of at least one hour or more must be met for each of the seven chemicals specified and is required for primary garment materials including visor, gloves, and boots. Any additional chemicals or specific chemical mixtures for which the manufacturer is certifying the garment must meet the same penetration performance requirements.

Liquid-tight integrity testing evaluates the garment for water leakage using an overall suit liquid penetration test. No liquid penetration of the garment can occur.

Physical durability testing evaluates burst strength and puncture propagation.

5-6.3.1 Members who provide functional support outside the hot zone during hazardous chemical emergencies shall be provided with and shall use support function protective garments. Support function protective garments shall meet the applicable requirements of NFPA 1993, *Standard on Support Function Protective Clothing for Hazardous Chemical Operations*.

5-6.3.2 Prior to use, the incident commander shall consult the technical data package, manufacturer's instructions, and manufacturer's recommendations as provided and required by Chapters 2 and 3 of NFPA 1993, *Standard on Support Function Protective Clothing for Hazardous Chemical Operations*, to assure that the garment is appropriate for the intended environment.

5-6.3.3 Members who engage in or are exposed to chemicals in support function environments during hazardous chemical emergencies shall be provided with and shall use either SCBA that meet the applicable requirements of Section 5-3 of this chapter or respiratory protective devices that are NIOSH certified under 42 *CFR* 84 as suitable for the specific environment. Additional outside air supplies shall be permitted to be utilized in conjunction with SCBA, provided such systems are positive pressure and have been certified by NIOSH under 42 *CFR* 84.

5-6.3.4 Support function protective garments shall not be used in any hot zone of any hazardous chemical operation.

5-6.3.5 Support function protective garments shall not be used for protection from chemicals or specific chemical mixtures with known or suspected carcinogenicity as indicated by any one of the following documents:

(a) N. Irving Sax, *Dangerous Properties of Industrial Chemicals*
(b) NIOSH *Pocket Guide to Chemical Hazards*
(c) U.S. Coast Guard *Chemical Hazard Response Information System (CHRIS)*, Volumes 1–3, "Hazardous Chemical Data"

5-6.3.6 Support function protective garments shall not be used for protection from chemicals or specific chemical mixtures with skin toxicity notations as indicated by the American Conference of Governmental Industrial Hygienists, *Threshold Limit Values and Biological Exposure Indices for 1996–1997*.

5-6.3.7* Support function protective garments shall not be used for any fire-fighting applications or for protection from radiological, biological, or cryogenic agents; from flammable or explosive atmospheres; or from hazardous chemical vapor atmospheres.

A-5-6.3.7 Materials used in support function protective garments are tested for limited thermal resistance; however, this testing only prevents the use of inherently flammable materials. There are no performance criteria provided in NFPA 1993, *Standard on Support Function Protective Clothing for Hazardous Chemical Operations*, to demonstrate protection of NFPA 1993-compliant support function protective garments during fire-fighting operations. There are no test requirements or performance criteria in NFPA 1993 addressing protection from radiological, biological, or cryogenic hazards.

5-6.3.8 Support function protective garments shall be permitted to be used for protection against solid chemical and particulates outside of the hot zone.

5-6.4 Inspection, Maintenance, and Disposal of Chemical-Protective Clothing.

5-6.4.1 All chemical-protective clothing shall be inspected and maintained as required by the technical data package, manufacturer's instructions, and manufacturer's recommendations.

5-6.4.2 All chemical-protective clothing that receives a significant exposure to a chemical or chemical mixture shall be disposed of if decontamination will not stop the chemical assault on the garment and the protective qualities will be diminished or nullified. Disposal shall be in accordance with applicable state or federal regulations.

5-7 Protective Clothing and Equipment for Wildland Fire Fighting

Section 5-7 was included with input from the United States Forest Service. Wildland protective clothing and shelters, and the environment in which wildland fire fighters operate, differ significantly from structural fire fighting. As stated in Chapter 3, fire fighters who operate in both environments need to be trained in the use of protective clothing and equipment for wildland fire fighting.

5-7.1*

The fire department shall establish standard operating procedures for the use of wildland protective clothing and equipment.

A-5-7.1 Fire departments that provide wildland and structural fire-fighting services should establish guidelines for members on which ensemble to wear for a given incident.

5-7.2

Members who engage in or are exposed to the hazards of wildland fire-fighting operations shall be provided with and use a protective ensemble that meets the requirements of NFPA 1977, *Standard on Protective Clothing and Equipment for Wildland Fire Fighting*.

5-7.3

Protective clothing for wildland fire-fighting operations shall be fitted so that an overlap of clothing is provided at the waist, ankles, and wrists.

5-7.4*

Members who engage in or are exposed to the hazards of wildland fire-fighting operations shall be provided with and use a protective helmet that meets the requirements of NFPA 1977, *Standard on Protective Clothing and Equipment for Wildland Fire Fighting.*

A-5-7.4 Structural fire-fighting helmets can be used for this purpose although these are overly heavy and can cause additional stress and fatigue for the member.

5-7.5

Members who engage in or are exposed to the hazards of wildland fire-fighting operations shall be provided with and use protective gloves that meet the requirements of NFPA 1977, *Standard on Protective Clothing and Equipment for Wildland Fire Fighting.*

5-7.6

Members who engage in or are exposed to the hazards of wildland fire-fighting operations shall be provided with and use protective footwear that meets the requirements of NFPA 1977, *Standard on Protective Clothing and Equipment for Wildland Fire Fighting.*

5-7.7

Members who engage in or are exposed to the hazards of wildland fire-fighting operations shall be provided with an approved fire shelter, in a crush-resistive case, and wear it in such a way as to allow immediate deployment.

5-7.7.1 Members shall be trained in the proper deployment of an approved fire shelter, at least annually.

5-7.8*

Each member who engages in or is exposed to the hazards of wildland fire-fighting operations shall be provided with 2 quarts of water. A process shall be established for the rapid replenishment of water supplies.

A-5-7.8 The importance of hydration during wildland fire-fighting operations cannot be over emphasized. This concept must be clearly understood and utilized by all members. A method of replenishment of this water supply should be in place to provide 8 to 12 quarts of water per day, per member.

5-7.9*

Members who engage in or are exposed to the hazards of wildland fire-fighting operations shall be provided with and use a laminated pocket card stating the 10 standard fire-fighting orders, the 18 "watch-out" situations, and the "LCES" (Lookouts, Communications, Escape routes, and Safety zones) safety orders.

A-5-7.9 Some wildland fire fighter fatalities have been attributed to the failure to follow the 10 standard orders, or a failure to recognize one or more of the 18 "watch-out" situations. The "LCES" model provides a quick reference for establishing a safe approach to wildland fire fighting. These 18 "watch-out" situations are listed below.

(a) *Fire Orders*

1. **F**ight fire aggressively but provide for safety first.
2. **I**nitiate all action based on current and expected fire behavior.
3. **R**ecognize current weather conditions and obtain forecasts.
4. **E**nsure instructions are given and understood.
5. **O**btain current information on fire status.
6. **R**emain in communication with crew members, your supervisor, and adjoining forces.
7. **D**etermine safety zones and escape routes.
8. **E**stablish lookouts in potentially hazardous situations.
9. **R**etain control at all times.
10. **S**tay alert, keep calm, think clearly, act decisively.

(b) *Common Denominators of Fire Behavior on Tragedy Fires*

1. Most incidents happen on the smaller fires or on isolated portions of larger fires.
2. Most fires are innocent in appearance before the "flare-ups" or "blow-ups." In some cases, tragedies occur in the mop-up stage.
3. Flare-ups generally occur in deceptively light fuels.
4. Fires run uphill surprisingly fast in chimneys, gullies, and on steep slopes.
5. Some suppression tools, such as helicopters or air tankers, can adversely affect fire behavior. The blasts of air from low-flying helicopters and air tankers have been known to cause flare-ups.

(c) *Watch-Out Situations*

1. Fire not scouted and sized up
2. In country not seen in daylight
3. Safety zones and escape routes not identified
4. Unfamiliar with weather and local factors influencing fire behavior
5. Uninformed on strategy, tactics, and hazards
6. Instructions and assignments not clear

7. No communication link with crew members or supervisor
8. Constructing line without safe anchor point
9. Building fireline downhill with fire below
10. Attempting frontal assault on fire
11. Unburned fuel between you and fire
12. Cannot see main fire, not in contact with someone who can
13. On a hillside where rolling material can ignite fuel below
14. Weather becoming hotter and drier
15. Wind increases and/or changes direction
16. Getting frequent spot fires across line
17. Terrain and fuels make escape to safety zone difficult
18. Taking nap near fireline

(d) *The four major common denominators of fire behavior on tragedy fires are as follows:*

1. Most incidents happen on smaller fires or on isolated sections of larger fires.
2. Flare-ups generally occur in deceptively light fuels, such as grass, herbs, and light brush.
3. Most fires are innocent in appearance before unexpected shifts in wind direction and/or speed result in flare-ups. In some cases, tragedies occur in the mop-up stage.
4. Fires respond to large and small scale topographic conditions, running uphill surprisingly fast in chimneys, gullies, and on steep slopes.

Section 5-7.9 was included in the revision to NFPA 1500 on recommendation of the report issued on the South Canyon, Colorado, fire in which 14 wildland fire fighters were killed. For additional information on this incident, see *South Canyon Fire Investigation,* prepared by the the U.S. Forest Service, the U.S. Bureau of Land Management, and the National Oceanic and Atmospheric Administration.

5-8 Personal Alert Safety System (PASS)

Using a PASS device should be as natural as putting on protective clothing. To be effective, though, the PASS device needs to be alarmed before the fire fighter enters the hazard area. Reports of recent fire fighter fatalities show members who were equipped with PASS devices that were not activated. See NFPA's report (Supplement 4 in Part Six of this handbook) on the Branford, Connecticut, Carpet Store Fire, Pang Warehouse Fire in Seattle, Washington, and the Chesapeake, Virginia, Auto Parts Store Fire.

5-8.1*

Each member shall be provided with and shall use a PASS device in the hazardous area. PASS devices shall meet the requirements of NFPA 1982, *Standard on Personal Alert Safety Systems (PASS) for Fire Fighters.*

A-5-8.1 The mandatory use and operation of a PASS by fire fighters involved in rescue, fire suppression, or other hazardous duty is imperative for their safety. The primary intent of this device is to serve as an audible device to warn fellow fire fighters in the event a fire fighter becomes incapacitated or needs assistance.

Past fire fighter fatality investigation reports document the critical need to wear and operate PASS devices when fire fighters operate in hazardous areas. Investigation results show that fire fighters most often failed to activate the PASS unit prior to entering a hazardous area.

Technology has provided the integration of PASS devices with SCBA. When the SCBA unit is activated to an operational mode, the PASS device is activated. Fire departments are encouraged to utilize this technology.

The use of PASS devices must be coupled with a solid incident management system, a personnel accountability system, and adequate communications to properly ensure for the safety of fire fighters.

Paragraph 5-8.1 links the use of PASS devices and fire department occupational safety and health programs. NFPA 1982, *Standard on Personal Alert Safety Systems (PASS) for Fire Fighters* (1993), specifies minimum performance criteria, functioning, and test methods for devices that emit an audible alarm signal to summon assistance if the fire fighter becomes incapacitated or needs assistance.

Recently, there have been several fire fighter fatality incidents in which fire fighters became entrapped, lost, or disoriented while performing interior structural fire fighting. In these incidents, some of the fire fighters were wearing PASS devices, but had failed to turn them on. Several manufacturers are already integrating PASS with SCBA so that the PASS will be automatically activated when the air supply is turned on. NFPA 1982 already allows for such integration of SCBA/PASS systems.

PASS cannot substitute for an individual's common sense, as it cannot substitute for an active incident management system, communications, and a functional and adequate personnel accountability system. Although a PASS does not guarantee safety, it is an important component to the fire fighter's personal protective ensemble.

5-8.2

Each PASS device shall be tested at least weekly and prior to each use, and shall be maintained in accordance with the manufacturer's instructions.

5-9 Life Safety Rope and System Components

The use of life safety rope and associated components is viewed sometimes as strictly a matter for special operations. In reality, however, fire service personnel utilize life safety rope in a number of different operations. Consequently, its care, use, and maintenance are as important as any other fire department tool. The inspection procedures addressed in NFPA 1983, *Standard on Fire Service Life Safety Rope and System Components* (1995), provide a safety margin to determine when rope should be removed from service. Documentation, as always, is an important part of the testing and maintenance process. Testing and maintenance records should be kept with other tool and apparatus records.

5-9.1

All life safety ropes, harnesses, and hardware used by fire departments shall meet the applicable requirements of NFPA 1983, *Standard on Fire Service Life Safety Rope* and System Components.

5-9.2

Rope used to support the weight of members or other persons during rescue, fire fighting, other emergency operations, or during training evolutions shall be life safety rope and shall meet the requirements of NFPA 1983, *Standard on Fire Service Life Safety Rope and System Components.* Life safety rope used for any other purpose shall be removed from service and destroyed.

5-9.3*

Life safety rope used for rescue at fires or other emergency incidents or for training shall be permitted to be reused if inspected before and after each such use in accordance with the manufacturer's instructions and provided that the following criteria are met:

(a) The rope has not been visually damaged by exposure to heat, direct flame impingement, chemical exposure, or abrasion.
(b) The rope has not been subjected to any impact load.
(c) The rope has not been exposed to chemical liquids, solids, gases, mists, or vapors of any material known to deteriorate rope.

If the rope used for rescue at fires or other emergency incidents or for training has been subjected to (a), (b), or (c) or fails the visual inspection, it shall be destroyed after such use. If there is any question regarding the serviceability of the rope after consideration of the above, the safe course of action shall be taken and the rope shall be placed out of service. Life safety rope used for any other purpose shall be removed from service and destroyed.

A-5-9.3 Life safety rope can be significantly weakened by abrasion, misuse, contamination, wear, and stresses approaching its breaking strength, particularly impact loading. Since there is no approved method to service test a rope without compromising its strength, rope rescue and training operations should be carefully observed and monitored for conditions that could cause immediate failure or result in undetectable damage to the rope. If a rope has been used in a situation that could not be supervised or where potential damage might have occurred, it must be removed from service and destroyed.

It is important that ropes be inspected for signs of wear by qualified individuals after each use. If indications of wear or damage are noted, or if the rope has been stressed in excess of the manufacturer's recommendations or impact loaded, it must be destroyed.

The destruction of the rope means that it must be removed from service and altered in such a manner that it could not be mistakenly used as a life safety rope. This alteration could include disposal or removal of identifying labels and attachments and cutting the rope into short lengths that could be used for utility purposes.

The assignment of "disposable" life safety ropes to members or to vehicles has proven to be an effective system to manage ropes that are provided for emergency use and are used infrequently. Special rescue teams, which train frequently and use large quantities of rope, should include members who are qualified to manage and evaluate the condition of their ropes and determine the limitations upon their reuse.

5-9.4

Rope inspection shall be conducted by qualified inspectors in accordance with rope inspection procedures established and recommended as adequate by the rope manufacturer to assure rope is suitable for reuse.

5-9.5

Records shall be maintained to document the use of each life safety rope used at fires and other emergency incidents or for training.

5-10 Eye and Face Protection

The 1997 edition of NFPA 1971, *Standard on Protective Ensemble for Structural Fire Fighting,* contains requirements for eye and face protection. Numerous questions have arisen concerning the purchase and use of certain types of face shields or goggles for protection. The equipment's ability to provide eye protection during operations is a significant safety factor.

5-10.1

Primary face and eye protection appropriate for a given specific hazard shall be provided for and used by members exposed to that specific hazard. Such primary face and eye protection shall meet the requirements of ANSI Z87.1, *Practice for Occupational and Educational Eye and Face Protection*.

5-10.2

The full facepiece of SCBA shall constitute face and eye protection when worn. SCBA that has a facepiece-mounted regulator that, when disconnected, provides a direct path for flying objects to strike the face or eyes, shall have the regulator attached in order to be considered eye and face protection.

5-10.3

When operating in the hazardous area at an emergency scene without the full facepiece of respiratory protection being worn, members shall deploy the helmet goggles for eye protection.

5-11 Hearing Protection

5-11.1*

Hearing protection shall be provided for and used by all members operating or riding on fire apparatus when subject to noise in excess of 90 dBA.

A-5-11.1 The use of personal protective equipment to limit noise exposure should be considered as an interim approach until the noise levels produced by vehicles, warning devices, and radios can be reduced. Protective ear muffs are recommended for fire fighters, due to the difficulties of proper fit and insertion of ear plugs.

Studies in some jurisdictions have indicated that the most harmful noise exposure can come from radios that are turned up loud enough to be heard over the noise of engines and warning devices. Ear muffs are available that provide effective sound attenuation and rapid donning. They should also be provided with built-in speakers and volume controls for radio and intercom communications. Ear muffs should be worn by operators of noisy equipment (in excess of 90 dBA) at the scene of incidents as well as during response. In some jurisdictions, traffic regulations might limit the use of hearing protection by drivers.

The fire apparatus standards require the noise level at any seated position to be a maximum of 90 dBA when measured as specified in the standard, without any warning devices in operation, as the vehicle proceeds at a speed of 45 mph on a level, hard, smooth surface road. However, it is recommended that the specification for new fire apparatus provide maximum sound requirements that would allow members to ride in those vehicles without using hearing-protective devices. A maximum limit of 85 dBA without audible warning devices and 90 dBA with warning devices in operation is recommended. Interior noise levels should be measured with the vehicle in motion at the speed that produces the highest noise level, up to 55 mph. All windows should be closed, and the noise level should be measured in each passenger area.

The requirement of paragraph 5-11.1 is also written into the requirements of NFPA 1901, *Standard for Automotive Fire Apparatus* (1996).

5-11.2*

Hearing protection shall be provided for and used by all members when exposed to noise in excess of 90 dBA caused by power tools or equipment, other than in situations where the use of such protective equipment would create an additional hazard to the user.

A-5-11.2 When operating in situations where other protective clothing and equipment is necessary, such as in structural fire fighting, the interface between hearing protection and other necessary protection might not be adequately addressed by currently used devices. For example, ear muffs might not interface with helmets, and foam plastic ear plugs could be dangerous in a fire environment due to the potential for melting. In addition, a reduction in hearing capability in an emergency operations setting could create additional hazards. Effective hearing protection should also be used during nonemergency activities such as equipment checks and engine warm-ups. Attention should be given to correcting the deficiencies through the advent of improved protective devices and through the use of alternate or improved procedures that create less noise.

5-11.3*

The fire department shall engage in a hearing conservation program to identify and reduce or eliminate potentially harmful sources of noise in the work environment. Where audiometric testing indicates a significant hearing loss for a member, the fire department shall address these conditions on an individual basis, as well as take steps to control potentially harmful noise exposure to any or all other members.

A-5-11.3 An effective hearing conservation program should address the regular audiometric testing of members to identify hearing loss, the development and implementation of steps to prevent further hearing loss by members exhibiting such loss, and the ongoing identification and reduction or elimination of potentially harmful noise sources in the work environment. The standards for hearing conservation included in 29 *CFR* 1910.95 should be used as a basic minimum approach to this problem.

Any approach to hearing conservation should address personal protective devices, audiometric testing, and the reduction of noise exposure that can be achieved by modifying existing equipment or changing procedures. Examples of modifications would include moving siren speakers and air horns down onto front bumpers, responding with windows closed, and installing sound-attenuating insulation in cabs of fire apparatus. The noise produced by audible warning devices should also be evaluated to determine the most effective balance between warning value and harmful characteristics. Some studies indicate that high-low alternating tone sirens and lower pitch air horns could be more effective warning devices and less damaging to hearing.

A longer-term approach to hearing conservation should deal with the purchase of apparatus and equipment that is less noisy by design, with noise standards included in the specifications. Improved radio equipment that produces higher clarity of sound with less output volume should also be considered.

For more information on fire department hearing conservation programs, consult the U.S. Fire Administration Publication, *Fire Department Hearing Conservation Program Manual.*

Paragraph 5-11.3 mandates hearing conservation programs. *(See Figure 1500-5.9.)* The department's program should address the following:

- The hearing process
- Occupational hearing loss
- The extra auditory effects of excessive noise exposure
- The measurement of sound
- Fire fighter noise exposure
- Noise control practices
- Workers' compensation and hearing loss
- A step-by-step approach to reduce excessive noise exposure for fire fighters and EMS personnel

What Does 85 dB Sound Like?

Source of Noise	*Typical Noise Level (dBA)*
Siren	105
Passing truck	100
Subway, machine shop	90
Home smoke detector, 10 feet away	85
Noisy restaurant	80
Inside car with closed windows	70
Office	60
Average home	50

Note: These noise levels are expressed in decibels on the A weighted scale (dBA), where 0 dBA is the weakest sound that can be heard in an extremely quiet location and where 140 dBA is a person's threshold of pain.

Figure 1500-5.9 *Hearing loss is an occupational hazard for fire fighters. This chart provides some comparisons of the noise levels to which fire fighters are exposed. (Chart courtesy of IFSTA, Oklahoma State University Fire Protection Publications)*

5-12 New and Existing Protective Clothing and Protective Equipment

5-12.1

All new protective clothing and protective equipment shall meet the requirements of the current edition, as specified in Chapter 11 of this standard, of the respective standards specified in 5-1.6, 5-2.1, 5-4.1, 5-5.1, 5-6.1.1, 5-6.2.1, 5-6.3.1, and 5-8.1 of this chapter.

5-12.2

Existing protective clothing and protective equipment shall have been in compliance with the edition of the respective NFPA standard that was current when the protective clothing or protective equipment was manufactured.

On August 20, 1989, a Formal Interpretation concerning 5-9.2 in the 1987 edition was issued by the Standards Council. In the 1997 edition paragraph 5-9.2 has been renumbered as 5-12.2. That Formal Interpretation is still valid and is reproduced here for the reader's convenience.

Formal Interpretation

Reference: 5-9.2

F.I. No.: 87-6

Question: Is it the intent of 5-9.2 to include, as acceptable, existing protective clothing and protective equipment that complied with OSHA requirements when purchased but did not comply with the appropriate NFPA standard when purchased?

Answer: No.

Issue Edition: 1987

Reference: 5-9.2

Issue Date: July 21, 1989

Effective Date: August 20, 1989

Paragraph 5-12.2 raises the sometimes difficult issue of compliance. If equipment was compliant when purchased, then is it still compliant? Why replace equipment if it is still compliant? Clothing and equipment have a limited life span. The amount of wear and tear will depend on amount of use, type of activity, and maintenance history. Is new equipment safer, lighter, or better ergonomically for the user? Health and safety committees must ask these types of questions as they develop specifications for new protective clothing.

CHAPTER 6

Emergency Operations

Chapter 6 has opened the door on more discussions than any other chapter in NFPA 1500. Since the first edition of NFPA 1500 in 1987, questions about staffing, deployment, response, strategy, tactics, and incident management have all evolved from this chapter. Many in the fire service assumed that the standard was attempting to dictate how an incident commander would run an incident scene. Many fire officers were offended and fought to remove or weaken Chapter 6.

Understanding Chapter 6 begins with understanding Chapter 2, "Organization." In defining the fire department's roles and mission (as required by Chapter 2), the AHJ determines the types of incidents the department will respond to, what level of service will be provided upon arrival, with how many personnel, and in what time frame. The answers to these questions are part of risk identification.

Over the years, the fire department has come to be expected to respond to *any* emergency situation. The response may or may not have been appropriate, either in level or expectations. As fire department management has become more complex, many departments face such questions as "What can we do?" "How do we train to do it?" and "At what level do we train and respond to an emergency?"

The transition from "fire responder" to first responder to many sorts of emergencies (hazardous material response, for example) has been an easily identifiable option for the fire service. Fire departments are encouraged to ask the following questions before emergency responses:

- Is there an identified need for fire department services?
- If so, does the fire department have the training and resources (people, capital, and knowledge) to respond safely and efficiently?
- If the fire department does respond, what is the level of response?
- If the fire department does not respond, what is the risk versus the benefit? Do the citizens (customers) understand the potential outcome?

The Technical Committee has responded to a number of issues in Chapter 6 since the 1987 edition of the document. What continues to dominate the controversy is that departments underestimate the importance of Chapter 2. If the fire department implementation plan addresses the issues in Chapter 2, then most of the issues in Chapter 6 are addressed.

The Technical Committee realizes that "one size does not fit all." The generic language included in the document allows the department to respond appropriately in its own jurisdiction.

Nonetheless, as the backbone of the fire department's function, emergency operations must be managed from a health and safety perspective. If personnel accept the risks of emergency scene operations, incident managers should have considered risk management as part of their decision-making process.

Fire departments interact with many agencies, and probably most frequently with their law enforcement counterparts. Fire fighters respond to non-fire incident scenes that are unsafe. These non-fire, unsafe scenes may include domestic violence calls, hostage incidents, or any type of special law enforcement operations. The incident commander needs to know when the incident scene is safe. This need furthers the point for integrated incident command training among agencies.

In special operations, specialized training, equipment, and medical support are necessary. The use of an incident management system is common in special operations and is usually coordinated in a multiagency unified command process.

The key change in this revision of Chapter 6 was text in paragraph 6-4.4, which concerns personnel required at an incident scene. Again, the chapter specifically addresses an interior working structural fire-fighting operation. The chapter also covers the initial response crew/team. The recent OSHA revision of its regulations (specifically 29 *CFR* 1910.134 and 29 *CFR* 1910.120) requires a backup team of at least two people, trained and equipped at the same level as those who are entering an actual or potential IDLH atmosphere.

Before the 1997 revision to NFPA 1500, there was some confusion between an OSHA interpretation of their regulations and OSHA's use of NFPA 1500 as a general duty clause citation on fire departments, that is, a clause used in OSHA citations when there was no specific paragraph or subsection to cite. The Technical Committee felt that including specific language would help clarify the relationship between OSHA regulations and NFPA 1500.

6-1 Incident Management

6-1.1

Emergency operations and other situations that pose similar hazards, including but not limited to training exercises, shall be conducted in a manner that recognizes hazards and prevents accidents and injuries.

6-1.2

An incident management system that meets the requirements of NFPA 1561, *Standard on Fire Department Incident Management System*, shall be established with written standard operating procedures applying to all members involved in emergency operations. All members involved in emergency operations shall be trained in the system. The incident management system shall be utilized at all emergency incidents. The incident management system shall also be applied to drills, exercises, and other situations that involve hazards similar to those encountered at actual emergency incidents and to simulated incidents that are conducted for training and familiarization purposes.

The use of an incident management system in all fire department operations, as introduced in paragraph 6-1.2, is a key safety behavior in protecting fire fighters and other emergency response personnel. *(See Figure 1500-6.1.)* Over the past few years, a common finding in fire fighter fatality investigations has been the lack of use of an incident management system. An incident management system, an incident command system (ICS), and a fireground command system contain common elements no matter what the system is called. These elements include an incident commander, a manageable span of control, supervisory levels, a communications plan, an incident action plan, defined strategic goals with obtainable tactical objectives, and an accountability process. NFPA 1561, *Standard on Fire Department Incident Management System* (1995), was developed from paragraph 6-1.2; see Part Three of this handbook. *(See Figures 1500-6.2 and 1500-6.3.)*

Figure 1500-6.1 *Incident scene management is a key health and safety component. It is included in a department's standard operating procedures and is used at all incidents. (Photo courtesy of Fairfax County, Virginia, Fire and Rescue Department)*

Figure 1500-6.2 *An incident management system is mandated by federal law for all emergency response personnel for hazardous materials incidents. (Photo courtesy of Fairfax County, Virginia, Fire and Rescue Department)*

Figure 1500-6.3 Special operations incidents, such as trench rescue, also require the use of an incident management system designed to meet the intricacies or complexity of the operation. (Photo courtesy of Virginia Beach Fire Department)

6-1.3*

At an emergency incident, the incident commander shall be responsible for the overall management of the incident and the safety of all members involved at the scene. As incidents escalate in size and complexity, the incident commander shall divide the incident into tactical-level management units and assign an incident safety officer to assess the incident scene for hazards or potential hazards.

A-6-1.3 The incident commander must automatically integrate fire fighter safety and survival into the regular command functions. When this integration occurs, the incident commander promotes fire fighter welfare by performing the standard job of command. Under fire conditions, the incident commander is at an extreme disadvantage to perform any additional tasks. The safety plan for the incident commander has to be the regular command plan.

6-1.4

At an emergency incident, the incident commander shall establish an organization with sufficient supervisory personnel to control the position and function of all members operating at the scene and to ensure that safety requirements are satisfied.

6-1.5*

At an emergency incident, the incident commander shall have the responsibility for the following:

(a) Arrive on-scene before assuming command.
(b) Assume and confirm command of an incident and take an effective command position.
(c) Perform situation evaluation that includes risk assessment.
(d) Initiate, maintain, and control incident communications.
(e) Develop an overall strategy and an incident action plan, and assign companies and members consistent with the standard operating procedures required by 6-1.2.
(f) Develop an effective incident organization by managing resources, maintaining an effective span of control, and maintaining direct supervision over the entire incident, and designate supervisors in charge of specific areas or functions.
(g) Review, evaluate, and revise the incident action plan as required.
(h) Continue, transfer, and terminate command.
(i) On incidents under the command authority of the fire department, provide for liaison and coordination with all other cooperating agencies.
(j) On incidents where other agencies have jurisdiction, implement a plan that designates one incident commander or that provides for unified command. Interagency coordination shall meet the requirements of Section 2-3 of NFPA 1561, *Standard on Fire Department Incident Management System.*

A-6-1.5

(a) The incident commander must always integrate fire fighter health and safety considerations into the command process. This integration ensures that safety will always be considered and will not be reserved for unusual or high-risk situations when the incident commander is under a high degree of stress. An incident action plan that addresses fire fighter safety should be a routine function of command.

(b) Early evaluation enables the incident commander to consider current conditions in a standard manner and then predict the sequence of events that will follow. The consideration of fire fighter safety must be incorporated in this evaluation and forecasting.

(c) Effective communications are essential to ensure that the incident commander is able to receive and transmit information, obtain reports to maintain an awareness of the situation, and communicate with all component parts of the incident organization to provide effective supervision and controls.

(d) Strategic decisions establish the basic positioning of resources and the types of functions they will be assigned to perform at the scene of a fire or emergency incident. The level of risk to which members are exposed is driven by the strategy; offensive strategy places members in interior positions where they are likely to have direct contact with the fire, while defensive strategy removes members from interior positions and high-risk activities. The attack plan is based on the overall strategy and drives the tactical assignments that are given to individual or groups of companies/crews and the specific functions they are expected to perform. Risk identification, evaluation, and management concepts must be incorporated in each stage of the command process.

(e) Tactical-level management unit people are command agents and are able both to monitor companies/crews at the actual location where the work is being done (geographic) and to provide the necessary support (functional). The incident commander uses a tactical-level management unit as off-site (from the command post) operational/communications/safety managers-supervisors. The incident commander uses the incident organization along with communications to stay connected. Some incident management systems identify tactical-level management units such as a "division" or a "group" for a functional position within the system, whereas other systems use the term "sectors" for either geographical or functional areas. As incidents escalate, the incident management system should be utilized to maintain an effective span of control ratio of 3-to-7. Good sector control = good safety control.

(f) The incident commander must routinely evaluate and re-evaluate conditions and reports of progress or lack of progress in reaching objectives. This process will allow the incident commander to determine if the strategy and attack plans should be continued or revised. The failure to revise an inappropriate or outdated attack plan is likely to result in an elevated risk of death or injury to fire fighters.

(g) Effective command and control must be maintained from the beginning to the end of operations, particularly if command is transferred. Any lapse in the continuity of command and the transfer of information increases the risk to fire fighters.

6-1.6

The fire department shall establish and ensure the maintenance of a fire dispatch and incident communication system that meets the requirements of Section 2-2 of NFPA 1561, *Standard on Fire Department Incident Management System.*

6-2 Risk Management During Emergency Operations

6-2.1*

The incident commander shall integrate risk management into the regular functions of incident command.

A-6-2.1 The incident commander has an ultimate responsibility for the safety of all fire department members operating at an incident and for any and all other persons whose safety is affected by fire department operations. Risk management provides a basis for the following:

(a) Standard evaluation of the situation
(b) Strategic decision-making
(c) Tactical planning
(d) Plan evaluation and revision
(e) Operational command and control

6-2.1.1*

The concept of risk management shall be utilized on the basis of the following principles:

(a) Activities that present a significant risk to the safety of members shall be limited to situations where there is a potential to save endangered lives.
(b) Activities that are routinely employed to protect property shall be recognized as inherent risks to the safety of members, and actions shall be taken to reduce or avoid these risks.
(c) No risk to the safety of members shall be acceptable when there is no possibility to save lives or property.

A-6-2.1.1 The risk to fire department members is the most important factor considered by the incident commander in determining the strategy that will be employed in each situation. The management of risk levels involves all of the following factors:

(a) Routine evaluation of risk in all situations
(b) Well-defined strategic options
(c) Standard operating procedures
(d) Effective training
(e) Full protective clothing ensemble and equipment
(f) Effective incident management and communications
(g) Safety procedures and safety officers
(h) Back-up crews for rapid intervention
(i) Adequate resources
(j) Rest and rehabilitation
(k) Regular evaluation of changing conditions
(l) Experience based on previous incidents and critiques

6-2.1.2* The incident commander shall evaluate the risk to members with respect to the purpose and potential results of their actions in each situation. In situations where the risk to fire department members is excessive, as defined by 6-2.1.1 of this section, activities shall be limited to defensive operations.

A-6-2.1.2 The acceptable level of risk is directly related to the potential to save lives or property. Where there is no potential to save lives, the risk to fire department members must be evaluated in proportion to the ability to save property of value. When there is no ability to save lives or property, there is no justification to expose fire department members to any avoidable risk, and defensive fire suppression operations are the appropriate strategy.

6-2.2

Risk management principles shall be routinely employed by supervisory personnel at all levels of the incident management system to define the limits of acceptable and unacceptable positions and functions for all members at the incident scene.

6-2.3*

At significant incidents and special operations incidents, the incident commander shall assign an incident safety officer that has the expertise to evaluate hazards and provide direction with respect to the overall safety of personnel.

A-6-2.3 An incident safety officer should be established at all major incidents and at any high-risk incidents. The incident safety officer should be assigned to operate under the incident commander. Depending on the specific situation, this assignment could require one or more members. If the fire department's safety officer is not available or doesn't have the expertise necessary for the incident, the incident commander should assign one or more members that have the expertise to assume this responsibility. All members should be familiar with the basic duties and responsibilities of an incident safety officer.

6-2.4

At civil disturbances or incidents involving the risk for physical violence, the incident commander shall ensure that appropriate protective equipment (e.g., body armor) is available and used before members are allowed to enter the hazard area.

As part of plans and logistics, the incident commander should have access to the appropriate personal protective equipment that will safeguard members operating at the incident. *(See Figure 1500-6.4.)*

Figure 1500-6.4 *This room houses the personal protective equipment for one department. (Photo courtesy of Virginia Beach Fire Department)*

6-2.5

At terrorist incidents or other incidents involving potential nuclear, biological, and chemical exposure, the incident commander shall exercise risk management practice and ensure that appropriate protective equipment is available for and used by members at risk.

6-3 Accountability

6-3.1*

The fire department shall establish written standard operating procedures for a personnel accountability system that is in accordance with Section 2-6 of NFPA 1561, *Standard on Fire Department Incident Management System*, and that provides for the tracking and inventory of all members operating at an emergency incident. The system shall provide a rapid accounting of all personnel at the incident scene.

A-6-3.1 A standard system to account for the identity and assignment of each member might be relatively simple when all members arrive as assigned crews on fire apparatus. The identity of each crew member should at least be recorded in a standard manner on the vehicle, and each company officer is responsible for those members. In fire departments where members arrive in their own vehicles or assemble at the scene, a system is required to record the identity of each member arriving and to organize them into companies or groups with appropriate supervision. This requires a standard system of "reporting in" at the incident and becoming part of the organized system of operations.

Paragraph 6-3.1 requires SOPs for a personnel accountability system. *(See Figure 1500-6.5.)* The personnel accountability system should be used in parallel with the department's incident management system. The system does not have to be complicated or expensive. However, it should provide the incident commander with a rapid accountability process and the ability to track personnel by location and function.

6-3.1.1 The fire department shall consider local conditions and characteristics in establishing the requirements of the personnel accountability system.

6-3.2

It shall be the responsibility of all members operating at an emergency incident to actively participate in the personnel accountability system.

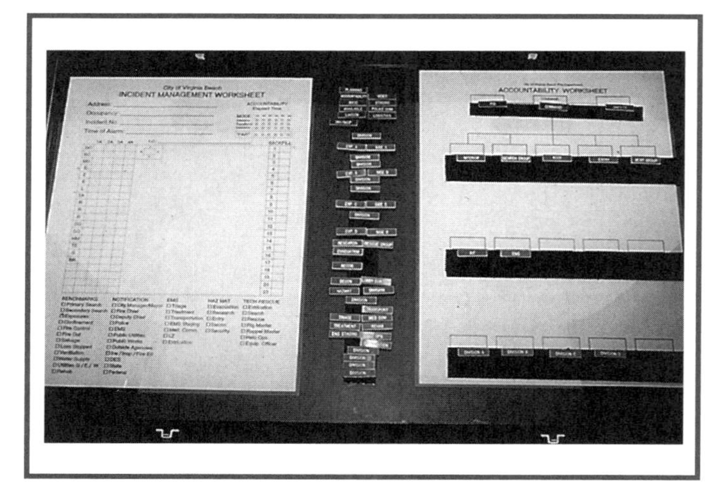

Figure 1500-6.5 An accountability process is critical for tracking personnel and provides a process for the tracking and deployment of the rapid intervention crews (RICs). (Photo courtesy of Virginia Beach Fire Department)

6-3.3

The incident commander shall be responsible for overall personnel accountability for the incident. The incident commander shall initiate an accountability and inventory worksheet at the very beginning of operations and shall maintain that system throughout operations.

6-3.3.1 The incident commander shall maintain an awareness of the location and function of all companies or units at the scene of the incident.

6-3.3.2 Officers assigned the responsibility for a specific tactical-level management unit at an incident shall directly supervise and account for the companies operating in their specific area of responsibility.

6-3.3.3 Company officers shall maintain an ongoing awareness of the location and condition of all company members.

6-3.3.4 Where assigned as a company, members shall be responsible to remain under the supervision of their assigned company officer.

6-3.3.5 Members shall be responsible for following personnel accountability system procedures.

6-3.4

The personnel accountability system shall be used at all incidents.

6-3.5*

The fire department shall develop the system components required to make the personnel accountability system effective.

A-6-3.5 There are many means of meeting these requirements. Some components can include tactical worksheets, command boards, apparatus riding lists, company personnel boards, electronic bar-coding systems, and so forth. These components can be used in conjunction with one another to facilitate the tracking of personnel by both location and function. The components of the personnel accountability system should be modular and expand with the size and complexity of the incident.

6-3.6*

The standard operating procedures shall provide the use of additional accountability officers based on the size, complexity, or needs of the incident.

A-6-3.6 These accountability officers should work with the incident commander and tactical-level management unit officers to assist in the ongoing tracking and accountability of members.

6-3.7

The incident commander and members who are assigned a supervisory responsibility for a tactical-level management unit that involves multiple companies or crews under their command shall have assigned a member(s) to facilitate the ongoing tracking and accountability of all assigned companies.

6-4 Members Operating at Emergency Incidents

6-4.1*

The fire department shall provide an adequate number of personnel to safely conduct emergency scene operations. Operations shall be limited to those that can be safely performed by the personnel available at the scene. No member or members shall commence or perform any fire-fighting function or evolution that is not within the established safety criteria of the organizational statement as specified in 2-1.2 of this standard.

A-6-4.1 The limitation of emergency scene operations to those that can be safely conducted by the number of personnel on the scene is intended to reduce the risk of fire fighter death or injury due to understaffing. While members can be assigned and arrive at the scene of an incident in many different ways, it is strongly recommended that interior firefighting operations not be conducted without an adequate number of qualified fire fighters operating in companies under the supervision of company officers.

It is recommended that a minimum acceptable fire company staffing level should be four members responding on or arriving with each engine and each ladder company responding to any type of fire. The minimum acceptable staffing level for companies responding in high-risk areas should be five members responding or arriving with each engine company and six members responding or arriving with each ladder company. These recommendations are based on experience derived from actual fires and in-depth fire simulations and are the result of critical and objective evaluation of fire company effectiveness. These studies indicate significant reductions in performance and safety where crews have fewer members than the above recommendations. Overall, five-member crews were found to provide a more coordinated approach for search and rescue and fire suppression tasks.

During actual emergencies, the effectiveness of companies can become critical to the safety and health of fire fighters. Potentially fatal work environments can be created very rapidly in many fire situations. The training and skills of companies can make a difference in the need for additional personnel and in reducing the exposure to safety and health risks to fire fighters where a situation exceeds their capabilities.

6-4.2

When inexperienced members are working at an incident, direct supervision shall be provided by more experienced officers or members. This requirement shall not reduce the training requirements contained in Chapter 3 of this standard.

6-4.3*

Members operating in hazardous areas at emergency incidents shall operate in teams of two or more. Team members operating in hazardous areas shall be in communication with each other through visual, audible, or physical means or safety guide rope, in order to coordinate their activities. Team members shall be in close proximity to each other to provide assistance in case of emergency.

A-6-4.3 For additional information see 29 *CFR* 1910.134 and U.S. Department of Labor, Occupational Safety and Health Administration, Memorandum for Regional Administration and State Designees, "Response to IDLH or Potential IDLH Atmospheres."

6-4.4*

In the initial stages of an incident where only one team is operating in the hazardous area at a working structural fire, a minimum of four individuals is required, consisting of two individuals working as a team in the hazard area and two individuals present outside this hazard area for assistance or rescue at emergency operations where entry into the danger area is required. The standby members shall be responsible for maintaining a constant awareness of the number and identity of members operating in the hazardous area, their location and function, and time of entry. The standby members shall remain in radio, visual, voice, or signal line communications with the team.

A-6-4.4 The assembling of four members for the initial fire attack can be accomplished in many ways. The fire department should determine the manner in which they plan to assemble members in their response plan. The four members assembled for initial fire-fighting operations can include an officer, chief officer, or any combination of members arriving separately at the incident.

Members that arrive on the scene of a working structural fire prior to the assembling of four persons can initiate exterior actions in preparation for an interior attack. These can include, but are not limited to, actions such as the establishment of a water supply, the shutting off of utilities, the placement of ladders, the laying of the attack line to the entrance of the structure, or exposure protection.

If members are going to initiate actions that would involve entering of a structure because of an imminent life-threatening situation where immediate action can prevent the loss of life or serious injury, and four members are not yet on the scene, the members should carefully evaluate the level of risk that they would be exposed to by taking such actions. If it is determined that the situation warrants such action, incoming companies should be notified so that they will be prepared to provide necessary support and backup upon arrival.

Fire departments respond to incidents based on staffing, location of stations, and type of department. Paragraph 6-4.4 requires the assembly of four personnel before beginning interior structural fire-fighting operations. This section, along with the text in paragraphs 6-4.4.1 and 6-4.4.2, provides the basis for the discussion of the "Two In and Two Out Rule" (i.e., 29 *CFR* 1910.134 and 29 *CFR* 1910.120).

6-4.4.1 The "initial stages" of an incident shall encompass the tasks undertaken by the first arriving company with only one team assigned or operating in the hazardous area.

The term *initial stages* of an incident delineates when the fire department is required to provide for backup for personnel. This requirement is explained further by the need for a trained rapid intervention crew, as described in Section 6-5.

6-4.4.2* One standby member shall be permitted to perform other duties outside of the hazardous area, such as apparatus operator, incident commander, or technician or aide, provided constant communication is maintained between the standby member and the members of the team. The assignment of any personnel, including the incident commander, the safety officer, or operators of fire apparatus, shall not be permitted as standby personnel if by abandoning their critical task(s) to assist or, if necessary, perform rescue, they clearly jeopardize the safety and health of any fire fighter working at the incident. No one shall be permitted to serve as a standby member of the fire-fighting team when the other activities in which he/she is engaged inhibit his/her ability to assist in or perform rescue, if necessary, or are of such importance that they cannot be abandoned without placing other fire fighters in danger.

A-6-4.4.2 The following examples show how a department might deploy a team of four members initially at the scene of a structure fire, regardless of how the team members are assembled:

(a) The team leader and one fire fighter could advance a fire-fighting hoseline into the IDLH atmosphere, and one fire fighter and the pump operator become the standby members.
(b) The team leader could designate the pump operator to be the incident commander. The team leader and one fire fighter enter the IDLH atmosphere, and one fire fighter and pump operator remain outside as the standby members.
(c) Two fire fighters could advance the hoseline in the IDLH atmosphere, and the team leader and pump operator remain outside as standby members.

6-4.4.3 The standby member shall be provided with at least the appropriate full protective clothing, protective equipment, and SCBA as required in Chapter 5 of this standard. The full protective clothing, protective equipment, and SCBA shall be immediately accessible for use by the outside team if the need for rescue activities inside the hazard area is necessary. The standby members shall don full protective clothing, protective equipment, and SCBA prior to entering the hazard area.

6-4.4.4 When only a single team is operating in the hazardous area in the initial stages of the incident, this standby member shall be permitted to assist, or if necessary perform, rescue for members of his/her team, providing abandoning his/her task does not jeopardize the safety or health of the team. Once a second team is assigned or operating in the hazardous area, the incident shall no longer be considered in the "initial stage," and at least one rapid intervention crew shall be required.

6-4.4.5 Initial attack operations shall be organized to ensure that, if upon arrival at the emergency scene, initial attack personnel find an imminent life-threatening situation where immediate action could prevent the loss of life or serious injury, such action shall be permitted with less than four personnel when conducted in accordance with Section 6-2 of this standard. No exception shall be permitted when there is no possibility to save lives. Any such actions taken in accordance with this section shall be thoroughly investigated by the fire department with a written report submitted to the fire chief.

6-4.5*

When members are performing special operations, the highest available level of emergency medical care shall be standing by at the scene with medical equipment and transportation capabilities. Basic life support shall be the minimum level of emergency medical care.

A-6-4.5 If advanced life-support personnel are available, this level of service would be preferred. Basic life support is the minimum acceptable level.

6-4.5.1 Emergency medical care and medical monitoring at hazardous materials incidents shall be provided by or supervised by personnel who meet the minimum requirements of NFPA 473, *Standard for Competencies for EMS Personnel Responding to Hazardous Materials Incidents.*

6-4.5.2 At all other emergency operations, the incident commander shall evaluate the risk to the members operating at the scene and, if necessary, request that at least basic life-support personnel and patient transportation be available.

Paragraph 6-4.5.2 requires the fire department to provide emergency medical care for emergency response personnel. This care can be provided by a third-party EMS provider, whether public or private. This EMS component of the incident management structure is beyond emergency medical requirements needed to treat civilians.

6-4.6

When members are operating from aerial devices, they shall be secured to the aerial device by an approved ladder belt that complies with the requirements of Section 5-8 of this standard.

6-4.7

When members are operating at an emergency incident and their assignment places them in potential conflict with motor vehicle traffic, they shall wear a garment with fluorescent retroreflective material.

Paragraph 6-4.7 is based on the need for members operating on roadways to be seen by oncoming traffic. Protective clothing reflective trim is not sufficient for drivers to see members at an incident scene. At times when members do not wear their protective clothing—such as when providing EMS care at a motor vehicle accident after responding in an EMS vehicle, rather than with an engine or ladder company—they should wear traffic vests similar to those worn by law enforcement personnel.

6-4.7.1 Apparatus shall be utilized as a shield from oncoming traffic wherever possible.

6-4.7.2* When acting as a shield, apparatus warning lights shall remain on, if appropriate, and fluorescent and retroreflective warning devices such as traffic cones, illuminated warning devices such as highway flares, or other appropriate warning devices shall be used to warn oncoming traffic of the emergency operations and the hazards to members operating at the incident.

A-6-4.7.2 Some studies have shown that headlights or warning lights of parked vehicles at emergency incidents have caused accidents instead of prevented accidents. The fire department should develop guidelines in conjunction with their local law enforcement agency to determine what is appropriate for local conditions.

As pointed out by paragraph A-6-4.7.2, the illumination of an incident scene and apparatus warning lights may, in fact, temporarily blind oncoming drivers. The location of apparatus and the use of warning lights should be part of an overall safety plan, developed in conjunction with the appropriate law enforcement agency, for operating on roadways.

6-5 Rapid Intervention for Rescue of Members

Section 6-5 introduces the concept of rapid intervention crews (RICs), first included in the 1992 edition of the standard. The use of a dedicated crew specifically for the rescue of lost or trapped fire fighters was not new to the fire service. For many years, the rescue company duties at an incident often included those of a rapid intervention crew. The duties of an RIC are no different from what is required in hazardous materials or other special operations.

The utilization and deployment of a rapid intervention crew are under the auspices of the incident commander. The requirements outlined in this section are reiterated in NFPA 1561, *Standard on Fire Department Incident Management System* (1995). *(See Part Three of this handbook.)* Because members respond to far more fire suppression incidents than hazardous materials or special operations incidents, it makes sense to include a rapid intervention crew in the response plan for fire suppression.

A sample SOP for a rapid intervention crew is available as Supplement 3 in Part Six of this handbook. The importance of a rapid intervention crew is illustrated in Supplement 4 by the NFPA Fire Investigation Report of a single fire fighter fatality incident in Branford, Connecticut, in 1996.

6-5.1

The fire department shall provide personnel for the rescue of members operating at emergency incidents if the need arises.

6-5.2

A rapid intervention crew shall consist of at least two members and shall be available for rescue of a member or a team if the need arises. Rapid intervention crews shall be fully equipped with the appropriate protective clothing, protective equipment, SCBA, and any specialized rescue equipment that might be needed given the specifics of the operation under way.

6-5.3

The composition and structure of rapid intervention crews shall be permitted to be flexible based on the type of incident and the size and complexity of operations. The incident commander shall evaluate the situation and the risks to operating teams and shall provide one or more rapid intervention crews commensurate with the needs of the situation.

6-5.4

In the early stages of an incident, which includes the deployment of a fire department's initial attack assignment, the rapid intervention crew(s) shall be in compliance with 6-4.4 and 6-4.4.2 and be either one of the following:

(a) On-scene members designated and dedicated as rapid intervention crew(s)
(b) On-scene members performing other functions but ready to redeploy to perform rapid intervention crew functions. The assignment of any personnel shall not be permitted as members of the rapid intervention crew if abandoning their critical task(s) to perform rescue clearly jeopardizes the safety and health of any member operating at the incident.

6-5.5

As the incident expands in size or complexity, which includes an incident commander's requests for additional resources beyond a fire department's initial attack assignment, the rapid intervention crews shall upon arrival of these additional resources be either one of the following:

(a) On-scene members designated and dedicated as rapid intervention crews
(b) On-scene company or companies located for rapid deployment and dedicated as rapid intervention crews

6-5.6

At least one rapid intervention crew shall be standing by with equipment to provide for the rescue of members that are performing special operations or for members that are in positions that present an immediate danger of injury in the event of equipment failure or collapse.

6-6 Rehabilitation During Emergency Operations

Section 6-6 covers the rehabilitation of members working at an incident scene and intends for rehabilitation to be more than "coffee and donuts." *(See Figure 1500-6.6.)* The dynamic stresses of the fire scene and exposure to weather conditions can take their toll on the body. During sustained operations, the incident commander should have sufficient personnel on-scene to relieve and rotate members. During rotation, members should be rehydrated in a temperature-controlled environment and medically evaluated before returning to work. Details of the rehabilitation process can be found in the United States Fire Administration publication *Emergency Incident Rehabilitation* (FA 114/July 1992); sample forms are included.

Figure 1500-6.6 *The process of establishing a rehabilitation sector is a critical component of fire fighter health and safety. A process should track personnel in and out of operations and provide a baseline medical evaluation, rehydration, and a place out of the elements. (Photo courtesy of the Longmeadow, Massachusetts, Fire Department)*

Rehabilitation is a component of incident management. Consequently, the incident commander needs to plan for "rehab," including plans for providing medical assistance. Those plans may include utilizing mutual-aid or private EMS providers. The fire department physician should assist in developing medical protocols for when members can or cannot return to work at an incident scene.

6-6.1*

The fire department shall develop standard operating procedures that outline a systematic approach for the rehabilitation of members operating at incidents. Provisions addressed in these procedures shall include medical evaluation and treatment, food and fluid replenishment, crew rotation, and relief from extreme climatic conditions.

A-6-6.1 Having a pre-planned rehabilitation program that is applicable to most incident types is essential for the health and safety of members. The rehabilitation plan should outline an ongoing rehabilitation for simple or short-duration incidents as well as a process to transition into the rehabilitation needs of a large or long-duration incident. Medical evaluation and treatment in the on-scene rehabilitation area should be conducted according to EMS protocols developed by the fire department in consultation with the fire department physician and the EMS medical director. If ALS personnel are available, this level of EMS care is preferred.

The use of a fire department physician in establishing medical protocols for return to duty from rehab provides an additional set of guidelines for the EMS provider to use. Vital signs, such as blood pressure, are only one indicator of a member's condition. Common sense would dictate asking the member, "How are you feeling?" Increased heart rate, blood pressure, and respiratory rate could result from the stresses in response, strenuous activity at the scene, and sheer adrenaline push—or they could be signs and symptoms of a serious medical condition. Other medical indicators, particular to that member, should provide guidance on allowing that member to return to the incident scene.

Medical evaluation and treatment in the on-scene rehabilitation area should be conducted according to EMS protocols developed by the fire department in consultation with the fire department physician and the EMS medical director. If ALS personnel are available, this level of service is preferred.

6-6.2*

The incident commander shall consider the circumstances of each incident and initiate rest and rehabilitation in accordance with the standard operating procedures and with NFPA 1561, *Standard on Fire Department Incident Management System.*

A-6-6.2 Weather factors during emergency incidents can impact severely on the safety and health of members, particularly during extremes of heat or cold. Where these factors combine with long-duration incidents or situations that require heavy exertion, the risks to members increase rapidly. The fire department should develop procedures, in consultation with the fire department physician, to provide relief from adverse climatic conditions.

Typical rehabilitation considerations for operations during hot weather extremes are (1) moving fatigued or unassigned personnel away from the hazardous area of the incident; (2) removal of personal protective equipment; (3) ensuring that personnel are out of direct sunlight; (4) ensuring that there is adequate air movement over personnel, either naturally or mechanically; (5) providing personnel with fluid replenishment, especially water; and (6) providing medical evaluation for personnel showing signs or symptoms of heat exhaustion or heat stroke.

Typical rehabilitation considerations for operations during cold weather extremes are (1) moving fatigued or unassigned personnel away from the hazardous area of the incident; (2) providing shelter from wind and temperature extremes; (3) providing personnel with fluid replenishment, especially water; and (4) providing medical evaluation for personnel showing signs or symptoms of frostbite, hypothermia, or other cold-related injury.

6-6.3*

Such on-scene rehabilitation shall include at least basic life-support care.

A-6-6.3 The assignment of an ambulance or other support crew to the rehabilitation function is essential during long-duration or heavy-exertion incident operations. This crew can assist with rehabilitation functions as well as be available to provide immediate life support needs for members.

6-6.4

Each member operating at an incident shall be responsible to communicate rehabilitation and rest needs to his/her supervisor.

6-7 Civil Unrest/Terrorism

Section 6-7 addresses the increased concerns about fire department response to acts of civil unrest and terrorism. Civil unrest, as well as domestic and international terrorism, increases the potential risk to fire department personnel. Additional specialized training, equipment, and interagency cooperation are components of responses to civil unrest and terrorism. *(See Figure 1500-6.7.)*

It is a hallmark of the fire-fighting profession that members will be called to respond to an unknown, unseen hazard. However, fire departments need to consider the safety concerns of their members before responding to incidents of this type. In many instances of civil unrest or terrorism, the fire department operates within a law enforcement incident management system. *(See Figure 1500-6.8.)*

Figure 1500-6.7 *Fire department operations that are included in law enforcement activities must provide a heightened degree of safety for fire personnel. These activities (such as response to terrorism incidents) are usually under a law enforcement ICS and require that the scene be secured by law enforcement personnel before the fire department becomes involved. [Photo courtesy of the United States Department of Treasury, Bureau of Alcohol, Tobacco, and Firearms (BATF)]*

Figure 1500-6.8 *Fire department special operations personnel should train with the other agencies and become familiar with their incident management systems. Clandestine drug labs, such as the one shown here, pose potentially fatal consequences for untrained fire personnel. (Photo courtesy of the United States Department of Justice, Drug Enforcement Administration)*

The incident scene should be secured before fire department involvement. When the fire department members arrive on-scene before law enforcement personnel, fire department company officers should assess the situation before entering a potentially hazardous area.

During civil unrest, fire department members may fall under attack. In referring to a department's risk management plan, incident commanders must understand and implement the plan that best protects their personnel. Questions that should be asked include the following:

- Should the fire department respond?
- What are the fire fighters' responsibilities?
- What egress routes are available for personnel?
- Is any benefit worth the potential risk?

6-7.1

The fire department shall develop and maintain written standard operating procedures that establish a standardized approach to the safety of members at incidents that involve violence, unrest, or civil disturbance. Such situations shall include but not be limited to riots, fights, violent crimes, drug-related situations, family disturbances, deranged individuals, and people interfering with fire department operations.

6-7.2

The fire department shall be responsible for developing an interagency agreement with its law enforcement agency counterpart to provide protection for fire department members at situations that involve violence.

6-7.2.1* The fire department shall develop a standard communication method that indicates that an incident crew is faced with a life and death situation requiring immediate law enforcement intervention.

A-6-7.2.1 Incidents that appear routine in nature can, after the arrival of responding crews, turn into a violent or hostile environment. A standard communication phrase, known only by communication personnel and other responders, can warn others to the dangers of the situation without triggering violence or hostilities.

6-7.3

Such violent situations shall be considered essentially a law enforcement event, and the fire department shall coordinate with the law enforcement incident commander throughout the incident.

6-7.4

The fire department incident commander shall identify and react to situations that do involve or are likely to involve violence.

6-7.5

In such violent situations, the fire department incident commander shall communicate directly with the law enforcement incident commander to ensure the safety of fire department members.

6-7.6

In such violent situations, the fire department incident commander shall stage all fire department resources in a safe area until the law enforcement agency has secured the scene.

6-7.7

When violence occurs after emergency operations have been initiated, the fire department incident commander shall either secure immediate law enforcement agency protection or shall withdraw all fire department members to a safe staging area.

6-7.8

Fire department companies or teams that provide support to law enforcement agency special weapons and tactics (SWAT) operations shall receive special training. Special standard operating procedures shall be developed that describe the training and safety of these fire department teams for such operations. These activities shall be considered as special operations for the purpose of this standard.

6-8 Post-Incident Analysis

In this edition of the standard, the Technical Committee changed the heading for Section 6-8 from post-incident critique to post-incident analysis. All too often, formal or informal critique sessions became finger-pointing sessions on who didn't do what or who did something unsafely. The term *critique* was felt to be too negative, since what was needed was to analyze and accentuate the positive actions at an incident. These positive actions include adherence to SOPs, absence of injuries to personnel, proper use of protective clothing and equipment, and successful use of incident management and personnel accountability systems.

The Technical Committee also felt that it would be beneficial for fire departments to discuss close calls. Close calls are sometimes too easily dismissed as sheer luck or an act of God. How and why personnel survive close calls should be discussed in a post-incident analysis. The safety officer needs to facilitate these meetings and emphasize the key safety factors that prevented a fatality or injury.

6-8.1

The fire department shall establish requirements and standard operating procedures for a standardized post-incident analysis of significant incidents or those that involved serious injury or death to a fire fighter.

Paragraph 6-8.1 grew from the committee's belief that a formalized incident investigation was needed whenever a fire fighter sustained serious injury or death. The investigation may involve outside agencies such as law enforcement agencies, federal and private agencies such as NFPA, as well as other agencies. (For example, the National Institute of Occupational Safety and Health is responsible for investigating all fire fighter fatalities.) The investigation and documentation of significant incidents or those involving serious injury or death to a fire fighter may be used to revise or develop NFPA codes and standards and standard operating procedures, identify training needs, or specify or upgrade protective clothing and equipment.

6-8.2

The fire department incident safety officer shall be involved in the post-incident analysis as defined in NFPA 1521, *Standard for Fire Department Safety Officer*.

6-8.3

The analysis shall conduct a basic review of the conditions present, the actions taken, and the effect of the conditions and actions on the safety and health of members.

6-8.4

The analysis shall identify any action necessary to change or update any safety and health program elements to improve the welfare of members.

6-8.5

The analysis process shall include a standardized action plan for such necessary changes. The action plan shall include the change needed and the responsibilities, dates, and details of such actions.

CHAPTER 7

Facility Safety

7-1 Safety Standards

7-1.1*

All fire department facilities shall comply with all legally applicable health, safety, building, and fire code requirements.

A-7-1.1 Where health, safety, building, and fire codes are not legally applicable to fire department facilities, steps should be taken to ensure that equivalent standards are applied and enforced. In the absence of local requirements, the provisions of NFPA 1, *Fire Prevention Code;* NFPA *101, Life Safety Code;* NFPA 70, *National Electrical Code®;* and a model plumbing, mechanical, and building code should be applied. In addition, the workplace safety standards specified in 29 *CFR* 1910 or an equivalent standard should be applied (*Code of Federal Regulations*, Workplace Safety Standards). Applicable requirements of the American with Disabilities Act, 1992 should be met.

Paragraph 7-1.1 is based on the fact that the fire department is not exempt from regulations that apply to the rest of the community. When facilities are built or renovated, the fire department should work with local inspectors to ensure that the facilities meet all requirements. In some instances, fire department personnel may need to cooperate with numerous inspectors, such as electrical, health, plumbing, zoning, and others.

7-1.2

Fire departments shall provide facilities for disinfecting, cleaning, and storage in accordance with NFPA 1581, *Standard on Fire Department Infection Control Program.*

NFPA 1581, *Standard on Fire Department Infection Control Program* (1995) (Part four of this handbook), and paragraph 7-1.2 do not only apply to departments that provide emergency medical services (EMS). In fact, NFPA 1581 and NFPA 1500 address all areas of disinfecting and cleaning, including protective clothing and equipment and fire apparatus. *(See Figure 1500-7.1.)* Disinfecting, cleaning, and storage are explained in greater detail in Chapters 3 through 5 of NFPA 1581.

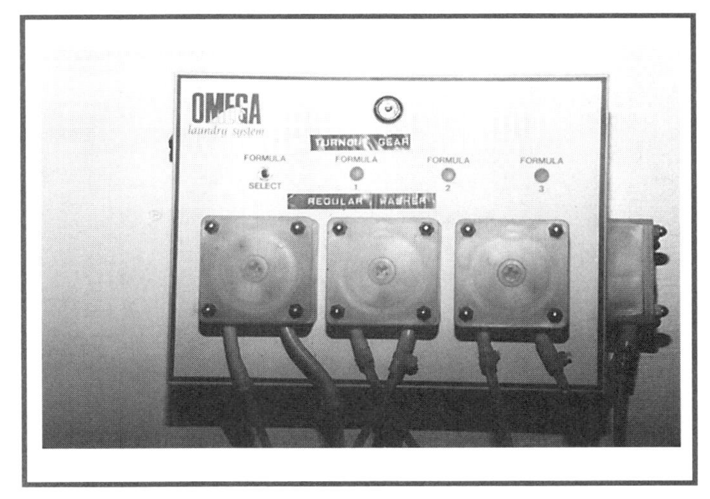

__Figure 1500-7.1__ Fire departments have installed sophisticated systems for safely disinfecting and cleaning protective clothing and equipment. This automatic cleaning agent measuring device saves money for the department and provides the right level of product for cleaning. (Photo courtesy of Virginia Beach Fire Department)

7-1.3

All existing and new fire stations shall be provided with smoke detectors in work, sleeping, and general storage areas. When activated, these detectors shall sound an alarm throughout the fire station.

7-1.4

All existing and new fire department facilities shall have carbon monoxide detectors installed in sleeping and living areas.

The requirements in paragraphs 7-1.3 and 7-1.4 address requirements that many jurisdictions mandate in residences. The same level of safety should be provided to those who use and live in fire department facilities.

Many departments allow their facilities to be used for community and civic functions. In addition, some departments have large halls or other public assembly areas where they hold functions. These public assembly areas should be fully protected and meet NFPA 101, *Life Safety Code* (1997). The liability and responsibility of a fire department with these facilities are significant: The fire department must provide for occupant safety. There have been several embarrassing cases in which inadequately protected fire department facilities have suffered significant fire damage. In some cases, the losses have even left the community without adequate fire protection.

7-1.5*

All fire stations and fire department facilities shall comply with NFPA *101*®, *Life Safety Code*®.

A-7-1.5 As new stations are constructed or existing stations are renovated, a separation between the apparatus floor and living quarters should be provided. The apparatus bay should be equipped with a designed exhaust ventilation system that meets local codes and applicable regulations. Exposure to diesel particulates can cause cancer, and elevated carbon monoxide levels are known to be toxic.

7-1.6

The fire department shall prevent exposure to fire fighters and contamination of living and sleeping areas to exhaust emissions.

Diesel exhaust emissions are a known carcinogen. The safe and efficient removal of these emissions will contribute to an overall safe atmosphere within the working environment. There are many ways to remove emissions, including use of equipment mounted to the exhaust system of the apparatus, large exhaust fans within the apparatus bays, and apparatus mounted filter systems. *(See Figure 1500-7.2.)*

Figure 1500-7.2 *Compliance with the intent of paragraph 7-1.6 can come in many forms. The exhaust removal system shown here attaches to the exhaust pipe of the apparatus and rides along a track. When the apparatus exits the apparatus bay, the unit deflates and falls off as the apparatus drives away. Upon return, before the apparatus is backed into its bay, the unit is placed back on the apparatus's exhaust pipe. This particular unit is connected to a duct and fan system for removal of the exhaust fumes. (Photo courtesy of Fairfax County, Virginia, Fire and Rescue Department)*

Many fire departments use a local or state department of labor or public health agency to monitor indoor air quality. Levels of carbon monoxide and of particulate are the key areas of concern. Air quality is a health issue and is complicated in a joint-use facility where the fumes can travel throughout the building via the heating and ventilation systems and can affect employees from other departments.

7-1.7

All fire department facilities shall have designated smoke-free areas that include work, sleeping, kitchen, and eating areas.

A smoke-free environment is an important contributor to a safe and healthy environment. Many public assembly areas or areas where the public has access (such as training rooms, offices that dispense permits, and function halls) are smoke free. Chapter 9 of NFPA 1500 endorses a smoking/tobacco use cessation. Departments and this standard require the use of SCBA in IDLH atmospheres and provide exhaust emissions systems; paragraph 7-1.7 extends respiratory protection to address the issue of tobacco smoke. Local, state, or provincial laws may also require fire department facilities to be smoke free.

7-2 Inspections

7-2.1*

All fire department facilities shall be inspected at least annually to provide for compliance with Section 7-1 of this chapter. Inspections shall be documented and recorded.

A-7-2.1 The following is a sample inspection form that can be used to document and record annual fire department facility inspections. Fire departments are encouraged to develop an inspection form that works for their jurisdiction.

The sample Facilities Safety Checklist and the sample Station Inspection Form that appeared in A-7-2.1 of the 1997 edition of *Fire Department Occupational Safety and Health Program* are not part of the requirements of the standard but are included with the standard for informational purposes only. For the convenience of readers, in this handbook these forms are included in Supplement 12 as Form S12-1 and Form S12-2 in full-size versions suitable for reproduction.

7-2.2

All fire department facilities shall be inspected at least monthly to identify and provide correction of any safety or health hazards.

7-3 Maintenance and Repairs

7-3.1*

The fire department shall have an established system to maintain all facilities and to provide prompt correction of any safety or health hazard or code violation.

A-7-3.1 In some jurisdictions fire department facilities are maintained by other agencies. In these situations fire departments should develop a process to expedite requests for repairs or modifications to the facility to address safety or health concerns.

Paragraph A-7.3.1 suggests that the fire department is ultimately responsible for providing well-maintained fire department facilities, regardless of which agency actually performs the maintenance. Facility maintenance and repair may not fall under the jurisdiction of the fire department. Many communities have a facility maintenance department to do the repair and upkeep. In some cases, these services may be contracted to another agency or outside organization. Regardless of who does the work, it is important to have a policy for the safe and efficient repair of any health and safety hazards to personnel. It is also important to document that maintenance and repair have been done and meet all applicable permit and code requirements.

CHAPTER 8

Medical and Physical

Chapter 8 provides general text requirements set forth in NFPA 1581, *Standard on Fire Department Infection Control Program* (1995) *(Part Four of this handbook),* and NFPA 1582, *Standard on Medical Requirements for Fire Fighters* (1997) *(Part Five of this handbook).* Fire departments provide a variety of services, with numerous personnel assigned to duties other than fire suppression or EMS. However, fire suppression is the one "entry" point into the department in many fire departments. The physical and medical requirements for the various functional positions within the department must be addressed. When the department identifies these positions, as required in the organizational structure in Chapter 2 of NFPA 1500, a task analysis should be included.

Many jurisdictions attempt to deal with issues raised by the Americans with Disabilities Act (ADA) at the suppression entry point, without a thorough task analysis of suppression positions. At the same time, those fire departments have made a "reasonable accommodation" for an incumbent (often injured) fire fighter in a non-suppression position (such as code enforcement or training) when those light-duty positions do not have an associated task analysis. A candidate for a suppression position who cannot meet physical requirements might then sue the department because reasonable accommodations were made for the incumbent assigned to a non-suppression position. NFPA 1582 applies to personnel who carry out structural fire fighting. The legal and medical issues of ADA are further explained in Appendix D of NFPA 1582. *(See Part Five of this handbook.)*

8-1 Medical Requirements

8-1.1

Candidates shall be medically evaluated and certified by the fire department physician. Medical evaluations shall take into account the risks and the functions associated with the individual's duties and responsibilities.

8-1.2

Candidates and members who will engage in fire suppression shall meet the medical requirements specified in NFPA 1582, *Standard on Medical Requirements for Fire Fighters*, prior to being medically certified for duty by the fire department physician.

The requirements of paragraph 8-1.2 are also required in NFPA 1001, *Standard on Fire Fighter Professional Qualifications* (1997), and as part of NFPA 1404, *Standard for a Fire Department Self-Contained Breathing Apparatus Program* (1996). The tasks outlined in NFPA 1001 require candidates and incumbents alike to be physically fit to operate safely and efficiently. These same requirements, specific to respiratory protection training, are addressed in NFPA 1404.

8-1.3

All members who engage in fire suppression shall be medically evaluated periodically as specified by NFPA 1582, *Standard on Medical Requirements for Fire Fighters*, on at least an annual basis, and before being reassigned to emergency duties after debilitating illnesses or injuries. Members who have not met the medical evaluation requirements shall not be permitted to engage in fire suppression. Where medical evaluations are conducted by a physician other than the fire department physician, the evaluation shall be subject to review and shall be approved by the fire department physician.

8-1.4

The medical evaluation shall be at no cost to the candidate, current fire fighter, or other member.

The costs of a medical evaluation should be borne by the AHJ. Funding medical evaluation is a critical part of risk management and should be a budgeted cost.

8-1.5*

Members who are under the influence of alcohol or drugs shall not participate in any fire department operations or other duties.

A-8-1.5 If any member, either career or volunteer, reports for duty under the influence of alcohol or drugs, or any other substance that impairs the member's mental or physical capacity, this situation cannot be tolerated.

Evidence of substance abuse could include a combination of various factors such as slurred speech, red eyes, dilated pupils, incoherence, unsteadiness on feet, smell of alcohol or marijuana emanating from the member's body, inability to carry on a rational conversation, increased carelessness, erratic behavior, inability to perform a job, or other unexplained behavioral changes.

The possibility of liability exists if a member who is under the influence of alcohol or drugs is allowed to remain on duty, to operate or drive vehicles or equipment on duty, or to drive a private vehicle from the duty site. A member who is believed to be under the influence of alcohol or drugs cannot be allowed to operate equipment or drive a vehicle, including a private vehicle, until the condition of the member has been determined and verified.

Members' use of alcohol and or drugs can impair ability and cause physical harm to them and to their coworkers. Serving alcohol in fire department facilities only compounds the problems of members responding under the influence. Off-duty members and volunteers who are under the influence should not respond in their personal vehicles, as this would violate motor vehicle laws. This risky behavior places the department in a position of severe liability.

8-2 Physical Performance Requirements

8-2.1

The fire department shall develop physical performance requirements for candidates and members who engage in emergency operations.

Departments have developed physical performance criteria that reflect the tasks their members will be required to perform. In some departments, the members are tested on an annual basis or can participate in a comprehensive fitness evaluation and education program. The Santa Ana College Wellness Program for Public Safety Personnel, for example, emphasizes the evaluation of health-related fitness components, including aerobic fitness, muscular endurance and strength, flexibility, and body composition. The program also provides tests, including a 12 lead resting and exercise electrocardiogram, pulmonary function test, blood chemistry, and coronary blood profile. To reinforce the importance of the foregoing health components, a series of lectures accompanies each program.

To meet stringent FAA requirements, the Aircraft Rescue Fire Fighter (ARFF) Department of the Cincinnati/Northern Kentucky International Airport uses a rigorous model to assess the physical agility of fire fighters and fire fighter candidates. All participants must first receive medical clearance, then successfully complete the following five job-related tasks within 7 minutes: stair climb with high-rise pack, hose hoist, forcible entry, hose advance, and victim rescue.

Additional information regarding performance criteria can be obtained from the following:

- Aircraft Rescue Fire Fighter Department, Cincinnati/Northern Kentucky International Airport, PO Box 752000, Cincinnati, OH 45275-2000 (606-767-3151; fax 606-767-3080)
- Fairfax County Fire and Rescue, Fairfax, VA 22033
- Santa Ana College, 1530 West 17th Street, Santa Ana, CA 92706
- International Association of Fire Fighters, 1750 New York Avenue, NW, Washington, DC 20006
- International Association of Fire Chiefs, 4025 Fair Ridge Drive, Fairfax, VA 22033 (703-273-0911)

8-2.2

Medical certification for the use of respiratory protection shall be conducted annually.

For information on implementing paragraph 8-2.2, see NFPA 1404 (1996) and the OSHA respiratory protection standard, OSHA 29 *CFR* 1910.134.

8-2.3

Candidates shall be certified by the fire department as meeting the physical performance requirements specified in 8-2.1 of this section prior to entering into a training program to become a fire fighter.

As part of the employment process, candidates (volunteers included) who are offered a position can be required to pass a physical performance test.

8-2.4

Members who engage in emergency operations shall be annually evaluated and certified by the fire department as meeting the physical performance requirements specified in

8-2.1 of this section. Members who do not meet the required level of physical performance shall not be permitted to engage in emergency operations.

8-2.5

Members who are unable to meet the physical performance requirements specified in 8-2.1 of this section shall enter a physical performance rehabilitation program to facilitate progress in attaining a level of performance commensurate with the individual's assigned duties and responsibilities.

Paragraphs 8-2.4 and 8-2.5 require the AHJ to provide a rehabilitation program so that fire fighters can meet the physical performance requirements. Members must not be allowed to begin or resume suppression duties until they pass the physical performance requirements.

8-3 Physical Fitness

Section 8-3 has led to intense discussions about voluntary versus mandatory physical fitness programs. Many users have incorrectly interpreted NFPA 1500 to require locations and equipment to supplement physical fitness programs. Some departments have paid for memberships in local health clubs, YMCAs, and the like, for fire department personnel. The successful physical fitness programs typically include nutritional and wellness components.

The purpose of the physical fitness program is not punitive, but is intended to reduce the potential of occupational injuries and illnesses.

8-3.1

The fire department shall establish and provide a physical fitness program to enable members to develop and maintain an appropriate level of fitness to safely perform their assigned functions. The maintenance of fitness levels specified in the program shall be based on fitness standards determined by the fire department physician that reflect the individual's assigned functions and activities and that are intended to reduce the probability and severity of occupational injuries and illnesses.

8-3.2

The fire department shall require the structured participation of all members in the physical fitness program.

On August 10, 1989, a Formal Interpretation concerning paragraphs 8-3.1 and 8-3.2 was issued by the Standards Council. That Formal Interpretation is still valid and is reproduced here for the reader's convenience.

Formal Interpretation

Reference: 8-3.1, 8-3.2

F.I. No.: 87-7

Question: Is it the intent of 8-3.1 and 8-3.2 to allow members to participate in a structured physical fitness program designed for individuals to carry out on an individual basis, when such plan includes a requirement for members to pass a physical fitness test designed by the fire department physician for each member, on a periodic basis and after a debilitating illness or injury?

Answer: Yes.

Issue Edition: 1987

Reference: 8-3.1, 8-3.2

Issue Date: July 21, 1989

Effective Date: August 10, 1989

8-3.3

The fire department health and fitness coordinator shall administer all aspects of the physical fitness and health enhancement program. The health and fitness coordinator shall act as a direct liaison between the fire department physician and the fire department in accordance NFPA 1582, *Standard on Medical Requirements for Fire Fighters*.

Paragraph 8-3.3 introduces the health fitness coordinator, who assists members in maintaining their physical fitness and coordinates the medical evaluations with the fire department physician. The coordinator may help develop educational programs in coordination with the fire department health and safety officer.

8-4 Confidential Health Data Base

As the title of Section 8-4 makes clear, information in the health data base is confidential — strictly between the member and the fire department physician. The tracking of these data could determine occupational risks for certain work groups or members who operated at a certain incident. Exposure tracking may provide long-term data on specific illnesses (such as cancer) afflicting fire fighters. (For a 1991 report on Occupational Cancer and the Fire Fighter, contact the IAFF at 1750 New York Avenue, NW, Washington, DC 20006.)

8-4.1*

The fire department shall ensure that a confidential, permanent health file is established and maintained on each individual member. The individual health file shall record the results of regular medical evaluations and physical performance tests, any occupational illnesses or injuries, and any events that expose the individual to known or suspected hazardous materials, toxic products, or contagious diseases.

A-8-4.1 The health data base for a fire department should include the reports of regular physical evaluations, injury and illness reports, and any supporting information that could be useful in tracking, analyzing, or predicting the health effects of various events on individuals or the group.

8-4.2*

Health information shall be maintained as a confidential record for each individual member as well as a composite data base for the analysis of factors pertaining to the overall health and fitness of the member group.

A-8-4.2 This information should be managed in a manner that respects the confidentiality of doctor-patient relationships. Electronic data processing is often employed to facilitate management of such a data base.

8-4.3*

If a member dies as a result of occupational injury or illness, autopsy results, if available, shall be recorded in the health data base.

A-8-4.3 The fire department should try to obtain autopsy or other medical information for all deceased employees or former employees. This information could be useful in establishing relationships between occupational factors and resulting fatalities at some time in the future. Autopsies for fire fatalities should be conducted and recorded according to a standard protocol.

8-5 Infection Control

NFPA 1581, *Standard on Fire Department Infection Control Program* (1995), elaborates on the requirements of Section 8-5. Part Four of this handbook provides text and commentary on NFPA 1581.

8-5.1*

The fire department shall actively attempt to identify and limit or prevent the exposure of members to infectious and contagious diseases in the performance of their assigned duties.

A-8-5.1 Where fire department members routinely respond to emergency medical incidents, the fire department should consult with medical professionals and agencies on measures to limit the exposure of members to infectious and contagious diseases. This should include the provision and maintenance of equipment to avoid or limit direct physical contact with patients, when feasible.

8-5.2

The fire department shall operate an infection control program that meets the requirements of NFPA 1581, *Standard on Fire Department Infection Control Program.* When appropriate, inoculations, vaccinations, and other treatment shall be made available.

8-6 Fire Department Physician

The role of fire department physician has expanded beyond the discipline of medical doctor. Today the fire department physician may also serve as EMS director or medical safety officer at an incident and assist with "rehab" operations at an incident scene. Physicians filling these multiple roles interact with the health and safety officer, health and safety committee, and the health fitness coordinator.

NFPA 1582, *Standard on Medical Requirements for Fire Fighters* (1997), primarily authored by fire department occupational physicians, is a framework from which their colleagues can administer an occupational medical and health program. Part Five of this handbook covers NFPA 1582 and describes the role of fire department physician.

8-6.1

The fire department shall have an officially designated physician who shall be responsible for guiding, directing, and advising the members with regard to their health, fitness, and suitability for various duties.

8-6.2

The fire department physician shall provide medical guidance in the management of the occupational safety and health program.

8-6.3*

The fire department physician shall be a licensed medical doctor or osteopathic physician qualified to provide professional expertise in the areas of occupational safety and health as they relate to emergency services.

A-8-6.3 A fire department physician should have specific expertise and experience relating to the needs of fire department members and a thorough knowledge of the physical demands involved in emergency operations. If possible, the fire department physician should be a specialist in the field of occupational medicine.

8-6.4*

The fire department physician shall be readily available for consultation and to provide professional services on an urgent basis. Availability shall be permitted to be accomplished by providing access to a number of qualified physicians.

A-8-6.4 Depending on the size and the needs of a fire department, the fire department physician might or might not be required on a full-time basis. A fire department should have a primary relationship with at least one officially designated physician. This physician can serve as the primary medical contact and, in turn, deal with a number of other physicians and specialists. A large fire department can designate more than one fire department physician or might determine that a relationship with a group practice or multiple provider system is more appropriate to its needs. In any case, the option to consult with a physician who is particularly aware of the medical needs of fire department members and who is available on an immediate basis should exist.

8-7 Post-Injury/Illness Rehabilitation

8-7.1*

It shall be an ongoing objective of the fire department to assist members affected by occupational injuries or illnesses in their rehabilitation and to facilitate their return to full active duty or limited duty where possible.

A-8-7.1 The fire department should be concerned with the members' ability to regain and maintain a comfortable, healthy, and productive life during and after their service with the fire department.

8-7.2*

Prior to a member returning to full duty from a debilitating injury, illness, or any other extended leave, a member shall have a physical performance assessment performed by the health and fitness coordinator under supervision by the fire department physician based on the individual's duties and responsibilities.

A-8-7.2 The minimum qualifications for the health and fitness coordinator should include emergency medical technician (EMT) state certification; health and fitness coordinator certification, which includes topics such as physical fitness training, exercise physiology, kinesiology, nutrition, weight control counseling, critical incident stress management, and substance abuse training and education; and NFPA 1041, *Standard for Fire Service Instructor Professional Qualifications,* Instructor II.

Certification in areas of physical fitness, training, exercise physiology, kinesiology, nutrition, and weight control can be acquired through agencies such as the American College of Sports Medicine (health and fitness instructor), Oklahoma State University Fire Service Division (fitness coordinator), and Cooper Institute (fitness coordinator).

CHAPTER 9

Member Assistance and Wellness Program

9-1 Member Assistance Program

Many cities and communities provide an employee assistance program for all employees and their families. Visiting nurse associations, mental health referral agencies, and other organizations help others help themselves. The fire department should provide access to these services for its members. On-the-job stresses that members encounter, as well as other problems, could compromise their ability to do their jobs safely. Possible impact on the health and safety of other members compounds the problem of a compromised ability to work safely. A resource directory for health, fitness, and wellness appears as Supplement 5 in Part Six of this handbook.

9-1.1*

The fire department shall provide a member assistance program that identifies and assists members and their immediate families with substance abuse, stress, and personal problems that adversely affect fire department work performance. The assistance program shall refer members and their immediate families, as appropriate, to the proper health care services for the purpose of restoring job performance to expected levels, as well as for the restoration of better health.

A-9-1.1 The fire department member assistance program does not have to be financed by the fire department. Many community/county/state mental health agencies provide such services free of charge or at a nominal fee. The fire department need have only the ability to identify when such problems exist and be able to offer confidential referrals to the professional who will provide the counseling. Although member assistance programs differ from one another in various ways according to the particular needs and resources of individual fire departments, member organizations, and members, there are certain components that are found in all quality programs. The following program standards set forth by the Association of Labor-Management Administrators and Consultants on Alcoholism (ALMACA) address these components and are strongly recommended:

The physical location of the member assistance program should facilitate easy access while ensuring confidentiality. There should be a review of medical and disability benefits to ensure that plans adequately cover appropriate diagnosis and treatment for alcohol, drug, and mental health problems. Where feasible, coverage should include outpatient and day treatment care. The member assistance program staff should be familiar with the provisions of the medical and disability benefit plans so they can advise clients clearly as to the extent, nature, and cost of the recommended treatment and the reimbursement available.

The member assistance program staff should combine two primary qualifications:

(a) Appropriate managerial and administrative experience
(b) Skills in identifying problems, interviewing, motivating, referring clients, and, where appropriate, in counseling or related fields; experience and expertise in dealing with alcohol-related problems is strongly recommended

It is important that members and their families are informed about the member assistance program and the services it offers and are continually updated on its existence, availability, and confidentiality. Information about the member assistance program should be made available to all new members and their families.

The member assistance program should maintain current information about alcoholism treatment services and other resources. These include Alcoholics Anonymous, Al-Anon, Alateen, and other self-help groups; appropriate health care; community services; and other professionals. Information about referral procedures, costs, and other relevant factors should be available. Professionally trained individuals should be immediately available to assist members involved in traumatic incidents to reduce or deal with the effects of psychological stress.

There should be a periodic review of the member assistance program to provide an objective evaluation of operation and performance. There should be an annual review of member assistance program staff performance.

9-1.2*

The fire department shall adopt a written policy statement on alcoholism, substance abuse, and other problems covered by the member assistance program.

A-9-1.2 The policy statement should acknowledge that alcoholism is a disease responsive to treatment and rehabilitation, and it should specify the responsibilities of management, member organizations, and members as they relate to the program. The member assistance program should not in any way alter management authority or responsibilities or the prerogatives of a member organization. Participation in the member assistance program should not affect future service or career advancement, nor should participation protect the member from disciplinary action for continued substandard job performance or rule infractions. Sponsorship of the program by management and the member organization is highly desirable.

9-1.3*

Written rules shall be established specifying how records are to be maintained, the policies governing retention and access to records, and the procedure for release of information. These rules shall identify to whom and under what conditions information can be released and what use, if any, can be made of records for purposes of research, program evaluation, and reports. Member records maintained by a member assistance program shall not become part of a member's personnel file.

A-9-1.3 Adherence to federal regulations on confidentiality of alcohol and other drug abuse records is required of programs receiving federal funds, directly or indirectly.

The confidentiality of this program is essential if it is to work. Members' records are personal and part of their counseling program. Members' assurance of the confidentiality of the member assistance program, both for them and for their families, must be conveyed to encourage participation in the program.

9-2 Wellness Program

9-2.1*

The wellness program shall provide health promotion activities that identify physical and mental health risk factors and shall provide education and counseling for the purpose of preventing health problems and enhancing overall well-being.

A-9-2.1 Health promotion should include, but not be limited to, the following activities: career guidance, family orientation, and educational programs on topics such as weight control, healthy heart, hypertension, stress management, nutrition, preventive medicine, substance abuse, smoking cessation, and retirement planning.

For additional guidance in the implementation and management of the stress management component of a member assistance program, consult the U.S. Fire Administration publication, *Stress Management Model Program for Maintaining Firefighter Well-Being.*

9-2.2*

The fire department shall provide a program on the health effects associated with the use of tobacco products. The fire department shall provide a smoking/tobacco use cessation program.

A-9-2.2 The fire department should develop a policy on the use of tobacco products for all members. The fire department should also develop a policy on the acceptance of new members into the fire department with regard to the use of tobacco products.

CHAPTER 10

Critical Incident Stress Program

10-1 General

Critical incident stress debriefing (CISD) is a component of a critical incident stress program (CISP). A critical incident stress debriefing session provides members with an opportunity to express thoughts and emotions with peers. This part of a CISP can provide both short- and long-term health and safety benefits for members.

In addition to debriefings, the program contains such components as follow-up counseling with professionals, medical monitoring, and diffusing of issues. The use of a CISP has come under fire lately as an overused tool forced on some members. For some members of a department that has suffered a fire fighter fatality, the CISD teams and meetings have become an additional burden to worry about, rather than a helpful way to put the issue behind them.

EMS providers, hospitals, mental health workers, social service agencies, and the fire department are key players of a CISP team. CISP partnerships involving these agencies may be local or regional. However, most fire departments lack the ability to provide a complete critical incident stress program. All too often the many stresses of fire department work play havoc on a member's ability to complete tasks safely and efficiently and also impact his or her family life.

10-1.1

The fire department physician shall provide medical guidance in the management of the critical incident stress program.

The medical guidance required by paragraph 10-1.1 covers a variety of situations and activities. As a result, the role of the fire department physician in assisting with critical incident stress should not be underestimated. The many situations that require CISD may include medical complications. The physician who is an integral part of the health and safety committee will be able to assist members in the critical incident stress process.

10-1.2*

The fire department shall adopt a written policy that establishes a program designed to relieve the stress generated by an incident that could adversely affect the psychological and physical well-being of fire department members. The policy shall establish criteria for implementation of the program.

A-10-1.2 Fire fighters frequently experience trauma, death, and sorrow. Critical incident stress is a normal reaction experienced by normal people following an event that is abnormal. The emotional trauma can be serious. It can break through a person's defenses suddenly, or slowly and collectively, so that the person can no longer function effectively. Critical incident stress is the inevitable result of trauma experienced by fire service personnel. It cannot be prevented, but it can be relieved. Experiencing emotional aftershocks following a traumatic event is a very normal reaction and should not be perceived as evidence of weakness, mental instability, or other abnormality.

Symptoms can appear immediately after the incident, hours later, or sometimes even days or weeks later. The symptoms can last for a few days, weeks, or months. Occasionally a professional counselor might be needed. Knowing the signs and symptoms and how to respond to them after the occurrence of a critical incident can greatly reduce the chance of more severe and long-term stress.

Rapid intervention, talking about the situation, and reassuring that these are normal reactions and feelings can help prevent more serious problems later on, such as family and marital problems.

To provide this intervention, the fire department should have access to a critical incident debriefing (CID) team. The main objective of the CID team is to lessen the impact of the critical incident, put it into the proper perspective, and help maintain a healthy outlook.

The CID team should consist of other fire fighters, support personnel, and mental health professionals specifically trained in stress-related counseling. The team should be well represented by all types of members whether volunteer, call, or career, and by all ranks. All members should have a minimum of a two-day training seminar with continuing education in stress-related training as an ongoing part of the team's regular meetings (monthly is recommended for active departments, while quarterly might be sufficient for less active departments).

Any individual should be able to initiate the debriefing procedure simply by contacting his/her supervisor or officer, or the dispatch center. A contact list of the debriefing team members should be available in the dispatch center.

Debriefings should be held for incidents that have the potential for having a stressful impact on members. It is important to remember that an event is traumatic when experienced as such.

Generally, debriefings should be held at a station within one to three hours after the incident. Debriefings should encourage brief discussions of the event, which in itself help to alleviate a good deal of the stress. Debriefings are strictly confidential and are not a critique of the incident. Information should be given on stress reactions and steps that members can take to relieve the symptoms so that they can continue their normal activities as soon as the debriefing is over. Some common signs and symptoms of critical incident stress are fatigue, headaches, inability to concentrate, anxiety, depression, inappropriate emotional behavior, intense anger, irritability, withdrawal from the crew and/or family, change in appetite, increased alcohol consumption, and a change in sleeping patterns.

To help alleviate some of the emotional pain, members can rest more; contact friends; maintain as normal a schedule as possible; eat well-balanced, scheduled meals; keep a reasonable level of activity to fight boredom; express feelings; and talk to loved ones. Recent studies and research also indicate that exercise, especially soon after an event, can greatly reduce mental pain. MAP should always be available to members. The CID team is often the first step in providing the help that is needed and should be ready to serve to help minimize stress-related injury.

The ability to deal with life and death situations varies from member to member. The ability of a supervisor or peers to recognize the signs and symptoms of fatigue, appetite loss, inability to sleep or function, and substance abuse is crucial. Any of these factors can reduce a member's ability to function safely at an incident scene. Obviously, the reduced capacity of one member impacts on the health and safety of other members.

10-1.3

The program shall be made available to members for incidents including but not limited to mass casualties, large life loss incidents, fatalities involving children, fatalities or injuries involving fire department members, and any other situations that affect the psychological and physical well-being of fire department members.

Critical incident stress may impact not only a member, but also the member's family. The compounded stresses of fire department activity and other factors can negatively influence the member's ability to function at home. Cases involving domestic violence, child abuse, and suicides are not uncommon. Members and supervisors, as well as family members, should participate in counseling as needed.

CHAPTER 11

Referenced Publications

11-1

The following documents or portions thereof are referenced within this standard as mandatory requirements and shall be considered part of the requirements of this standard. The edition indicated for each referenced mandatory document is the current edition as of the date of the NFPA issuance of this standard. Some of these mandatory documents might also be referenced in this standard for specific informational purposes and, therefore, are also listed in Appendix C.

11-1.1 NFPA Publications.

National Fire Protection Association, 1 Batterymarch Park, P.O. Box 9101, Quincy, MA 02269-9101.

NFPA 10, *Standard for Portable Fire Extinguishers*, 1994 edition.

NFPA *101*®, *Life Safety Code*®, 1997 edition.

NFPA 472, *Standard for Professional Competence of Responders to Hazardous Materials Incidents*, 1997 edition.

NFPA 473, *Standard for Competencies for EMS Personnel Responding to Hazardous Materials Incidents*, 1997 edition.

NFPA 600, *Standard on Industrial Fire Brigades*, 1996 edition.

NFPA 1001, *Standard on Fire Fighter Professional Qualifications*, 1997 edition.

NFPA 1002, *Standard for Fire Department Vehicle Driver/Operator Professional Qualifications*, 1993 edition.

NFPA 1003, *Standard for Airport Fire Fighter Professional Qualifications*, 1994 edition.

NFPA 1021, *Standard for Fire Officer Professional Qualifications*, 1997 edition.

NFPA 1041, *Standard for Fire Service Instructor Professional Qualifications*, 1996 edition.

NFPA 1051, *Standard for Wildland Fire Fighter Professional Qualifications*, 1995 edition.

NFPA 1403, *Standard on Live Fire Training Evolutions*, 1997 edition.

NFPA 1404, *Standard for a Fire Department Self-Contained Breathing Apparatus Program*, 1996 edition.

NFPA 1405, *Guide for Land-Based Fire Fighters Who Respond to Marine Vessel Fires*, 1996 edition.

NFPA 1521, *Standard for Fire Department Safety Officer*, 1997 edition.

NFPA 1561, *Standard on Fire Department Incident Management System*, 1995 edition.

NFPA 1581, *Standard on Fire Department Infection Control Program*, 1995 edition.

NFPA 1582, *Standard on Medical Requirements for Fire Fighters*, 1997 edition.

NFPA 1901, *Standard for Automotive Fire Apparatus*, 1996 edition.

NFPA 1906, *Standard for Wildland Fire Apparatus*, 1995 edition.

NFPA 1911, *Standard for Service Tests of Pumps on Fire Department Apparatus*, 1997 edition.

NFPA 1914, *Standard for Testing Fire Department Aerial Devices*, 1997 edition.

NFPA 1931, *Standard on Design of and Design Verification Tests for Fire Department Ground Ladders*, 1994 edition.

NFPA 1932, *Standard on Use, Maintenance, and Service Testing of Fire Department Ground Ladders*, 1994 edition.

NFPA 1961, *Standard on Fire Hose*, 1997 edition.

NFPA 1962, *Standard for the Care, Use, and Service Testing of Fire Hose Including Couplings and Nozzles*, 1993 edition.

NFPA 1964, *Standard for Spray Nozzles (Shutoff and Tip)*, 1993 edition.

NFPA 1971, *Standard on Protective Ensemble for Structural Fire Fighting*, 1997 edition.

NFPA 1975, *Standard on Station/Work Uniforms for Fire Fighters*, 1994 edition.
NFPA 1976, *Standard on Protective Clothing for Proximity Fire Fighting*, 1992 edition.
NFPA 1977, *Standard on Protective Clothing and Equipment for Wildland Fire Fighting*, 1993 edition.
NFPA 1981, *Standard on Open-Circuit Self-Contained Breathing Apparatus for Fire Fighters*, 1997 edition.
NFPA 1982, *Standard on Personal Alert Safety Systems (PASS) for Fire Fighters*, 1993 edition.
NFPA 1983, *Standard on Fire Service Life Safety Rope and System Components*, 1995 edition.
NFPA 1991, *Standard on Vapor-Protective Suits for Hazardous Chemical Emergencies*, 1994 edition.
NFPA 1992, *Standard on Liquid Splash-Protective Suits for Hazardous Chemical Emergencies*, 1994 edition.
NFPA 1993, *Standard on Support Function Protective Clothing for Hazardous Chemical Operations*, 1994 edition.
NFPA 1999, *Standard on Protective Clothing for Emergency Medical Operations*, 1997 edition.

11-1.2 American Conference of Governmental Industrial Hygienists Publication.

6500 Glenway Avenue, Bldg. D7, Cincinnati, OH 45211.

Threshold Limit Valves and Biological Exposure Indices for 1996-1977, 1996.

11-1.3 ANSI Publications.

American National Standards Institute, 11 West 42nd Street, New York, NY 10036.

ANSI/CGA G7.1, *Commodity Specification for Air*, 1989.
ANSI Z87.1, *Practice for Occupational and Educational Eye and Face Protection*, 1989.

11-1.4 U.S. Coast Guard Publication.

U.S. Coast Guard Commandant Instruction M 16465, Department of Transportation, Washington, DC.

U.S. Coast Guard *Chemical Response Information System (CHRIS)*, Volumes 1–3, "Hazardous Chemical Data," October 1978.

11-1.5 U.S. Government Publications.

U.S. Government Printing Office, Superintendent of Documents, Washington, DC 20402.

NIOSH Pocket Guide to Chemical Hazards, U.S. Department of Health and Human Services, Public Health Services, Publication DHHS No. 85-114, September 1985.
Title 42, *Code of Federal Regulations*, Part 84 (42 *CFR* 84), July 1995.

11-1.6 Other Publication.

Sax, N. Irving, *Dangerous Properties of Industrial Chemicals*, 6th ed., Van Nostrand Reinhold, NY, 1988.

REFERENCES CITED IN COMMENTARY

The *Americans with Disabilities Act of 1990*, 42 U.S.C. §12101 et seq., U.S. Government Printing Office, Washington, DC 20402.
ASTM F 1001, *Standard Guide for Chemicals to Evaluate Protective Clothing Materials*, 1989.
CDC, *A Curriculum Guide for Public Safety and Emergency Response Workers, Prevention of Transmission of Human Immunodeficiency Virus and Hepatitis B Virus*, February 1989.
IAFF, *Occupational Cancer and the Fire Fighter*, 1991.
NIIMS, *Incident Command System*, Oklahoma State University Fire Protection Publications, 1983.
Report of the South Canyon Fire Investigation Team (joint report of Departments of Agriculture, the Interior, and Commerce), August 17, 1994.
29 *CFR* 1910.120, *Hazardous Waste Operations and Emergency Repair* (HAZWOPER), U.S. Government Printing Office, Washington, DC, 1989.
29 *CFR* 1910.134, *OSHA Rule on Respiratory Protection*, U.S. Government Printing Office, Washington, DC, 1997.
29 *CFR* 1910.1030, *Occupational Exposure to Bloodborne Pathogens*, U.S. Government Printing Office, Washington, DC, 1991.
U.S. Fire Administration, *Emergency Incidents Rehabilitation*, FA 114/July 1992.

APPENDIX A

The material contained in Appendix A of this standard is not part of the requirements of the code but is included for informational purposes only. For the convenience of readers, in this handbook the Appendix A material is interspersed among the verbiage of Chapters 1 through 10 and, therefore, is not repeated here.

APPENDIX B

Fire Service Occupational Safety and Health Program Worksheet

This appendix is not a part of the requirements of this NFPA document but is included for informational purposes only.

The worksheet in this appendix was developed by technical committee members to provide a template for fire departments that are beginning an occupational safety and health program or that are evaluating the current status of their programs. This worksheet provides a tool for assessing the yearly progress of the program and for developing a fiscal policy plan to achieve compliance with the applicable requirements of the standard. In the second, third, or fourth column, the user can record whether his or her department has achieved total compliance, partial compliance, or compliance that was effected by either administrative order or legislative action. If the department has not achieved compliance, the date(s) that compliance is expected to be completed can be recorded in the fifth column. There are some compliance issues that require budgetary action and would be included in either an operating budget or a capital planning budget. When compliance is achieved, this can be recorded in the sixth column. For budget items that are planned for two or three years in the future, those costs and anticipated compliance dates can be included in the seventh and eighth columns. Any remarks or changes should be included in the last column for explanatory purposes. This is not a "one size fits all" worksheet and can be modified to meet the user's needs.

The following paragraphs are extracted from the standard to reiterate the fact that an implementation plan should be implemented and annually evaluated.

1-2 PURPOSE

1-2.1

The purpose of this standard is to specify the minimum requirements for an occupational safety and health program for a fire department and to specify safety guidelines for those members involved in rescue, fire suppression, emergency medical services, hazardous materials operations, special operations, and related activities.

1-2.2

Many of the performance objectives of this standard can be achieved in a variety of ways. The achievement of these objectives is intended to help prevent accidents, injuries, and exposures and to reduce the severity of those accidents, injuries, and exposures that do occur. They will also help to prevent exposure to hazardous materials and contagious diseases and to reduce the probability of occupational fatalities, illnesses, and disabilities affecting fire service personnel.

1-2.3

Nothing herein shall be intended to restrict any jurisdiction from exceeding these minimum requirements.

1-3 IMPLEMENTATION

1-3.1

When this standard is adopted by a jurisdiction, the authority having jurisdiction shall set a date or dates for achieving compliance with the requirements of this standard and shall be permitted to establish a phase-in schedule for compliance with specific requirements of this standard.

1-3.2

The fire department shall adopt a risk management plan as specified in Section 2-2 of this standard. This risk management plan shall include a written plan for compliance with this standard.

The Occupational Safety and Health Program that appeared in Appendix B of the 1997 edition of *Fire Department Occupantional Safety and Health Program* is not part of the requirements of the standard but is included with the standard for informational purposes only. For the convenience of readers, in this handbook the worksheet is included in Supplement 12 as Form S12-3 in a full-size version suitable for reproduction.

APPENDIX C

Referenced Publications

C-1

The following documents or portions thereof are referenced within this standard for informational purposes only and are thus not considered part of the requirements of this standard unless also listed in Chapter 11. The edition indicated here for each reference is the current edition as of the date of the NFPA issuance of this standard.

C-1.1 NFPA Publications.

National Fire Protection Association, 1 Batterymarch Park, P.O. Box 9101, Quincy, MA 02269-9101.

NFPA 1, *Fire Prevention Code*, 1997 edition.
NFPA 30, *Flammable and Combustible Liquids Code*, 1996 edition.
NFPA 70, *National Electrical Code®*, 1996 edition.
NFPA *101®*, *Life Safety Code®*, 1997 edition.
NFPA 472, *Standard for Professional Competence of Responders to Hazardous Materials Incidents*, 1997 edition.
NFPA 901, *Standard Classifications for Incident Reporting and Fire Protection Data,* 1995 edition.
NFPA 1001, *Standard on Fire Fighter Professional Qualifications*, 1997 edition.
NFPA 1041, *Standard for Fire Service Instructor Professional Qualifications,* 1996 edition.
NFPA 1401, *Recommended Practice for Fire Service Training Reports and Records*, 1996 edition.
NFPA 1451, *Standard for a Fire Service Vehicle Operations Training Program*, 1997 edition.
NFPA 1581, *Standard on Fire Department Infection Control Program,* 1995 edition.
NFPA 1582, *Standard on Medical Requirements for Fire Fighters*, 1997 edition.
NFPA 1971, *Standard on Protective Ensemble for Structural Fire Fighting,* 1997 edition.
NFPA 1975, *Standard on Station/Work Uniforms for Fire Fighters*, 1994 edition.
NFPA 1981, *Standard on Open-Circuit Self-Contained Breathing Apparatus for Fire Fighters*, 1997 edition.
NFPA 1991, *Standard on Vapor-Protective Suits for Hazardous Chemical Emergencies*, 1994 edition.
NFPA 1992, *Standard on Liquid Splash-Protective Suits for Hazardous Chemical Emergencies*, 1994 edition.
NFPA 1993, *Standard on Support Function Protective Clothing for Hazardous Chemical Operations*, 1994 edition.
NFPA 1999, *Standard on Protective Clothing for Emergency Medical Operations*, 1997 edition.
NFPA *Fire Protection Handbook*, 18th edition, 1997.

C-1.2 ANSI Publication.

American National Standards Institute, 11 West 42nd Street, New York, NY 10036.

ANSI Z88.5, *Practices for Respiratory Protection for the Fire Service*, 1981.

C-1.3 ASTM Publications.

American Society for Testing and Materials, 100 Barr Harbor Drive, West Conshohocken, PA 19428-2959.

ASTM F 739, *Test Method for Resistance of Protective Clothing Materials to Permeation by Liquids or Gases*, 1986.
ASTM F 903, *Standard Test Method for Resistance of Protective Clothing Materials to Penetration by Liquids*, 1990.
ASTM F 1052, *Standard Practice for Pressure Testing of Gas-Tight Totally Encapsulating Chemical Protective Suits*, 1987.
ASTM F 1359, *Practice for Evaluating the Liquid-Tight Integrity of Chemical Protective Suits and Ensembles Under Static Conditions*, 1991.

C-1.4 ICMA Publication.

International City Management Association, 777 N. Capitol Street NE, Washington, DC 20002.

Managing Fire Services, 2nd edition, 1988.

C-1.5 USFA Publications.

U.S. Fire Administration, Emmitsburg, MD 21727.

Fire Department Hearing Conservation Program Manual, 1991.

Stress Management Model Program for Maintaining Firefighter Well-Being, 1990.

C-1.6 U.S. Government Publications.

U.S. Government Printing Office, Superintendent of Documents, Washington, DC 20402.

American with Disabilities Act, 1992.

Center for Disease Control and Prevention, "Guidelines for Preventing the Transmission of *Mycobacterium Tuberculosis* in Health-Care Facilities," 1994, October, 1994.

Federal Register, Vol. 60, No. 110, June 8, 1995.

General Services Administration, Federal Specification KKK-A-1822D for Ambulances.

OSHA Enforcement Policy and Procedures for Occupational Exposure to Tuberculosis, October 8, 1993.

U.S. Department of Labor, Occupational Safety and Health Administration, Memorandum for Regional Administration and State Designees, "Response to IDLH or Potential IDLH Atmospheres," May 1, 1995.

Title 29, *Code of Federal Regulations*, Part 1910 [29 *CFR* 1910.95, 29 *CFR* 1910.120, and 29 *CFR* 1910.134], July 1, 1992.

Title 40, *Code of Federal Regulations*, Part 311 [40 *CFR* 311] (EPA), March 1991.

C-1.7 VOSH Publication.

Virginia Occupational Safety and Health, Department of Labor and Industry, Powers-Taylor Building, 13 S. 13th Street, Richmond, VA 23219.

VOSH Standard 1900.1200.

PART TWO

NFPA 1521

Standard for Fire Department Safety Officer and Commentary

Part Two of this handbook includes the complete text of the 1997 edition of NFPA 1521, *Fire Department Safety Officer*. This standard was initially developed in 1977, and the first two editions were numbered as NFPA 1501. This 1997 edition expands on the safety officer requirements of NFPA 1500 and focuses on the distinctions between the incident scene safety officer (ISO) and health officer (HSO). Additionally, it shows how each of these positions fits into a fire department's risk management plan, which is a key component of an overall occupational safety and health program.

The mandatory provisions found in Chapters 1 through 5 of the NFPA 1521 were prepared by the Technical Committee on Fire Service Occupational Safety within the framework of NFPA's consensus codes- and standards-making system. Because these provisions are designed to be suitable for adoption into law or for reference by other codes and standards, the text is concise, without extended explanation.

The material found in Appendix A of NFPA 1521 was also developed by the Technical Committee on Fire Service Occupational Safety within NFPA's codes- and standards-making system to assist users in understanding and interpreting the mandatory provisions of the standard. It is not considered part of the requirements of the standard; it is advisory or informational. An asterisk (*) following a paragraph number in the standard indicates that advisory appendix material pertaining to that paragraph appears in Appendix A. For the reader's convenience, in this handbook, Appendix A material has been repositioned to appear immediately following its base paragraph in the body of the standard. The text of the standard and the Appendix A material are printed in black in this handbook.

Explanatory commentary, which was prepared by Captain Murrey E. Loflin of the Virginia Beach Fire Department, immediately follows the standard text it discusses and is printed in blue for easy identification. The commentary is intended to provide the reader with a deeper understanding of the standard and to serve as a resource and reference for implementing its provisions. It is not a substitute for the actual wording of the standard or the text of any code or standard that may be incorporated by reference.

Loflin, who has been employed by the Virginia Beach Fire Department since 1983, is currently company officer assigned to Engine 19. He first served as a fire fighter/EMT and was later assigned as department safety officer. After being promoted to the rank of captain in 1988, he continued to serve as safety officer and assumed the duties of infection control officer. Loflin has been a member of the American Society of Safety Engineers, Greater Tidewater Chapter, since 1983, serving as president for the 1992–1993 term. He serves as chairman of the NFPA Fire Service Section Executive Board, as chairman of NFPA's Technical Committee on Fire Service Medical and Health, and as a member of NFPA's Technical Committee on Fire Service Occupational Safety. He is an adjunct faculty member and course developer for the National Fire Academy in Emmitsburg, Maryland.

Loflin has a Master of Science Degree in Occupational Health and Safety from Marshall University in Huntington, West Virginia.

CHAPTER 1

Administration

1-1 Scope

The 1997 edition of NFPA 1521 is a complete revision and separates, for the first time, the duties and responsibilities of the health and safety officer and the incident safety officer. NFPA 1521 provides minimum requirements for the positions of health and safety officer and incident safety officer. Nothing prohibits a department from exceeding these requirements when establishing these positions. In fact, departments are encouraged to exceed these requirements to assure compliance with this standard.

Public fire departments provide the majority of fire and emergency medical services in the United States. Organizations such as military, private, and industrial fire departments often use both a health and safety officer and an incident safety officer. In larger departments, these functions are handled through a battalion or division assignment. By contrast, in smaller departments, one person often functions as both the health and safety officer and the incident safety officer. Regardless of department size, NFPA 1521 intends that the fire department provide an adequate occupational safety and health program and an effective incident scene safety program.

This standard does not apply to industrial fire brigades; however, most companies with an industrial fire brigade also have a safety department or division. Safety department personnel may use this standard to assure the safety and health of industrial fire brigade members.

1-1.1

This standard contains minimum requirements for the assignment, duties, and responsibilities of a health and safety officer and an incident safety officer for a fire department or other fire service organization.

1-1.2

These requirements shall be applicable to organizations providing rescue, fire suppression, emergency medical services, hazardous materials mitigation, special operations, and other emergency services, including public, military, private, and industrial fire departments.

1-1.3

This standard does not apply to industrial fire brigades that also can be known as emergency brigades, emergency response teams, fire teams, plant emergency organizations, or mine emergency response teams.

1-2 Purpose

1-2.1

The purpose of this standard shall be to specify the minimum requirements for a fire department health and safety officer and an incident safety officer.

1-2.2

This standard shall be intended to meet the requirements of Section 2-5 of NFPA 1500, *Standard on Fire Department Occupational Safety and Health Program.*

Paragraph 1-2.2 links this standard with NFPA 1500. Section 2-5 of NFPA 1500 states that the fire chief shall appoint a designated fire department health and safety officer to be responsible for the management of the occupational safety and health program. *(See Part One of this handbook.)* An effective program requires that the fire chief appoint a qualified member to function in this capacity. Although there is only one health and safety officer, the fire chief can appoint additional members to the program if needed. Based upon the needs of the department, the fire chief shall assign additional assistant safety officers and needed resources to fulfill the requirements of the occupational safety and health program. Although there are many participants in the occupational safety and health program, the health and safety officer is the focal point.

The fire chief may appoint a command officer as the incident safety officer, or the health and safety officer may respond as the incident safety officer. The department must appoint an incident safety officer by automatic dispatch or on-scene appointment, as discussed in Chapter 4.

1-2.3

Many of the performance objectives of this standard shall be permitted to be achieved in a variety of ways. Nothing herein shall be intended to restrict any jurisdiction from exceeding these minimum requirements.

1-3 Equivalency

Section 1-3 on equivalency first appeared in the 1997 edition of NFPA 1500, primarily for departments that do not use the National Fire Protection Association's professional qualifications standards. The professional qualifications of the health and safety officer must be as equivalent in training, education, competency, and safety as possible. Members' training, education, and competency must be commensurate with the functions they are expected to perform.

1-3.1

The authority having jurisdiction shall be permitted to approve an equivalent level of qualifications for the requirements specified in 2-2.1 of this standard provided that the fire department has technical documentation to demonstrate equivalency.

1-3.2

The approved equivalent levels shall secure as nearly equivalent training, education, competency, and safety as possible and shall require that training, education, and competency be commensurate with those functions that the members are expected to perform. In no case shall the equivalency afford less competency of members or safety to members than that which, in the judgment of the authority having jurisdiction, would be provided by compliance with the provisions of the specified paragraph.

1-4 Definitions

Accident. Any unexpected event that interrupts or interferes with the orderly progress of fire department operations and can include personal injury or property damage.

Approved.* Acceptable to the authority having jurisdiction.

A-1-4 Approved. The National Fire Protection Association does not approve, inspect, or certify any installations, procedures, equipment, or materials; nor does it approve or evaluate testing laboratories. In determining the acceptability of installations, procedures, equipment, or materials, the authority having jurisdiction may base acceptance on compliance with NFPA or other appropriate standards. In the absence of such standards, said authority may require evidence of proper installation, procedure, or use. The authority having jurisdiction may also refer to the listings or labeling practices of an organization that is concerned with product evaluations and is thus in a position to determine compliance with appropriate standards for the current production of listed items.

Assistant Safety Officer. A member of the fire department assigned and authorized by the fire chief to assist the fire department health and safety officer or incident safety officer in the performance of the duties and responsibilities specified in this standard.

Authority Having Jurisdiction.* The organization, office, or individual responsible for approving equipment, an installation, or a procedure.

A-1-4 Authority Having Jurisdiction. The phrase "authority having jurisdiction" is used in NFPA documents in a broad manner, since jurisdictions and approval agencies vary, as do their responsibilities. Where public safety is primary, the authority having jurisdiction may be a federal, state, local, or other regional department or individual such as a fire chief; fire marshal; chief of a fire prevention bureau, labor department, or health department; building official; electrical inspector; or others having statutory authority. For insurance purposes, an insurance inspection department, rating bureau, or other insurance company representative may be the authority having jurisdiction. In many circumstances, the property owner or his or her designated agent assumes the role of the authority having jurisdiction; at government installations, the commanding officer or departmental official may be the authority having jurisdiction.

Driver/Operator. A person having satisfactorily completed the requirements of driver/operator as specified in NFPA 1002, *Standard for Fire Department Vehicle Driver/Operator Professional Qualifications.*

Emergency Incident. A specific emergency operation.

Emergency Medical Care. The provision of treatment to patients, including first aid, cardiopulmonary resuscitation, basic life support, advanced life support, and other medical procedures that occur prior to arrival at a hospital or other health care facility.

Emergency Operations. Activities of the fire department relating to rescue, fire suppression, emergency medical care, and special operations, including response to the scene of the incident and all functions performed at the scene.

Fire Apparatus. A fire department emergency vehicle used for rescue, fire suppression, or other specialized functions.

Fire Chief. The highest ranking officer in charge of a fire department.

Fire Department. An organization providing rescue, fire suppression, and related activities. The term "fire department" shall include any public, governmental, private, industrial, or military organization engaging in this type of activity.

Fire Department Facility. Any building or area owned, operated, occupied, or used by a fire department on a routine basis. This does not include locations where a fire department might be summoned to perform emergency operations or other duties, unless such premises are normally under the control of the fire department.

Fire Department Member. See Member.

Fire Department Safety Officer. Functions comprised of the health and safety officer and the incident safety officer. These roles can be performed by one member or several members as designated by the fire chief. See Health and Safety Officer and Incident Safety Officer.

The term *fire department safety officer* remains in the standard because it generically refers to the all-encompassing position of safety officer. The title "safety officer" will continue to be used, but the two roles—that is, health and safety officer and incident safety officer—better define this position. As fire departments increasingly fill the position of fire department safety officer, the two roles will become more distinct.

Fire Department Vehicles. Any vehicle operated by a fire department, including fire apparatus.

Fire Suppression. The activities involved in controlling and extinguishing fires. Fire suppression shall include all activities performed at the scene of a fire incident or training exercise that expose fire department members to the dangers of heat, flame, smoke, or other products of combustion, explosion, or structural collapse.

Hazard. The potential for harm or damage to people, property, or the environment. Hazards include the characteristics of facilities, equipment systems, property, hardware, or other objects, and the actions and inactions of people that create such hazards.

Health and Safety Officer. The member of the fire department assigned and authorized by the fire chief as the manager of the safety and health program and who performs the duties and responsibilities specified in this standard. This individual can be the incident safety officer or it can also be a separate function.

Health Hazard. Any property of a material that either directly or indirectly can cause injury or incapacitation, either temporary or permanent, from exposure by contact, inhalation, or ingestion.

Imminent Hazard. An act or condition that is judged to present a danger to persons or property that is so urgent and severe that it requires immediate corrective or preventive action.

Incident Action Plan. The objectives reflecting the overall incident strategy, tactics, risk management, and member safety that are developed by the incident commander. The incident action plan must be continually updated throughout the incident.

The term *incident action plan* is used within the U.S. Forest Service to describe the plan established by the incident commander to mitigate an incident and is now widely used by the fire service. The incident action plan must address risk management and the safety of the members operating at the incident. The incident commander must formalize an incident action plan and communicate this information to all members on-scene. Through the communicated incident action plan, every member will know exactly which strategy and tactics will be employed for a safe and effective operation. The incident action plan is not a static process, but rather a dynamic one that has to be updated as each tactical benchmark is completed.

Incident Commander. The fire department member in overall command of an emergency incident.

Incident Management System (IMS). An organized system of roles, responsibilities, and standard operating procedures used to manage and direct emergency operations. Such systems are often referred to as incident command systems (ICS).

Incident Safety Officer. An individual appointed to respond to or assigned at an incident scene by the incident commander to perform the duties and responsibilities specified in this standard. This individual can be the health and safety officer or it can be a separate function.

Incident Safety Plan. The strategies and tactics developed by the incident safety officer based upon the incident commander's incident action plan and the type of incident encountered.

The incident safety officer develops an incident safety plan based on the incident commander's incident action plan. The incident commander must brief the incident safety officer so that the incident action plan is understood before the safety officer formulates an incident safety plan. As the incident action plan changes, so does the incident safety plan.

The incident safety plan is a strategy used by the incident safety officer to provide for the safety of members operating at the incident scene. The incident safety plan also provides information for the incident safety officer's role in the postincident analysis required by Section 6-8 of NFPA 1500, *Standard on Fire Department Occupational Safety and Health Program* (1997). *(See Part One of this handbook.)*

Incident Scene. The location where activities related to a specific incident are conducted. This shall include the entire area subject to incident-related hazards and all areas used by fire department members and equipment in proximity to the incident.

Incident Scene Rehabilitation. The tactical level management unit that provides for medical evaluation, treatment, monitoring, fluid and food replenishment, mental rest, and relief from climatic conditions of the incident.

Industrial Fire Department.* An organization providing rescue, fire suppression, and related activities. It can also provide emergency medical services, hazardous material operations, or other activities. These activities can occur at a single facility or facilities under the same management, whether for profit, not for profit, or government owned or operated, including occupancies such as industrial, commercial, mercantile, warehouse, and institutional. The industrial fire department is generally trained and equipped for specialized operation based on site-specific hazards present at the facilities.

Groups or teams organized to perform specialized rescue services, but who do not perform fire suppression activities, are not considered as industrial fire departments.

A-1-4 Industrial Fire Department. Industrial fire departments should be distinguished from industrial fire brigades. Industrial fire departments are similar in mission to municipal fire departments and usually employ fire apparatus, mobile water supplies, large-diameter hose, and specialized equipment based on the site-specific hazards present within the occupancy. These occupancies can have separate organizations, covered by separate organizational statements, operating as industrial fire brigades or teams providing rescue unrelated to fire incidents. Membership in these organizations can overlap.

Member. A person involved in performing the duties and responsibilities of a fire department under the auspices of the organization. A fire department member can be a full-time or part-time employee or a paid or unpaid volunteer, can occupy any position or rank within the fire department, and can engage in emergency operations.

Occupational Illness. An illness or disease contracted through or aggravated by the performance of the duties, responsibilities, and functions of a fire department member.

Occupational Injury. An injury sustained during the performance of the duties, responsibilities, and functions of a fire department member.

Occupational Safety and Health Program. The overall program to provide occupational safety and health in a fire department as defined in NFPA 1500, *Standard on Fire Department Occupational Safety and Health Program.*

Procedure. An organizational directive issued by the authority having jurisdiction or department that establishes a specific policy that must be followed.

Rescue. Those activities directed at locating endangered persons at an emergency incident, removing those persons from danger, treating the injured, and providing for transport to an appropriate health care facility.

Risk Management. Identification and analysis of exposure to hazards, selection of appropriate risk management techniques to handle exposures, implementation of chosen techniques, and monitoring of results, as respects the health and safety of members.

Safety Specialist. An individual who has the expertise, knowledge, and professional experience to achieve control or reduction of occupational hazards and exposures. The individual is assigned to assist the health and safety officer as part of the safety staff.

The safety specialist is a qualified individual assigned to the occupational safety and health program who may or may not be a uniformed member of the fire department. The safety specialist may be a certified industrial hygienist (CIH) or a certified safety professional (CSP) who administers occupational safety and health programs, such as hearing conservation, protective clothing and equipment, infection control, air quality, and other health and environmental concerns. This specialist also conducts technical research to ensure compliance with applicable laws, codes, and standards. For example, research and development of methods to reduce heat stress in fire fighters' protective clothing and equipment would be a task for the safety specialist.

Safety Unit. A member or members assigned to assist the incident safety officer. The tactical level management unit that can be comprised of the incident safety officer alone or with additional assistant safety officers assigned to assist in providing the level of safety supervision appropriate for the magnitude of the incident and the associated hazards.

The term *safety unit* is incident management terminology designating the incident safety officer and any additional members assigned as assistant incident safety officers. The term *safety unit* could be utilized when the incident safety officer is in charge of a group of assistant safety officers.

Service Testing. The regular, periodic inspection and testing of apparatus and equipment, according to an established schedule and procedure, to ensure that it is in safe and functional operating condition.

Shall. Indicates a mandatory requirement.

Should. Indicates a recommendation or that which is advised but not required.

Special Operations. Those emergency incidents to which the fire department responds that require specific and advanced training and specialized tools and equipment. Special operations include water rescue, extrication, hazardous materials, confined space entry, high-angle rescue, aircraft rescue and fire fighting, and other operations requiring specialized training.

Standard Operating Procedure.* A written organizational directive that establishes or prescribes specific operational or administrative methods to be followed routinely for the performance of designated operations or actions.

A-1-4 Standard Operating Procedure. It is a requirement of the authority having jurisdiction to develop and utilize a policy or guideline for organizational directives for the operation of the fire department.

During the public comment period for NFPA 1521, a comment was submitted to replace the term *standard operating procedure* with the term *standard operating guideline*. The public comment prompted intense technical committee debate. The technical committee decided that the term *standard operating procedure* was more appropriate as used in relation to occupational safety and health. Standardization of policy, operating procedures, and operating guidelines terminology becomes imperative, especially as more fire departments establish such procedural documents.

Tactical Level Management Unit. A management unit identified in an incident management system commonly known as "division," "group," or "sector."

CHAPTER 2

Organization

2-1 Assignment

2-1.1*

The fire chief shall have the ultimate responsibility for the fire department occupational safety and health program as specified in NFPA 1500, *Standard on Fire Department Occupational Safety and Health Program.* A health and safety officer shall be assigned to manage the fire department occupational safety and health program.

A-2-1.1 The fire chief is responsible for the overall management and authority of the fire department, including member safety and health. The fire chief delegates this responsibility to a health and safety officer. The health and safety officer is the program manager or administrator of the occupational safety and health program.

The fire chief is ultimately responsible for the development, implementation, and management of the occupational safety and health programs. In practice, the responsibility to manage the daily operations of the occupational safety and health program is delegated to the health and safety officer.

2-1.2

The health and safety officer shall report directly to the fire chief or to the fire chief's designated representative.

The appointed health and safety officer works directly for the fire chief or designee (such as the Deputy Chief of Operations). The intent of paragraph 2-1.2 is to provide the safety officer with a supervisor who has the authority to effect change. Furthermore, 2-1.2 gives the safety officer visibility within the organizational structure, which increases the officer's ability to impact change within the fire department.

2-1.3*

Each fire department shall have a designated health and safety officer. The health and safety officer shall be permitted to be assigned as a full-time or part-time position, depending on the size and character of the fire department.

A-2-1.3 The determination of whether the fire department safety officer will be a full-time or part-time assignment should be made by the fire chief. This should depend on the size and structure of the organization, the activity level, the level of risk in the fire department's work environment, and the history of accidents, injuries, occupational illnesses, fatalities, and exposures.

Paragraph 2-1.3 gives the department flexibility in appointing a full- or part-time health and safety officer. The size of the fire department dictates whether the health and safety officer is a full-time or part-time position. However, the extensive duties and responsibilities of the health and safety officer virtually dictate that this be a full-time position, especially since the department will greatly benefit. If the fire department cannot afford a full-time health and safety officer, then the training officer may be the logical person to share duties (especially when the training officer has a full-time position).

2-1.3.1 Additional assistant health and safety officers shall be appointed when the activities, size, or character of the fire department warrants extra safety personnel. If the health and safety officer is not available, additional assistant health and safety officers shall be appointed to ensure proper coverage.

The size and needs of the department dictate the need for additional assistant safety officers. In large departments, assistant safety officers may be assigned to a shift while the health and safety officer is assigned to an 8-hour workday schedule. All assistant safety officers report directly to the health and safety officer.

2-1.3.2* In the absence of the health and safety officer and assistant health and safety officer(s), alternate personnel shall be assigned to perform the duties and responsibilities of the position that require immediate attention.

A-2-1.3.2 A large fire department should have one or more assistant health and safety officer(s) working in the area of safety and health, under the direction of the health and safety officer. A small department can have one individual assigned as the health and safety officer, which can be on a part-time basis. This individual can depend upon assistance from members of the occupational safety and health committee, who have expertise in various areas of fire fighter safety and health.

2-1.4

The incident commander shall have ultimate responsibility for incident scene safety as specified in NFPA 1561, *Standard on Fire Department Incident Management System.*

2-1.4.1* An incident safety officer shall be appointed when activities, size, or need occurs. The incident safety officer function shall be permitted to be a pre-designated position or appointed by the incident commander as needed. If the pre-designated incident safety officer is not available, the incident commander shall appoint an incident safety officer.

A-2-1.4.1 There are circumstances at emergency incidents that require the immediate response or attention of the incident safety officer. It is unrealistic to assume that one individual would be available on a continual basis to fulfill these requirements. The system should provide for additional assistant incident safety officers to assume these responsibilities in the absence of the incident safety officer. The response of the incident safety officer to an emergency incident might be delayed by distance, simultaneous events, or other circumstances. When the need for an incident safety officer is a priority at an incident scene and none is available, the incident commander should assign a qualified member to establish a safety unit and assume those duties and responsibilities on a temporary basis. All members should be aware of the basic functions and responsibilities of the incident safety officer at an incident scene.

2-1.4.2 Additional assistant incident safety officer(s) shall be appointed when the activities, size, or need warrants extra safety personnel.

The incident commander has the ultimate responsibility for safety, health, and welfare of all members operating at the scene of an emergency. Safety and health authority is commonly delegated to the incident safety officer when this position is utilized. At the majority of incidents, the incident commander will function as the incident safety officer. However, the size, type, or severity of an incident dictates the response or appointment of an incident safety officer.

The fire department's response matrix dictates the automatic response of the incident safety officer. The incident safety officer should be dispatched to the following:

- Working commercial fires
- All second-alarm fires
- Incidents involving fire fighter injury
- Hazardous materials incidents
- Technical rescue operations
- Mass casualty incidents

The incident commander may appoint an interim incident safety officer until the incident safety officer arrives on-scene.

At working incidents, the incident safety officer may require assistant safety officers due to the area (e.g., commercial building), height (e.g., high-rise building), type of incident (e.g., hazardous materials), or any other situation that would dictate assistance.

2-2 Qualifications of the Health and Safety Officer (HSO)

The position of health and safety officer requires commitment, time management, understanding, honesty, and self-motivation. The health and safety officer must be able to evaluate programs and projects fairly. The National Fire Academy's *Health and Safety Officer (HSO)* 16-hour course is an excellent overall training resource for newly appointed health and safety officers.

2-2.1

The health and safety officer shall be a fire department officer and shall meet the requirements for Fire Officer Level 1 specified in NFPA 1021, *Standard for Fire Officer Professional Qualifications.*

The all-encompassing nature of the health and safety officer position is the basis for the requirement of 2-2.1.

2-2.2*

The health and safety officer shall have and maintain a knowledge of current applicable laws, codes, and standards regulating occupational safety and health to the fire service.

A-2-2.2 The standard requires the health and safety officer to have and maintain a knowledge of current applicable laws, codes, and standards. Such current knowledge requires continuing efforts to be aware of the developing bodies of knowledge and experience pertaining to fire service occupational safety and health. This can be gained through reading journals and periodicals, attending classes and seminars, and regularly reviewing additions and changes in applicable laws, codes, and standards.

Paragraph 2-2.2 intends to include OSHA standards, NFPA codes and standards, and departmental regulations.

2-2.3*

The health and safety officer shall have and maintain a knowledge of occupational safety and health hazards involved in emergency operations.

A-2-2.3 The health and safety officer must recognize safety and health hazards associated with emergency operations and how to reduce the severity of these hazards. Safety and health hazards can be identified as, but not limited to, respiratory hazards, exposure to communicable diseases and hazardous materials, failure to wear or improper use of protective clothing and equipment, and apparatus and vehicle safety.

An effective health and safety officer must have served as both a fire fighter and a fire officer to have the experience, knowledge, and understanding of the occupational safety and health hazards encountered during incident operations. Live fire training evolutions provide the health and safety officer an excellent environment for learning during controlled fireground operations.

2-2.4*

The health and safety officer shall have and maintain a knowledge of the current principles and techniques of safety management.

A-2-2.4 The health and safety officer must utilize safety management as a basis for establishing the fire department's occupational safety and health program. This process includes accident prevention, accident investigation, identifying unsafe acts and unsafe conditions, accident and injury analysis, training and education, and use of protective clothing and equipment.

The health and safety officer must understand the basics of safety management, including the theory and practical application of accident and loss prevention, accident investigation, accident and injury analysis, basic components of safety management, protective clothing and equipment, and risk management. Colleges or universities that offer occupational safety and health courses usually provide a basic course in safety management. Several companies in private industry, as well as professional associations such as the American Society of Safety Engineers, offer safety management courses for a fee.

2-2.5*

The health and safety officer shall have and maintain a knowledge of current health maintenance and physical fitness issues that affect the fire service members.

A-2-2.5 The health and safety officer must be familiar with health maintenance issues such as disabling injuries and illnesses, respiratory and heart diseases, cancer and related diseases, a medical monitoring program for members, the need for members to maintain an appropriate level of fitness, and wellness programs for fire fighters.

Paragraph 2-2.5 introduces health and wellness as a topic for the fire department safety officer. Health and wellness issues are relatively new and untraversed within the fire service yet are very important because they address the fire department's most valuable resource—its members. The health and safety officer can learn about health and wellness through local physical fitness agencies, local universities, or professional associations such as the American College for Sports Medicine. Information on health and wellness is also available through the NFPA's Public Fire Protection Division, its Fire Analysis and Research Division, or Charles S. Morgan Technical Library and the United States Fire Administration.

2-2.6*

The health and safety officer shall have and maintain a knowledge of infection control practice and procedures as required in NFPA 1581, *Standard on Fire Department Infection Control Program.*

A-2-2.6 The health and safety officer can utilize NFPA 1581, *Standard on Fire Department Infection Control Program,* to develop and implement an infection control program and serve as a resource for infection control issues.

Paragraph 2-2.6 acknowledges that, for most fire departments, providing emergency medical services (EMS) involves many incidents that require an aggressive infection control program. As a result, the health and safety officer must understand the components of infection control. An infection control officer is sometimes appointed in conjunction with the appointment as health and safety officer. The health and safety officer must have a basic knowledge of infection control practices even if the department has an infection control officer. NFPA 1581, *Standard on Fire Department Infection Control Program* (1995), provides the key components for the operation of an effective infection control program. *(See Part Four of this handbook.)* That standard provides the necessary procedures for ensuring compliance with 29 *CFR* 1910.134, *Bloodborne Pathogens*.

2-3 Authority of the Health and Safety Officer (HSO)

2-3.1

The health and safety officer shall have the responsibility to identify and cause correction of safety and health hazards.

2-3.2

The health and safety officer shall have the authority to cause immediate correction of situations that create an imminent hazard to members.

2-3.3

Where nonimminent hazards are identified, a health and safety officer shall develop actions to correct the situation within the administrative process of the fire department. The fire department health and safety officer shall have the authority to bring notice of such hazards to whomever has the ability to cause correction.

Upon implementation of an occupational safety and health program, the fire chief must grant the health and safety officer the authority to immediately correct hazards that jeopardize the safety and health of members. The following three types of hazards may exist:

- *Nonemergency.* These hazards involve training, apparatus, facilities, and other nonemergency situations.
- *Imminent dangers.* These hazards include potential building collapse, severe weather conditions, and lost or trapped personnel and pose an immediate danger to life and health. Consequently, the health and safety officer must have the authority to stop operations until the hazard is eliminated. The health and safety officer must have the necessary resources available to properly eliminate the hazard.
- *Long-term, nonimminent dangers.* These hazards require the health and safety officer to develop an action plan that identifies the time frame in which the hazard will be eliminated. This plan can include long-range planning, funding, and an action plan for compliance with applicable laws, codes, and standards. Examples of nonimminent hazards that require an action plan include diesel exhaust emissions, decontamination facilities for infection control, and compliance with general industry safety standards for nonimminent hazards such as those of OSHA and the Centers for Disease Prevention and Control.

The occupational safety and health program must address and eliminate imminent hazards. Nonimminent hazards must be prioritized based on their level of importance—*not* on funding.

2-4 Qualifications of the Incident Safety Officer (ISO)

As seen in Section 2-4, the requirements for incident safety officer are very similar to those for health and safety officer. The exceptions to that general statement are the following:

- Knowledge of building construction
- Knowledge of the personnel accountability system (PAS)
- Knowledge of incident scene rehabilitation

An incident safety officer may be appointed on-scene rather than predesignated. The member who serves in this capacity must (1) understand incident scene safety and (2) observe and correct, if necessary, any imminent safety hazards at the incident scene. The incident safety officer must develop an incident safety plan based on the incident action plan. Developing the incident safety plan requires the incident safety officer to work within the incident management system and to serve as a part of the command staff.

2-4.1

The incident safety officer shall be a fire department officer and shall meet the requirements for Fire Officer Level 1 specified in NFPA 1021, *Standard for Fire Officer Professional Qualifications*.

2-4.2*

The incident safety officer shall have the knowledge, skill, and abilities to manage incident scene safety as defined in Chapter 4 of this standard.

A-2-4.2 It is imperative that the member that functions as the incident safety officer be qualified to assume this function. Training, experience, and knowledge in incident scene operations are excellent qualifiers for an incident safety officer. The incident safety officer must have an understanding of the operations of the particular incident, the hazards associated with these operations, risk management, incident management system, and personnel accountability.

2-4.3*

The incident safety officer shall have and maintain a knowledge of safety and health hazards involved in emergency operations.

A-2-4.3 Safety and health hazards could include lack of or improper use of protective clothing and equipment, structural conditions, scene safety, infection control, hazardous materials, conditions associated by technical rescue incidents, personnel accountability, or any hazard that affects the safety and health of personnel operating at the incident scene.

2-4.4*

The incident safety officer shall have and maintain a knowledge of building construction.

A-2-4.4 Identification of building construction problems or concerns has a direct impact on fire fighter safety. The incident safety officer must be able to identify building conditions such as truss roof construction, lightweight truss construction, fire protection systems, reinforcement rods ("stars") that could impact, and any other building construction factor that affects fire fighter safety. Prefire planning must be incorporated into this process.

Building construction is a major consideration during incident operations due to the number of fire fighter fatalities associated with truss construction. Pre-incident identification of truss construction is part of the risk management toolbox and plays a significant role in fireground safety because it allows the incident safety officer and members to inspect the facility's construction before an emergency.

2-4.5

The incident safety officer shall have and maintain a knowledge of the fire department's personnel accountability system.

As required by paragraph 2-4.5, the incident safety officer must understand the department's personnel accountability system, a risk management tool that is vital to fire fighter safety and health. One of the primary functions of the incident safety officer is to make sure that on-scene personnel do not freelance, that is, operate independently or become separated from their crew.

2-4.6*

The incident safety officer shall have and maintain a knowledge of incident scene rehabilitation.

A-2-4.6 Incident scene "rehab" is a critical part of incident scene safety. The incident safety officer is not responsible for establishing "rehab," but must ensure that this tactical level management unit is established and adequately staffed with personnel and resources. The key components of the "rehab" process are rest, hydration, and medical monitoring.

Rehab consists of moving members out of the environment, rest, medical evaluation, hydration, and food (for long-term operations). Rehab must be established during weather extremes, during extended operations, and any other time that members need rest and rehabilitation during emergency operations. The incident safety officer is not necessarily responsible for establishing rehab but must ensure that this process has been established.

See also paragraph 4-2.2.

2-5 Authority of the Incident Safety Officer (ISO)

2-5.1

At an emergency incident where activities are judged by the incident safety officer to be unsafe or to involve an imminent hazard, the incident safety officer shall have the authority to alter, suspend, or terminate those activities. The incident safety officer shall immediately inform the incident commander of any actions taken to correct imminent hazards at the emergency scene.

2-5.2

At an emergency incident where an incident safety officer identifies unsafe conditions, operations, or hazards that do not present an imminent danger, the incident safety officer shall take appropriate action through the incident commander to mitigate or eliminate the unsafe condition, operation, or hazard at the incident scene.

2-5.3

At an emergency incident, assistant incident safety officer(s) shall be granted the authority as authorized in 2-5.1.

The requirements of Section 2-5.1 first appeared in NFPA 1501, *Standard on Fire Department Safety Officer.* (NFPA 1501 was renamed NFPA 1521 after the adoption of NFPA 1500.) The requirements have been modified to give the incident safety officer full authority to alter, suspend, or terminate operations due to unsafe operations or an imminent hazard. Assistant safety officers, if present, are granted this same authority by 2-5.3. The fire department's incident management system must fulfill the intention of Section 2-5 of NFPA 1521 so that the incident safety officer is granted this full authority.

Upon discovery of an unsafe operation or condition, the incident safety officer has the authority to take immediate corrective action. This action includes immediate and direct communications with the incident commander, which may lead to an instant change in the incident action plan. Examples of unsafe operations or conditions include the following:

- Freelancing (i.e., a member acting independently)
- Venting a truss roof or a roof that is already elsewhere vented by fire
- Inadequate protective clothing or equipment
- Entering an improperly shored trench
- Failure to adequately define hot, warm, or cold zones at a hazardous materials incident

In many other cases, common sense indicates that something is wrong and corrective action is needed.

The incident safety officer must take action to correct unsafe conditions or operations and nonimminent hazards before they become serious problems, that is, imminent hazards. The incident safety officer may be able to correct the problem without involving the incident commander. However, if assistance is needed from the incident commander, then the incident safety officer must advise him or her. Nonimminent hazards may not affect the incident action plan, but the incident safety officer needs to communicate to the incident commander any changes that may affect operations.

CHAPTER 3

Functions of the Health and Safety Officer

Chapter 3 is a valuable resource for those fire departments developing a job description for the health and safety officer. See also the position description for Safety Officer in Figure 1500-2.6 (Part One of this handbook) provided by the National Wildfire Coordinating Group and a position description from the Virginia Beach Fire Department (Supplement 6 in Part 6 of this handbook).

3-1 Risk Management

Risk management is a broad topic, but Section 3-1 focuses on the safety and health aspects of risk management. Private industry has successfully used risk management for years with great success to lower the number of accidents and injuries and to reduce the cost of workers' compensation insurance and medical expenses. Incorporating risk management into fire department operations can greatly decrease fire fighter fatalities, occupational injuries and illnesses, and health exposures.

3-1.1*

The health and safety officer shall be involved in the development, implementation, and management of the official written risk management plan as specified in Chapter 2 of NFPA 1500, *Standard on Fire Department Occupational Safety and Health Program.*

A-3-1.1 Risk management is a vital component to any organization's operation, especially a fire department. The health and safety program is one of many elements that comprise the risk management process. The risk management process enables an organization to control the risks associated with fire department operations. Due to the inherent risks faced by members during emergency and nonemergency operations, a risk management plan will reduce the frequency and severity of risks.

Paragraph 3-1.1 requires the health and safety officer to participate in developing the fire department's risk management plan. In fact, the health and safety officer is often the primary author of the department's risk management plan. A classic risk management plan includes the following:

- Risk identification
- Evaluation of risks
- Prioritization of risks
- Control measures
- Monitoring

A copy of the Virginia Beach Fire Department's Risk Management Plan is included as Supplement 7 in Part 6 of this handbook.

3-1.1.1 The health and safety officer shall communicate the health and safety aspects of the risk management plan to all members through training and education.

3-1.1.2 The health and safety officer shall make available the written risk management plan to all fire department members.

3-1.2

The health and safety officer shall monitor the effectiveness of the risk management plan and shall ensure the risk management plan is revised annually as it relates to fire fighter health and safety.

Paragraph 3-1.2 prevents a risk management plan from becoming frozen. Risk management planning is a dynamic process in which the plan is continually evaluated and updated. Updates are needed at least annually so that run statistics, community risk assessment, accident and injury data, training needs and requirements, and any other factors that impact the risk management plan can be evaluated. Monitoring the plan will also play a significant role in determining needed changes and/or additions.

3-1.3

The health and safety officer shall develop an incident risk management plan that is implemented into the fire department's incident management system. This risk management plan shall meet the requirements of Chapter 6 of NFPA 1500, *Standard on Fire Department Occupational Safety and Health Program.*

3-2 Laws, Codes, and Standards

Section 3-2 establishes that determining which laws, codes, and standards apply to the fire department from a safety and health perspective is an important responsibility of the health and safety officer. Examples of applicable laws, codes, and standards include those of the EPA, NFPA, and OSHA, as well as state motor vehicle codes, state legislation, local ordinances, and jurisdictional policies. The health and safety officer must develop a strategic plan for compliance with applicable laws, codes, and standards. Monitoring department policy and standard operating procedures and/or guidelines with respect to these regulations is another function of the health and safety officer; any discrepancy must be reported to the fire chief or designated representative.

The health and safety officer is responsible for compliance with applicable laws, codes, and standards. The fire chief must grant the health and safety officer the authority to achieve compliance with all regulations for the sake of workplace safety. *This is the same authority granted to the incident safety officer to alter, suspend, or terminate operations.* In situations where corrective action is needed, the health and safety officer must be granted the authority to take such action.

3-2.1*

The health and safety officer shall develop, review, and revise rules, regulations, and standard operating procedures pertaining to the fire department occupational safety and health program. Based upon the directives and requirements of applicable laws, codes, and standards, the health and safety officer shall develop procedures that ensure compliance with these laws, codes, and standards. These recommended or revised rules, regulations, or standard operating procedures shall be submitted to the fire chief or the fire chief's designated representative by the health and safety officer.

A-3-2.1 A sample safety procedure or statement can read as follows: It is the intent of the Anytown Fire Department to provide for the safety, health, and welfare of all its members. Through the implementation of the occupational safety and health program, our goal is to reduce the frequency and severity of accidents, injuries, occupational illnesses, and occupational exposures. The occupational safety and health program governs all activities, emergency and nonemergency, of all members of this department and of any other persons involved in fire department operations.

3-2.2

The health and safety officer shall periodically report to the fire chief or the fire chief's designated representative on the adequacy of, effectiveness of, and compliance with the rules, regulations, and standard operating procedures specified in 3-2.1 of this section.

3-2.3

The fire chief shall define the role of the health and safety officer in the enforcement of the rules, regulations, and standard operating procedures.

3-3 Training and Education

3-3.1*

The health and safety officer shall ensure that training in safety procedures relating to all fire department operations and functions is provided to fire department members. Training shall address recommendations arising from the investigation of accidents, injuries, occupational deaths, illnesses, and exposures and the observation of incident scene activities.

A-3-3.1 The health and safety officer is not the only safety trainer. To fulfill this function properly, even in a small fire department, the health and safety officer should act as a clearinghouse for information and training programs related to occupational safety and health.

3-3.2

The health and safety officer shall cause safety supervision to be provided for training activities, including all live burn exercises. All structural live burn exercises shall be conducted in accordance with NFPA 1403, *Standard on Live Fire Training Evolutions.* The health and safety officer or qualified designee shall be personally involved in preburn inspections of any acquired structures to be utilized for live fire training.

The health and safety officer must ensure that safety training occurs in the fire department, both during recruit training and annually thereafter. He or she is also responsible (through the instructor) for safety during training operations. OSHA requires annual safety training in the use of respiratory protection, hazardous waste operations and emergency response (HAZWOPER), infection control, confined space, protective clothing and equipment, and fire fighting operations (Title 29, *CFR*, Part 1910.120). The health and safety officer may provide instruction or determine that the training is completed and properly documented. Should a fatality, serious injury, or near miss occur, safety training needs to be conducted to address the incidence and recommendations made to prevent the incident from repeating.

3-3.3

The health and safety officer shall develop and distribute safety and health information for the education of fire department members.

Paragraph 3-3-3 intends that the health and safety officer remain current on safety and health issues that affect the fire service and distribute current information to other fire department members. As part of ongoing safety training, the health and safety officer will distribute information through written reports, videotapes, training packages, state and national training programs, the Internet, and any other media.

3-4 Accident Prevention

Accident prevention is an integral part of any occupational safety and health program, regardless of the occupation or industry. Section 3-4 integrates accident prevention with a fire department occupational safety and health program. As a result, the health and safety officer must address accident prevention in the development of the fire department's occupational safety and health program. Unfortunately, some members of the fire service have the mistaken belief that occupational accidents, injuries, and illnesses are an unchangeable part of the profession. In fact, accident prevention will take the fire service a long way in reducing fatalities, occupational accidents, injuries, illnesses, and health exposures.

3-4.1

The health and safety officer shall manage an accident prevention program that addresses the items specified in this section. The health and safety officer shall be permitted to delegate the development, direct participation, review, or supervision of this program.

3-4.2

The accident prevention program shall provide instruction in safe work practices for all fire department members. This shall include safe work practices for emergency and nonemergency operations.

3-4.3

The accident prevention program shall address the training and testing of all fire department drivers, including all fire apparatus driver/operators.

3-4.4

The health and safety officer shall periodically survey operations, procedures, equipment, and fire department facilities with regard to maintaining safe working practices and procedures. The health and safety officer shall report any recommendations to the fire chief or the fire chief's designated representative.

3-5 Accident Investigation, Procedures, and Review

3-5.1

The health and safety officer shall develop and implement procedures to ensure that a member(s) suffering a life-threatening occupational injury or illness is provided immediate emergency medical care and transportation to medical facilities. These procedures shall also ensure that all occupational injuries and illnesses are treated at the most appropriate health care facilities.

Paragraph 3-5.1 requires in-place procedures to provide immediate emergency medical care for the member(s) involved in a catastrophic incident. Facilities for treating serious burns, orthopedic injuries, and cardiac problems, for example, need to be identified. In the event of an occupational exposure, procedures must be in place for proper prophylaxis, counseling, and recordkeeping, as well as follow-up care. The same approach applies to an occupational exposure to a hazardous material.

3-5.2

The health and safety officer shall investigate, or cause to be investigated, all occupational injuries, illnesses, exposures, and fatalities, or other potentially hazardous conditions involving fire department members and all accidents involving fire department vehicles, fire apparatus, equipment, or fire department facilities.

The intent of 3-5.2 is for the fire department to conduct a complete investigation in order to learn from mistakes and to prevent the incident from happening again. The fire department must take corrective action and institute change to prevent a recurrence. Outside agencies involved in such an investigation process must be identified before an incident occurs. Once a fatality or serious injury occurs, it is too late to start developing investigative procedures.

Accidents involving fire department vehicles, apparatus, and equipment must be investigated by the proper authorities, including law enforcement. A thorough investigation will result in a properly documented report, which may be especially important to self-insured fire departments.

3-5.3

The health and safety officer shall develop corrective recommendations that result from accident investigations. The health and safety officer shall submit such corrective recommendations to the fire chief or the fire chief's designated representative.

3-5.4

The health and safety officer shall develop accident and injury reporting and investigation procedures and shall periodically review these procedures for revision. These accident and injury reporting procedures shall comply with all local, state, and federal requirements.

Among the most important procedures to be developed, but hopefully never used, is how to investigate a fire fighter fatality, serious injury, or near miss. Information available from the International Association of Fire Fighters (IAFF) and the International Association of Fire Chiefs (IAFC) will assist the fire department in developing its procedures. The Public Safety Officer's Benefit (PSOB) Act, from both a federal and a state level, addresses specific procedures for handling a fire fighter fatality. Fire fighter fatality reports typically include a recommendation section on actions that could have prevented the fatality or serious injury. The health and safety officer must disseminate this information to the fire department.

The fire department has the right to conduct an independent investigation to determine what went wrong and why. Outside agencies will conduct investigations as well, and information has to be shared. *The intent of investigations is not to conceal information or place blame, but to determine what happened and why.*

The health and safety officer must periodically evaluate the adequacy of procedures used in accident and injury investigation. If changes are needed, they must be made. The primary focus for procedures is to determine all the facts of the incident and present an unbiased report.

3-5.5

The health and safety officer shall review the procedures employed during any unusually hazardous operation. Wherever it is determined that incorrect or questionable procedures were employed, the health and safety officer shall submit corrective recommendations to the fire chief or the fire chief's designated representative.

3-6 Records Management and Data Analysis

3-6.1*

The fire department shall maintain records of all accidents, occupational deaths, injuries, illnesses, and exposures in accordance with Chapter 2 of NFPA 1500, *Standard on Fire Department Occupational Safety and Health Program.* The health and safety officer shall manage the collection and analysis of this information.

A-3-6.1 Data management refers to the collection and assimilation of information related to fire department safety and health and the use of this data to enhance the efforts of the occupational safety and health program. The data management process serves several important functions, as follows:

(a) It provides a summary of fire department experience in different categories (i.e., fire fighter injuries, vehicular accidents, work-related illnesses).
(b) It provides a measure of how the experience of a particular fire department compares with other fire departments, with national trends, and with other occupations or industries.
(c) It provides a systematic method to record information for future reference and use.

Data management provides a means of determining trends and program effectiveness, whether problems are becoming worse, whether accidents and injuries are being reduced, and whether the costs associated with accidents and injuries are increasing or decreasing.

Occupational safety and health laws require employers to maintain records of job-related injuries and illnesses.

The health and safety officer manages record keeping and documentation—two vital components of the occupational safety and health program. To reap the benefits of accident and injury data, the health and safety officer will collect and analyze the data and use the results to improve the occupational safety and health program. The health and safety officer should publish an annual report that identifies the year's significant incidents, including accidents, occupational fatalities, injuries, illnesses, or exposures. More importantly, the report must identify corrective actions to improve fire fighter safety and health.

3-6.2

The health and safety officer shall identify and analyze safety and health hazards and shall develop corrective actions to deal with these hazards.

3-6.3

The health and safety officer shall ensure that records on the following are maintained as specified in Chapter 2 of NFPA 1500, *Standard on Fire Department Occupational Safety and Health Program:*

(a) Fire department safety and health standard operating procedures
(b) Periodic inspection and service testing of apparatus and equipment
(c) Periodic inspection and service testing of personal safety equipment
(d) Periodic inspection of fire department facilities

3-6.4

The health and safety officer shall maintain records of all recommendations made and actions taken to correct safety and health hazards or unsafe practices.

3-6.5

The health and safety officer shall maintain records of all measures taken to implement safety and health procedures and accident prevention methods.

Paragraphs 3-6.4 and 3-6.5 make the health and safety officer responsible for the occupational safety and health paper trail. As the health and safety officer develops policy or procedural change regarding health and safety, informational files must be maintained. Written procedures to correct unsafe acts, conditions, or health hazards must be maintained by the health and safety officer.

3-6.6

The health and safety officer shall issue a report to the fire chief, at least annually, on fire department accidents, occupational injuries, illnesses, deaths, and exposures.

3-7 Apparatus and Equipment

3-7.1

The health and safety officer shall review specifications for new apparatus, equipment, protective clothing, and protective equipment for compliance with the applicable safety standards, including the provisions of Chapters 4 and 5 of NFPA 1500, *Standard on Fire Department Occupational Safety and Health Program.*

The health and safety officer monitors all new apparatus and equipment purchased for compliance with Chapters 4 and 5 of NFPA 1500, *Standard on Fire Department Occupational Safety and Health Program* (1997), as well as other applicable codes and standards. *(See Part One of this handbook.)* Whether or not the health and safety officer is a member of the fire department's apparatus and/or protective clothing and equipment committees, the officer will review and approve specifications for new apparatus and equipment. Among the most important factors to be considered is the mounting of tools and equipment in compliance with manufacturers' recommendations and Chapter 4 of NFPA 1500.

3-7.2

The health and safety officer shall assist and make recommendations regarding the evaluation of new equipment and its acceptance or approval by the fire department in accordance with the applicable provisions of Chapter 4 of NFPA 1500, *Standard on Fire Department Occupational Safety and Health Program.*

3-7.3

The health and safety officer shall assist and make recommendations regarding the service testing of apparatus and equipment to determine its suitability for continued service and in accordance with Chapter 4 of NFPA 1500, *Standard on Fire Department Occupational Safety and Health Program.*

Chapter 4 of NFPA 1500 requires annual service testing for pumps, ladders, hose, and other equipment. *(See Part One of this handbook.)* The health and safety officer is responsible for the completion and proper documentation of service testing.

3-7.4

The health and safety officer shall develop, implement, and maintain a protective clothing and protective equipment program that will meet the requirements of Chapter 5 of NFPA 1500, *Standard on Fire Department Occupational Safety and Health Program,* and provide for the periodic inspection and evaluation of all protective clothing and equipment to determine its suitability for continued service.

Protective clothing and equipment are to be inspected annually, according to Chapter 5 of NFPA 1500. *(See Part One of this handbook.)* The health and safety officer develops an inspection program that determines suitability for continued service. For a nominal fee, the Fire Industry Equipment Research Organization (FIERO) offers a care, use, and maintenance document that complies with paragraph 3-7.4. (Contact: Robert D. Tutterow, Jr., Charlotte F.D., 1200 Otis St., Charlotte, NC 28208, 704-336-5609)

3-8 Facility Inspection

The health and safety officer must review plans for new or renovated facilities to monitor compliance with applicable codes and standards. Personal hygiene, infection control, diesel exhaust emissions, fire protection, and other safety and health issues must be addressed and incorporated into the facility design. See also NFPA 1500, Chapter 7, and NFPA 1581, *Standard on Fire Department Infection Control Program* (1995). *(See Parts One and Four of this handbook.)*

3-8.1

The health and safety officer shall ensure all fire department facilities are inspected in accordance with Chapter 7 of NFPA 1500, *Standard on Fire Department Occupational Safety and Health Program.*

Chapter 7 of NFPA 1500 requires that all facilities be inspected at least annually. *(See Part One of this handbook.)* Hopefully, the fire department will require its facilities to be inspected more frequently. For example, a monthly inspection should identify any safety and health issues that need to be corrected. Sample checklists that can be utilized for the inspection process are in the appendix of NFPA 1500.

3-8.2

The health and safety officer shall ensure that any safety or health hazards or code violations are corrected in a prompt and timely manner.

3-9 Health Maintenance

3-9.1

The health and safety officer shall ensure that the fire department complies with the requirements of Chapter 8 of NFPA 1500, *Standard on Fire Department Occupational Safety and Health Program.*

3-9.2

The health and safety officer shall incorporate medical surveillance, wellness programs, physical fitness, nutrition, and injury and illness rehabilitation into the health maintenance program.

The health and welfare of fire department members are paramount. As a result, the health and safety officer must effectively manage health maintenance programs. Chapter 8 of NFPA 1500 requires a health maintenance program that addresses the following:

- Medical surveillance (annual medical evaluations and examinations)
- Educational programs and information
- Wellness issues
- Physical fitness
- Nutrition
- Cessation programs
- Injury and illness rehabilitation

An aggressive, proactive health maintenance program must be established by working with the fire department physician. The physician may be an employee or a contractor of the fire department or the authority having jurisdiction. See also Section 8-6 of NFPA 1500 and Section 2-2 of NFPA 1582, *Standard on Medical Requirements for Fire Fighters* (1997). *(See Parts One and Five of this handbook.)*

3-10 Liaison

3-10.1

The health and safety officer shall be a member of the fire department occupational safety and health committee.

The intent of 3-10.1 is to identify the various personnel, departments, and agencies with whom the health and safety officer interacts to provide an effective occupational safety and health program. The health and safety officer serves as a member of the fire department's occupational safety and health committee and will communicate any committee recommendations to the appropriate authority. Any recommendations made by the health and safety officer to enhance occupational safety and health in the fire department must be made to the appropriate authority.

3-10.2

The health and safety officer shall report the recommendations of the fire department occupational safety and health committee to the fire chief or the fire chief's designated representative.

3-10.3

The health and safety officer shall submit recommendations on occupational safety and health to the fire chief or the fire chief's designated representative.

3-10.4

The health and safety officer shall provide information and assistance to officers and fire fighters for surveying their districts, so they will be able to identify and report safety and health hazards that could have adverse effects on fire department operations.

3-10.5

The health and safety officer shall maintain a liaison with staff officers regarding recommended changes in equipment and procedures and in recommended methods to eliminate unsafe practices and reduce existing hazardous conditions.

Paragraph 3-10.5 establishes a departmentwide liaison. The health and safety officer works with district, battalion, and company officers to identify and report any safety and health issues that affect fire department operations. An excellent example is identifying truss roof construction and its adverse effects in an emergency.

3-10.6

The health and safety officer shall maintain a liaison with equipment manufacturers, standards-making organizations, regulatory agencies, and safety specialists outside the fire department regarding changes to equipment and procedures and methods to eliminate unsafe practices and reduce existing hazardous conditions.

When unsafe practices or hazardous conditions are identified by the incident safety officer or by another member, the health and safety officer must take the steps necessary to eliminate these situations. Through educational means or additional training, the health and safety officer must be assured that the unsafe acts are changed and hazardous conditions are corrected. When problems occur with protective clothing and equipment and/or apparatus, the health and safety officer will work with the manufacturer to eliminate the problem.

3-10.7

The health and safety officer shall maintain a liaison with the fire department physician to ensure that needed medical advice and treatment are available to the members of the fire department.

As discussed in Section 3-9, the health and safety officer works with the fire department physician so that medical advice, consultation, treatment, and care are available for all members of the fire department.

3-11 Occupational Safety and Health Committee

Section 3-11 establishes the relationship of the health and safety officer and the occupational safety and health committee. The health and safety officer ensures that the fire department establishes an occupational safety and health committee, as required by Chapter 2 of NFPA 1500. *(See Part One of this handbook.)* This committee provides the members of the fire department with a voice in the safety and health program and assists the health and safety officer in addressing safety and health issues.

3-11.1

The health and safety officer shall ensure that an occupational safety and health committee is established by the fire department.

3-11.2

The health and safety officer shall ensure that the occupational safety and health committee meets the requirements of Chapter 2 of NFPA 1500, *Standard on Fire Department Occupational Safety and Health Program,* and Section 3-9 of this standard.

3-12 Infection Control

3-12.1

The health and safety officer shall ensure that the fire department's infection control program meets the requirements of 29 CFR 1910.1030, *Occupational Exposure to Bloodborne Pathogens,* and NFPA 1581, *Standard on Fire Department Infection Control Program.*

3-12.2

The health and safety officer shall maintain a liaison with the person or persons designated as infection control officer to assist in achieving the objectives of the infection control program as specified in NFPA 1581, *Standard on Fire Department Infection Control Program.*

3-12.3

The health and safety officer shall function as the fire department infection control officer if an infection control officer position does not exist in the fire department.

Many fire departments provide emergency medical services to the communities they serve. A critical part of fire fighter safety and health is a proactive infection control program. The health and safety officer must ensure that the infection control program meets the requirements of NFPA 1581, *Standard on Fire Department Infection Control Program* (1995), and 29 *CFR* 1910.1030, *Occupational Exposure to Bloodborne Pathogens.* NFPA 1581 provides a foundation for a thorough infection control program; in fact, compliance with NFPA 1581 assures compliance with 29 *CFR* 1910.1030.

The health and safety officer serves as the infection control officer if the position is not staffed. If the infection control officer position is staffed, the health and safety officer assists him or her.

3-13 Critical Incident Stress Management

3-13.1

The health and safety officer shall ensure that the fire department establishes a critical incident stress management (CISM) program. The critical incident stress management program shall meet the requirements of Chapter 10 of NFPA 1500, *Standard on Fire Department Occupational Safety and Health Program.*

3-13.2

The health and safety officer shall ensure that the critical incident stress management program is incorporated into the fire department's member assistance program.

As with many occupational safety and health programs, the health and safety officer may not be part of the process, but must be sure that it exists. A departmental policy or procedure, as well as training and continuing education, must be available so that department members understand the importance of critical incident stress management.

3-14 Postincident Analysis

3-14.1

The health and safety officer shall develop procedures to ensure that safety and health issues are addressed during postincident analysis.

Postincident analysis is a vital component of the occupational safety and health program. The health and safety officer must be sure that fire fighter safety and health concerns are addressed during the postincident analysis.

3-14.2

The health and safety officer shall provide a written report that includes pertinent information about the incident relating to safety and health issues.

Paragraph 3-14.2 requires the health and safety officer to submit a written report that addresses safety and health issues resulting from an incident; the incident safety officer must do the same. In other words, in fire departments where these two functions are separate, two different reports will be submitted. The reports will be in a format acceptable to the fire department and submitted to a designated staff officer. This reporting process is essential, especially after a fire fighter fatality, serious injury, or near miss. For a sample postincident analysis report, see Supplement 8 in Part 6 of this handbook.

3-14.3

The health and safety officer shall include information based upon input from the incident safety officer. This information shall include the incident action plan and the incident safety officer's incident safety plan.

3-14.4

The health and safety officer shall include information about issues relating to the use of protective clothing and equipment, personnel accountability system, rehabilitation operations, and other issues affecting the safety and welfare of personnel at the incident scene.

Paragraph 3-14.4 specifies certain issues to be covered in the health and safety officer's report. Ideally, the report will address the following:

- Protective clothing and equipment
- Use of pre-incident planning information
- Risk management
- Apparatus and equipment malfunctions or problems
- Personnel accountability
- Incident scene rehabilitation

The incident action plan and the incident safety plan must be (1) identified in the written report and (2) discussed during the postincident analysis. This issue is critical if there are problems with the incident action plan, especially if the problems impacted the issues listed above.

CHAPTER 4

Functions of the Incident Safety Officer

4-1 Incident Management System

4-1.1*

The incident safety officer shall be integrated with the incident management system as a command staff member, as specified in NFPA 1561, *Standard on Fire Department Incident Management System.*

A-4-1.1 The function of incident scene safety must be carried out at all incidents. It is the responsibility of the incident commander who cannot perform this function due to the size or complexity of the incident to assign or request response of an incident safety officer to this function. There are, however, incidents that require immediate response or appointment of an incident safety officer, such as a hazardous materials incident or special operations incidents. These types of incidents should be defined in the fire department's response policy or procedure to ensure that the incident safety officer responds. Likewise, some situations require an incident safety officer to respond after members are on the scene, such as a working fire or at the request of the incident commander.

The fire department must have an incident management system that complies with the requirements of NFPA 1561, *Standard on Fire Department Incident Management System* (1995), so that each participant understands the rules for incident management. *(See Part Three of this handbook.)* The incident management system must incorporate the incident safety officer as a member of the command staff. The incident management process must be in place in order to manage an emergency effectively and safely.

4-1.2*

Standard operating procedures shall define criteria for the response or appointment of an incident safety officer.

If the incident safety officer is designated by the incident commander, the fire department shall establish criteria for appointment based upon 4-1.1 of this standard.

A-4-1.2 A fire department should develop response procedures for an incident safety officer that is on call or designated to respond. Examples could be as follows:

(a) Commercial fires
(b) Multiple alarm
(c) Fire fighter injury or fire fighter transported for treatment
(d) Hazardous materials incident
(e) Technical rescue incident
(f) At the request of the incident commander

In-place procedures will define the response criteria for dispatching an incident safety officer. For example, the incident safety officer should be dispatched on all commercial working fires, second alarms, hazardous materials incidents, special operations, when a member is seriously injured, and when requested by the incident commander. The procedures should clearly define response criteria so that an incident safety officer is dispatched as required. The fire department should also initiate procedures to appoint an incident safety officer on-scene; such procedures will make sure that the incident commander makes needed appointments.

The incident safety officer is dispatched to a variety of incidents. The uniqueness and safety concerns of each incident may require different members to function as incident safety officer. Some members may simply have better knowledge, skills, and abilities to respond to a particular incident. The issue of individual capabilities must be clearly addressed *before* any emergency response. The department must define a minimum response of personnel and equipment when responding on automatic or mutual aid. The response should include a command officer and an incident safety officer who are responsible for the safety and welfare of department members responding to the incident.

4-1.3*

The incident safety officer and assistant incident safety officer(s) shall be readily identifiable on the incident scene.

A-4-1.3 This can be accomplished by wearing a highly visible vest, helmet, or other indicator.

Paragraph 4-1.3 requires that the fire department identify the incident safety officer and assistant incident safety officer(s). Identification is especially important when the incident safety officer and assistant(s) are appointed on-scene or when the fire department responds on automatic or mutual response.

4-2 Incident Scene Safety

4-2.1

The incident safety officer shall monitor conditions, activities, and operations to determine whether they fall within the criteria as defined in the fire department's risk management plan. When the perceived risk(s) is not within these criteria, the incident safety officer shall take action as outlined in Section 2-5.

There is a very fine line between acceptable and unacceptable risk. The first arriving officer(s), the incident commander, and the incident safety officer will evaluate the risks involved based on assessment of the situation and will decide which tactics to use. At times, difficult decisions must be made regarding the risk to fire fighters and the individuals they are trying to rescue. Effective risk control measures will help make this process safer.

The first arriving officer must provide a risk assessment on arrival at the scene and communicate this information to the incident commander and all members on-scene. The tactics taken should match the risk management plan established by the fire department. Very simply stated, the risk management plan should be as follows:

- Risk a lot to save a lot.
- Risk a little to save a little.
- Risk nothing to save nothing.

By monitoring incident scene safety and operations, the incident safety officer matches operations on-scene to the established risk management plan. If risk and operations do not match each other, the incident safety officer has authority to alter, suspend, or terminate the operations.

4-2.2

The incident safety officer shall ensure that the incident commander establishes an incident scene rehabilitation tactical level management unit during emergency operations.

Paragraph 4-2.2 makes the incident safety officer responsible for the incident commander's action to initiate rehabilitation. Rehabilitation is especially important during weather extremes, long-term operations, hazardous materials incidents, or special operations incidents. As with many other activities, the incident safety officer does not necessarily personally implement or manage rehabilitation, but needs to know that "rehab" is properly established, staffed, and equipped.

4-2.3

The incident safety officer shall monitor the scene and report the status of conditions, hazards, and risks to the incident commander.

Paragraph 4-2.3 makes communication an occupational safety and health issue: Missed, misunderstood, or incomplete communications can result in serious injury to members. Communication between the incident safety officer and the incident commander is key during incident operations. In fact, the incident commander and the incident safety officer must communicate from the time of arrival until after the incident is over. The incident safety officer and the incident commander must routinely confer, especially when tactical benchmarks are met and the incident action plan changes. When communication is lacking, it is very difficult for the incident scene to run effectively or safely.

4-2.4

The incident safety officer shall ensure that the fire department's personnel accountability system is being utilized.

4-2.5

The incident commander shall provide the incident safety officer with the incident action plan. The incident safety officer shall provide the incident commander with a risk assessment of incident scene operations.

4-2.6

The incident safety officer shall ensure that established safety zones, collapse zones, hot zone, and other designated hazard areas are communicated to all members present on scene.

By monitoring activities at the incident scene, the incident safety officer will identify unsafe conditions, hazards, and risks. As building conditions deteriorate or hazards expand, the incident safety officer will develop a safety zone and/or a collapse zone to provide for the safety of members on-scene and the public. Barrier tape can establish safety or collapse zones.

4-2.7

The incident safety officer shall evaluate motor vehicle scene traffic hazards and apparatus placement and take appropriate actions to mitigate hazards.

Every year, fire fighters are killed or severely injured while working on roadways or highways during emergency operations. The fire department should establish a procedure or policy for traffic safety.

4-2.8

The incident safety officer shall monitor radio transmissions and stay alert to transmission barriers that could result in missed, unclear, or incomplete communication.

4-2.9*

The incident safety officer shall communicate to the incident commander the need for assistant incident safety officers due to the need, size, complexity, or duration of the incident.

A-4-2.9 The need, size, complexity, or duration of an incident can necessitate the need for additional assistant incident safety officers. Incidents such as high-rise fires, hazardous materials incidents, and special operations require additional assistance. In these cases, the incident safety officer should request from the incident commander the need to establish a safety unit. Under the direction of the incident safety officer, assistant incident safety officers can be assigned to handle scene monitoring, action planning, risk management, interior safety at a high-rise incident, or operations safety at hazardous materials incidents or special operations, or serve as relief for the incident safety officer during extended incident operations.

4-2.10

The incident safety officer shall survey and evaluate the hazards associated with the designation of a landing zone and interface with helicopters.

The surveying and evaluating of hazards required by 4-2.10 include noting overhead wires, debris, people, vehicles, equipment, and any other object or material that could cause a hazard.

4-3 Fire Suppression

The basis for Section 4-3 is tragically simple: The many members who are injured or killed during fire-fighting operations make the incident safety officer's role on the fireground absolutely critical. The incident safety officer will be proactive in ensuring safe fireground operations. However, members must clearly understand that they are responsible and accountable for their actions or inactions at an emergency incident. The incident safety officer is not a "safety cop." Members must think for themselves and follow the basics of fire fighter safety and survival. The incident safety officer looks at the overall incident, not just the operations of a company or sector. Forecasting to determine what might happen in the near future based on the current operations is a major activity for the incident safety officer.

4-3.1

The incident safety officer shall meet provisions of Section 4-2 of this standard during fire suppression operations.

4-3.2

The incident safety officer shall ensure that a rapid intervention crew meeting the criteria in Chapter 6 of NFPA 1500, *Standard on Fire Department Occupational Safety and Health Program,* is available and ready for deployment.

After personnel are accounted for in the personnel accountability system and they understand their tactical assignments within the incident action plan, the incident safety officer will next make sure that a rapid intervention crew (RIC) is available. The need for a rapid intervention crew is discussed with the incident commander, and resources are made available to staff the rapid intervention crew as needed. See also Chapter 6 of NFPA 1500, *Standard on Fire Department Occupational Safety and Health Program* (1997). *(See Part One of this handbook.)*

4-3.3

Where fire has involved a building or buildings, the incident safety officer shall advise the incident commander of hazards, collapse potential, and any fire extension in such building(s).

4-3.4

The incident safety officer shall evaluate visible smoke and fire conditions and advise the incident commander, tactical level management units officers, and company officers on the potential for flashover, backdraft, blow-up, or other fire event that could pose a threat to operating teams.

From the occupational safety and health perspective, assessing building construction includes determining the type of building construction, roof construction, fire extension, and collapse concerns or any other hazard that could jeopardize fire fighter safety.

The incident safety officer must also monitor smoke and fire conditions as they relate to potential problems. The incident safety officer must ascertain an approximate length of time that the fire has been burning and the presence of other problems that might lead to building collapse or otherwise threaten members' safety.

4-3.5

The incident safety officer shall monitor the accessibility of entry and egress of structures and the effect it has on the safety of members conducting interior operations.

4-4 Emergency Medical Service Operations

The incident safety officer must understand some very basic components of emergency medical services (EMS). These components can be summarized in a checklist or other convenient reminder format for the incident safety officer. (For a sample checklist, see Supplement 9 in Part Six of this handbook.)

At a minimum, the incident safety officer must understand the following in relation to EMS operations:

- Infection control, including protective clothing and equipment, hygiene issues, and so on
- Incident scene rehabilitation
- Critical incident stress management
- Traffic safety
- Personnel accountability

4-4.1

The incident safety officer shall meet provisions of Section 4-2 of this standard during EMS operations.

4-4.2

The incident safety officer shall ensure compliance with the department's infection control plan and NFPA 1581, *Standard on Fire Department Infection Control Program,* during EMS operations.

4-4.3

The incident safety officer shall ensure that incident scene rehabilitation and critical incident stress management are established as needed at EMS operations, especially mass casualty incidents (MCI).

4-5 Hazardous Materials Operations

The incident safety officer is the overall safety officer. A safety officer will be assigned to the operational tactical level management unit, which oversees the safety of the members working in the hot zone.

4-5.1*

The incident safety officer shall meet provisions of Section 4-2 of this standard during hazardous materials incidents.

A-4-5.1 Hazardous materials incidents require an incident safety officer for the following:

(a) Potential risks to members
(b) Substantial number of members to control an incident
(c) Duration of the incident

4-5.2*

The hazardous materials incident safety officer shall meet the requirements of Chapter 4 of NFPA 472, *Standard for Professional Competence of Responders to Hazardous Materials Incidents.*

A-4-5.2 Due to the knowledge and expertise required at a hazardous materials incident, the incident safety officer needs to have an understanding of these operations. This can be achieved by being trained to the Hazardous Materials Technician level of NFPA 472, *Standard for Professional Competence of Responders to Hazardous Materials Incidents.*

4-5.3

The incident safety officer shall attend strategic and tactical planning sessions and provide input on risk assessment and member safety.

The incident safety officer must be included in all planning sessions, briefings, or meetings to ensure that the requirements of 29 *CFR* 1910.120, *Hazardous Waste Operations and Emergency Response,* are met. Each zone will be properly marked for the safety of members, other personnel, and the public.

4-5.4

The incident safety officer shall ensure that a safety briefing, including an incident action plan and an incident safety plan, is developed and made available to all members on the scene.

4-5.5

The incident safety officer shall ensure that hot, warm, decontamination, and other zone designations are clearly marked and communicated to all members.

4-5.6

The incident safety officer shall meet with the incident commander to determine rehabilitation, accountability, or rapid intervention needs. For long-term operations, the incident safety officer shall ensure that food, hygiene facilities, and any other special needs are provided for members.

Since most true hazardous materials incidents are lengthy, the incident safety officer must consider long-term care such as food, hygiene, water, and additional protective clothing and equipment. Hazardous materials incidents may require using all the incident management system components, such as personnel accountability systems, incident scene rehabilitation, and rapid intervention crews, for a successful outcome. The incident safety officer will work with the incident commander so that operational safety and health and welfare needs are met throughout the incident. In addition, if an exposure to a hazardous material occurs, medical treatment and care must be provided. Forecasting relates to fire fighter safety and health and is a good tool during hazardous materials and special operations incidents.

4-6 Special Operations

Risk control measures used during special operations incidents are similar to those used during hazardous materials incidents, although the hazards and risks differ. The incident safety officer needs proper knowledge, skills, and abilities to be effective. The incident safety officer must participate in all planning sessions, briefings, or meetings so that all safety provisions meet the requirements of 29 *CFR* 1910.146, *Permit Required Confined Space*. The incident safety officer must establish and designate safety and collapse zones for the safety of members, other personnel, and the public.

4-6.1*

The incident safety officer shall meet provisions of Section 4-2 of this standard during special operations incidents. The individual that serves as the incident safety officer for special operations incidents shall have the appropriate education, training, and experience in special operations.

A-4-6.1 Some functions are performed best by individuals with specific expertise, particularly in highly technical areas. The fire department should endeavor to have more than one qualified individual to perform all essential functions within the incident management system.

4-6.2

The incident safety officer shall attend strategic and tactical planning sessions and provide input on risk assessment and member safety.

4-6.3

The incident safety officer shall ensure that a safety briefing, including an incident action plan and an incident safety plan, is developed and made available to all members on the scene.

4-6.4

The incident safety officer shall meet with the incident commander to determine rehabilitation, accountability, or rapid intervention needs. For long-term operations, the incident safety officer shall ensure that food, hygiene facilities, and any other special needs are provided for members.

The incident safety officer must take an overall view of special operations. In addition to operational safety, health and welfare needs must be addressed. When operations exceed several hours, such issues as food, personal hygiene needs, and shelter must be given priority. The incident safety officer must be part of this process so that all needs are considered and met.

4-7 Accident Investigation and Review

4-7.1

Upon notification of a member injury, illness, or exposure, the incident safety officer shall immediately communicate this to the incident commander to ensure that emergency medical care is provided.

4-7.2

The incident safety officer shall initiate the accident investigation procedures as required by the fire department.

Section 4-7 makes accident investigation and review primarily a function of the health and safety officer, but in most situations the investigation and review are initiated by the incident safety officer. The incident safety officer must be familiar with departmental procedures to conduct an effective investigation.

4-7.3

In the event of a serious injury, fatality, or other potentially harmful occurrence, the incident safety officer shall request assistance from the health and safety officer.

Most accident investigations can be handled by the incident safety officer and the immediate supervisor. However, for accidents involving a serious injury or fatality, the incident safety officer requires assistance and will be assisted by the health and safety officer. Department procedures should specify the necessary assistance required to conduct a thorough investigation and ensure that such assistance is available.

4-8 Postincident Analysis

The intent of the postincident analysis required by Section 4-8 is not to determine fault or blame, but to identify and learn from both mistakes and proper actions. Without an avenue for identifying and correcting mistakes, the little mistakes become bigger—and more dangerous—mistakes that might kill or seriously injure fire fighters. The incident safety officer needs adequate time to provide input and direction to the postincident analysis, based on what was observed during the operation.

4-8.1*

The incident safety officer shall prepare a written report for the postincident analysis that includes pertinent information about the incident relating to safety and health issues. The incident safety officer shall participate in the postincident analysis.

A-4-8.1 The incident safety officer should document pertinent information about the incident, including assignments given by the incident commander, the incident safety plan, procedures that worked well, obstacles encountered and how to correct them, and significant accidents and/or injuries.

It is important to include successful or positive actions as well as those actions that require training or procedural changes to improve incident safety and health for all members.

4-8.2

The incident safety officer shall include information about issues relating to the use of protective clothing and equipment, personnel accountability system, rapid intervention crews, rehabilitation operations, and other issues affecting the safety and welfare of members at the incident scene.

The incident safety officer must participate in the formal postincident analysis and prepare a written report outlining pertinent information about the incident as it relates to fire fighter safety and health. The incident safety officer must ensure that information that needs discussion—such as protective clothing and equipment, personnel accountability, rapid intervention crews, rehab, and any other safety or health issue—is addressed during the postincident analysis.

CHAPTER 5

Referenced Publications

5-1

The following documents or portions thereof are referenced within this standard as mandatory requirements and shall be considered part of the requirements of this standard. The edition indicated for each referenced mandatory document is the current edition as of the date of the NFPA issuance of this standard. Some of these mandatory documents might also be referenced in this standard for specific informational purposes and, therefore, are also listed in Appendix C.

5-1.1 NFPA Publications.

National Fire Protection Association, 1 Batterymarch Park, P.O. Box 9101, Quincy, MA 02269-9101.

NFPA 472, *Standard for Professional Competence of Responders to Hazardous Materials Incidents,* 1997 edition.

NFPA 1002, *Standard for Fire Department Vehicle Driver/Operator Professional Qualifications,* 1993 edition.

NFPA 1021, *Standard for Fire Officer Professional Qualifications,* 1997 edition.

NFPA 1403, *Standard on Live Fire Training Evolutions,* 1997 edition.

NFPA 1500, *Standard on Fire Department Occupational Safety and Health Program,* 1997 edition.

NFPA 1561, *Standard on Fire Department Incident Management System,* 1995 edition.

NFPA 1581, *Standard on Fire Department Infection Control Program,* 1995 edition.

5-1.2 U.S. Government Publication.

U.S. Government Printing Office, Washington, DC 20402.

29 *Code of Federal Regulations* 1910.1030, *Occupational Exposure to Bloodborne Pathogens.*

REFERENCES CITED IN COMMENTARY

29 *CFR* 1910.120, *Hazardous Waste Operations and Emergency Responses,* U.S. Government Printing Office, Washington, DC 20402.

29 *CFR* 1910.1030, *Occupational Exposures to Bloodborne Pathogens,* U.S. Government Printing Office, Washington, DC 20402.

29 *CFR* 1910.146, *Permit Required Confined Space,* U.S. Government Printing Office, Washington, DC 20402.

APPENDIX A

Explanatory Material

The material contained in Appendix A of this standard is not part of the requirements of the code but is included with the code for informational purposes only. For the convenience of readers, in this handbook the Appendix A material is interspersed among the verbiage of Chapters 1 through 4 and, therefore, is not repeated here.

APPENDIX B

Sample Forms

The sample Facilities Safety Checklist and the sample Station Inspection Form that appeared in Appendix B of the 1997 edition of *Standard for Fire Department Safety Officer* are not part of the requirements of the standard, but are included with the standard for informational purposes only. For the convenience of readers, in this handbook the forms are included in Supplement 12 as Form S12-1 and S12-2 in full-size versions suitable for reproduction.

APPENDIX C

Referenced Publications

C-1

The following documents or portions thereof are referenced within this standard for informational purposes only and are thus not considered part of the requirements of this standard unless also listed in Chapter 5. The edition indicated here for each reference is the current edition as of the date of the NFPA issuance of this standard.

C-1.1 NFPA Publications.

National Fire Protection Association, 1 Batterymarch Park, P.O. Box 9101, Quincy, MA 02269-9101.

NFPA 30, *Flammable and Combustible Liquids Code,* 1996 edition.

NFPA 472, *Standard for Professional Competence of Responders to Hazardous Materials Incidents,* 1997 edition.

NFPA 1581, *Standard on Fire Department Infection Control Program,* 1995 edition.

NFPA 1582, *Standard on Medical Requirements for Fire Fighters,* 1997 edition.

NFPA 1975, *Standard on Station/Work Uniforms for Fire Fighters,* 1994 edition.

C-1.2 VOSH Publication.

Virginia Occupational Safety and Health, Department of Labor and Industry, Powers-Taylor Building, 13 S. 13th Street, Richmond, VA 23219.

VOSH standard 1910.1200.

PART THREE

NFPA 1561

Standard on Fire Department Incident Management Systems and Commentary

Part Three of this handbook includes the complete text of the 1995 edition of NFPA 1561, *Fire Department Incident Management Systems*. The first edition of NFPA 1561 was published in 1990 to identify the essential considerations for safety and health in incident management systems and to encourage the fire service to utilize such systems to manage all emergency incidents. This second edition emphasizes that incident management includes more than fireground operations, and it contains new and expanded text covering such topics as accountability, use of rapid intervention crews to rescue members, and interagency cooperation.

The mandatory provisions found in Chapters 1 through 5 of NFPA 1561 were prepared by the Technical Committee on Fire Service Occupational Safety within the framework of NFPA's consensus codes- and standards-making system. Because these provisions are designed to be suitable for adoption into law or for reference by other codes and standards, the text is concise, without extended explanation.

The material found in Appendix A of NFPA 1561 was also developed by the Technical Committee on Fire Service Occupational Safety within NFPA's codes- and standards-making system to assist users in understanding and interpreting the mandatory provisions of the standard. It is not considered part of the requirements of the standard; it is advisory or informational. An asterisk (*) following a paragraph number in the standard indicates that advisory appendix material pertaining to that paragraph appears in Appendix A. For the reader's convenience, in this handbook, Appendix A material has been repositioned to appear immediately following its base paragraph in the body of the standard. The text of the standard and the Appendix A material are printed in black in this handbook.

Explanatory commentary, which was prepared by Margaret Dimmick, Planning Section Chief for the Nike World Masters Games Public Safety Committee, immediately follows the standard text it discusses and is printed in blue for easy identification. The commentary is intended to provide the reader with a deeper understanding of the standard and to serve as a resource and reference for implementing its provisions. It is not a substitute for the actual wording of the standard or the text of any code or standard that may be incorporated by reference.

In her current position as Planning Section Chief for the Nike World Masters Games Public Safety Committee, Dimmick is responsible for coordinating the planning for law enforcement, fire, and emergency medical response to the Games. Prior to this assignment, she spent ten years as the emergency management coordinator for the city of Gresham, Oregon. During that time, she also served on the NFPA 1600 Technical Committee on Disaster Management and became well known for facilitating innovative uses of the NIIMS Incident Command System in all-risk and multiagency applications. Dimmick spent her early career with the federal wildland fire management agencies and traveled extensively throughout the United States assisting with response to catastrophic wildfires.

CHAPTER 1

Administration

1-1 Scope

1-1.1*

This standard contains the minimum requirements for an incident management system to be used by fire departments to manage all emergency incidents.

A-1-1.1 This document establishes minimum requirements for the development and implementation of an incident management system. The system is intended to apply to operations conducted at the scene of emergency incidents by a fire department. While this document is written largely in terms that relate to a single-agency system, it is intended to integrate with emergency management systems that apply to multiple agencies and large-scale situations.

1-1.2*

These requirements shall be applicable to organizations providing rescue, fire suppression, emergency medical care, special operations, and other emergency services including public, military, and private fire departments and fire brigades.

Paragraph 1-1.2 lists the many types of organizations involved in an incident management system. For effective use of an incident management system, it should be acknowledged that emergency incidents are rarely truly single-discipline events. The fire agency's incident management system must be known to participants and integrated with similar systems of other public safety entities (such as law enforcement), private emergency medical service providers, and public works agencies. In fact, it is in the best interest of the fire agency to promote the use of a standard system on an interagency and interdisciplinary basis.

A-1-1.2 An incident management system also should be used by other types of organizations engaging in activities that involve similar risks to personnel. The basic principles contained within this standard should have broad application in the delivery of emergency services and activities conducted in a high risk environment.

1-1.3*

This standard shall not apply to fire brigades organized only to fight incipient stage fires as defined in OSHA, 29 *CFR*, Part 1910.155(c)(26).

A-1-1.3 The intent of this requirement is to ensure that industrial fire brigades that perform fire fighting beyond the incipient stage comply with the requirements of this standard. Based upon the organizational statement of the industrial fire brigade, the types or potential types of fires (i.e., fires that develop beyond the incipient stage) encountered, and other job tasks performed by personnel, dictate the required compliance with NFPA 1561. These requirements should be addressed through training, standard operating guidelines, and company or corporate policy.

1-2 Purpose

1-2.1

The purpose of this standard is to define and describe the essential elements of an incident management system.

1-2.2*

The purpose of an incident management system is to provide structure and coordination to the management of emergency incident operations in order to provide for the safety and health of fire department personnel and other persons involved in those activities. This standard is intended to meet the requirements of NFPA 1500, *Standard on Fire Department Occupational Safety and Health Program*, Chapter 6, and OSHA, 29 *CFR*, Part 1910.120(q)(3).

A-1-2.2 This standard establishes minimum performance requirements for an incident management system based on concerns for the safety and health of fire department personnel. The benefits of an incident management system extend far beyond this single concern, but personnel health and safety is considered to be the most important reason to implement an incident management system. This standard also may be permitted to be used for guidance in meeting the requirements for an incident command system as outlined in other NFPA documents, including NFPA 471, *Recommended Practice for Responding to Hazardous Materials Incidents*, and NFPA 472, *Standard for Professional Competence of Responders to Hazardous Materials Incidents.*

Paragraph 1-2.2 establishes the purpose of an incident management system. The term *management* implies a host of related issues and activities, including personnel safety and health. Providing for the safety and health of responding personnel is rightfully the primary purpose of an incident management system. The effective use of an incident management system also supports the effective and efficient use of resources. This efficiency and effectiveness reduces incident cost, exposure of personnel and equipment to hazards, and impact on the availability of critical resources to respond to other emergencies. It is easy to underestimate both the critical nature of management requirements and the demands they make on the attention of the incident commander. The use of a carefully designed and comprehensive incident management system helps assure that all the duties of the incident commander are effectively carried out while other personnel focus on tactical operations and safety. *(See also 2-1.1.)*

1-2.2.1* The incident management system shall integrate risk management into the regular functions of incident command.

A-1-2.2.1 The incident commander has the ultimate responsibility for the safety of all fire department personnel operating at an incident and for any and all other persons whose safety is affected by fire department operations. Risk management provides a basis for the following:

(a) Standard evaluation of the situation;
(b) Strategic decision-making;
(c) Tactical planning;
(d) Plan evaluation and revision;
(e) Operational command and control.

The primary focus of risk management, as described in paragraph A-1-2.2.1, is to reduce the risk to the safety and health of responders. However, risk management considerations should also help the incident commander reduce the potential liability incurred as a result of actions taken on an emergency scene.

1-2.3*

Many of the performance objectives of this standard can be achieved in a variety of ways. This standard is not intended to restrict any jurisdiction from exceeding these minimum requirements or from adopting a system tailored to meet local needs while satisfying the minimum requirements of this standard.

A-1-2.3 Many of the requirements of this standard could be satisfied by adopting a "model" system (such as the Incident Command System) that is intended to provide for a uniform approach to incident management while providing for some variations to meet local requirements.

Agencies must carefully weigh the advantages of creating an in-house system that is crafted to meet the department's individual skills, resources, and risks against the equal advantages of adopting a "model" system that is understood by and easily incorporates the resources of other disciplines, mutual aid agencies, and levels of government. The best of all possible worlds is an incident management system that is acceptable to all public safety agencies and at the same time permits agency and incident-specific tailoring.

1-2.3.1* The incident management system described in this standard is to be used by trained individuals and applied in a manner that meets the needs of each particular situation. The many different and complex situations encountered by emergency responders require a considerable amount of judgment in the application of the incident management system. The incident commander shall apply the system in a manner that is appropriate for the circumstances of each specific situation.

A-1-2.3.1 An incident management system is intended to provide a standard approach to the management of emergency incidents. The primary objective is always to manage the incident, not to fully implement and utilize the incident management system. The command officer should be able to apply the incident management system in a manner that supports effective and efficient management of the incident. The use of the system should not create an additional challenge for the incident commander.

Paragraphs 1-2.3.1 and A-1-2.3.1 recognize that no two emergency incidents are the same. As a result, it is impossible to develop an SOP or a specific incident management staffing pattern that works effectively under all conditions. Effective incident management systems (and incident commanders) promote "structured improvisation." The incident management structure and departmental SOPs provide the framework or the "rules of the game"; responders can (and often must) improvise tactically, while taking care not to abandon the framework. Strict adherence to structure and protocol that is too specific will result in a system that cannot adapt quickly to rapidly changing conditions. For additional information, see the sample Incident Action Planning Process presented as Supplement 10 in Part Six of this handbook.

1-3 Definitions

Command Staff. Positions that are established to assume responsibility for key activities in the incident management system that are not a part of the line organization.

Clear Text. The use of plain English in radio communications transmissions. Ten codes or agency-specific codes shall not be used when using clear text.

Emergency Incident. Any situation to which the fire department responds to deliver emergency services, including rescue, fire suppression, emergency medical care, special operations, and other forms of hazard control and mitigation.

Fire Brigade. A group of people organized to engage in rescue, fire suppression, and related activities.

Fire Department. An organization providing rescue, fire suppression, emergency medical care, special operations, and related activities. The term "fire department" shall include any public, governmental, private, industrial, or military organization engaging in this type of activity.

Imminent Hazard. An act or condition that is judged to present a danger to persons or property that is so urgent and severe that it requires immediate corrective or preventive action.

Incident Commander. The fire department individual in overall command of an emergency incident.

Incident Scene. The location where activities related to a specific incident are conducted. This shall include the entire area subject to incident related hazards and all areas used by fire department personnel and equipment in proximity to the incident scene.

Incident Termination. The conclusion of fire department operations at the scene of an incident, usually the departure of the last unit from the scene.

Incipient Stage Fire. A fire that is in the initial or beginning stage and that can be controlled or extinguished by portable fire extinguishers, Class II standpipe, or small hose systems without the need for protective clothing or breathing apparatus.

Intermediate Level of Supervision. A level of supervision within the incident management system that groups fire companies and other resources working toward common objectives or in a particular area under a supervisor responsible for the objective(s) or area.

Liaison. The coordination of activities between the fire department and other agencies.

Member. A person involved in performing the duties and responsibilities of a fire department, under the auspices of the organization. Fire department personnel can be full-time or part-time employees, paid or unpaid volunteers, can occupy any position or rank within the fire department, and might or might not engage in emergency operations.

Personnel. Fire department personnel or any individual participating within the incident scene.

Resources. Personnel and equipment that are utilized or available to be utilized at the scene of an incident.

Risk. A measure of the probability and severity of adverse effects. These adverse effects result from an exposure to a hazard.

Shall. Indicates a mandatory requirement.

Should. Indicates a recommendation or that which is advised but not required.

Special Operations. Those emergency incidents to which the fire department responds that require specific and advanced training and specialized tools and equipment. Special operations include water rescue, hazardous materials, confined space entry, high-angle rescue, and other operations requiring specialized training.

Staging. A specific function where resources are assembled in an area at or near the incident scene to await instructions or assignments.

Standard Operating Guideline. An organizational directive that establishes a course of action or policy.

Supervisor. Fire department personnel who have supervisory authority and responsibility over other personnel.

Unified Command. A standard method to coordinate command of an incident where multiple agencies have jurisdiction.

CHAPTER 2

System Structure

2-1 Implementation

2-1.1*

The fire department shall adopt an incident management system to manage all emergency incidents. The system shall be designed to meet the particular characteristics of the fire department based on size, complexity, and operating environment.

A-2-1.1 The fire department should evaluate existing recognized systems to develop or adopt a system that meets its own particular requirements and provides compatibility with systems used by other agencies that would reasonably be expected to work together at emergency incidents.

Paragraph 2-1.1 calls for a system to manage *all* emergency incidents. Because the vast majority of emergency incidents are routine, most agencies adopt a system tailored to their size, resources, and environment. Nonetheless, the system must allow for modular expansion when the large or unusual event does occur. It is unlikely that any department will be able to preplan for the range of possible incidents. (Consider the bombing of the Murrah Federal Building in Oklahoma City.) However, an incident management system that can readily expand to assist the incident commander faced with a catastrophe puts the agency in a position to succeed.

2-1.2

The incident management system shall be defined and documented in writing. Standard operating guidelines shall include the requirements for implementation of the incident management system and shall describe the options that are available for application according to the needs of each particular situation.

Implementation of the incident management system for the routine incident is relatively simple and generally documented by internal SOP. Intermediate-to-large incidents, especially those that escalate rapidly, are more difficult to commit to hard-and-fast rules of implementation. The larger an incident, the more likely it is to be at least interdisciplinary, if not interagency or interjurisdictional. For example, implementation guidelines must consider transfers of command to ranking officers in the fire department, to officers from other fire agencies, or to personnel from other disciplines, levels of government, or jurisdictions. Careful consideration and documentation of when transfers are appropriate and how to manage them will protect long-term interagency relationships.

2-1.3*

The fire department shall prepare and adopt written plans, based on the incident management system, to address the requirements of the different types of incidents that can be anticipated. These plans shall address both routine and unusual incidents and shall provide standardized guidelines and supervisory assignments that can be applied to the needs of situations of different types, sizes, and complexities.

A-2-1.3 Fire departments respond to a wide variety of incidents. Most of these incidents are considered "routine" and involve a small commitment of resources, while a few incidents involve large commitments of resources, complex situations, and potential high-risk operations. It is important for an incident management system to accommodate all types and sizes of incidents and to provide for a regular process of escalation from the arrival of the first responding units to the largest and most complex incidents. The system always should be applied, even to routine incidents, in order to provide for familiarity with the system, to be prepared for escalation, and to be cognizant of the risks that exist at all incidents.

Paragraph 2-1.3 links an incident management system and preplanning. A standardized incident management system can easily be incorporated into the preplanning process. Identifying the general tactical activities required to respond to an incident at a specific site (evacuation, primary search, ventilation, etc.) is usually simple. These activities provide the basic outline of the organization needed to manage the event. Details of tactics may be best left to the time of response, but knowing ahead of time how the organization would coordinate makes for smoother implementation of the ICS. Using the standard ICS incident action planning forms *(Figures 1561-2.1 through 1561-2.5)* to document incident preplans can be a useful way to ensure a thorough preplan and to facilitate an actual response. These forms are included in Supplement 13 in Part Six of this handbook in full-size versions suitable for reproduction.

INCIDENT OBJECTIVES (ICS 202)

1. INCIDENT NAME	2. DATE PREPARED	3. TIME PREPARED

4. OPERATIONAL PERIOD (DATE/TIME)

5. GENERAL CONTROL OBJECTIVES FOR THE INCIDENT (INCLUDE ALTERNATIVES)

6. WEATHER FORECAST FOR OPERATIONAL PERIOD

7. GENERAL/SAFETY MESSAGE

8. ATTACHMENTS (✓ IF ATTACHED)

- ☐ ORGANIZATION LIST (ICS 203)
- ☐ DIVISION ASSIGNEMENT LISTS (ICS 204)
- ☐ COMMUNICATIONS PLAN (ICS 205)
- ☐ MEDICAL PLAN (ICS 206)
- ☐ INCIDENT MAP
- ☐ TRAFFIC PLAN
- ☐ ____________
- ☐ ____________
- ☐ ____________

ICS 202	9. PREPARED BY (PLANNING SECTION CHIEF)	10. APPROVED BY (INCIDENT COMMANDER)

Figure 1561-2.1 *ICS 202 outlines the general objectives for an operational period, usually 0700 to 1900 or 1900 to 0700. The times should be standard, and all agencies should have a copy of this form. (See Form S13-2 in Supplement 13 in Part Six of this handbook for a full-size version of this form that is suitable for reproduction.) (Adapted from Incident Command System, Fire Protection Publications, Oklahoma State University, Stillwater, OK, 1983)*

2-1.4*

The incident management system shall be utilized at all emergency incidents. The incident management system also shall be applied to drills, exercises, and other situations that involve hazards similar to those encountered at actual emergency incidents and to simulated incidents that are conducted for training and familiarization purposes.

A-2-1.4 The fire department should use the same basic approach for all situations, including drills, to ensure that personnel are fully familiar and confident with the incident management system. Drills and simulated incidents often involve risks that are similar in nature to those of actual incidents.

It is virtually impossible to understate the necessity of paragraph 2-1.4. An incident management system that is not used daily on emergencies and for training will

ORGANIZATION ASSIGNMENT LIST (ICS 203)

1. INCIDENT NAME	2. DATE PREPARED	3. TIME PREPARED

4. OPERATIONAL PERIOD (DATE/TIME)

POSITION	NAME
5. INCIDENT COMMANDER AND STAFF	
INCIDENT COMMANDER	
DEPUTY	
SAFETY OFFICER	
INFORMATION OFFICER	
LIAISON OFFICER	
6. AGENCY REPRESENTATION	
AGENCY	NAME
7. PLANNING SECTION	
CHIEF	
DEPUTY	
RESOURCES UNIT	
SITUATION UNIT	
DOCUMENTATION UNIT	
DEMOBILIZATION UNIT	
TECHNICAL SPECIALISTS	
8. LOGISTICS SECTION	
CHIEF	
DEPUTY	
a. SUPPORT BRANCH	
DIRECTOR	
SUPPLY UNIT	
FACILITIES UNIT	
GROUND SUPPORT UNIT	
b. SERVICE BRANCH	
DIRECTOR	
COMMUNICATIONS UNIT	
MEDICAL UNIT	
FOOD UNIT	
9. OPERATIONS CHIEF	
CHIEF	
DEPUTY	
a. BRANCH I – DIVISIONS/GROUPS	
BRANCH DIRECTOR	
DEPUTY	
DIVISION/GROUP	
DIVISION/GROUP	
DIVISION/GROUP	
DIVISION/GROUP	
DIVISION/GROUP	
b. BRANCH II – DIVISIONS/GROUPS	
BRANCH DIRECTOR	
DEPUTY	
DIVISION/GROUP	
DIVISION/GROUP	
DIVISION/GROUP	
DIVISION/GROUP	
DIVISION/GROUP	
c. BRANCH III – DIVISIONS/GROUPS	
BRANCH DIRECTOR	
DEPUTY	
DIVISION/GROUP	
DIVISION/GROUP	
DIVISION/GROUP	
DIVISION/GROUP	
DIVISION/GROUP	
d. AIR OPERATIONS BRANCH	
AIR OPERATIONS BR. DIR.	
AIR ATTACK SUPERVISOR	
AIR SUPPORT SUPERVISOR	
HELICOPTER COORDINATOR	
AIR TANKER COORDIANTOR	
10. FINANCE SECTION	
CHIEF	
DEPUTY	
TIME UNIT	
PROCURMENT UNIT	
COMPENSATION/CLAIMS UNIT	
COST UNIT	

ICS 203	PREPARED BY (RESOURCES UNIT)

Figure 1561-2.2 *ICS 203 identifies who is filling which position within the incident command system. (See Form S13-3 in Supplement 13 in Part Six of this handbook for a full-size version of this form that is suitable for reproduction.) (Adapted from Incident Command System, Fire Protection Publications, Oklahoma State University, Stillwater, OK, 1983)*

1. BRANCH	2. DIVISION/GROUP	DIVISION ASSIGNMENT LIST (ICS 204)
3. INCIDENT NAME		4. OPERATIONAL PERIOD DATE ______ TIME ______

5. OPERATIONS PERSONNEL

OPERATIONS CHIEF ______ DIVISION/GROUP SUPERVISOR ______

BRANCH DIRECTOR ______ AIR ATTACK SUPERVISOR ______

6. RESOURCES ASSIGNED THIS PERIOD

STRIKE TEAM/TASK FORCE/ RESOURCE DESIGNATOR	LEADER	NUMBER PERSONS	TRANS. NEEDED	DROP OFF PT./TIME	PICK UP PT./TIME

7. CONTROL OPERATIONS

8. SPECIAL INSTRUCTIONS

9. DIVISION/GROUP COMMUNICATION SUMMARY

FUNCTION		FREQ.	SYSTEM	CHAN.	FUNCTION		FREQ.	SYSTEM	CHAN.
COMMAND	LOCAL REPEAT				SUPPORT	LOCAL REPEAT			
DIV./GROUP TACTICAL					GROUND TO AIR				

PREPARED BY (RESOURCE UNIT LDR.)	APPROVED BY (PLANNING SECT. CH.)	DATE	TIME

Figure 1561-2.3 ICS 204 is used to list division/group assignments. (See Form S13-4 in Supplement 13 in Part Six of this handbook for a full-size version of this form that is suitable for reproduction.) (Adapted from Incident Command System, Fire Protection Publications, Oklahoma State University, Stillwater, OK, 1983)

remain a "paper plan." Struggling to use an unfamiliar system with its accompanying terminology and lines of responsibility and authority adds stress to the incident commander, adds to scene confusion, and compromises scene and personnel safety and tactical efficiency. Constant practice is required for the system to be implemented when needed. Therefore, a system designed to be used only during "the big one" is doomed to failure.

2-2 Communications

2-2.1*

The incident management system shall include standard operating guidelines for radio communications that provide for the use of standard protocols and terminology at all types of incidents. Plain English *(see definition of clear text)* for radio communications shall be used to reduce the confusion that can be created when radio codes are used.

COMMUNICATIONS PLAN (ICS 205)	1. INCIDENT NAME	2. DATE/TIME PREPARED	3. OPERATIONAL PERIOD TO

4. COMMUNICATIONS RESOURCE ALLOCATION

SYSTEM/CACHE	TALK GROUP/ FREQUENCY	FUNCTION	KNOW POSITION CHANNEL/PHONE #	ASSIGNMENT	REMARKS

PREPARED BY (COMMUNICATIONS UNIT LEADER)

Figure 1561-2.4 ICS 205, Communications Plan, identifies who is operating on what frequency or radio channel. (See Form S13-5 in Supplement 13 in Part Six of this handbook for a full-size version of this form that is suitable for reproduction.) (Adapted from Incident Command System, Fire Protection Publications, Oklahoma State University, Stillwater, OK, 1983)

A-2-2.1 The intent of the use of plain English (clear text) for radio communications is to reduce confusion at incidents, particularly where different agencies work together.

While a traditional part of emergency communications for most emergency response agencies, the use of radio codes often leads to confusion and miscommunication, especially on mutual aid and interdisciplinary incidents.

2-2.2

Standard operating guidelines for communications shall be established to support the escalation of operations from small to large or from routine to unusual without necessitating major changes or transitions. The communications system shall meet the requirements of the fire department for routine and large-scale emergencies. In a small fire department, one radio channel for dispatch and one fire ground communications channel might be sufficient for most situations. The radio capabilities shall also provide for communications with mutual aid resources or other agencies that could be expected to respond to a major incident. A larger fire department shall require several additional radio channels to provide for the volume of communications relating to

MEDICAL PLAN (ICS 206)	1. INCIDENT NAME	2. DATE PREPARED	3. TIME PREPARED	4. OPERATIONAL PERIOD

5. INCIDENT MEDICAL AID STATIONS

MEDICAL AID STATIONS	LOCATION	PARAMEDICS	
		YES	NO

6. TRANSPORTATION

A. AMBULANCE SERVICES

NAME	ADDRESS	PHONE	PARAMEDICS	
			YES	NO

B. INCIDENT SERVICES

NAME	LOCATION	PARAMEDICS	
		YES	NO

7. HOSPITALS

NAME	ADDRESS	TRAVEL TIME		PHONE	HELIPAD		BURN CENTER	
		YES	NO		YES	NO	YES	NO

8. MEDICAL EMERGENCY PROCEDURES

ICS 206	9. PREPARED BY (MEDICAL UNIT LEADER)	10. REVIEWED BY (SAFETY OFFICER)

Figure 1561-2.5 *ICS 206, Medical Plan, is used by the medical unit leader. It is especially useful on large-scale or multiple-casualty incidents. (See Form S13-6 in Supplement 13 in Part Six of this handbook for a full-size version of this form that is suitable for reproduction.) (Adapted from Incident Command System, Fire Protection Publications, Oklahoma State University, Stillwater, OK, 1983.)*

routine incidents and for the complexity of multiple alarm situations. The system shall be developed to provide reserve capacity for unusually complex situations where effective communications could become critical.

Paragraph 2-2.2 highlights the role of communications planning in the incident management system. A systematic approach to communication planning, both before and during an emergency incident, is necessary for adequate communication capability. While radio communication is the backbone of emergency communication, other modes of communication, such as cellular phone, should be considered, particularly in areas with limited radio frequencies. Within ICS, the communications unit leader prepares the incident communications plan. Depending on the complexity of the incident, all of the following steps may be required:

- Attend planning meeting.
- Obtain division/group assignment lists (ICS 204, as shown in Figure 1561-2.3 and in a full-size version in Supplement 13 as Form S13-4) or determine organizational structure.
- Determine radio, phone, and cellular phone requirements.
- Establish required radio nets. ("Net" includes both 800 MHz talk groups and non-800 radio frequencies.)
- Establish required land and cellular phone links.
- Establish required amateur radio network.
- Prepare incident communications plan (ICS 205, as shown in Figure 1561-2.4 and in a full-size version in Supplement 13 as Form S13-5).
- Prepare communications portion of division/group assignment lists (ICS 204, as shown in Figure 1561-2.3 and in a full-size version in Supplement 13 as Form S13-4).
- Monitor and maintain the system.

Additional discussion on the communication planning part of the incident management system is found in Supplement 11 in Part Six of this handbook.

2-2.3*

Standard terminology shall be established to transmit information, including strategic modes of operation, situation reports, and emergency notifications of imminent hazards.

A-2-2.3 A change in strategic mode of operation would include, as an example for structural fire fighting, the switch from offensive strategy (interior fire attack with hand lines) to defensive strategy (exterior operation with master streams and hand lines). In such an instance, it is essential to notify all affected personnel of the change in strategic modes, ensure that all personnel withdraw from the structure, and account for everyone who was operating offensively before initiating any exterior stream application with either hand lines or master streams.

Paragraph 2-2.3 calls for standard terminology in specific instances. "Clear text" should also be applied in these situations. What seems perfectly clear to one department or discipline may mean something substantially different to another. A classic (and tragic) illustration is the final words from the nonnative English speakers of an airline cockpit crew seconds before impact, "What does 'pull-up' mean?" A second example occurred after the Air Florida crash into the Potomac River, when the incident commander requested additional "rescues"—he received ambulances instead of the expected apparatus carrying rescue tools, cutting torches, and so forth.

2-2.4*

The communications system shall provide a standard method to give priority to the transmission of emergency messages and notification of imminent hazards to all levels of the incident command structure over that of routine communications.

A-2-2.4 The emergency notification system should provide a means to rapidly warn all persons who might be in danger if an imminent hazard is identified or if a change in strategy is made. An emergency message format with distinctive alert tones and definitive instructions should be used to make such notifications.

2-2.5

The incident management system shall provide standard operating guidelines for communication operators and dispatchers to provide support to emergency incident operations. Operators and dispatchers shall be trained to function effectively within the incident management system.

The need for paragraph 2-2.5 is based on an unfortunate fact: *The relationship between the incident management organization and the dispatch center is poorly defined in emergency response.* During day-to-day operations, dispatchers commonly provide incident commanders with a variety of logistical services ranging from resource procurement to frequency management. To perform their duties efficiently, dispatchers need a general familiarity with the incident management system used by the organizations they support. In the case of the ICS, dispatchers' duties are also listed under position descriptions in the incident management organization. Incident commanders who are accustomed to "ordering up" (i.e., requesting additional resources) from dispatch may have difficulty establishing an effective ordering process when the logistics function is staffed and the supply unit takes over the ordering process. In addition, depending on its size and capabilities, the dispatch organization may be able to provide either large-incident logistical support or 911 service; many dispatch organizations will be unable to provide both. Careful preplanning is required to ensure effective support for the incident, continued 911 service, and a functional relationship with dispatch.

2-3 Interagency Coordination

2-3.1*

The fire department shall develop an integrated incident management system in coordination with other agencies that are involved in emergency incidents.

A-2-3.1 The incident management system should be a component of interagency and multijurisdictional planning for emergency operations. A fire department is seldom the only agency involved in activities at the scene of emergency incidents, particularly large-scale incidents. While this standard is based upon the requirements for an incident management system for a fire department, any system should, as a minimum, provide for coordination with police departments and other emergency service agencies within the same jurisdiction, as well as mutual aid fire departments. Any other agencies that have an established role at emergency incidents also should be included.

The fire department incident management system also should integrate with plans for major emergencies that could involve activities at different sites. In these circumstances, the incident management system defined in this document should apply specifically to activities conducted at a particular site and should integrate with larger-scale plans for the coordination of activities at multiple sites.

As paragraph 2-3.1 makes clear, few incidents are truly solely fire department events. Even relatively simple incidents may require assistance from law enforcement agencies for traffic and crowd control or from public works agencies for water supply and other tactical and logistical activities. Large incidents may include not only partner agencies from the same jurisdiction, but also mutual aid providers and other levels of government. Homegrown incident management systems that focus only on fire department activities often make it difficult to coordinate the activities of all participants at emergency incidents. At best, failure to coordinate will result in inefficient response; more seriously, a lack of coordination may compromise the health and safety of all responders.

2-3.2*

The incident management system shall provide a plan to coordinate operations with other agencies that have jurisdiction at the incident scene. This plan shall include a standard guideline to designate one incident commander or to establish unified command.

A-2-3.2 At large-scale and complex incidents, several agencies could become involved and could have legal jurisdiction over different aspects of the situation or different areas that are involved in the incident.

Paragraph 2-3.2 requires the fire department to build into its incident management system a system for interaction and coordination with other agencies. This is best accomplished by developing an integrated system in cooperation with all of the agencies that would be expected to work together at routine or large-scale incidents.

It is possible that other agencies might be unwilling to develop fully integrated incident management systems with the fire department. In these circumstances, the fire department should utilize its own capabilities to develop and implement an incident management system that meets the intent of this standard.

If plans are not established in advance, the authority for overall command of the incident could be in question. Most emergency incidents occur clearly within the jurisdictional area of one fire department. The agency having jurisdiction is normally responsible for designating the incident commander, although pre-established plans could provide for an individual from a different agency to assume command under some circumstances. The basic concept should be to designate one fire department incident commander, even where several fire departments are involved in the incident.

Where multiple jurisdictions are involved, the plan should incorporate a process to assign, divide, or share overall command responsibilities in a standard manner. It is essential to establish the roles, responsibilities, and relationships among the different agencies that could be involved in advance of a major incident.

One approach that is used for multijurisdictional incidents is "unified command." In this system, each agency having jurisdiction can have its own designated incident commander, with all of the incident commanders working together to develop one unified plan of action. This approach should be used only within a well-established interagency standard operating guideline.

Another approach that is employed in some cases, where different agencies have specific jurisdiction over different aspects of an incident, is a "lead agency" concept. Under a lead agency structure, one agency assumes overall command of the incident, while other agencies fulfill their jurisdictional responsibilities under the coordination of the lead agency's incident commander. The lead agency role can be transferred at different stages of an incident, as objectives are accomplished and priorities change. Each agency can operate using its own incident management structure under the overall coordination.

Integrated incident management systems always work best when there is either a single incident commander or a unified command directing a single incident management organization. The practice of separate incident commanders directing separate organizations from separate command posts is a recipe for disjointed incident management. The guideline establishing command at interagency incidents should be clear, but provide enough flexibility for incident managers to accommodate the inevitable range of authority, expertise, and jurisdictional issues that accompany interagency incidents. Establishing unified command is generally easier where geography is the deciding factor, but the disciplines are the same. (For example, fire agencies responding to an incident on the border between jurisdictions will share the same objectives; establishing command becomes a simple process of identifying the highest-ranking and best-qualified officer at the scene.) It is often more difficult to establish unified command with other disciplines or other levels of government, especially if the incident is unusual or the agencies lack day-to-day working relationships. Ideally, issues of command are identified before an incident through preplanning, training, and exercise; in reality, agency representatives often meet for the first time at the incident. This reality is further complicated by incompatible incident management systems.

The following questions may prove useful in determining the makeup of a unified command organization:

1. Does the other agency or jurisdiction have legal authority over part of the geographic area affected by the incident, or over a specific activity or tactic required to manage the incident?
2. Does the other agency or jurisdiction control a large number of resources that will be responding to the incident? (While this in itself is not a textbook reason for establishing unified command, the incident may run more smoothly if representatives from such agencies or jurisdictions are included in the command structure.)
3. Is the incident likely to expand to include other jurisdictions or agencies?

If the answer to any of the preceding questions is yes, unified command may be appropriate. In situations that are less clear, an option to unified command is to assign a single command from a lead agency with deputies from the other disciplines, agencies, or jurisdictions. This approach has the advantages of single command, while still addressing some of the issues identified above.

Unified command does *not* imply "management by committee." While consensus is certainly desirable, it is more important that the objectives and related tactics of each incident commander are included in the incident action plan. The commonly used "Life safety, Incident stabilization, Property conservation" hierarchy can be used to set priorities of a unified command organization. *(See commentary for paragraph 4-1.2.)* Each agency or jurisdiction identifies its objectives under each category, tactics are developed, and resources are assigned. The result is an integrated plan that reflects the authority and objectives of each command participant.

2-3.3*

Where the incident is under the command authority of the fire department, the incident commander shall provide for liaison and coordination with all other cooperating agencies.

A-2-3.3 Designated representatives should be assigned by other agencies involved in emergency incidents to ensure that all functions performed by their agencies support and are coordinated with fire department activities. There should be an established system for representatives of cooperating agencies to report to the command post. Where necessary, the incident commander should assign a designated liaison officer to manage interaction with representatives of other agencies. Where fire departments routinely work together under mutual aid or automatic aid systems, standard operating guidelines and communications capabilities should provide for activities to be managed routinely by one incident commander under a management system that does not necessarily require representatives of each fire department to be present at the command post.

How to meet paragraph 2-3.3 is the subject of considerable discussion among incident commanders. Incident commanders are often tempted to provide tactical liaison and coordination with cooperating and assisting agencies through the liaison officer. This temptation is especially strong for incidents requiring assistance from other disciplines, such as law enforcement on a hazardous materials incident or structural fire support on a wildland fire.

The "Liaison Officer" position is staff to the incident commander and has no line authority. Consequently, the position is ideally situated for top-level coordination with the managers of cooperating and assisting jurisdictions or agencies. For example, evacuations and traffic control on a hazardous materials incident are tactical activities commonly conducted by law enforcement personnel. Because law enforcement personnel are outside the purview of the fire service incident commander, he or she may be tempted to work with representatives of the law enforcement agencies through the liaison process. However, fire tactics on such incidents must often be carefully sequenced with evacuations and traffic control. Without involving law enforcement representatives in tactical planning, and operations supervision during implementation, sequencing may prove difficult or impossible.

Incident commanders' reluctance to incorporate cooperating and assisting agencies in the operations function and the planning process is often an issue of comfort level. Few fire department incident commanders or operations section chiefs have a multidisciplinary background, and even fewer will feel comfortable directing other disciplines. When comfort is an issue, the incident commander may assign deputy incident commanders and operations section chiefs from the other agencies or disciplines.

2-3.4*

Where the incident is under the overall jurisdiction of an agency other than the fire department, the fire department shall utilize the incident management system to manage its own operations and coordinate its activities with the agency having overall jurisdiction.

A-2-3.4 At incidents where extensive interaction is required, the agency having overall jurisdiction should request a designated fire department representative to be assigned to the command post to provide liaison and coordinate activities. This should be part of an established interagency standard operating guideline for incident management.

Paragraph 2-3.4 addresses the reverse of the issue identified in paragraph 2-3.3. When the fire department is the cooperating or assisting agency, incident managers should incorporate their tactical activities into the operations section and the formal planning process. At the very least, fire department incident managers should insist on observing planning sessions and obtaining copies of incident action plans. Failure to be very well versed in the tactical plans of the incident will at best jeopardize the fire department's ability to fulfill its mission on the incident, and may put members or other resources in harm's way.

2-4 Command Structure

2-4.1*

The incident management system shall provide a series of supervisory levels that are available for implementation to create a command structure. *(See Form S13-7, ICS 207, Incident Organization Chart, in Appendix 13.)* The particular levels to be utilized in each situation shall depend on the nature of the incident and the scale and complexity of fire department activities at the scene.

A-2-4.1 For further information on incident management systems, see Appendix B.

When implementing the additional levels of supervision required by 2-4.1, it is important to observe two organizational guidelines. First, a span of control that is appropriate to the incident's complexity and hazards must be observed. Second, the organizational structure must preserve the unity of command. In other words, each individual on the incident must report directly to only one supervisor. *(See Figure 1561-2.6.)*

2-4.2

The incident management system shall be modular to allow the application of only those elements that are necessary at a particular incident and to allow elements to be activated or deactivated as the needs of the incident change with time. The system shall provide for a routine process of escalation as additional resources are utilized.

The predefined modular nature of the incident command system, as required by paragraph 2-4.2, allows the organization to expand and contract its functions to meet the changing management requirements of the incident. Managers within the system should monitor the progress toward accomplishment of the incident commander's objectives and the accompanying support requirements and adjust the organizational structure up or down accordingly. The elements to be implemented depend on a combination of incident characteristics and the comfort level and preferences of the incident commander.

2-4.3

The incident commander shall determine which levels and elements of the incident management system are to be implemented in each case and shall develop the command structure for each incident by assigning supervisory responsibilities according to standard operating guidelines.

As paragraph 2-4.3 makes clear, standard operating guidelines should clearly define supervisory responsibilities. Does each section chief have the authority and responsibility for activating the organizational elements that fall under his or her management, or does each additional activation require command approval? Can branch directors or division or group supervisors alter assigned tactics without the approval of the supervisor above? Where possible, these questions should be answered in SOPs or be the subject of drills and exercises.

2-4.4*

The command structure for each incident shall maintain an effective supervisory span of control at each level of the organization. An effective span of control shall be determined by the ability of each supervisor to monitor the activ-

Figure 1561-2.6 *It is imperative that the first arriving unit establish command and that a process is in place to ensure proper transfer of command. (Photo courtesy of Phoenix Fire Department)*

ities of assigned subordinates and to communicate effectively with them.

A-2-4.4 The most important factor in establishing supervisory levels within the command structure is the need to maintain an effective span of control. Where the number of individuals reporting to the incident commander exceeds a span of control that can be effectively managed, the incident commander should consider activating an additional level. In many cases, this condition can be anticipated and the incident commander can activate these levels early in the incident to begin building the command structure.

A span of control of between 3 and 7 is considered desirable in most cases.

An effective span of control should be maintained at each level of the command structure, and the organization should be expanded to meet this objective wherever the need is identified. This can be accomplished by adding levels or reassigning responsibilities within existing levels, or a combination of both.

The incident commander also should consider activating additional levels within the command structure where activities become highly complex or are conducted over a large geographic area. In these cases, the benefit could be increased overall coordination and more direct supervision over complex activities.

The two basic levels of the incident management system are the incident commander and the company or unit level. The grouping of companies or units, according to task or location, creates an intermediate level of supervision. The incident commander has the option of assigning additional intermediate levels within the command structure for more complex incidents.

The incident commander should begin to assign intermediate level supervisors as soon as it becomes evident that the number of companies or units that will be used at an incident exceeds the number that can be effectively directed by the incident commander (3 to 7 companies). It is preferable to establish intermediate levels of the command structure as early as possible rather than to establish them after companies have gone into action. The early designation of intermediate level supervisors allows them to plan the utilization of resources that will be assigned, as opposed to regrouping resources that have already initiated action.

In many cases, the officer of the first company assigned to a particular area or function is designated as an intermediate level supervisor. The company officer can be relieved of this additional responsibility when a higher level officer is assigned by the incident commander.

Additional levels of the command structure should be available to the incident commander as an option for activation in complex and large-scale incidents. Plans for large-scale incidents should provide standard organization charts for command structures.

The ability of each supervisor to monitor the activities and to communicate effectively with assigned subordinates is a function of geography, task complexity, and degree of hazard, as well as sheer numbers. The recommended span of control for emergency operations is generally one supervisor to three to seven subordinates. A good practice, when assessing whether or not organizational span of control is appropriate, is to look at the most hazardous tactical activity first. This activity is likely both to be most complex and to put personnel at greatest risk. It is important that the span of control for hazardous tactical activities be carefully limited. On the other hand, an assignment where the tactical activity is not complex may be handled with a span of control exceeding the three to seven normally recommended.

2-4.5*

The incident management system shall define standardized supervisory assignments. These assignments shall be activated upon assignment by the incident commander.

A-2-4.5 The intent of defining standardized assignments is to provide for efficient communications when assignments are made. Instead of explaining each assignment in detail, the incident commander makes assignments that are predefined and described in the standard operating guidelines. The incident commander determines which standardized assignments to utilize, depending on the situation. When an assignment is made, both the incident commander and assigned personnel know what is expected, based on their knowledge of the written standard operating guideline.

Standard operating guidelines can define certain assignments that would be assumed automatically by designated individuals, such as the fire department safety officer, upon arrival at the scene. The preassigned individuals should make the incident commander aware of their presence upon arrival and assume their predesignated functions unless otherwise instructed by the incident commander. This could involve relieving an individual who had been assigned to the function pending the arrival of the designated individual.

2-4.5.1* Standardized supervisory assignments shall define the role, authority, and responsibilities of assigned personnel. Assignments shall be defined by function or by location at the scene of the incident, or by a combination of function and location. The scope of authority to be delegated at each supervisory level shall be outlined in standard operating guidelines.

A-2-4.5.1 In addition to defining the role, authority, and responsibilities, standard operating guidelines should provide guidance or direction on how an assignment will be performed.

Standardized supervisory assignments are required by paragraph 2-4.5.1 and are an integral part of a fire department incident management system. The flexible organizational structure of the ICS easily accommodates functional, geographic, or combination organizational options. The supervisory hierarchy established in this standardized system provides several advantages. For example, predefined supervisory roles allow for training and exercise in advance of real incidents. Predefined position titles and job descriptions summarize a wealth of information about the organizational structure and position relationships and responsibilities. A fire fighter assigned as a ventilation group supervisor, for example, knows the following:

- The role is functional, not geographic in nature. He or she will be expected to perform the role at the most appropriate (potentially more than one) location on the incident.
- The assignment is within the operations function.
- The assignment is limited to performing ventilation.
- He or she reports to either a branch director, the operations section chief, or directly to the incident commander.
- His or her peers in the organization are other group supervisors and division supervisors.
- The position is supervisory. Strike teams, task forces, or single resources will work for the ventilation group.

All of the preceding information is implicit in the title "Ventilation Group Supervisor." Although learning the detailed terminology of the ICS takes time and effort, the role clarity that the terminology provides is worth the effort.

2-4.5.2* An assignment that is defined by function shall be based on performing or supervising a particular function or set of functions.

A-2-4.5.2 Examples of assignments by function include safety officer, public information officer, and water supply officer. These functions generally are performed without geographic limitation and interact with different levels of the command structure. Other functional assignments, such as staging or medical treatment, could refer to both the function and a designated location where it is applied.

Paragraph A-2.4.5.2 provides examples of functional assignments. Even though an assignment is functional, it will most likely take place in someone else's geographic assignment. A "division" is identified as a specific geographical location. For example, in a structural fire in a three-story building, a primary search group would probably operate in all three divisions. The fact that a group may move from one division to another to accomplish its tasks requires close coordination and communication with the division supervisors of the geographic assignments on the incident.

2-4.5.3* An assignment that is defined by location shall be based on supervising all activities that are conducted within a designated area. The area shall be defined by standard terminology or specified by the incident commander at the time of assignment.

A-2-4.5.3 Location assignments generally address the supervision of all activities that are conducted within a specified area. A specified area could include one exterior side of a building, the roof or a particular floor of a building, or a section of an interior. A location assignment could include any subdivision of the area where emergency activities are being conducted. It is important that the limits of the area are defined sufficiently to avoid overlap or omission of areas. Standard terminology should be used to define commonly used subdivisions of the incident scene.

A geographic assignment includes all activities required to manage the incident in that location *except* those assigned to groups. For example, the division 2 supervisor on the structural fire in the three-story building discussed in the commentary on paragraph A-2-4.5.2 would understand that with a primary search group assigned, he or she is responsible for all tactics in division 2 except primary search. The division and group supervisors must communicate clearly to coordinate their activities. For example, the division 2 supervisor needs to know when the search group entered the division and when the search was completed.

2-4.6

The incident commander shall have the authority to modify standard assignments or to apply them in a manner that suits the particular needs of an incident. It shall be the responsibility of the incident commander to identify the parameters of an assignment clearly where deviating from the standard assignments.

2-5 Training and Qualifications

2-5.1*

All personnel who could be involved in emergency operations shall be trained in the incident management system.

A-2-5.1 In addition to being familiar with the basic structure of the incident management system, all personnel should be trained to assume initial command of an incident in the absence of a more qualified individual. This applies to a situation where an individual could be the first arriving at the scene of an incident and, therefore, responsible for initiating command responsibilities at the scene.

2-5.2

Personnel who are expected to perform as incident commanders or to be assigned to supervisory levels within the command structure shall be trained in and familiar with the incident management system and the particular levels at which they are expected to perform. The fire department shall define training and experience requirements for supervisors.

In addition to meeting the requirements of paragraph 2-5.2, incident commanders or section chiefs need a good working understanding of the roles and responsibilities of *all* section chiefs. *(See Figure 1561-2.7.)* While in-depth cross training is not necessary, coordinating activities requires the following basic understandings:

- The operations section chief must understand the planning function and the analytical services it provides, the constraints that may reduce the logistics function's ability to support operations activities, and the role of the finance function in coordinating the use of contracted resources.
- Planning section staff should have enough operations background to be able to perform detailed contingency planning and situation analysis. They should also understand the logistics resource ordering process to estimate the availability of scarce resources and to effectively incorporate communications and medical planning into the planning process. The planning section staff must also understand the role the finance function plays in estimating the overall cost of the incident.
- Logistics staff should have sufficient understanding of the operations function to anticipate resource needs and locate resources, to design an effective communications system, and to provide appropriate medical and rehabilitation support. Logistics staff must understand the planning process and the portions of the incident action plan that are the responsibility of logistics. Finally, they must understand the role of the finance section, especially the procurement unit, in acquiring resources.
- Finance staff must have enough understanding of the other functions to facilitate the flow of information about costs, equipment, and personnel and to negotiate and administer contracts. Finance staff must also understand the time constraints imposed by emergency incidents and be able to facilitate emergency procurement procedures and authorities to order a resource.

Figure 1561-2.7 *Shown are command personnel staff operating inside the command post. The command post provides quiet communications and planning facilities. (Photo courtesy of Phoenix Fire Department)*

Similarly, while it is not necessary for the incident commander to have a detailed understanding of the intricacies of the planning, logistics, and finance functions, the incident commander must understand enough to know when it is appropriate to staff the functions. It is also important to know expected outputs of the functions so the incident commander can tell how well the functions are working.

2-5.3*

The incident commander shall make assignments based on the availability, qualifications, and expertise of individuals.

A-2-5.3 Some functions are performed best by individuals with specific expertise, particularly in highly technical areas. The fire department should endeavor to have more than one qualified individual to perform all essential functions within the incident management system.

2-6 Personnel Accountability

2-6.1

The incident management system shall provide for personnel accountability at the incident scene.

2-6.2*

The fire department shall adopt and routinely use a system to maintain accountability for all personnel assigned to the incident. This system shall provide a rapid accounting of all personnel at the incident scene.

A-2-6.2 One purpose of the system is to provide rapid determination if any personnel are missing in the event that an area should be required to be evacuated, or if a structural collapse or other unplanned event occurs.

The personnel accountability system required by Section 2-6 applies to non-fire department responders. While most fire departments are well aware of the need to track their own resources at the scene of an incident, they are often less likely to track personnel from assisting and supporting agencies or assigned from outside the operations section. Paragraph 2-6.2 requires that a system track *all* personnel assigned to an incident.

2-6.3*

All supervisors shall maintain a constant awareness of the position and function of all personnel assigned to operate under their supervision. This awareness shall serve as the basic means of accountability that shall be required for operational safety.

A-2-6.3 The incident management system should account for the degree of danger that is involved in specific activities and should provide more direct supervision over personnel exposed to greater risks.

With the passport method of fulfilling the requirement of paragraph 2-6.3, personnel assigned to apparatus are tracked by means of three "passports." Personnel reporting for duty place their name badges on all three passports. The primary passport has the names of all personnel assigned to the apparatus on that shift and is normally attached (with Velcro) on the inside of the officer's door on the apparatus. *(See Figure 1561-2.8.)*

Figure 1561-2.8 *Shown are passport tags used to identify personnel assigned to and responding on paramedic engine 33. (Photo courtesy of Phoenix Fire Department)*

This passport is given to the incident commander or the supervisor to whom the apparatus is assigned. When the assignment is completed or changed, the officer retrieves the passport, and it is either returned to the apparatus upon departure or given to the next supervisor.

A secondary passport with the same information (i.e., the names and ranks of assigned personnel) is kept on the driver's side of the apparatus and normally remains there while the apparatus is at the scene. However, the secondary passport is useful to the planning section's resource unit, which may collect the secondary passport. The passport system assists in overall incident resource tracking and at the same time reduces the chance of uncontrolled demobilization. *(See Figure 1561-2.9.)*

The third passport remains at the home station of the apparatus for the duration of the shift. Personnel responding without apparatus follow the same procedure by putting their name tags on an apparatus after they arrive at the scene.

In addition to the passports, magnetic helmet shields can be used to identify personnel assigned to an incident. After being assigned, a fire fighter's helmet shield is attached to the helmet, providing an easy visual reference to anyone who sees the fire fighter. Anyone not displaying the shield has not been checked in and either may be freelancing or is not being tracked.

The passport system is designed for use within the operations function and provides supervisors with a valuable tool in monitoring the location of tactical personnel. The system is often less effective on larger incidents involving personnel assigned to other functions or who are unfamiliar with the passport system. In incidents like this, the resource unit within the planning section may be staffed to provide the overall incident resource tracking. Staffing the resource unit does not negate the need for the passport system or a similar tracking process within the operations function: On large incidents, it is unlikely that the resource unit will be able to monitor the movement of personnel into and out of the hot zone.

2-6.3.1 The incident management system shall maintain accountability for the location and function of each company or unit at the scene of the incident. Personnel who respond to the incident on fire apparatus shall be identified by a system that provides an accurate accounting of those personnel actually responding to the scene with each company or on apparatus.

Paragraph 2-6.3.1 extends the concept of personnel accountability by specifically covering each company or unit, as well as personnel on fire apparatus. Many resource tracking systems refer to apparatus number or position call sign only. However, the actual personnel staffing the apparatus or position change with each shift, and even within the shift due to illness,

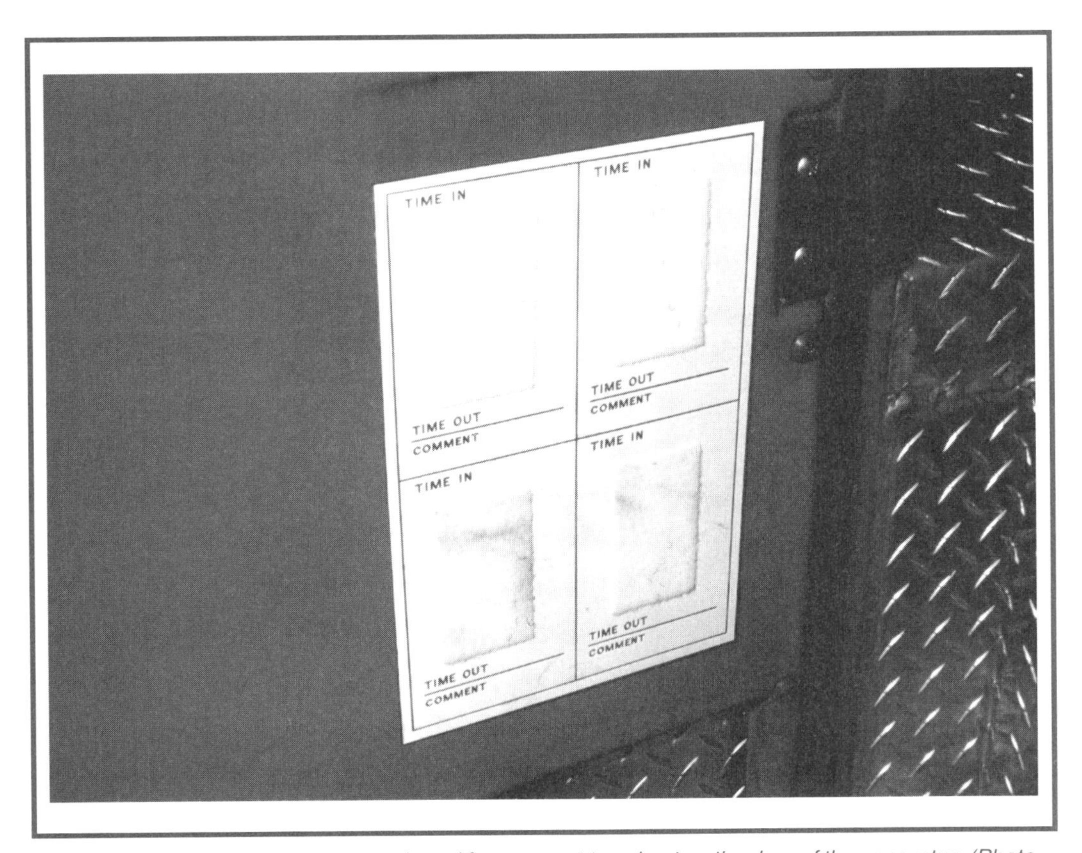

Figure 1561-2.9 *Shown is a status board for passport tags kept on the door of the apparatus. (Photo courtesy of Phoenix Fire Department)*

vacation, or other assignments. As a result, apparatus number, position call sign, and even shift designation are not reliable methods of tracking personnel at an incident. Systems such as the passport provide the additional level of detail needed for operational safety. *(See Figure 1561-2.10.)*

2-6.3.2 Personnel who arrive at the scene of the incident by means other than fire apparatus shall be identified by a system that accounts for their presence and their assignment at the incident scene.

Individuals without an apparatus assignment are frequently overlooked in the initial organizational phase of an incident. This fact makes them more likely to operate informally within the organization and to be left out of the resource tracking system. They may also be more tempted to freelance, creating additional issues of safety and accountability. *(See Figure 1561-2.11.)*

2-6.4

The system shall include a specific means to identify and keep track of personnel entering and leaving hazardous areas, such as confined spaces or areas where special protective equipment is required.

Paragraph 2-6.4 covers hot zone operations, which are the most hazardous and hence the most heavily regulated activities of a response. The resource tracking system must provide detailed tracking of movements into and out of these hazardous areas.

2-6.5*

The incident management system shall include a standard operating guideline to evacuate personnel from an area where an imminent hazard condition is found to exist and to account for their safety. This guidance shall include a method to notify immediately all personnel in the affected area by means of audible warning devices, and by radio signals in accordance with the requirements specified in 2-2.4.

A-2-6.5 The intent of this requirement is to provide assurance that all personnel are notified of urgent safety warnings and to account for all personnel in the event of an unanticipated emergency situation. The system should include all personnel and any other individuals who are operating in areas where they could be endangered. *(See also 2-2.4.)*

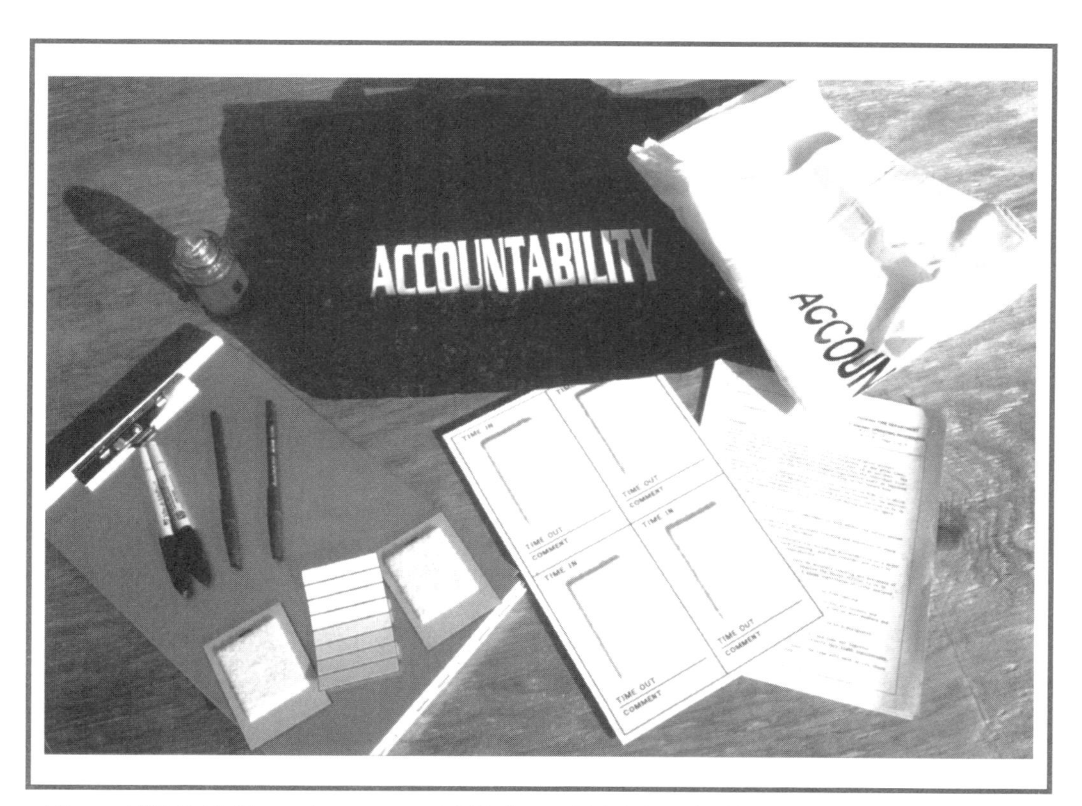

Figure 1561-2.10 *Shown is an accountability bag, which is kept inside a supervisor's or chief officer's vehicle. It contains additional passports, individual name tags, clip boards, and necessary resources to assist in tracking personnel. (Photo courtesy of Phoenix Fire Department)*

Figure 1561-2.11 Accountability at the rehabilitation sector involves tracking personnel in and out of "rehab." (Photo courtesy of Phoenix Fire Department)

Paragraph 2-6.5 reinforces the need for effective communication planning and procedures. The ability to maintain accountability for all personnel and to rapidly account for them in the event of an emergency is a function of both resource tracking and communication. Knowing where personnel are assigned, without a reliable method of communicating with them, does not offer operational safety.

2-7 Emergency Incident Rehabilitation

2-7.1*

The incident commander shall consider the circumstances of each incident and make suitable provisions for the rest and rehabilitation of personnel operating at the scene. These provisions shall include medical evaluation and treatment, food and fluid replenishment, and relief from extreme climatic conditions, according to the circumstances of the incident.

A-2-7.1 Weather factors during emergency incidents can impact severely on the safety and health of personnel, particularly during extremes of heat or cold. Where these factors combine with long-duration incidents or situations that require heavy exertion, the risks to personnel increase rapidly. The fire department should develop guidelines, in consultation with the fire department physician, to provide relief from adverse climatic conditions.

For more information on emergency incident rehabilitation, see the United States Fire Administration Publication FA-114, *Emergency Incident Rehabilitation.*

2-7.2

All supervisors shall maintain an awareness of the condition of personnel operating within their span of control and shall ensure that adequate measures are taken to provide for their safety and health. The command structure shall request relief and reassignment of fatigued crews.

The intent of paragraph 2-7.2 is for commanders to consider both mental and physical health when assessing the condition of personnel operating at an incident scene. Each department should have access to critical incident stress counseling and should consider making counseling mandatory on incidents likely to result in extreme mental stress. *(See Figures 1561-2.12 and 1561-2.13.) [See also Chapter 10 of NFPA 1500, Fire Department Occupational Safety and Health Program (1997), in Part One of this handbook.]*

Figure 1561-2.12 *Communication is an important part of accountability. Supervisory personnel track personnel in and out of the sector. As crews are released they may be reassigned as needed. (Photo courtesy of Phoenix Fire Department)*

Figure 1561-2.13 *The rehab sector provides medical evaluation, rehydration, and a location for personnel to rest before being reassigned. (Photo courtesy of Phoenix Fire Department)*

CHAPTER 3

System Components

3-1 Incident Commander

3-1.1*

The incident management system shall clearly identify who is in overall command at the scene for the duration of the incident. The incident management system shall provide for the transfer of the assignment of "incident commander" to take place one or more times during the course of an incident.

A-3-1.1 There should be one, clearly identifiable incident commander for the duration of the incident, from the arrival of the first fire department unit until the incident is terminated. While a succession of individuals could assume the role of incident commander, there should be no question of who is in command. When a transfer of command takes place, it should be performed in a standard manner.

An exception to the "one incident commander" requirement may be permitted where two or more agencies have specific jurisdictional responsibility for an incident. In such circumstances a "unified command" guideline may be permitted to be employed, by prior agreement, with two or more individuals working together to command the incident. (*See also A-2-3.2.*)

Paragraph 3-1.1 acknowledges that the transfer of command during an incident is a fact of emergency response life. Unfortunately, at each transfer, the potential exists for loss of continuity and key information. *(See Figure 1561-3.1.)* A briefing process must be developed and followed to ensure that vital information is transferred with the title of "Incident Commander." The ICS 201 Incident Briefing form is designed to assist in this process. *(See Appendix 13, Form S13-1.)* It captures a sketch of the incident scene, resources assigned and en route, the current organizational structure, and action taken. The ICS 201 Incident Briefing form is a simple way for the current incident commander to organize information for the efficient and thorough transfer of command.

3-1.2*

Standard operating guidelines shall provide for one individual to assume the role of incident commander from the beginning of operations at the scene of each incident.

A-3-1.2 The incident management system should be applied to every incident from arrival of the first individual until termination. At small-scale incidents, the assumption of command may be permitted to be informal, but the principle of one individual in overall command of the incident always should apply. Routine application of the system is intended to increase familiarity with the concepts and guidelines, even where the need to apply a formal command structure is not obvious. The officer in charge of the first arriving company or the first arriving individual of the fire department, regardless of rank or function, should be the incident commander until relieved by more qualified personnel. All personnel should be sufficiently familiar with basic responsibilities and communications protocols in order to assume the role of initial-arriving incident commander, if only until a more qualified individual arrives.

3-1.3*

Standard operating guidelines shall define the circumstances and guidelines for transferring command and shall specify to whom command shall be transferred.

A-3-1.3 The fire department should establish a protocol of command authority based on rank structure, assignments, and qualifications to define a hierarchy for transferring command. The qualifications required to perform as incident commander should increase with the size and complexity of the incident. Standard operating guidelines should

Figure 1561-3.1 Command posts should be clearly identified and provide adequate resources and work space for personnel in support and command staff functions. (Photo courtesy of Phoenix Fire Department)

define the circumstances under which an officer at a higher level should respond to an incident and whether the transfer of command to an officer at a higher level is mandatory or discretionary.

In certain cases, an individual with a higher level of command authority arriving at the scene may be permitted to direct the current incident commander to continue in this role. The higher level officer is responsible for the command of the incident, but could act as an observer or advisor to allow the incident commander to benefit from the experience. The exercise of this option should be at the discretion of the higher level officer.

The guidelines required by paragraph 3-1.3 should identify incidents and conditions under which command is transferred to non-fire personnel, as well as establish procedures for internal transfer, that is, within the fire department. Fire personnel are often first on the scene at law enforcement incidents, or are involved in incidents that may begin with the fire department in a command role but require command to be shifted after the completion of the life safety-related tactics operations. For example, most aircraft accidents have, in their initial phases, a clear fire command role. However, once the fire is suppressed and survivors are transported, law enforcement personnel secure the scene for investigation. At this point, fire department members are usually released, and command shifts to law enforcement. This transfer of command must be treated with the same thoroughness as transfer of command within the fire discipline.

3-1.4

The incident commander shall be responsible for overall personnel accountability for the incident. The incident commander shall initiate an accountability and inventory worksheet at the very beginning of operations and shall maintain that system throughout operations.

The first arriving incident commander initiates the personnel accountability system and retains the overall responsibility for system maintenance throughout the incident. *(See Figure 1561-3.2.)* However, the hands-on task of actually maintaining the personnel accountability system must be delegated throughout the organization. For example, the incident commander must expect all supervisors to maintain the system. On larger incidents, it may be necessary to staff the resource unit to provide additional tracking capability. *(See Figures 1561-3.3 and 1561-3.4.)* See also Section 2-6.

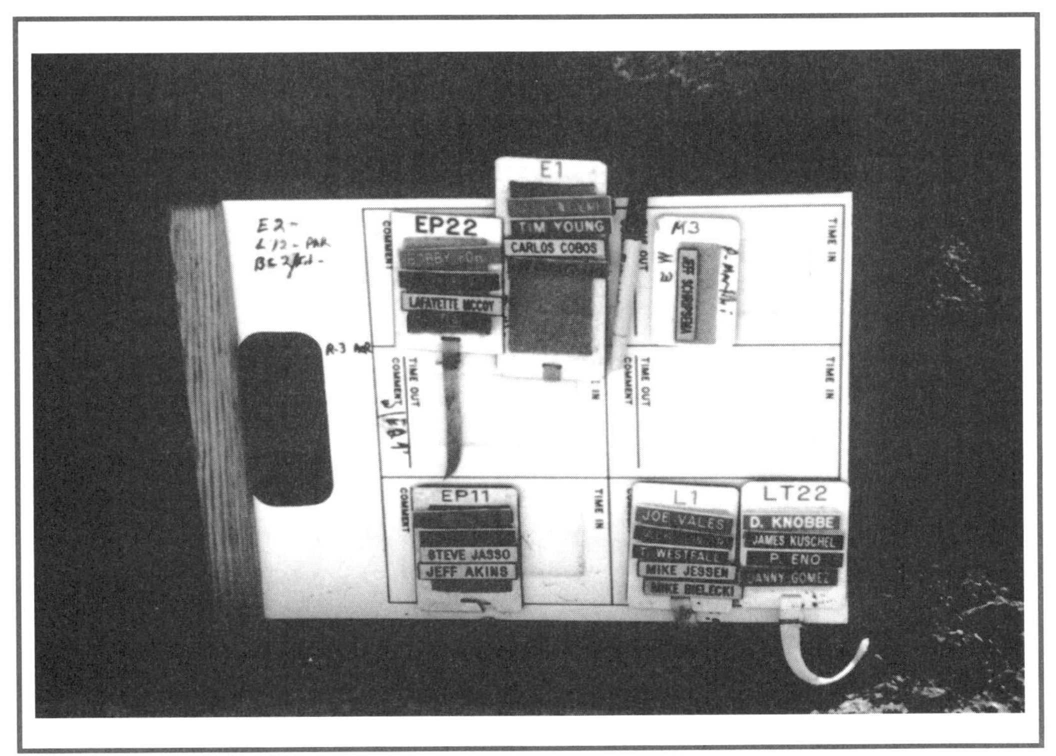

Figure 1561-3.2 An accountability board is used by the accountability section to track personnel both by location and by function. (Photo courtesy of Phoenix Fire Department)

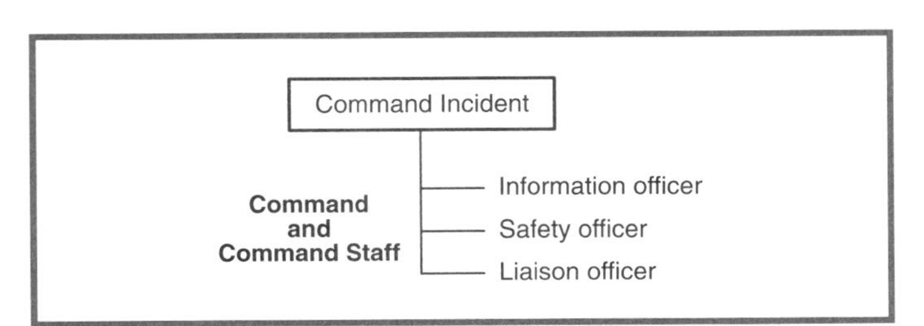

Figure 1561-3.3 This chart shows ICS incident commander and command staff. (Adapted from Incident Command System, Fire Protection Publications, Oklahoma State University, Stillwater, OK, 1983)

3-1.5*

The incident commander shall provide for appropriate control of access to the incident scene.

A-3-1.5 The incident management system should include standard operating guidelines to protect personnel from hazards and to keep unauthorized persons out of hazardous areas. All supervisors should be aware of hazards and should take the necessary steps to control access to areas under their supervision. The incident commander should provide for control of access to the entire incident scene and, where appropriate, should exclude, establish limitations for, or provide an escort for non-fire department personnel.

Controlled access to the incident scene, covered in paragraph 3-1.5, is strongly tied to scene safety. Stories of injuries and even deaths sustained due to uncontrolled access to the incident scene abound. In the initial response, establishing control is difficult and often means removing witnesses, civilian volunteers (well-meaning, but usually untrained and unprotected), and even self-dispatched emergency personnel. However difficult, controlled scene access is a critical objective to be addressed very early in the incident.

3-2 Command Staff

3-2.1*

Command staff functions shall be those elements of the incident management system that operate in direct support of the incident commander and contribute to the overall management of the incident.

A-3-2.1 The command staff generally includes those personnel who work at the command post and provide direct support to the incident commander. This includes personnel who fulfill specifically assigned duties. *(See Figure A-3-2.1.)*

Figure 1561-3.4 Shown is the Phoenix Fire Department command van. (Photo courtesy of Phoenix Fire Department)

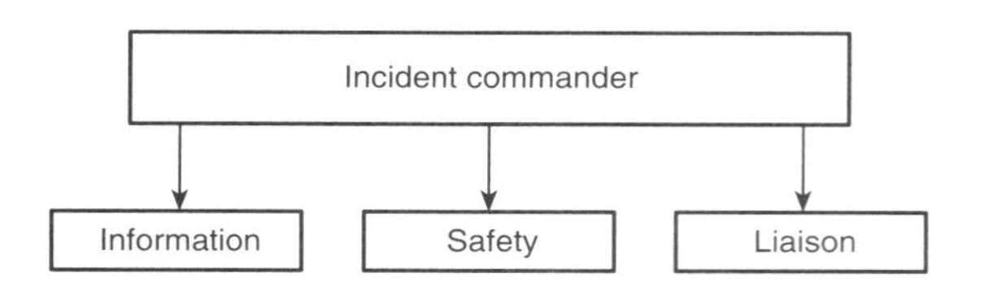

Figure A-3-2.1. *Command structure from IMS book.*

3-2.2*

Standard operating guidelines shall define the roles and responsibilities of personnel assigned to command staff functions. Three specific staff positions shall be identified as information officer, safety officer, and liaison officer. Additional staff functions shall be assigned, depending upon the nature and location of the incident or upon requirements established by the incident commander.

A-3-2.2 The incident management system should include command staff functions that are automatically activated upon escalation of an incident or with multiple alarms. Specific individuals should be designated to respond and assume command staff duties automatically.

3-2.2.1 The information officer shall provide liaison between the media and the incident commander. The information officer shall consult with the incident commander regarding any constraints on the release of information and shall prepare press briefings.

Except in very rare circumstances, the media will be at or near a major incident. In some incidents, the incident commander needs the media's help to inform the public about protective action. Dealing with the media, especially during a significant incident, calls for special training and skills. The information officer, as introduced in paragraph 3-2.2.1, can remove an enormous load from the shoulders of the incident commander. *(See Figure 1561-3.5.)* Few incident commanders have the time, training, or skills necessary to meet the needs of the press at the scene of an emergency incident.

The "Information Officer" position, especially if filled by someone with a constructive ongoing relationship with the local media, can play a key role in incident management. The information officer is often the first member of the incident management organization to sense shifts in public perception about the incident. He or she may detect trends in questions asked, the general tenor of the relationship with the press, and other indicators of potential public relations issues. In some situations, the incident commander will adjust

Figure 1561-3.5 A public information officer (PIO) provides information to media, as authorized by the incident commander. (Photo courtesy of James C. Smalley)

tactics to address public information issues. For example, despite disaster research to the contrary, public concern about looting after a natural disaster is common. To address the public perception that looting is a threat, incident managers may need to deploy personnel for security and patrols. The public is the ultimate judge of incident management teams, and preventing long-term public relations damage is sometimes part of sound incident management.

The proposed 1998 edition of NFPA 1035, *Professional Qualifications for Fire and Life Safety Educator,* includes job performance requirements for the public information officer.

3-2.2.2 Safety officers shall have the authority to immediately correct situations that create an imminent hazard to personnel.

At an emergency incident, where activities are judged by a safety officer to be unsafe and to involve an imminent hazard, the safety officer shall have the authority to alter, suspend, or terminate those activities. The safety officer shall immediately inform the incident commander of any actions taken to correct imminent hazards at an emergency scene.

At an emergency incident where a safety officer identifies unsafe conditions, operations, or hazards that do not present an imminent danger, the safety officer shall take appropriate action through the incident commander to mitigate or eliminate the unsafe condition, operation, or hazard.

To fulfill the requirements of paragraph 3-2.2.2, the position of "Safety Officer" requires equal parts tact and firmness, detailed knowledge of the incident command system, understanding of applicable safety rules and regulations, and extensive tactical experience. Rarely will an individual safety officer have all of the required background for all possible scenarios. Assistant safety officers may be needed, either because the incident is so large that a single safety officer cannot effectively monitor scene safety, or because additional technical knowledge is needed to cover the incident's range of hazards and tactics. In addition to monitoring the scene for safe tactical operations, the safety officer provides a vital service in assisting in the development of strategy and choosing appropriate objectives and tactics. Discussions among the command, operations, and planning functions and the safety officer should occur early and often during the planning process. [For additional information, see NFPA 1521, *Standard for Fire Department Safety Officer* (1997) in Part Two of this handbook.]

3-2.2.3 The liaison officer shall provide a point of contact for assisting and cooperating agencies. The liaison officer shall identify current or potential interagency needs.

Paragraph 3-2.2.3 introduces the liaison officer, who assists the incident commander by establishing and maintaining contact with the managers of cooperating and assisting agencies. The "Liaison Officer" position is the least frequently used and often the least understood of the three command staff positions. Besides relieving the incident commander of the need to speak personally with officials from other agencies, the liaison officer plays a key role in the effective use of resources provided by cooperating and assisting agencies. As discussed in the commentary to paragraph 2-3.3, this position is not well suited to coordinate the tactical activities provided by other agencies. On the other hand, the liaison officer is capable of identifying limits or restrictions on the use of resources, informing the sending agency about incident activities, and discussing problems with resources during the incident.

The position also provides managers of cooperating and assisting agencies with a conduit to the incident commander. *(See also paragraph 2-3.3.)*

3-2.3*

Personnel performing command staff functions shall operate with delegated authority to issue orders and instructions in the name of the incident commander. The scope of this authority shall be established in standard operating guidelines. The assigned personnel shall keep the incident commander informed of significant occurrences.

A-3-2.3 The basic function of the command staff is to support the incident commander. The assigned individuals should be able to differentiate between routine actions and those that could have a significant impact on the overall incident. Part of their responsibility is to inform the incident commander of significant information and to request direction when major decisions are necessary.

3-3 Planning Functions

3-3.1

Planning staff functions shall include those components of the incident management system that are involved with information management to support the incident commander and other levels of the incident command structure.

Through the collection, interpretation, packaging, and dissemination of information about the incident and the resources assigned to it, the planning function provides the glue that holds the incident management organization together. *(See Figure 1561-3.6.)* In the incident command system, the planning section also assists the incident commander in the facilitation of the planning process, strategy and contingency planning, documentation of actions taken on the incident, and the orderly return to service of resources when the incident has been concluded.

Within the ICS, the tasks of the management of information are divided among the four units of the planning section. The following is a brief outline of the responsibilities of each unit:

- *Resource unit:* The resource unit is responsible for checking in, tracking, and displaying the status of all personnel and equipment assigned to the incident.
- *Situation unit:* The situation unit is responsible for the collection, interpretation, packaging, and display of information about the status of the incident, progress of tactical operations, and contingency planning. It also supplies mapping and photographic services.
- *Documentation unit:* The documentation unit gathers and packages all documentation and paperwork generated by the incident. This documentation includes, but is not limited to, all incident action plans, press releases, accident and injury reports, resource orders, financial records, and resource lists.
- *Demobilization unit:* The demobilization unit is responsible for designing a plan for the orderly dismantling of the incident organization and the return to service of tactical resources.

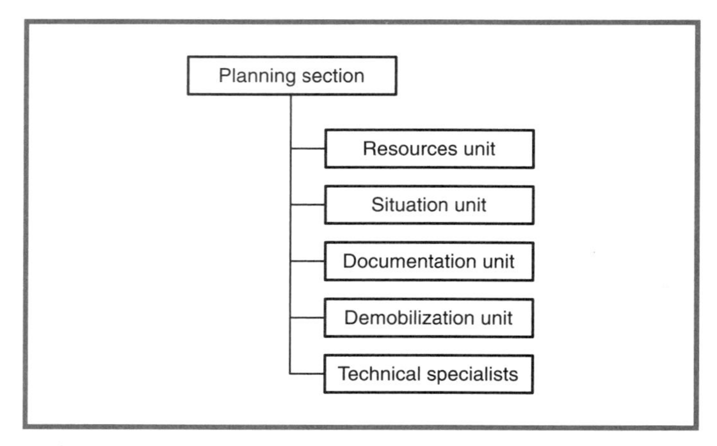

Figure 1561-3.6 *This chart shows the ICS planning section organization. (Adapted from Incident Command System, Fire Protection Publications, Oklahoma State University, Stillwater, OK, 1983)*

On large, long-term incidents, the entire range of information management activities is standardized in the formal planning process. *(See Figure 1561-3.7.) (See Supplement 10 in Part Six of this handbook for a description of the incident action planning process.)*

3-3.2*

The incident management system shall include a standard approach for the collection, evaluation, dissemination, and use of information. The planning staff shall account for the organizational structure, availability of resources, deployment of resources, and situation status reports.

A-3-3.2 The incident management system should provide standard worksheets, charts, diagrams, and other forms to assist the incident commander in keeping track of pertinent information and to provide for the transfer of information in a standard format when command is transferred. The planning staff function should be able to provide information such as accountability, pre-fire plans, reference information, maps, diagrams, and other pertinent information to the incident commander as needed.

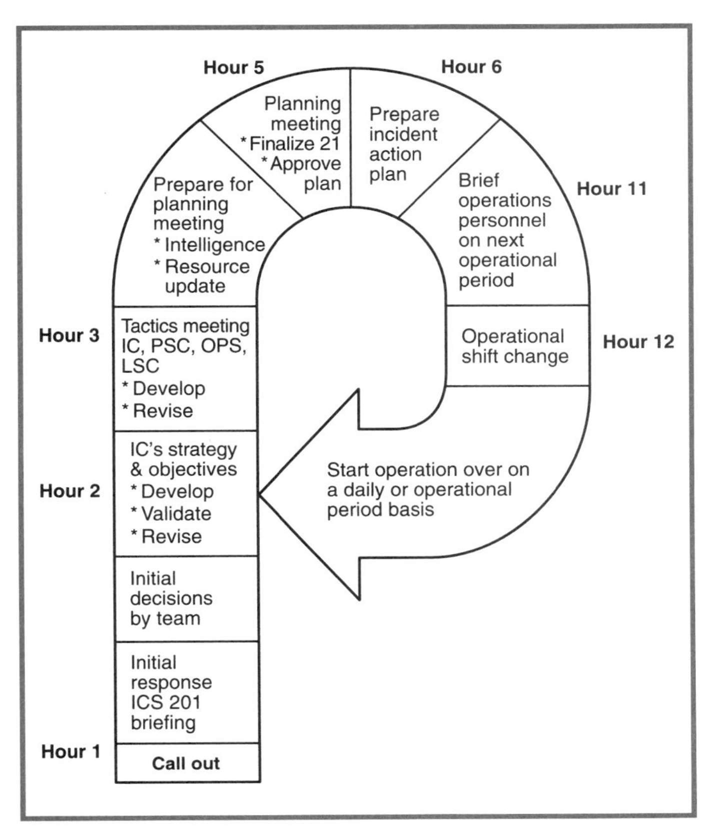

Figure 1561-3.7 This flow chart shows a 12-hour operational period at an incident scene.

The responsibilities of the planning function break into two major categories: resource tracking and situation analysis. In a fully staffed planning section, the former responsibility is assigned to the resource unit, the latter to the situation unit. See Form S13-9, ICS 215, Operational Planning Worksheet, in Appendix 13.

3-3.3

The incident management system shall include standard methods and terminology to record and track the assignment of resources for the duration of an incident.

Paragraph 3-3.3 covers resource tracking throughout an incident. The resource unit is responsible for checking in and tracking all resources assigned to the incident. Status is identified as either "assigned" (actively working the incident), "available" (such as at the incident base or in staging), and "out of service" (for rest or because of injury or mechanical failure). The resource unit must be aggressive in its attempts to monitor the changes in resource status. Proactive monitoring may mean sending personnel to various locations on-scene to check in resources and monitoring operational radio frequencies for changes in location of resources. The resource unit must also display the resource status in a method that is easily accessible and understood by all incident managers. While computers can enhance resource tracking, a computerized system must be easily used by all who need to know the location and status of resources.

3-3.4

The incident management system shall include a standard approach to utilize technical advisors to support the development of strategic plans and to assist the incident commander.

In the ICS, technical specialists may be assigned wherever their assistance is needed in the organization. However, technical specialists are frequently assigned to the situation unit within the planning section and are most frequently used for situation analysis and contingency planning. Often, technical specialists do not have an emergency response background and lack ICS training. In such circumstances, the situation unit may assign a supervisor to assure that the technical specialists' expertise results in timely, usable products.

3-4 Logistics Functions

3-4.1

Logistics provides services and support systems to all the organizational components involved in the incident including facilities, transportation, supplies, equipment maintenance, fueling, feeding, communications, and medical services, including responder rehabilitation.

The logistics function provides a broad array of support functions to the entire organization. *(See Figure 1561-3.8.)* On very large, long-term incidents, the logistics staff may supervise a large number of personnel. Because of the number of units within the logistics section, branch directors may be assigned to reduce the span of control for the section chief. A brief description of the responsibilities of each unit follows:

- *Communications unit:* The communications unit is responsible for the design and maintenance of the incident communication system. On small incidents, the dispatch center may handle this task by separating the tactical operations into separate frequencies. On very large incidents, the communications responsibility may include staffing the incident dispatch center, designing stand-alone communications systems, and incorporating the

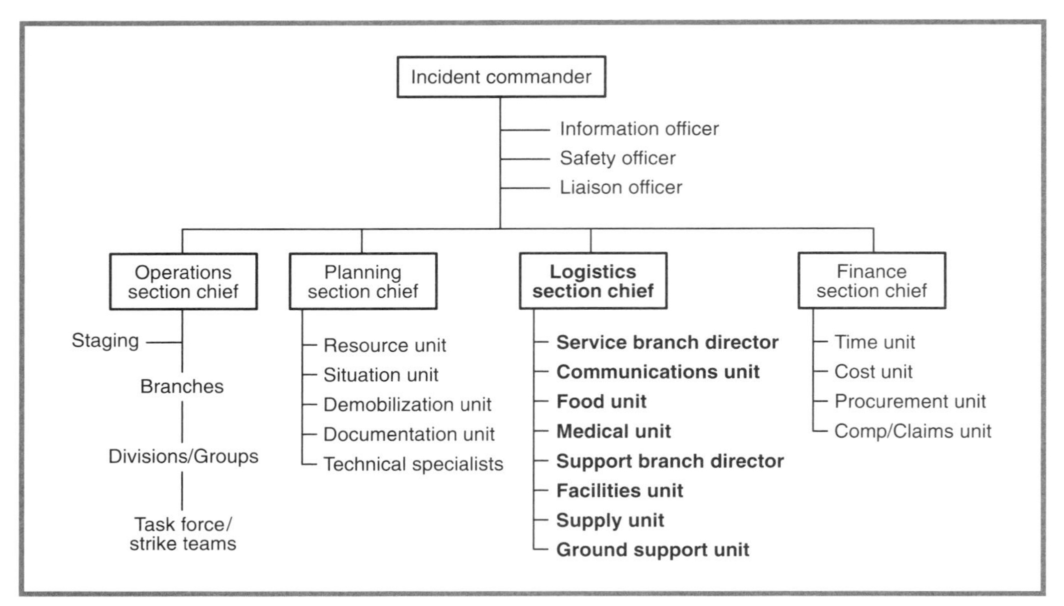

Figure 1561-3.8 *This chart shows the ICS logistics section organization. (Adapted from Incident Command System, Fire Protection Publications, Oklahoma State University, Stillwater, OK, 1983)*

communications resources of mutual aid organizations, amateur radio, and land line and cellular telephones.

The communications unit is also responsible for developing a communication plan (ICS 205) for the written incident action plan and for making sure communications equipment is assigned appropriately, tracked, and maintained. The "Communications Unit Leader" is a highly technical position, requiring extensive knowledge of the communications assets available, as well as a good understanding of the current organizational structure.

- *Food Unit:* The food unit procures food and drink for the organization and coordinates meal times with operations and meal delivery with the ground support unit.
- *Medical unit:* The medical unit provides medical support to incident personnel. This responsibility may include establishing baseline physical readings, monitoring physical condition, and providing first aid. The "Medical Unit Leader" is responsible for developing the medical plan (ICS 206), as illustrated in Figure 1561-3.8, and for the written incident action plan, and works closely with the safety officer to provide a safe working environment for responders.
- *Facilities unit:* The facilities unit is responsible for the management, furnishing, and maintenance of facilities needed during the incident. This may include an emergency operations center, incident command post, incident base, and long-term staging areas. Additional considerations for the facilities unit may include sleeping, feeding, and sanitation support for incident personnel.
- *Supply unit:* The supply unit is the single point for resource ordering on the incident scene. Without this focus, the incident commander will find it difficult to determine what resources have been ordered, on whose authority, and the status of the orders. The incident commander should work out the details of the resource ordering process with the logistics section chief and then make sure everyone in the organization follows the process. The supply unit also receives, documents, stores, and distributes resources and works closely with the finance section to document expenses and to facilitate the procurement of contracted resources. The most significant challenge to the logistics function is the timely procurement of resources. It may be helpful to staff the supply unit with personnel with procurement experience, as well as a working knowledge of department, mutual aid, and other emergency resources.
- *Ground support unit:* The ground support unit provides vehicle maintenance and fueling services, as well as transportation for personnel and supplies to and from the incident. The "Ground Support Unit Leader" plays a key role in traffic planning for the incident.

3-5 Operations Functions

3-5.1

Operations functions shall refer to those tactical components of the incident management system that are directly involved in rescue, fire suppression, emergency medical care, special operations, and other activities that are within the primary mission of the fire department.

In addition to tactical components within the primary mission of the fire department, ICS operations organizations may also incorporate tactical components from other disciplines. Figures 1561-3.9 and 1561-3.10 illustrate the organizational structure.

3-5.2*

The incident commander shall assign intermediate levels of supervision and organize resources following standard operating guidelines in accordance with Section 2-4 and based on the scale and complexity of operations.

A-3-5.2 The command structure should be assembled by the incident commander by grouping resources, assigning supervisors, and adding additional levels of supervision, as described in Section 2-4, to meet the objectives for an effective span of control at each level. This provides a degree of supervision that enhances the safety of all personnel.

To fulfill paragraph 3-5.2, the incident commander has several levels of supervisory organization available in combination to meet his or her preferences and management needs. As long as the organizational "rules of the game" (span of control, unity of command, organizational hierarchy and terminology) are followed, no one organizational structure is any more "correct" than any other. Ordinarily, it is most efficient to manage at the lowest supervisory level possible, then work up through the next available organizational elements, rather than organize from the top down. Working from the lowest to the highest supervisory level reduces confusion as additional management layers are added. The next five figures illustrate the activation of succeeding levels of supervision. *(See Figure 1561-3.11.)*

The approach illustrated by Figures 1500-3.11 and 1500-3.12 is most frequently used on wildland and wildland/urban interface fires, where large numbers of single resources (such as a single engine company or a crew, which could be assembled with personnel from different companies) must be integrated into an appropriate span of control. On most other kinds of incidents, single resources are often integrated directly into divisions or groups, as shown in Figure 1561-3.13.

In Figure 1561-3.13, the incident commander supervises two divisions, two groups, and a single tactical

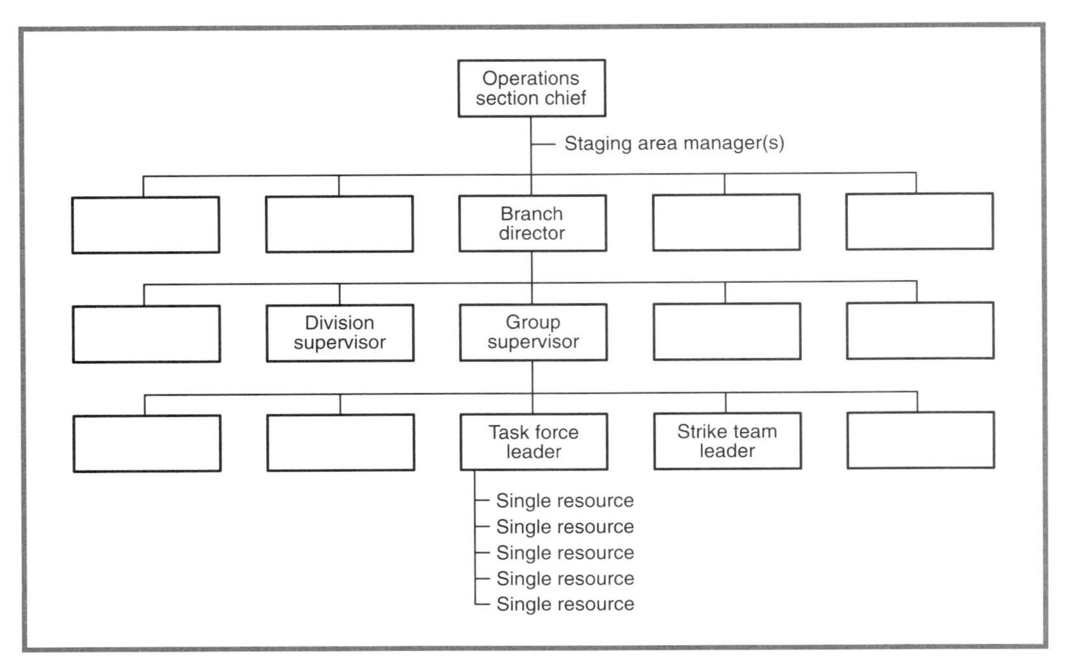

Figure 1561-3.9 *This chart shows the ICS operations section organization. (Adapted from Incident Command System, Fire Protection Publications, Oklahoma State University, Stillwater, OK, 1983)*

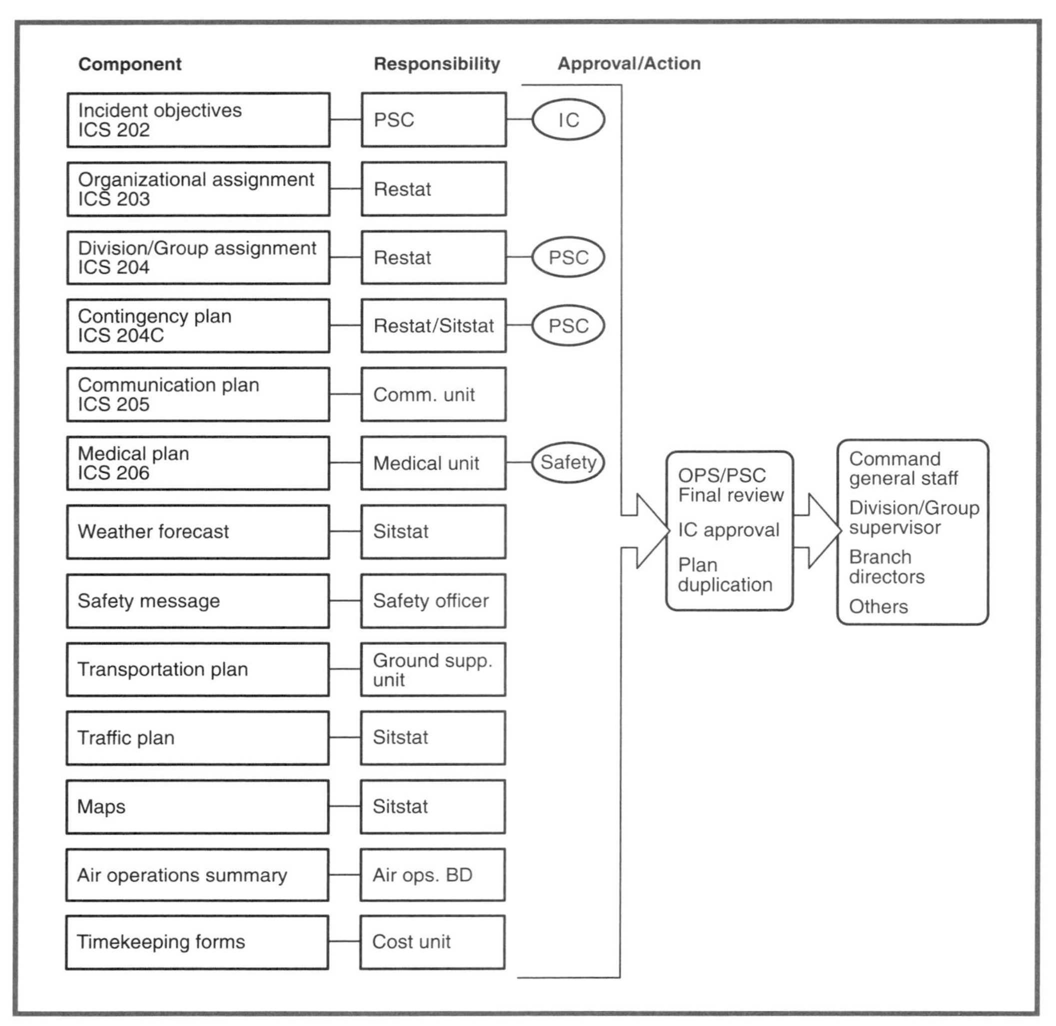

Figure 1561-3.10 Shown is the ICS flow chart for the decision-making process. (Adapted from Incident Command System, Fire Protection Publications, Oklahoma State University, Stillwater, OK, 1983)

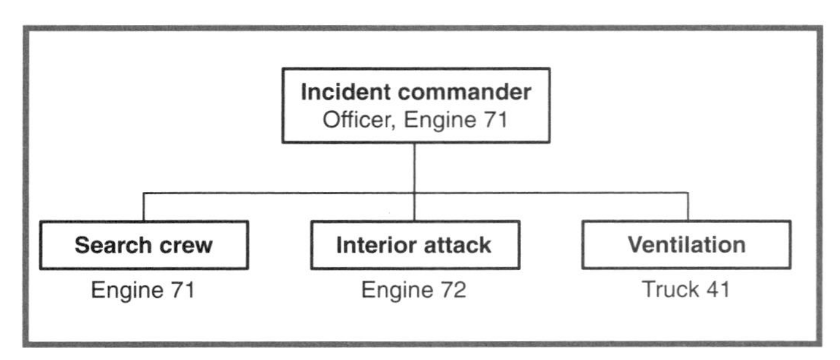

Figure 1561-3.11 Incident command begins with the first arriving company. This simple organizational chart shows how the first arriving company officer assigns resources to special tactical objectives. (Adapted from Incident Command System, Fire Protection Publications, Oklahoma State University, Stillwater, OK, 1983)

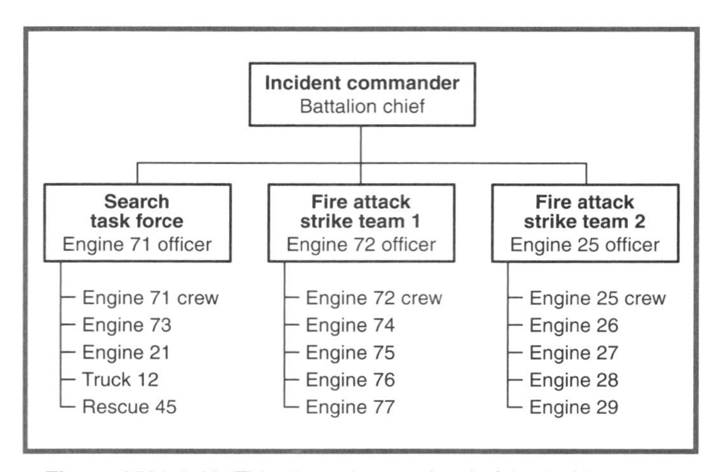

Figure 1561-3.12 This chart shows a level of the incident command system where task forces and strike teams are used to assist with span of control issues. (Adapted from Incident Command System, Fire Protection Publications, Oklahoma State University, Stillwater, OK, 1983)

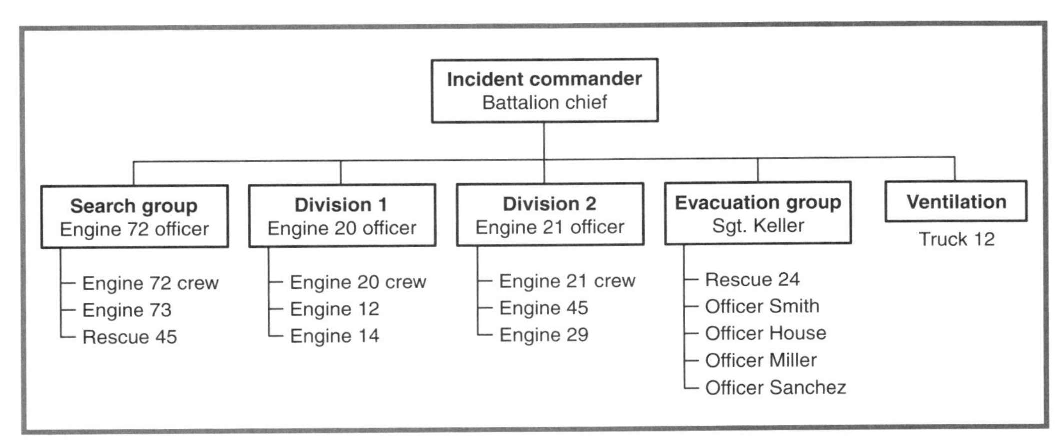

Figure 1561-3.13 *This chart shows an ICS supervisory level to assist with span of control problems. (Adapted from Incident Command System, Fire Protection Publications, Oklahoma State University, Stillwater, OK, 1983)*

assignment. One of the groups includes resources from an assisting agency (in this case, from another discipline as well). While the span of control is still an acceptable one to five, an escalating incident will begin to place additional management demands on the incident commander. Figure 1561-3.14 continues this example to the next organizational level.

As illustrated in Figure 1561-3.14, the incident's increasing size and complexity have led the incident commander to activate the command staff positions of information officer and safety officer, and to staff the planning and logistics section chief positions. Staging has also been established. The rescue group's assignment has been completed; those resources have been reassigned to manage the staging area and to assist in the two divisions. Ventilation has also been completed, and the resource has been staged. To reduce the span of control and to "package" resources into discipline-specific chains of command, the fire resources assigned to the two divisions have been organized in a fire branch. Law enforcement and rescue resources have been assigned to the evacuation group, and a new

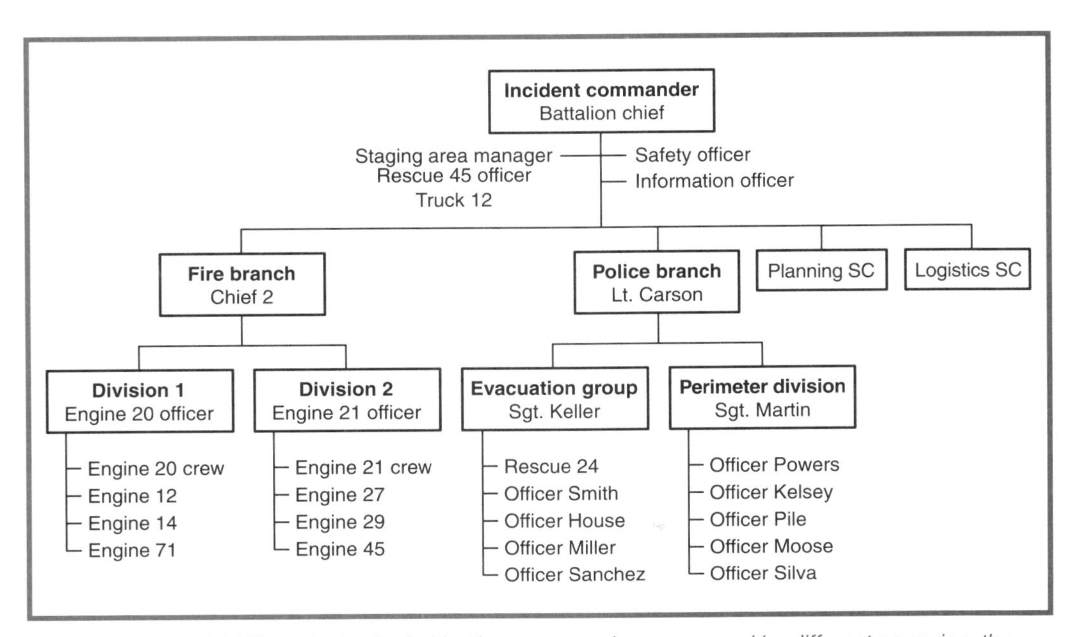

Figure 1561-3.14 *When the tactical objectives grow and are managed by different agencies, the "Branch Director" position may be used to assist with span of control issues. The tactical objectives are still coordinated by the incident commander. (Adapted from Incident Command System, Fire Protection Publications, Oklahoma State University, Stillwater, OK, 1983)*

perimeter division has been organized under a police branch. The span of control continues to be one to five. (Command staff positions are considered extensions of the command function and are not counted in the span of control.)

Figure 1561-3.15 indicates that the incident has continued to increase in complexity. Adding the operations section chief has reduced the span of control for the incident commander and maintained an effective span of control in operations. Staging has moved to report to the operations section chief. Because the organization is built from the bottom up, adding the section chief to the structure impacts only the branch directors and the staging area manager. That is, no other chain of command has been changed. An arson investigator has joined the fire branch. Reflecting the interagency and interdisciplinary aspects of this incident, the incident commander has added the liaison officer to the command staff. Both planning and logistics have added staff to support the incident.

While span of control is a common reason for staffing the "Operations Section Chief" position, it is not the only reason. Another frequent use of the position is to support an incident commander with limited tactical experience with the kind of incident. This position is also used when the incident requires extensive management at other functional levels, as illustrated in Figure 1561-3.15. Use of the position in this complex an incident allows an organization to place its best-qualified tactical staff at the level of the organization where most needed, while continuing to take advantage of the skills of other top managers.

3-5.3*

All supervisors assigned to operations functions shall support an overall strategic plan, as directed by the incident commander, and shall work toward the accomplishment of tactical objectives.

A-3-5.3 The strategic plan should identify the broad goals of emergency incident activities and the basic manner in which operations should be conducted. An offensive strategic plan involves operations to provide search and rescue and to control and extinguish the fire. A defensive strategic plan involves operations directed toward protecting exposures. Offensive and defensive operations should not be conducted in an area that would create unnecessary risk to fire department personnel.

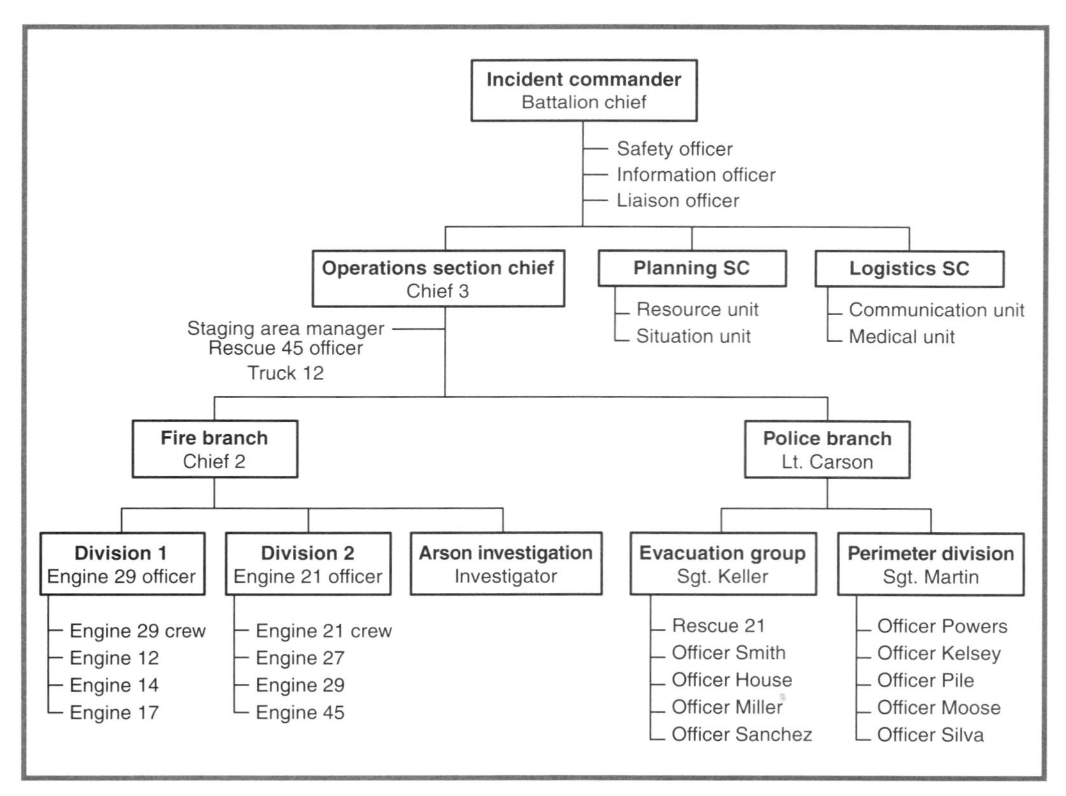

Figure 1561-3.15 This chart describes an escalating incident using the "Operations Section Chief" position to reduce the incident commander's span of control. (Adapted from Incident Command System, Fire Protection Publications, Oklahoma State University, Stillwater, OK, 1983)

Tactical objectives should be based on the strategic plan and assigned by the incident commander to supervisors within the command structure. Each supervisor should be expected to direct the assigned resources to accomplish one or more tactical objectives. The accomplishment of tactical objectives should support successful completion of the strategic plan. An example of a tactical objective is to ensure that all occupants are removed from the second floor of a building and to control the fire on that floor.

Paragraph 3-5.3 provides for acceptance of the incident commander's strategic plan by supervisors. An effective planning process, as described in paragraph 3-3.1, will yield reasonable and achievable objectives, strategy, and tactics. All levels of the organization must monitor progress toward achieving the incident's objectives and let the incident commander know if the objectives are no longer appropriate or will not be met. In the ICS, the operations section chief has the authority to adjust tactics as necessary to achieve objectives and strategies. Changes to objectives and strategies, on the other hand, must have the concurrence of the incident commander.

3-5.4

Supervisors assigned to operations functions shall be accountable for all resources assigned under their span of control and for coordination with higher levels of the command structure and with other supervisors at the same level. The safety and health of all personnel shall be primary considerations.

Paragraph 3-5.4 connects occupational safety and health to supervisory activities. Coordinating the functional assignments of groups or branches with the supervisors of the geographic divisions or branches is especially important, as discussed in the commentary to paragraph A-2-4.5.2.

3-6 Staging

3-6.1*

The incident management system shall provide a standard system to manage reserves of personnel and other resources at or near the scene of the incident.

A-3-6.1 Staging provides a standard method to keep reserves of personnel, apparatus, and other resources ready for action at the scene or close to the scene of an incident. Staging also provides a standard method to control and record the arrival of such resources and their assignment to specific activities. When units are dispatched to assist at working incidents, they should be dispatched to a designated "staging" or "base" area where they can be ready for assignment when required by the incident commander. This process helps the incident commander to keep track of the resources that are on the scene and available for assignment, where they are located, and where specific units have been assigned. The incident commander always should attempt to keep reserves of personnel, equipment, and supplies available to rotate assignments with fatigued crews and to go into action quickly when changing conditions require a rapid commitment of resources. Equipment failures should be anticipated and supplies should be ordered to the scene in time and in sufficient quantities to provide a safe margin over anticipated needs. The ability to provide these reserves is necessarily dependent on the amount of resources that are available, but each fire department should have plans to utilize its available resources to maximum advantage and should have contingency plans to obtain resources from other sources that might be available.

Staging assists in resource management in the following ways:

- Staging allows the incident commander to gather personnel and other resources in an accessible location until they can be effectively assigned. During the initial phases of a rapidly escalating incident, staging allows for more considered use of resources and reduces the management load of the incident commander.
- Staging provides a location to which personnel not responding with apparatus can report, thereby reducing convergence and scene clutter.
- Staging provides a pool of readily available resources, thereby reducing response time.
- Staging reduces freelancing and enhances scene safety.

3-6.2*

Where emergency activities are being conducted in a location where there would be a delay in activating standby resources, the incident commander shall establish staging areas close to the area where the need for those resources is anticipated.

A-3-6.2 It generally is desirable to keep staged resources in locations where they can be ready for action within two minutes. In some cases, particularly where imminent hazards exist, it is advisable to keep an immediate response capability in a state of readiness in a safe location that provides immediate access to the area.

The term "base" is often used to refer to a more remote location where standby resources are gathered but are not available for immediate action. As needed, resources can be moved up to a staging location where they are ready for immediate action. An example is a high-rise building where apparatus is parked at a safe distance from the building, and personnel and equipment are moved in to stand by on a safe floor below the fire level.

Paragraph A-3-6.2 distinguishes between a staging area and a base. The needs of the incident, the proximity of a suitable location, and safety will dictate the actual location of the staging area. It is important that staged resources maintain their readiness. If the staging area begins to resemble an incident base (rest and recreation), resources may not be able to respond quickly when needed. Because staging areas are usually located as close as possible to the incident scene, it is not unusual to need to relocate the staging area quickly if the incident escalates.

3-7 Finance/Administration

3-7.1*

The incident management system shall provide for financial/administrative services where necessary.

A-3-7.1 Where resources necessary for the safe conduct of an incident reach beyond the procurement authority of the incident commander, a finance/administrative function should be provided to authorize and expedite procurement of necessary resources.

The finance/administration function required by paragraph 3-7.1 is the least often used function in the incident command system. *(See Figure 1561-3.16.)* However, on incidents in which reimbursement is expected, and for responses to disasters, financial record keeping becomes critical. Fire departments without internal financial support staff will need to look to the finance staff of their jurisdictions for these services. Coordinating this effort is critical during the preplanning phase.

The ICS finance/administration function has four units. Brief descriptions of their responsibilities follow:

- *Time unit:* The time unit is responsible for maintaining time records for personnel and equipment assigned to the incident.
- *Cost unit:* The cost unit provides periodic (usually on a 12- or 24-hour basis) estimates of incident costs to date. The estimates should include costs for personnel, equipment, supplies, food, and so forth. The unit should also assist with cost-benefit analysis on specific tactics or on specific pieces of equipment.

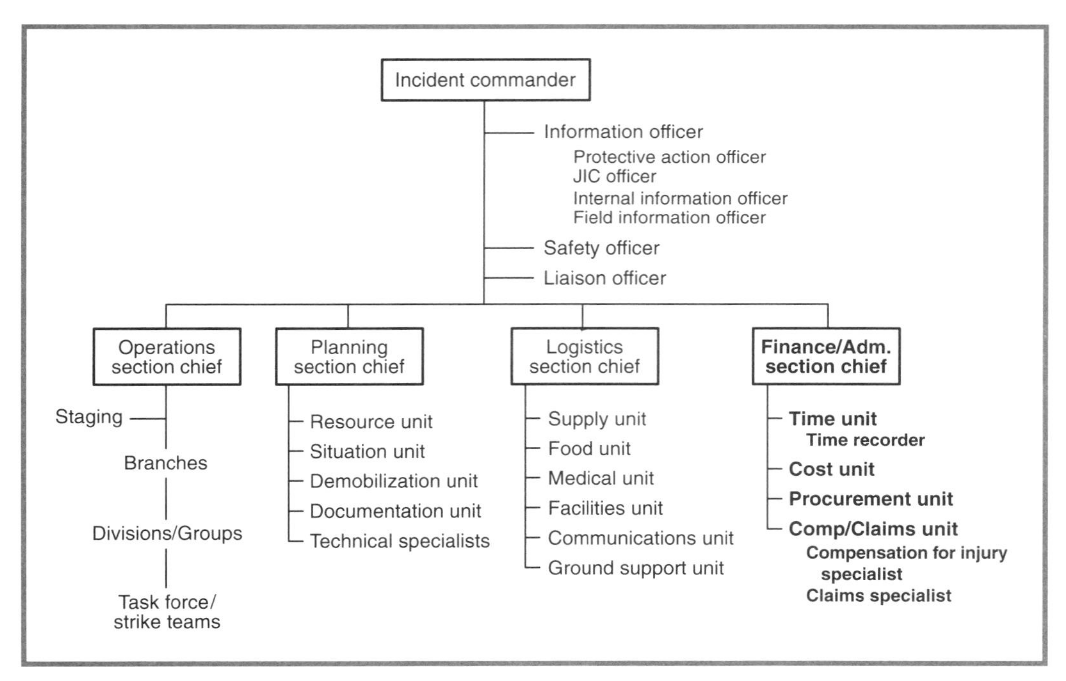

Figure 1561-3.16 *The finance/administration function might not be staffed by emergency personnel and could be staffed by someone from city/town government. (Adapted from Incident Command System, Fire Protection Publications, Oklahoma State University, Stillwater, OK, 1983)*

- *Procurement unit:* The procurement unit negotiates and administers contracts. It ensures that the organization does not assume unwarranted liability and that contract terms are fulfilled. The unit works closely with the logistics function.
- *Compensation/claims unit:* The compensation/claims unit is responsible for documenting and processing accident and injury reports and workers' compensation forms for incident personnel. The unit also investigates and documents any claims against the organization for damage to mutual aid equipment or private property The compensation/claims unit is a valuable asset in overall incident risk management and works closely with the safety officer and the medical unit leader.

3-7.2*

The incident commander shall assign finance/administrative functions based on the needs or complexity of the incident.

A-3-7.2 The finance/administration section is established for incidents where the agency(ies) that is involved has a specific need for financial services. Not all agencies require the establishment of a specific finance/administration section. In some cases, where only one specific function is required (i.e., cost analysis), the position of Technical Specialist in the Planning Section could be established. (*See Figure A-3-7.2.*)

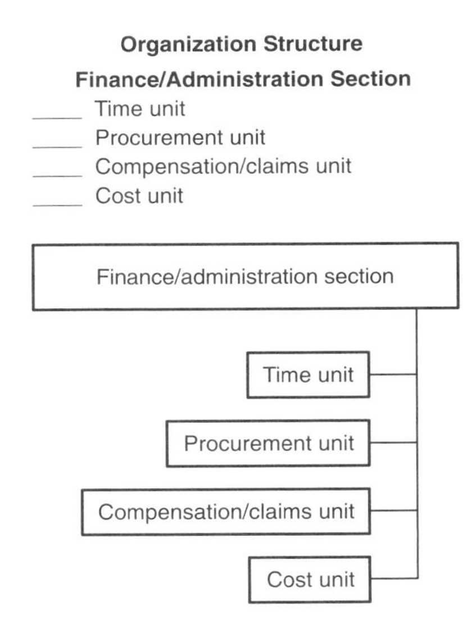

Figure A-3-7.2.

Frequently, finance/administration duties can be accomplished off-scene and completed after the incident has been demobilized. Following disasters, the finance/administration responsibilities may carry over into the recovery phase and last for months or years. In these long-term situations, it is important to capture as much of the relevant information (time records, expenditures, etc.) as possible before demobilization. Once the incident has been demobilized, it is difficult to recreate the information necessary for cost recovery.

CHAPTER 4

Roles and Responsibilities

4-1 Incident Commander

4-1.1*

The incident commander shall be responsible for the overall coordination and direction of all activities at an incident. This shall include overall responsibility for the safety and health of all personnel and for other persons operating within the incident management system.

A-4-1.1 The incident commander should be located at a fixed command post and should be visible and accessible to authorized individuals. The fixed command post should be established as early as possible, preferably in a location that provides a view of the incident scene.

For small-scale incidents, the command post could be as simple as the cab of a piece of fire apparatus or the incident commander's response vehicle. Being inside a vehicle is usually helpful in providing a functional work environment for the incident commander. Specially equipped command post vehicles are often used for major incidents, where the incident commander is assisted by several command staff personnel and liaison personnel from other agencies.

Paragraph 4-1.1 covers overall coordination and direction. Tactically focused incident commanders may neglect the "big picture" management demands of a major incident. Operations and tactics are most often the experience base for fire department incident commanders, so the comfort zone is squarely in the operations function. The ICS is designed to help the incident commander carry out the additional management requirements of major incidents, including an enhanced focus on scene safety, interagency liaison, public information, resource and situation tracking and analysis, logistical support, and fiscal management. Early activation of these support functions will greatly enhance the ability of the incident commander to accomplish "overall coordination and direction of all activities at an incident."

4-1.2*

The concept of risk management shall be utilized on the basis of the following principles:

(a) Activities that present a significant risk to the safety of personnel shall be limited to situations where there is a potential to save endangered lives.
(b) Activities that are routinely employed to protect property shall be recognized as inherent risks to the safety of personnel, and actions shall be taken to reduce or avoid these risks.
(c) No risk to the safety of personnel shall be acceptable where there is no possibility to save lives or property.

A-4-1.2 The risk to fire department personnel is the most important factor considered by the incident commander in determining the strategy that will be employed in each situation. The management of risk levels involves all of the following factors:

(a) Routine evaluation of risk in all situations;
(b) Well-defined strategic options;
(c) Standard operating guidelines;
(d) Effective training;
(e) Full protective clothing and equipment;
(f) Effective incident management and communications;
(g) Safety guidelines and safety officers;
(h) Back-up crews for rapid intervention;
(i) Adequate resources;
(j) Rest and rehabilitation;
(k) Regular reevaluation of conditions;
(l) Pessimistic evaluation of changing conditions;
(m) Experience based on previous incidents and critiques.

In essence, paragraph 4-1.2 requires the incident commander to use risk management in making decisions and setting priorities. A simple memory device frequently used by the fire service to establish incident priorities is "*LIP*," which stands for *l*ife safety, *i*ncident stabilization, and *property* conservation. The acronym also presents the generally accepted order of priority: life safety first, then incident stabilization, followed by property conservation. This order of priority can be further expanded as follows:

(a) Life safety

1. Responders
2. Populations at risk
3. General public

(b) Incident stabilization

1. Actions to contain the incident
2. Actions to keep the incident from escalating
3. Actions to minimize the impact of the incident

(c) Property/environmental conservation

1. Essential infrastructure
2. Environment with health/safety implications
3. Environment in general
4. Property in general

Although incident priorities should be set in this order, they may be acted upon tactically in a different order, depending upon the incident. For example, it may be necessary to aggressively attack a structure fire (incident stabilization) in order to accomplish a rescue (life safety). The LIP process provides a template when developing priorities for a specific incident.

4-1.3*

The incident commander shall evaluate the risk to personnel with respect to the purpose and potential results of their actions in each situation. In situations where the risk to fire department personnel is excessive, as defined in 4-1.2, activities shall be limited to defensive operations.

A-4-1.3 The acceptable level of risk is directly related to the potential to save lives or property. Where there is no potential to save lives, the risk to fire department personnel must be evaluated in proportion to the ability to save property of value. Where there is no ability to save lives or property, there is no justification to expose fire department personnel to any avoidable risk, and defensive fire suppression operations are the appropriate strategy.

4-1.4

The incident commander shall be responsible for establishing a command structure that meets the needs of the particular situation, for determining the overall strategy that will be employed, for summoning and assigning adequate resources to deal with the situation, for evaluating progress and changing the strategy as appropriate, for communicating directions and interpreting progress reports from assigned persons in the command structure, and for bringing the incident to a termination.

4-1.5

The incident commander shall make assignments and provide direction, as demanded by the nature and circumstances of the incident, in order to manage the activities of all personnel and other resources at the incident scene.

4-1.6

The incident commander shall assign supervisory duties and responsibilities to create an organizational structure, within the framework of the incident management system, based on the needs of each particular incident. The established structure shall provide a manageable span of control at all levels of the organization to exercise supervision over all aspects of the incident.

4-1.6.1 As the incident increases in size and complexity and as additional personnel and units are assigned to operate at the scene, the incident commander shall expand the command structure to maintain effective levels of supervision and span of control.

4-1.6.2 The assignment of duties and responsibilities to individuals also shall include the delegation of the authority necessary to accomplish the assignments. The standard operating guidelines adopted by the fire department shall define the scope of authority to be delegated at each level of the organization.

The ICS is not rank-based. Positions are filled by qualified individuals regardless of their rank in the organization. In fact, it is not uncommon for ranking officers to be assigned subordinate duties within the system. Personnel operating within the incident management system need the authority of the position; other personnel must understand and accept this principle.

4-1.7

The incident commander shall utilize standardized terminology and predefined job descriptions to make supervisory assignments.

Like paragraph 2-4.5.1, paragraph 4-1.7 requires the use of a standardized system, including position titles and job descriptions, which makes assignments at incidents much more efficient. It is not necessary to define job expectations in detail because participants understand the job, its responsibilities, and its relationships to others in the organization.

4-1.8

The fire department shall provide personnel for the rescue of individuals operating at emergency incidents if the need arises. A rapid intervention crew shall consist of at least two individuals and shall be available for rescue of personnel if necessary.

4-1.9

The incident commander shall ensure that any change in strategy is communicated to all affected supervisors.

Paragraph 4-1.9 clearly makes the incident commander responsible for communicating changed strategy. It is simply sound management to communicate changes in objectives and strategy broadly throughout the organization. Changes in tactics, which affect only those responsible for carrying them out, do not merit broad communication. On the other hand, changes in objectives and strategy have broad ramifications for the entire organization (including the support functions of planning, logistics, and finance). To be effectively incorporated throughout the organization, changes in objectives and strategy must be communicated to all.

4-2 Supervisory Personnel

4-2.1

Risk management principles shall be employed routinely by supervisory personnel at all levels of the incident management system to define the limits of acceptable and unacceptable positions and functions for all personnel at the incident scene.

4-2.2*

Supervisors shall assume responsibility for activities within their span of control, including responsibility for the safety and health of personnel and other authorized persons within their designated areas.

A-4-2.2 Supervisors should be visible and recognizable to their subordinates and to other persons who would need to communicate with them. First level supervisors, such as company officers, are often identified by distinctively colored helmets or other markings. Intermediate level supervisors also should be identified, particularly in situations where personnel from different agencies are directly involved in operations. Colored helmets, vests, and other means are often used to identify intermediate level supervisors.

The incident command post also should be visible and recognizable. This can be accomplished by displaying a colored light, flag, banner, or other symbol to mark the location. Where special command post vehicles are used, such vehicles are usually marked with distinctive identification to make the command post recognizable.

4-2.3*

Supervisors shall work toward assigned objectives within the overall strategy defined by the incident commander. They shall, on a regular basis, report progress, or lack of progress, in meeting those objectives and any deviation from established plans.

A-4-2.3 The fire department should establish a standard time interval for progress reports from supervisors. Routine progress reports should be provided at intervals of 10 to 15 minutes. If conditions change significantly at any time, this information should be transmitted promptly to the higher level supervisor. Any report relating to the safety of personnel should have the highest priority.

4-2.4

Supervisors at each level of the command structure shall receive direction from and provide progress reports to supervisors at a higher level.

See Form S13-8, ICS 209, Incident Status Summary, in Appendix 13.

4-2.5

Supervisors shall be alert to recognize conditions and actions that create a hazard within their span of control. All supervisors shall have the authority and responsibility to take immediate action to correct imminent hazards and to advise the appropriate supervisor regarding these actions.

Paragraph 4-2.5 incorporates the philosophy that every supervisor—in fact, every member of the organization—is a "safety officer." Supervisors are responsible for the safety and health of those assigned to them; individuals are responsible for following safety requirements imposed by the organization and for reporting observed unsafe conditions. Supervisors should employ the span of control tools at their disposal so that the resources they supervise have adequate oversight and communication capability. Supervisors should also communicate the expectation that anyone observing an unsafe act or condition will take corrective actions and report to the appropriate supervisory level.

4-2.6

Supervisors shall coordinate their activities with other supervisors at the same level and shall provide direction to supervisors at a lower level or personnel within their span of control.

4-2.7*

Where conflicting orders are received at any level of the incident management system, the individual receiving the conflicting order shall inform the individual giving the order that a conflict exists. If the conflicting order is required to be carried out, the individual giving the conflicting order shall so inform the individual who provided the initial order.

A-4-2.7 **The guideline for clarifying conflicting orders should not apply to imminent hazard situations where immediate action is necessary to avoid a dangerous situation.**

Conflicting orders jeopardize the safety of all operating at the incident. Once personnel have agreed to the action plan, how they accomplish the tactical objectives is incumbent upon them. There are times when the tactical objective (for example, ventilation coordinated with fire attack and search and rescue) is done at the tactical level.

The ICS operates on the principle of direct access to information. If one element of the organization has information needed by another, it is not necessary to observe the organizational chain of command to seek it out. However, it is critical that the chain of command be observed when giving or changing direction. The only exception to this rule of thumb should be in the instance of safety. Any other changes in instructions should be coordinated with the supervisor of the resource that is receiving the new direction.

CHAPTER 5

Referenced Publications

5-1

The following documents or portions thereof are referenced within this standard and shall be considered part of the requirements of this document. The edition indicated for each reference is the current edition as of the date of the NFPA issuance of this document.

5-1.1 NFPA Publication.

National Fire Protection Association, 1 Batterymarch Park, P.O. Box 9101, Quincy, MA 02269-9101.

NFPA 1500, *Standard on Fire Department Occupational Safety and Health Program*, 1992 edition.

5-1.2 Other Publications.

5-1.2.1 U.S. Government Publications. U.S. Government Printing Office, Superintendent of Documents, Washington, DC 20402.

Title 29, *Code of Federal Regulations*, Part 1910, Section 120 (29 *CFR* 1910.120(q)(3)); March 6, 1989.

Title 29, *Code of Federal Regulations*, Part 1910, Section 155 (29 *CFR* 1910.155(c)(26)); July 1, 1987.

REFERENCE CITED IN COMMENTARY

Incident Command System, Fire Protection Publications, Oklahoma State University, Stillwater, OK, 1983.

APPENDIX A

Explanatory Material

The material contained in Appendix A of this standard is not part of the requirements of the code but is included with the code for informational purposes only. For the convenience of readers, in this handbook the Appendix A material is interspersed among the verbiage of Chapters 1 through 4 and, therefore, is not repeated here.

APPENDIX B

This Appendix is not a part of the requirements of this NFPA document but is included for informational purposes only.

This standard provides performance requirements for incident management systems for emergency situations. The emphasis of the standard is on safety and health considerations to ensure that emergency scene operations are conducted in a manner that provides an appropriate emphasis on the welfare and survival of fire department personnel and other emergency response personnel. These objectives may be permitted to be satisfied by a variety of systems that meet the specified criteria and can provide benefits beyond those of safety and health.

In the development of this standard, it was considered more important to specify the required performance criteria for any system and encourage fire departments to adopt or modify an effective existing system that meets their particular needs, rather than to require all users to adopt one particular system. The user has the option to adopt a model system, to adapt an existing system to meet local conditions, or to develop a different system.

It was noted that several different incident management systems are already in existence. These systems have been successfully adopted and employed and address many or all of the requirements of this standard. Upon close examination, it was evident that there are many similarities among these systems, and the differences were considered to be less significant than the benefits of meeting the overall performance objectives. Some differences in terminology and specific guidelines were noted. This standard was developed to allow for local options, while recognizing the benefits of standardization and compatibility among systems.

The following points are considered to be key factors in any incident management system for a fire department.

(a) Overall authority and responsibility is assigned to the incident commander.
(b) The incident management system provides structured authority and responsibilities for different command levels and positions.
(c) There is a structured hierarchy reporting system with a manageable span of control at each level.
(d) The system is used to coordinate all incident scene operations.
(e) Individuals performing command functions must be trained and qualified.
(f) Everyone involved in operations at the incident scene has a relationship to the system that includes reporting and receiving assignments in a standard manner.
(g) The system is documented in written standard operating guidelines.
(h) The system is simple and familiar and is used routinely at all incidents.
(i) Supervisory assignments are based on functions or locations or, in some cases, both.
(j) Communications protocols are structured to match the command system.
(k) There is a structured system for the response of resources and for summoning additional resources.
(l) The system provides for expansion, escalation, transfer, and transition of command roles and responsibilities.
(m) The system requires safety and health to be managed as major strategic and operational priorities in all cases.
(n) The system employs standard tactical approaches that are applied to different situations and circumstances.
(o) The system leads to the eventual termination of the incident.

(See Appendix C for resources.)

APPENDIX C

Referenced Publications

C-1

The following documents or portions thereof are referenced within this standard for informational purposes only and thus are not considered part of the requirements of this document. The edition indicated for each reference is the current edition as of the date of the NFPA issuance of this document.

C-1.1 NFPA Publications.

National Fire Protection Association, 1 Batterymarch Park, P.O. Box 9101, Quincy, MA 02269-9101.

NFPA 471, *Recommended Practice for Responding to Hazardous Materials Incidents*, 1992 edition.

NFPA 472, *Standard for Professional Competence of Responders to Hazardous Materials Incidents*, 1992 edition.

NFPA 1500, *Standard on Fire Department Occupational Safety and Health Program,* 1997 edition.

NFPA 1521, *Standard for Fire Department Safety Officer*, 1992 edition.

C-1.2

U.S. Fire Administration Publication. USFA, 16825 S. Seton Ave., Emmitsburg, MD 21727.

Emergency Incident Rehabilitation (FA-114).

C-1.3

The following are examples of two existing incident management systems that illustrate how the performance objectives of the standard might be achieved. These examples do not signify any approval or endorsement of the systems:

Fire Command System, available from the NFPA, 1 Batterymarch Park, P.O. Box 9101, Quincy, MA 02269-9101.

National Fire Academy, Incident Command System, available from the National Fire Academy, 16825 South Seton Avenue, Emmitsburg, MD 21727.

C-1.4

The following is an available document regarding structural fire fighting application for up to 25 companies:

The National Fire Service Incident Management System (NFIMS) Consortium has developed a "Model Procedures Guide for Structural Firefighting," which is an application of Fire Command System tactics and strategy as applied to the National Fire Academy's Incident Command System (ICS) and designed for structural fire fighting for incidents up to 25 companies. It is available from Fire Protection Publications, Oklahoma State University, Stillwater, Oklahoma 74078.

PART FOUR

NFPA 1581

Standard on Fire Department Infection Control Programs and Commentary

Part Four of this handbook includes the complete text of the 1995 edition of NFPA 1581, *Fire Department Infection Control Programs.* The first edition of NFPA 1581 was developed in 1990 to address fire department infection control practices, programs, and policies that would be compatible with federal guidelines and regulations applicable to public safety and emergency response personnel. This second edition contains new and expanded text dealing with decontamination and other issues related to a proactive program for maintaining a safe and healthy work environment.

The mandatory provisions found in Chapters 1 through 6 of NFPA 1581 were prepared by the Technical Committee on Fire Service Occupational Safety within the framework of NFPA's consensus codes- and standards-making system. Because these provisions are designed to be suitable for adoption into law or for reference by other codes and standards, the text is concise, without extended explanation.

The material found in Appendix A of NFPA 1581 was also developed by the Technical Committee on Fire Service Occupational Safety within NFPA's codes- and standards-making system to assist users in understanding and interpreting the mandatory provisions of the standard. Appendix A is not considered part of the requirements of the standard; it is advisory or informational. An asterisk (*) following a paragraph number in the standard indicates that advisory appendix material pertaining to that paragraph appears in Appendix A. For the reader's convenience, in this handbook, Appendix A material has been repositioned to appear immediately following its base paragraph in the body of the standard. The text of the standard and the Appendix A material are printed in black in this handbook.

Explanatory commentary, which was prepared by Gordon Sachs, former Chief of Training and Safety with Marion County (Florida) Fire-Rescue, immediately follows the standard text it discusses and is printed in blue for easy identification. The commentary is intended to provide the reader with a deeper understanding of the standard and to serve as a resource and reference for implementing its provisions. It is not a substitute for the actual wording of the standard or the text of any code or standard that may be incorporated by reference.

Sachs has 20 years of fire and EMS experience in both the career and volunteer services and is nationally recognized as an emergency services educator and author. As a former program manager with the U.S. Fire Administration, he coordinated and directed federal projects dealing with fire and EMS management and operations, responder health and safety, incident command, and EMS public education. Sachs has served on several national committees dealing with emergency service management operations. He also served as chairman of the NFPA Task Group on Infection Control and is a former member of the NFPA Technical Committee on Fire Service Occupational Safety and Health. He is currently a member of the NFPA Technical Committee on Fire Service Occupational Health.

CHAPTER 1

Administration

1-1 Scope

1-1.1

This standard contains minimum requirements for a fire department infection control program.

1-1.2

These requirements shall be applicable to organizations providing fire suppression, rescue, emergency medical care, and other emergency services including public, military, private, and industrial fire departments.

1-1.3

This standard shall not apply to industrial fire brigades that also might be known as emergency brigades, emergency response teams, fire teams, plant emergency organizations, or mine emergency response teams.

NFPA 1581 addresses the infection control concerns of fire departments and emergency medical services. *(See Figure 1581-1.1.)* The scope is written essentially the same as NFPA 1500, *Standard on Fire Department Occupational Safety and Health Program* (1997) (Part One of this handbook), but is further intended to include any emergency response agency whose members may be reasonably anticipated to come in contact with blood or other body fluids as a part of their duties. Thus, any agency that routinely responds in any capacity to medical emergencies, traffic crashes, rescue incidents, or fires with burn victims is covered under this standard.

Figure 1581-1.1 *NFPA 1581 applies not only to fire department EMS providers, but to any public or private EMS provider. (Photo courtesy of Fairfax County Fire and Rescue Dept., Fairfax, Virginia)*

1-2 Purpose

1-2.1

The purpose of this standard is to provide minimum criteria for infection control in the fire station, at an incident scene, and at any other area where fire department members are involved in routine or emergency operations.

1-2.2*

The requirements of this standard are intended to meet or exceed applicable federal regulations of the Occupational Safety and Health Administration and guidelines of the Centers for Disease Control and Prevention.

A-1-2.2 "Applicable federal regulations from the Occupational Safety and Health Administration" refers specifically to 29 *CFR* Part 1910.1030, "Bloodborne Pathogens," Final Rule.

"Guidelines from the Centers for Disease Control and Prevention" refers specifically to *Guidelines for Prevention of Transmission of Human Immunodeficiency Virus and Hepatitis B Virus to Health Care and Public Safety Workers.*

1-2.3

The requirements in this standard are designed to exceed those of an exposure control program and to provide minimum levels of protection for members and patients, and for the public at fire department facilities.

1-2.4

Nothing herein is intended to restrict any jurisdiction from exceeding these minimum requirements.

NFPA 1581 addresses fire service and EMS infection control from a different perspective than the OSHA bloodborne pathogen regulation, 29 *CFR* Part 1910.1030, as it applies not only to bloodborne pathogens, but also to airborne and foodborne pathogens and to protecting both patients and emergency responders.

NFPA 1581 was written to meet all applicable OSHA requirements for employee exposure protection, including CDC guidelines on patient exposure protection. It addresses infection control policy, risk management, training and education, health maintenance, and exposure incidents. It addresses the need for a designated "Infection Control Officer," as does the *Ryan White Comprehensive AIDS Resources Emergency (CARE) Act of 1990* (popularly known as the *Ryan White Law*). It also treats the many infection control issues found at fire department facilities, including those related to kitchen areas, sleeping areas, bathrooms, laundry areas, storage areas, cleaning and disinfecting areas, and areas for the disposal of waste. Finally, NFPA 1581 covers protective measures needed during emergency medical operations, as well as cleaning, disinfecting and disposal procedures. Appendix A includes sample policy statements and resource material.

1-3* Definitions

A-1-3 For a more complete glossary of terms associated with infection control, refer to the United States Fire Administration Publication #FA-112, *Guide to Developing and Managing an Emergency Service Infection Control Program.*

Airborne Pathogens. Pathogenic microorganisms that are present in airborne secretions and can cause diseases in humans. These pathogens shall include, but shall not be limited to, chicken pox, German measles (rubella), influenza, measles, meningococcal meningitis, mononucleosis, mumps, tuberculosis, and whooping cough (pertussis).

Blood. Human blood, human blood components, and products made from human blood.

Bloodborne Pathogens. Pathogenic microorganisms that are present in human blood and can cause diseases in humans. These pathogens shall include, but shall not be limited to, human immunodeficiency virus (HIV), hepatitis B virus (HBV), hepatitis C virus (HCV), other non-A/non-B hepatitis viruses, and syphilis.

Body Fluids. Fluids that the body produces including, but not limited to, blood, semen, mucus, feces, urine, vaginal secretions, breast milk, amniotic fluids, cerebrospinal fluid, synovial fluid, pericardial fluid, and any other fluids that might contain HIV or HBV viruses.

Body Substance Isolation. An infection control strategy that considers *all* body substances potentially infectious.

Cleaning. The physical removal of dirt and debris. This generally is accomplished with soap and water and physical scrubbing.

Cleaning Gloves. See Gloves.

Contaminated. The presence or the reasonably anticipated presence of blood, body fluids, or other potentially infectious materials on an item or surface.

Contaminated Sharps. Any contaminated object that can penetrate the skin including, but not limited to, needles, lancets, scalpels, broken glass, and jagged metal or other debris.

Decontamination. The use of physical or chemical means to remove, inactivate, or destroy bloodborne, airborne, or foodborne pathogens on a surface or item to the point where they are no longer capable of transmitting infectious particles and the surface or item is rendered safe for handling, use, or disposal. *(See A-5-3.8.)*

Disease Transmission. The process that includes a sufficient quantity of an infectious agent, such as a virus or bacteria; a mode of transmission, such as blood for HBV and HIV or airborne droplets for tuberculosis; a portal of entry, such as a needle stick injury, abraded skin, or mucous membrane contact; and a susceptible host.

Disinfection. The process used to inactivate virtually all recognized pathogenic microorganisms but not necessarily all microbial forms, such as bacterial endospore. Disinfection is not the same as sterilization.

Emergency Medical Care. The provision of treatment to patients, including first aid, cardiopulmonary resuscitation, basic life support (EMT level), advanced life support (Paramedic level), and other medical procedures that occur prior to arrival at a hospital or other health care facility.

Emergency Medical Operation. Delivery of emergency medical care and transportation prior to arrival at a hospital or other health care facility.

Environmental Surface. Interior patient care areas, both stationary and in vehicles, and other surfaces not designed for intrusive contact with the patient or contact with mucosal tissue.

Exposure Incident. A specific eye, mouth, other mucous membrane, non-intact skin, or parenteral contact with blood, body fluids, or other potentially infectious materials, or inhalation of airborne pathogens.

Eyewear. See Splash-Resistant Eyewear.

Face Protection Devices. Devices constructed of protective clothing materials, designed and configured to cover part or all of the wearer's face or head. Face protection devices might include splash-resistant eyewear, hooded visors, or respirators.

Fire Department. An organization providing rescue, fire suppression, and related activities, including emergency medical operations. The term "fire department" shall include any public, private, or military organization engaging in this type of activity.

Fire Department Facility. Any building or area owned, operated, occupied, or used by a fire department on a routine basis. This does not include locations where a fire department could be summoned to perform emergency operations or other duties, unless such premises are normally under the control of the fire department.

Fire Department Member. See Member.

Fluid-Resistant Clothing. Clothing worn for the purpose of isolating parts of the wearer's body from contact with body fluids.

Foodborne. Pathogenic microorganisms that are present in food or food products and can cause diseases in humans. These pathogens include, but are not limited to, hepatitis A virus and salmonella bacteria.

Garment. An item of clothing that covers any part of the wearer's skin, excluding accessory items such as gloves or face protection devices, including but not limited to full body clothing such as suits, coveralls, and patient/victim isolation bags; and non-full body clothing such as aprons, sleeve protectors, and shoe covers.

Gloves.*

Cleaning Gloves. Multipurpose, multiuse gloves that provide limited protection from abrasion, cuts, snags, and punctures during cleaning and that are designed to provide a barrier against body fluids, cleaning fluids, and disinfectants.

Emergency Medical Gloves. Single-use, patient examination gloves that are designed to provide a barrier against body fluids meeting the requirements of NFPA 1999, *Standard on Protective Clothing for Emergency Medical Operations.*

Structural Fire Fighting Gloves. Gloves meeting the requirements of NFPA 1973, *Standard on Gloves for Structural Fire Fighting.*

A-1-3 Gloves. The requirement for FDA registration provides further benefit to the emergency responder. The FDA currently does not require that medical gloves used in emergency medical response be registered as medical devices. Yet, these same gloves, when worn by emergency personnel inside hospitals and other health care provision organizations, must be registered as Class 1 medical devices with the FDA. While FDA registration is not a certification of the product, it is a process by which the manufacturer must provide substantiation for any and all claims made regarding the performance of the product (e.g., its viral barrier performance, levels of quality assurance, and sterility) in either product packaging or marketing literature. The FDA neither affirms nor denies these claims. Therefore, this requirement helps to ensure that the fire service and emergency medical service personnel are provided with accurate information about the products they purchase.

Handwashing Facility. A facility providing an adequate supply of running potable water, soap, and single-use towels or hot-air drying machines.

HBV. Hepatitis B virus.

HCV. Hepatitis C virus.

HIV. Human immunodeficiency virus.

Health Data Base. A compilation of records and data relating to the health experience of a group of individuals, maintained in such a manner that it is retrievable for study and analysis over a period of time.

Immunization. The process or procedure by which a person is rendered immune.

Industrial Fire Department. An organization providing rescue, fire suppression, and related activities at a single facility or facilities under the same management, whether for profit, not for profit, or government owned or operated, including industrial, commercial, mercantile, warehouse, and institutional occupancies. The industrial fire department generally is trained and equipped for specialized operations based on site-specific hazards present at the facilities.

Infection Control Officer. The person or persons within the fire department who are responsible for managing the department infection control program and for coordinating efforts surrounding the investigation of an exposure.

Infection Control Program. The fire department's formal policy and implementation of procedures relating to the control of infectious and communicable disease hazards where employees, patients, or the general public could be exposed to blood, body fluids, or other potentially infectious materials in the fire department work environment.

Kitchen. An area designated for storage, preparation, cooking, and serving of food for members. Cleaning and washing of food service equipment and utensils also are conducted in this area.

Leakproof Bags. Bags that are sufficiently sturdy to prevent tearing or breaking and can be sealed securely to prevent leakage. Such bags are red in color or display the universal biohazard symbol.

Mask. A device designed to limit exposure of the nasal, oral, respiratory, or mucosal membranes to airborne pathogens.

Medical Gloves. See Gloves.

Medical Waste. Items to be disposed of that have been contaminated with human waste, blood, or body fluids; or human waste, human tissue, blood, or body fluids for which special handling precautions are necessary.

Member. A person involved in performing the duties and responsibilities of a fire department, under the auspices of the organization. For the purposes of this standard, a fire department member can be a full-time or part-time employee, can be a paid or unpaid volunteer, shall be permitted to occupy any position or rank within the fire department, and might or might not engage in emergency operations.

Mucous Membrane. A moist layer of tissue that lines the mouth, eyes, nostrils, vagina, anus, or urethra.

Needle. A slender, usually sharp, pointed instrument used for puncturing tissues, suturing, drawing blood, or passing a ligature around an artery.

Occupational Exposure. Reasonably anticipated skin, eye, mucous membrane, or parenteral contact with blood, body fluids, or other potentially infectious materials that might result from the performance of a member's duties.

Other Potentially Infectious Materials. Any body fluid that is visibly contaminated with blood; all body fluids in situations where it is difficult or impossible to differentiate between body fluids; sputum, saliva, and other respiratory secretions; and any unfixed tissue or organ from a living or dead human.

Patient. An individual, living or dead, whose body fluids, tissues, or organs could be a source of exposure to the member.

Parenteral. Piercing of the mucous membranes or the skin barrier due to such events as needle sticks, human bites, cuts, and abrasions.

Personal Protective Equipment. Specialized clothing or equipment worn by a member for protection against an infectious or communicable disease hazard. Personal protective equipment for cleaning and disinfecting shall include splash-resistant eyewear, cleaning gloves, and fluid-resistant clothing.

Pocket Mask. A double-lumen device that is portable, pocket-size, and designed to protect the emergency care provider from direct contact with the mouth/lips or body fluids of a patient while performing artificial respiration.

Regulated Waste. Liquid or semiliquid blood, body fluids, or other potentially infectious materials; contaminated items that would release blood, body fluids, or other potentially infectious materials in a liquid or semiliquid state if compressed; items that are caked with dried blood, body fluids, or other potentially infectious materials and are capable of releasing these materials during handling; contaminated sharps; and pathological and microbiological wastes containing blood, body fluids, or other potentially infectious materials.

Resuscitation Equipment. Respiratory assist devices such as bag-valve masks, oxygen demand valve resuscitators, pocket masks, and other ventilation devices that are designed to provide artificial respiration or assist with ventilation of a patient.

Risk. A measure of the probability and severity of adverse effects. These adverse effects result from an exposure to a hazard.

Shall. Indicates a mandatory requirement.

Sharps Containers. Containers that are closable, puncture-resistant, disposable, and leakproof on the sides and bottom; red in color or display the universal biohazard symbol; and designed to store sharp objects after use.

Should. Indicates a recommendation or that which is advised but not required.

Source Individual. Any individual, living or dead, whose blood, body fluids, or other potentially infectious materials could be a source of occupational exposure to a member.

Splash-Resistant Eyewear. Safety glasses, prescription eyewear, goggles, or chin-length faceshields that, when properly worn, provide limited protection against splashes, spray, spatter, droplets, or aerosols of body fluids or other potentially infectious material. (*See Face Protection Devices.*)

Sterilization. The use of a physical or chemical procedure to destroy all microbial life, including highly resistant bacterial endospores. This procedure typically is not performed at fire department facilities or by members.

Structural Fire Fighting Gloves. See Gloves.

Structural Fire Fighting Protective Clothing. Garments primarily intended for structural fire fighting and rescue operations including, but not limited to, coats, trousers, gloves, hoods, footwear, and helmets.

Universal Precautions. An approach to infection control in which human blood and certain human body fluids are treated as if known to be infectious for HIV, HBV, and other bloodborne pathogens. Under circumstances in which differentiation between body fluids is difficult or impossible, all body fluids shall be considered potentially infectious materials. (*See Body Substance Isolation.*)

The list of definitions in NFPA 1581 is fairly comprehensive. A more extensive list (related to the emergency services) can be found in the U.S. Fire Administration publication *Guide to Developing and Managing an Emergency Service Infection Control Program*. Some terminology, occasionally used but not addressed in the definitions in the standard, includes "Designated Officer" (another term for "Infection Control Officer") and "standard precautions" (the principles of protection used in both "universal precautions" and "body substance isolation").

CHAPTER 2

Program Components

2-1 Policy

2-1.1*

The fire department shall have a written infection control policy with the goal of identifying and limiting the exposure of members to infection during the performance of their assigned duties and within the fire department working and living environment.

A-2-1.1 Sample Policy Statements. The following examples are reprinted from the United States Fire Administration Publication #FA-112, *Guide to Developing and Managing an Emergency Service Infection Control Program.*

Example 1: The______Fire Department recognizes the potential exposure of its fire fighters, in the performance of their duties, to communicable diseases. To minimize the risk of exposure, the______Fire Department will implement an infection control program.

The infection control program will include standard operating procedures; initial training and continuing education in infection control practices; a vaccination program; the provision of proper infection control clothing and equipment; decontamination procedures for clothing and equipment; procedures for the disposal of medical waste; a system for reporting and managing exposures; a system for tracking exposures and ensuring confidentiality; monitoring of compliance with the standard operating procedures; the design of fire department facilities to minimize risk of infection; and a public information campaign.

Finally, exposure to communicable disease shall be considered an occupational health hazard, and any communicable disease contracted as the result of a documented workplace exposure shall be considered occupationally related.

Example 2: The______Fire Department recognizes the potential exposure of its members to communicable diseases in the performance of their duties and in the normal work environment. The______Fire Department is committed to a program that will reduce this exposure to a minimum and will take whatever measures are feasible to protect the health of its members.

In the emergency care setting, the infectious disease status of patients is frequently unknown by fire department personnel. All patients must be considered infectious. Blood and body fluid precautions must be taken with all patients.

To minimize the risk of exposure, the______Fire Department will provide its members with proper infection control protective equipment, including disposable medical gloves, face masks, gowns, and eyewear, and will provide necessary cleaning and disinfecting supplies. The ______Fire Department also will provide initial instruction and continuing education in preventative health care practices so that fire fighters possess a basic awareness of infectious diseases, understand the risks and severity of various types of exposures, and exhibit proper skills in infection control.

Standard prophylactic medical treatment will be given to exposed members, and necessary immunizations will be made available to protect members from potential exposure to infectious disease.

______Fire Department members will contact the fire department infection control representative after any actual or suspected exposure to a contagious disease. The infection control representative will contact the hospital to initiate patient follow-up and determine the need for treatment of the exposed individual. A contagious disease exposure tracking system is a component of the medical records system that is maintained for each member.

The______Fire Department believes that its members have the right to be fully informed if a patient is found to carry a communicable disease and if a probable exposure occurred. The responsibility for informing the______Fire Department should rest with the medical institution receiving the patient and should occur as soon as possible after the medical institution becomes aware of the condition.

The______Fire Department also recognizes the health concerns that may be involved in the station work environment, where a number of members share living quarters and work areas and, in some cases, use the same equipment. There is a particular need to isolate this environment from the infectious hazards that members may encounter in providing emergency care to the general public. There is also a need to provide facilities and equipment that do not expose members to additional health risks. This also extends to preventing the spread of health risks encountered in the work environment to a member's home, family, and friends.

The______Fire Department also believes that infectious disease exposure should be considered an occupational health hazard and supports the presumption that contracting a contagious disease should be considered an occupationally related condition.

Therefore, the______Fire Department hereby adopts NFPA 1581, *Standard on Fire Department Infection Control Program.*

It is possible that an existing program or policy may be permitted to satisfy the requirements of this standard; if so, it may be permitted to be adopted in whole or in part, in order to comply with this standard. An example of such an existing policy or program might be a corporate infection control program or an employee immunization program.

A policy statement makes the members aware that the department considers infection control to be an important issue.

The written policy statement should define the purpose, scope, and philosophy of the infection control program clearly.

Sample
Infection Control Program
Policy Statement

Purpose: To provide a comprehensive infection control system which maximizes protection against communicable diseases for all members, and for the public that they serve.

Scope: This policy applies to all members, career and volunteer, providing fire, rescue, or emergency medical services.

This department recognizes that communicable disease exposure is an occupational health hazard. Communicable disease transmission is possible during any aspect of emergency response, including in-station operations. The health and welfare of each member is a joint concern of the member, the chain of command, and this department. While each member is ultimately responsible for his or her own health, the department recognizes a responsibility to provide as safe a workplace as possible. The goal of this program is to provide all members with the best available protection from occupationally acquired communicable disease.

It is the policy of this department:

- To provide fire, rescue, and emergency medical services to the public without regard to known or suspected diagnoses of communicable disease in any patient.
- To regard all patient contacts as potentially infectious. Universal precautions will be observed at all times and will be expanded to include all body fluids and other potentially infectious material (body substance isolation).
- To provide all members with the necessary training, immunizations, and personal protective equipment (PPE) needed for protection from communicable diseases.
- To recognize the need for work restrictions based on infection control concerns.
- To encourage participation in member assistance and CISD (Critical Incident Stress Debriefing) programs.
- To prohibit discrimination of any member for health reasons, including infection and/or seroconversion with HIV or HBV.
- To regard all medical information as strictly confidential. No member health information will be released without the signed written consent of the member.

2-1.2

As part of the overall fire department safety and health program, the fire department shall implement an infection control program that meets the requirements of this standard.

2-1.3

The fire department shall provide for the cleaning and disinfection or disposal of personal protective equipment, structural fire fighting protective equipment, station/work uniforms, other clothing, and emergency medical equipment.

2-1.4*

Members with infections that constitute, in the course of performing their duties, a risk of infection to patients or other members shall be evaluated by a physician to determine those functions the member can perform.

A-2-1.4 Table A-2-1.4 summarizes information on the specific diseases/infections that are of greatest concern.

2-1.5

Members with extensive skin lesions or severe dermatitis on hands, arms, head, face, or neck shall not engage in direct patient contact, handle patient care equipment, or handle medical waste.

The first three paragraphs of Section 2-1 are intended to meet the exposure control program

Table A-2-1.4 Disease Information for Emergency Response Personnel

Disease/Infection	Mode of Transmission	Is Vaccine Available?	Signs and Symptoms
AIDS/HIV (human immunodeficiency virus)	Needle stick, blood splash into mucous membranes (e.g., eyes, mouth), or blood contact with open wound	No	Fever, night sweats, weight loss, cough
Chickenpox	Respiratory secretions and contact with moist vesicles	No	Fever, rash cutaneous vesicles (blisters)
Diarrhea: Campylobacter Cryptosporidium Giardia Salmonella Shigella Viral Yersinia	Fecal/oral	No	Loose, watery stools
German measles (rubella)	Respiratory droplets and contact with respiratory secretions	Yes	Fever, rash
Hepatitis A (infectious hepatitis)	Fecal/oral	No	Fever, loss of appetite, jaundice, fatigue
Hepatitis B (HBV) (serum hepatitis)	Needle stick, blood splash into mucous membranes (e.g., eye or mouth), or blood contact with open wound. Possible exposure during mouth-to-mouth resuscitation	Yes	Fever, fatigue, loss of appetite, nausea, headache, jaundice
Hepatitis C	Same as hepatitis B	No	Same as hepatitis B
Hepatitis D	Same as hepatitis B. Dependent on HBV (past or present) to cause infection.	No	A complication of HBV infection and can increase the severity of HBV infection
Other non-A/non-B hepatitis	Several viruses with different modes of transmission (These are called "non- A/non-B" because there are no specific tests to identify them.)	No	Fever, headache, fatigue, jaundice
Herpes simplex (cold sores)	Contact of mucous membrane with moist lesions. Fingers are at particular risk for becoming infected	No	Skin lesions located around the mouth area
Herpes zoster (shingles) localized disseminated (see chickenpox)	Contact with moist lesions.	No	Skin lesions
Influenza	Airborne	Yes	Fever, fatigue, loss of appetite, nausea, headache
Lice: Head Body Pubic	Close head to head contact. Both body and pubic lice require intimate contact (usually sexual) or sharing of intimate clothing.		Severe itching and scratching, often with secondary infection. Scalp and hairy portions of body may be affected. Eggs of head lice (nits) attach to hairs as small, round, gray lumps.
Measles	Respiratory droplets and contact with nasal or throat secretions. Highly communicable	Yes	Fever, rash, bronchitis

(continues)

Table A-2-1.4 Continued

Disease/Infection	Mode of Transmission	Is Vaccine Available?	Signs and Symptoms
Meningitis:			
Meningococcal	Contact with respiratory secretions	No	Fever, severe headache, stiff neck, sore throat
Haemophilus influenza (usually seen in very young children)	Contact with respiratory secretions	No	(Same)
Viral meningitis	Fecal/oral	No	(Same)
Mononucleosis	Contact with respiratory secretions or saliva, such as with mouth-to-mouth resuscitation	No	Fever, sore throat, fatigue
Mumps (infectious parotitis)	Respiratory droplets and contact with saliva	Yes	Fever, swelling of salivary glands (parotid)
Salmonellosis	Foodborne	No	Sudden onset of fever, abdominal pain, diarrhea, nausea, and frequent vomiting
Scabies	Close body contact	No	Itching, tiny linear burrows or "tracks," vesicles—particularly around fingers, wrists, elbows, and skin folds
Syphilis	Primarily sexual contact; rarely through blood transfusion	No	Genital and cutaneous lesions, nerve degeneration (late)
Tuberculosis, pulmonary	Airborne	No	Fever, night sweats, weight loss, cough
Whooping cough (pertussis)	Airborne, direct contact with oral secretions	Yes	Violent cough at night, whooping sound when cough subsides

requirements of the OSHA bloodborne pathogen regulation. Each department must have a written exposure control policy and a complete program to address members' safety and health in relation to bloodborne pathogens. In contrast to OSHA requirements, NFPA 1581 also applies to airborne and foodborne pathogens.

Paragraph A-2-1.1 includes sample policy statements. A policy statement informs members that the department considers infection control to be an important issue. The written policy statement should clearly define the purpose, scope, and philosophy of the infection control program.

The fire department must provide for the protection of its personnel in real terms, not just in policy form. This includes having all necessary personal protective equipment, training, and vaccination programs for any disease that members may be exposed to in the course of their duties. Table A-2-1.4 identifies the specific diseases that are of concern to the emergency services, modes of transmission, the signs and symptoms, and whether a vaccine is available.

Members must be monitored for exposure to infectious or communicable disease and for the potential to be infectious or communicable. For example, a member with severe skin lesions or large lacerations must completely cover the affected areas, or must not be allowed to provide patient care until the areas are covered or healed. The member, in this case, faces a great risk of a disease if an infected patient's body fluid splashes into the non-intact skin. Likewise, a patient who has an open wound or burn could face a severe exposure if the member's wound or lesion oozes or bleeds onto the patient.

Appropriate policy must be established to deal with exposure incidents. Such a policy would include access to medical expertise to help determine whether a member should be temporarily taken off-line. *(See also Section 2-6 of this standard.)*

2-2* Risk Management

A-2-2 The risk to personnel of exposure to infection poses a real hazard and should be properly addressed through a written infection control program which includes but is not limited to:

- Training and education,
- Personal protective equipment,
- Health maintenance and vaccinations,
- Appropriate supervision,
- Incident operations,
- Facility safety,
- Medical follow-up for an occupational exposure.

Infection control should be integrated into the department's overall risk management process. By utilizing the risk management process, risks are identified by the services that a department provides. These risks should be evaluated based upon the probability and severity of occurrence within the community. Control measures should be implemented based upon the risk evaluation and services performed by the department. A monitoring process evaluates the effectiveness of the risk control techniques.

This is an ongoing process that should be continually evaluated and revised based upon the needs and requirements of the department. The health and safety officer, infection control officer, and the department's occupational safety and health committee should ensure that evaluations and revisions occur at least annually.

2-2.1

In accordance with NFPA 1500, *Standard on Fire Department Occupational Safety and Health Program*, Section 2-2, the fire department shall adopt a written risk management plan that addresses infection control.

2-2.2

The written risk management plan shall include risk assessment and control measures for department facilities, emergency medical operations, cleaning and disinfecting of personal protective equipment, and any other situation that poses an occupational risk to personnel due to infection.

Section 2-2 reiterates the requirement in NFPA 1500 (1997) (Part One of this handbook) for each department to adopt a written risk management plan. The section further specifies that the risk management plan must address infection control.

The areas to be covered include risk assessment and risk control measures for all aspects of emergency services operations and facilities (including training and education, personal protective equipment, health maintenance and vaccinations, incident operations, facility safety, post-exposure protocols, cleaning and disinfection, and any other situation that could pose a risk to members). Appropriate supervisory issues must also be addressed.

2-3 Training and Education

2-3.1*

The fire department shall conduct annual training and education programs for all members.

A-2-3.1 For infectious disease training guidelines, consult Infection Control for Emergency Response Personnel:The Supervisor's Role (Student Manual), U.S. Fire Administration, National Fire Academy; or A Curriculum Guide for Public Safety and Emergency Response Workers, Prevention of Transmission of Human Immunodeficiency Virus and Hepatitis B Virus, U.S. Department of Health and Human Services, Public Health Service, Centers for Disease Control and Prevention.

2-3.2

The training program shall include proper use of personal protective equipment, standard operating procedures for safe work practices in infection control, proper methods of disposal of contaminated articles and medical waste, cleaning and decontamination, exposure management, and medical follow-up.

2-3.3*

The education program shall provide information on epidemiology, modes of transmission, and prevention of diseases including, but not limited to, meningitis, childhood communicable diseases, herpes viruses, hepatitis A, hepatitis B, non-A/non-B or hepatitis C, human immunodeficiency virus, tuberculosis, lice, and scabies.

A-2-3.3 A list of applicable government regulations relating to infection control are listed in Appendix B.

2-3.4

Members shall be educated in the potential reproductive health risks to the individual as well as to the fetus.

As Section 2-3 makes clear, training is one of the most important aspects of an infection control program. Section 2-3, like the OSHA bloodborne pathogen regulation, identifies specific topics that must be covered in the training/education program. The OSHA bloodborne pathogen regulation requires that specific information be provided on Hepatitis B vaccinations; NFPA 1581 additionally requires that information be provided on potential reproductive hazards to the member and the fetus.

There are several training programs available for purchase and/or use by fire and EMS departments. Several states have developed mandatory programs, which are available to local departments. The American Red Cross has some programs available; also there are commercially available programs. (Note that the OSHA bloodborne pathogen regulation requires someone "knowledgeable" in infection control to be present to answer questions during the training program.) The National Fire Academy course, *Infection Control for Emergency Response Personnel: The Supervisor's Role,* is now available through state fire and EMS training agencies or for purchase through the National Technical Information Service. The NFA course is designed to meet the training requirements of NFPA 1581, the OSHA bloodborne pathogen regulation, and the Centers for Disease Control guidelines. However, that course is aimed at supervisory-level members of the emergency services.

2-4 Infection Control Officer

2-4.1

The fire department shall designate one or more members or other qualified persons as the infection control officer.

2-4.2*

The infection control officer shall be responsible for maintaining communication among the fire department, the fire department physician, the health care facility, appropriate city, county, or state health officials, and other health care professionals.

A-2-4.2 The infection control officer does not necessarily need to be of an officer rank. The member or members in this position are intended to fulfill the requirements of a "designated officer" as required in Public Law 101-381, *The Ryan White Comprehensive AIDS Resources Emergency (CARE) Act of 1990.*

2-4.3

When notified of an exposure incident, the infection control officer shall ensure the notification, verification, treatment, and follow-up of members. The infection control officer also shall ensure that proper documentation of the exposure incident is recorded as specified in 2-6.4 of this standard.

2-4.4

The infection control officer shall examine compliance procedures and engineering controls to ensure their effectiveness in accordance with Chapter 3 of this standard.

2-4.5

The infection control officer shall be a designated member of the fire department's occupational safety and health committee.

Section 2-4 addresses the infection control officer position, or "designated officer," as the position is sometimes called. The infection control officer does not have to be a separate position within a department. For example, the health and safety officer or EMS coordinator can fill this role effectively. The infection control officer is the primary point of contact between the hospital and the department on issues related to infection control and occupational exposures. The *Ryan White Law* requires each emergency response agency to have a "designated officer" (hence the term) who can be notified whenever the department transports a patient with an airborne-transmissible disease to the hospital. The designated officer would then contact the members involved for any follow-up testing or treatment. The infection control officer also contacts the hospital when a member has an occupational exposure to blood or other body fluid to ensure that all documentation, verification, and follow-up were completed appropriately.

The need for a single person to be the point of contact with hospitals is primarily based on the need for confidentiality. For example, consider what happens when a crew takes a child to the hospital, and later at the hospital it is determined that the child has infectious meningitis. The hospital must notify the fire department to send members for testing and/or treatment. The crew involved will quite possibly be at another station, on a call, or off duty by the time the hospital calls. For timely alerting of members, the hospital needs an after-hours number for the designated officer. Without these safeguards, days could pass before the members are actually notified of an exposure. By that time, a message that began as "You need to come in for an evaluation" could have easily become "You have acquired a disease." Having a designated, trained point of contact will minimize such dangerous delays.

It is also important that the designated officer serve as liaison to the various hospitals, infection control physicians, other department infection control officers, and similar outside resources. This individual should monitor the effectiveness of the department's infection control program and keep abreast of any changes in the infection control field that may warrant a change in policy and/or procedure.

2-5 Health Maintenance

2-5.1*

The fire department shall make available or ensure that members have access to an appropriate immunization program, including vaccination against hepatitis B.

A-2-5.1 Members that choose to decline immunizations offered by the department shall sign a written declination. The declination shall become part of the member's confidential health data base as specified in NFPA 1500, *Standard on Fire Department Occupational Safety and Health Program*, Section 8-4.

2-5.2

The fire department shall ensure that all members have adequate immunity, as determined through consultation with a physician, to tetanus, diphtheria, rubella, measles, polio, mumps, and influenza.

2-5.3

The fire department shall make available or ensure that members have access to tuberculosis screening at least annually.

2-5.4

Members shall meet the medical requirements specified in NFPA 1582, *Standard on Medical Requirements for Fire Fighters*, prior to being medically certified for duty by the fire department physician.

2-5.5

In the event of any perceived occupational exposure, the member shall receive a confidential medical evaluation, post-exposure prophylaxis where medically indicated, counseling, and evaluation of reported illness by the fire department physician.

2-5.6

A confidential health data base shall be established and maintained for each member. Any exposures shall become part of a member's confidential health data base as specified by NFPA 1582, *Standard on Medical Requirements for Fire Fighters*, and in accordance with 29 *CFR*, Part 1910.20, "Access to Employee Exposure and Medical Records."

Section 2-5 of NFPA 1581 addressees member health maintenance aspects of infection control. The section requires that the fire department provide access to hepatitis B vaccinations and other appropriate vaccinations. In addition, the department must ensure that each member has immunity to the various childhood diseases.

In fact, members should be up-to-date on all vaccines, including hepatitis B, which is now a typically required childhood vaccine. Each member must be provided with (or have access to) annual tuberculosis screening, which is very important due to the difficulty in determining exposure and the rapid rise of cases of different types of tuberculosis. Vaccination programs and TB screening can often be provided through a city or county health department, at little or no cost to the fire department.

Paragraph 2-5.6 requires all members to meet NFPA 1582, *Standard on Medical Requirements for Fire Fighters* (1997) (Part Five of this handbook). NFPA 1500, *Standard on Fire Department Occupational Safety and Health Program* (1997) (Part One of this handbook), also cites fulfilling medical requirements as a mandated fire fighter safety component. NFPA 1582 requires annual medical evaluations and periodic medical examinations by a physician.

A confidential post-exposure medical evaluation, appropriate prophylaxis, and counseling are also required, according to paragraph 2-5.5, after actual and perceived exposures, as both can affect work performance and member safety and health. Most exposures will probably be evaluated as posing little or no risk of disease transmission, and no prophylaxis is necessary. However, the stress of real or perceived exposure is significant, and appropriate counseling may be necessary.

The fire department must establish a confidential health data base, which includes injuries, illnesses, and exposures, as well as medical evaluation and examination results. Such a data base is addressed in NFPA 1500, NFPA 1582, and OSHA regulations on bloodborne pathogens and medical record keeping. The data base does not have to be elaborate, or even computerized. *(See Figure 1581-2.1.)* It must, however, be confidential and have all appropriate records accessible in one place. This way, if a member contracts an illness in ten years, all appropriate documentation of previous medical evaluations and exposures can be accessed and reviewed. The data base can be especially useful if a member has left the department, or if the member has died and survivors, workers' compensation agents, or OSHA officials are researching medical history.

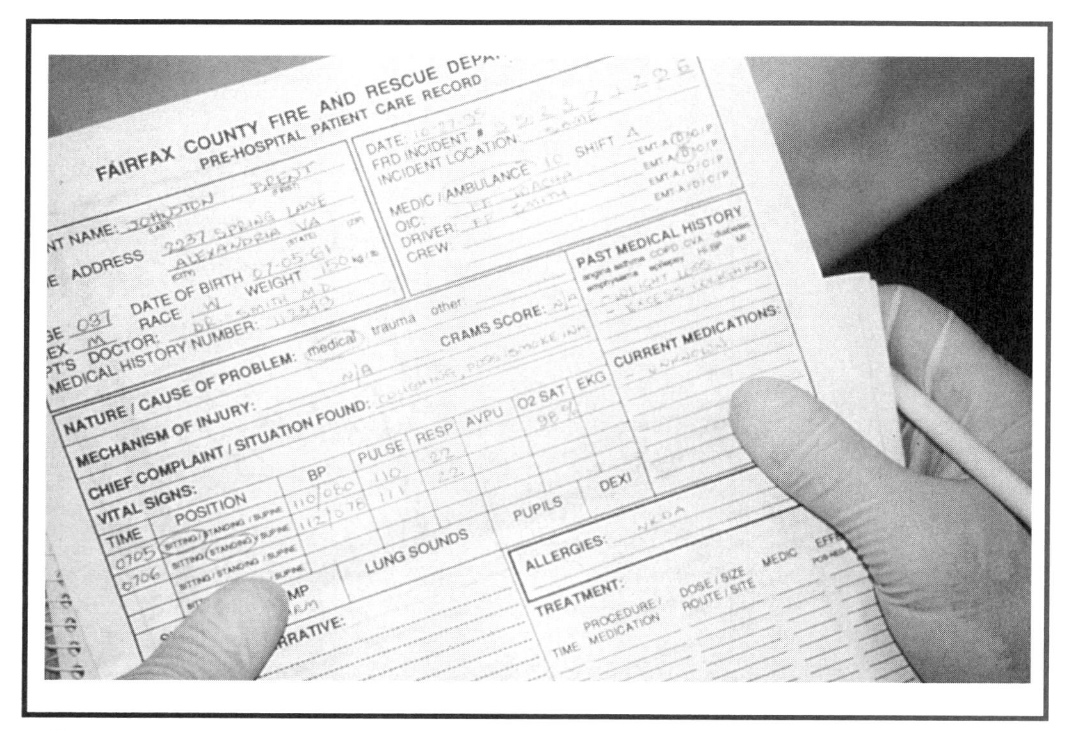

Figure 1581-2.1 *EMS providers must document any incident data, including patient medical treatment and exposure. (Photo courtesy of Fairfax County Fire and Rescue Dept., Fairfax, Virginia)*

2-6 Exposure Incidents

2-6.1

If a member has sustained an exposure incident, the exposed area shall be thoroughly washed immediately using water on mucosal surfaces, and soap and running water on skin surfaces. If soap and running water are not available, waterless soap, antiseptic wipe, alcohol, or other skin cleaning agents that do not need running water shall be used until soap and running water can be obtained.

2-6.2

The fire department shall have an established procedure for members to report an exposure incident immediately and for the infection control liaison to be notified within 3 hours of the exposure incident.

2-6.3*

The fire department shall ensure that a member who has experienced an exposure incident receives medical guidance, evaluation, and, where appropriate, treatment as soon as practical but at least within 24 hours. Appropriate, confidential, post-exposure counseling and testing shall be made available.

A-2-6.3 For appropriate post-exposure guidelines, consult 29 CFR 1910.1030, Occupational Exposure to "Bloodborne Pathogens," Final Rule; *Guidelines for Prevention of Transmission of Human Immunodeficiency Virus and Hepatitis B Virus to Health Care and Public Safety Workers*; and *Guidelines for Infection Control in Hospital Personnel*, by Walter Williams, MD, MPH, Hospital Infections Program, Center for Infectious Disease, Centers for Disease Control and Prevention, Atlanta, Georgia.

For guidance on post-exposure counseling, consult "Public Health Service Guidelines for Counseling and Antibody Testing to Prevent HIV Infection and AIDS," *Morbidity and Mortality Weekly Review*, Centers for Disease Control and Prevention.

2-6.4*

All exposure incidents shall be recorded in writing as soon as possible after the incident using a standardized form designed to allow for efficient follow-up. Included in the record shall be a description of the tasks being performed when the exposure incident occurred, the means of transmission, the portal of entry, the personal protective equipment utilized, and the disposition of medical management.

A-2-6.4 Recordkeeping should be done in accordance with the requirements of 29 *CFR*, Part 1910.1030, Occupational Exposure to "Bloodborne Pathogens," Final Rule.

Figure A-2-6.4 is an example of a report form.

The Infectious Exposure Form that appeared in paragraph A-2-6.4 of the 1995 edition of the *Standard for Fire Department Safety Officer* is not part of the requirements of the standard, but is included with the standard for informational purposes only. For the convenience of readers, in this handbook the form is included in Supplement 12 as Form S12-4 in a full-size version suitable for reproduction.

2-6.5

The record of exposure incidents shall become part of the member's confidential health data base as specified in NFPA 1500, *Standard on Fire Department Occupational Safety and Health Program*, Section 8-4.

2-6.6

A complete record of the member's exposure incidents shall be available to the member upon request.

2-6.7

Exposure incident data, without personal identifiers, also shall be added to the fire department health data base as specified in NFPA 1500, *Standard on Fire Department Occupational Safety and Health Program*, Section 8-4.

2-6.8

Due to the hazardous nature of some communicable diseases, members shall be required to report to the infection control officer when the member has received a confirmed exposure incident and is being medically treated or tested due to presenting signs or symptoms. Verbal notification shall be followed up with a note or letter from the member's physician describing the disease to which the member has been exposed, treatment required, and fitness for regular fire department duties relative to communicability hazard to fellow workers and civilians at emergency incidents.

Section 2-6 of NFPA 1581 expands on Section 2-5, Health Maintenance, by detailing the requirements of a fire department post-exposure program. Obviously, a member who comes in contact with a patient's blood or body fluids must be washed thoroughly with soap and water or a waterless cleanser. After this initial cleansing, the fire department's post-exposure program begins.

The post-exposure process consists of four basic steps: (a) notification, (b) verification, (c) documentation, and (d) treatment/follow-up. All of the following steps should be initiated as quickly as possible:

(a) Notification of an actual or possible exposure should be made immediately or as soon as possible to the member's supervisor, and subsequently to the department's infection control officer. Notification protects the employee by removing any question at a later date that the incident actually occurred. Some departments use a form for notification purposes (separate from an exposure report form); others make an entry in the appropriate station log book.

(b) Verification investigates the exposure incident, not for preventability or blame, but to determine whether an exposure did occur or whether it was a perceived exposure. Verification must be done by someone specifically trained in infection control and exposure risk identification. Terminology can make a difference in the stress level of an employee. With a "perceived exposure," there may actually have been contact with body fluids, but the person verifying the exposure determines that there is no risk of transmission of disease. With a "true exposure," the person verifying the exposure determines that there is a risk of transmission. While both perceived and true exposures need to be documented, rarely does a perceived exposure need treatment/followup care beyond counseling.

(c) Documentation depends on a standard form used for all exposures so that all the appropriate information is captured consistently. (See Form S12-4 in Supplement 12 for a sample form.) This information becomes part of the confidential health data base, and is listed in the standard as including a description of the tasks performed when the exposure incident occurred, the means of transmission, the portal of entry, the personal protective equipment utilized, and the administration of medical care. The information (without personal identifiers) should be included in a tabulated listing of occupational illnesses, injuries, and exposures that is posted at all work locations at least annually. This information can help identify trends or areas that need improvement in the infection control program.

(d) The final step in the post-exposure process is treatment and follow-up. This step includes medical evaluation, examination, testing, prophylaxis, treatment, and counseling as necessary. The extent of this step is determined by a physician or through standing protocols for certain types of exposures (such as exposure to certain types of meningitis).

An off-duty member who has an exposure should follow the same routine, but the data will not be counted in the cumulative departmental data.

Any exposure could potentially affect the job of an emergency responder, and a physician may feel that the member should be temporarily suspended from duty for any number of reasons following a true exposure. In the event that a member does contract a disease (on or off duty), the physician should determine the duty status of the member and the precautions that may be needed in the work environment.

CHAPTER 3

Fire Department Facilities

3-1 General

3-1.1*

All fire department facilities shall comply with applicable and appropriate health and infection control laws, regulations, and standards for public use facilities.

A-3-1.1 State and local laws and regulations are usually very specific about infection control standards for public use facilities. Public health agencies can provide standards for food storage, preparation, and handling, as well as for disposal of general and medical or other regulated waste. Hotel bureaus might be able to provide standards for sleeping areas and bathrooms.

Emergency response agencies can learn important lessons from these state and local agencies, which monitor infection control in public use facilities. Such agencies can serve as valuable resources in developing standard operating procedures or guidelines for infection control in fire department facilities and in designing or remodeling facilities.

The local public health department can be very helpful in meeting the requirements of Section 3-1. A fire station, for example, has some of the same features as a hotel, a restaurant, an assisted living facility, or a retirement home. Using established codes for these types of occupancies on a voluntary basis can improve fire station health and safety.

3-2 Kitchen Areas

3-2.1

All food preparation surfaces shall be of a nonporous material. All surfaces directly used for holding or hanging food preparation containers and utensils shall be of a nonporous material.

3-2.2

Shelving shall be provided above sinks to drip-dry cleaned food preparation containers. All drainage from shelving shall run into a sink or drainage pan that empties directly into a sanitary sewer system or septic system.

3-2.3

All kitchens shall have sinks with a double basin or two sinks. A sprayer attachment shall be provided. Sinks, adjacent countertops and dish drainage areas, and splash guards around the sink shall be of a nonporous material.

3-2.4*

Kitchens in fire department facilities shall have kitchen appliances, including a range, an oven, at least one refrigerator, and a dishwasher.

A-3-2.4 Because of the potential for excessive use by a large number of people, commercial grade appliances are needed in many fire department facilities. Such appliances often have a larger capacity and more durability for continuous or repeated use.

When determining the number of refrigerators needed, consideration should be given to the number of members who will be using a refrigerator or the amount of use the refrigerator will receive. A large number of people using a small refrigerator can result in the door being opened often; thus, the refrigerator might not be able to maintain a proper temperature. This could lead to spoilage of food or the harboring of bacteria or other sources of foodborne diseases.

3-2.5

Perishable food requiring cold storage shall be kept at a temperature of 38°F (3°C) or less. Perishable food requiring freezer storage shall be kept at a temperature of 0°F (–18°C) or less. All foods removed from their original manufactured packaging shall be kept in tightly sealed food containers or shall be wrapped with plastic food wrap.

3-2.6

Kitchens equipped with a dishwasher shall be capable of supplying 140°F (64°C) water for washing.

3-2.7

Food preparation and storage areas shall meet local health standards.

Surprisingly, a fire station kitchen, if not properly managed, can be a major health hazard. Section 3-2 identifies requirements to help prevent foodborne diseases such as salmonella and other food poisoning. Most of the items listed in Section 3-2 are standard in any kitchen built today: double sinks with sprayer, modern appliances, and so forth. Most refrigerators recommend a setting at or below 40°F (approximately 3°C), and freezers at or below 0°F (–18°C). Most dishwashers require a water temperature of 140°F (64°C). Thus, there are few burdensome requirements in this section.

3-3 Sleeping Areas

3-3.1*

A minimum of 60 ft^2 (5.57 m^2) of floor space per bed shall be provided in sleeping areas.

A-3-3.1 Separate bedding lockers and clothing lockers should be provided for each member requiring a bed.

The required floor space per bed (bedroom density) is designed to (1) reduce the chances of a member with a cold or other airborne disease from spreading it to other members and (2) make sleep easier. A rested and healthy body is more resistant to disease and injury.

3-3.2

Proper ventilation, heating, and cooling shall be provided in sleeping areas.

3-4 Bathrooms

3-4.1*

Doors, sinks, and other bathroom fixtures shall be designed to prevent or minimize the spread of contaminants.

A-3-4.1 Bathrooms can be a significant source of infection if they are improperly designed, or if members fail to practice proper hygiene, or both.

Bathrooms should have push-to-open doors for egress, without handles. This assists in eliminating a place for infectious agents to accumulate and breed. It should not be necessary for the user to grasp sink faucets in order to turn them off or on. If grasping is necessary, the user should use a paper towel to turn faucets off after drying.

Hand-drying materials should be disposable, or an air-drying machine should be available. This decreases the possibility of infectious agents accumulating or breeding on a cloth that is used repeatedly.

The flush valve on toilets and urinals should be of a foot operated or electric eye type that does not require the use of hands to operate.

3-4.2

A clearly visible sign reminding members to wash their hands shall be posted prominently in each bathroom.

3-4.3

Bathrooms shall meet local standards.

The requirements of Section 3-4 are basic: Use common sense to reduce the spread of bacteria or other organisms. The sign is important, as a fire department facility is typically a public building, and often food is prepared for several people. For information on local standards, contact the local public health agency.

3-5 Laundry Areas

Obviously, clean materials should not be stored with dirty or contaminated materials. Potentially contaminated personal protective equipment (PPE) is an everyday hazard—structural fire-fighting PPE may be loaded with potential contaminants after every fire! For this reason, it is recommended that all members who have been in a smoke-filled environment be rinsed prior to removing their PPE at the scene. Rinsing will remove many (but not all) contaminants. If PPE becomes contaminated with blood or other body fluids, the garment(s) should be removed immediately, placed in a leakproof bag, and decontaminated as soon as possible. After the incident, PPE should be stored in a dedicated, well-ventilated area in a fire or EMS station. Manufacturer's instructions should be followed (e.g., do not store in direct sunlight).

3-5.1*

The fire department shall provide for the cleaning of protective clothing and station/work uniforms. Such cleaning shall be performed by either a cleaning service that is equipped to handle contaminated clothing or a fire department facility that is equipped to handle contaminated clothing.

A-3-5.1 Commercial models of washers (front-loading washers) and dryers are recommended to prevent agitator damage to clothing.

3-5.2

Where such cleaning is conducted in fire stations, the fire department shall provide at least one washing machine for this purpose in the designated cleaning area as specified in Section 3-7.

3-5.3

Laundry areas shall be kept neat and orderly.

Section 3-5 is intended to prevent contaminated protective clothing and station/work uniforms from being taken home for laundering. Home laundering of contaminated clothing can cause cross-contamination and place family members at risk. Most fire departments comply with Section 3-5 by (1) installing a washer and dryer in each station for laundering station/work uniforms and by (2) contracting out the laundering of personal protective equipment (PPE) or (3) using one or more centrally located commercial washers for laundering personal protective clothing. Some departments have a laundry service for uniforms and PPE.

Commercial washers or extractors can be expensive, since they may have special requirements for plumbing, drainage, and mounting. Similarly, contracting with a professional cleaning company can also be expensive. It may be worth contacting other local departments to establish a joint purchasing agreement for decontamination of PPE.

3-6 Equipment Storage Areas

3-6.1*

Emergency medical supplies and equipment stored in fire department facilities, other than those stored on vehicles, shall be stored in a dedicated, enclosed area to protect from damage and contamination. The storage area shall be secured properly and labeled appropriately.

A-3-6.1 The intent of this requirement is to ensure that emergency medical supplies are located in an area, separate from other functional areas, to minimize contamination. Room temperature should be maintained at 68°F to 90°F (20°C to 32°C).

3-6.2

Open and reusable emergency medical supplies and equipment shall not be stored in kitchen, living, sleeping, recreation, or personal hygiene areas, unless physically separated in a locker or room, nor shall they be stored in personal clothing lockers.

3-6.3

Potentially contaminated personal protective equipment shall be stored in a dedicated, well-ventilated area or room and shall not be stored in kitchen, living, sleeping, recreation, or personal hygiene areas, nor shall they be stored in personal clothing lockers.

3-6.4

Areas or containers for the temporary storage of contaminated medical supplies or equipment prior to disinfection or disposal shall be separated physically from members in facilities or on vehicles. Such areas or containers shall not be used for any other purpose.

As required by Section 3.6, to prevent contamination or damage, medical supplies and equipment must be stored in a locker or closet, or in closed, labeled containers in a designated area. Open or reusable medical supplies or equipment must never be stored in a kitchen, bathroom, personal hygiene area, living or recreation area, furnace room, shop area, or any location where they might be damaged or where any latent contamination might endanger members. Supplies and equipment can, however, be stored in these areas if they are in a labeled locker or closet that is physically separated from the activities in these areas.

3-7 Cleaning Areas

3-7.1

A designated cleaning area shall be provided in each fire station for the cleaning of personal protective equipment, portable equipment, and other clothing. This cleaning area shall have proper ventilation, lighting, and drainage connected to a sanitary sewer system or septic system.

3-7.2

The designated cleaning area shall be physically separate from areas used for food preparation, cleaning of food and cooking utensils, personal hygiene, sleeping, and living areas.

3-7.3

The designated cleaning area shall be physically separate from the disinfecting facility.

3-8 Disinfecting Facilities

3-8.1*

Fire departments that provide emergency medical operations shall provide or have access to disinfecting facilities for the cleaning and disinfecting of emergency medical equipment. Medical equipment shall be disinfected at a fire station only where a disinfecting facility that meets the requirements of this section is provided. Disinfection shall not be conducted in fire station kitchen, living, sleeping, or personal hygiene areas.

A-3-8.1 Where the fire department provides only emergency medical operations at the first responder level, there should be at least one disinfecting facility available. Where the fire department provides basic life-support or advanced life-support emergency medical operation, there should be a disinfecting facility in each fire station from which such services are provided.

3-8.2

Disinfecting facilities in fire stations shall be lighted properly, vented to outside environment, fitted with floor drains connected to a sanitary sewer system or septic system, and designed to prevent contamination of other fire station areas.

3-8.3

Disinfecting facilities shall be equipped with rack shelving of nonporous material. Shelving shall be provided above sinks to drip-dry cleaned equipment. All drainage from shelving shall run into a sink or drainage pan that empties directly into a sanitary sewer system or septic system.

3-9 Disposal Areas

3-9.1

Medical waste or other regulated waste shall be disposed of in a designated disposal area. Such waste shall not be disposed of in fire station kitchen, living, sleeping, or personal hygiene areas.

3-9.2

The designated disposal area shall be physically separate from areas used for food preparation, cleaning of food and cooking utensils, personal hygiene, sleeping, and living areas.

3-9.3

The designated disposal area shall be physically separate from the designated cleaning area and the disinfecting facility.

3-9.4

The designated disposal area shall be properly secured and appropriately labeled.

3-9.5

The designated disposal area, and the handling, storage, transportation, and disposal of medical waste or other regulated waste, shall comply with all applicable state and local laws and regulations.

Whenever possible, contaminated waste or medical equipment should be placed in a leakproof bag and transported with the patient for disposal or disinfection at the hospital. Occasionally, however, the fire department does not transport the patient, or required rapid transport delays the cleanup of the scene until later. These situations create a need for specific areas in a fire or EMS station to be designated for cleaning, disinfecting, and temporary storage of biohazardous waste or contaminated medical equipment. The cleaning area should be physically separate from all kitchen, hygiene, and clean storage areas. Contaminated equipment must never be cleaned in the kitchen or bathroom areas. The cleaning area should have a sink with an appropriate drainage system into the sanitary, sewer, or septic system. The disinfecting and cleaning areas should be separate from the storage area (as everything that enters and leaves the storage area must be clean). The use of disinfectant solutions requires the disinfecting area to be vented directly to the outside. Equipment should be easy to transport from the disinfecting area to the clean storage area.

The disposal area can be a separate room or simply a leakproof container. In either case, precautions must to be taken to properly secure and label disposal areas. These precautions protect members from accidental contamination. All contaminated items must be kept physically separate from (1) cleaning and disinfecting areas, (2) all living, kitchen, and hygiene areas, and (3) clean supplies and equipment. Contaminated items must never be disposed with regular waste in any of these areas. Any containers used for temporary storage of contaminated waste must be decontaminated or disposed, that is, must be used for no other purpose.

CHAPTER 4

Emergency Medical Operations Protection

4-1 Personnel

Chapter 4 describes the fundamental rules of personnel protection related to infection control during emergency medical operations (*see Figure 1581-4.1*). These rules may be summarized as follows:

- All non-intact skin on emergency responders must be covered.
- Gloves must be worn during all patient contact.
- Splash protection (eye/face and body) should be used whenever there is a potential for splash or spray of blood or body fluids.
- Resuscitation equipment should be used in lieu of mouth-to-mouth resuscitation.
- Sharps (needles, syringes, etc.) should never be recapped.
- Hands should be washed immediately following removal of gloves and whenever there is contact with blood or other body fluids.

Of course, for members to use the personal protective equipment, it must be provided by the department and carried on emergency response vehicles.

4-1.1

Prior to any contacts with patients, members shall cover all areas of abraded, lacerated, chapped, irritated, or otherwise damaged skin with adhesive dressings, provided the member is not restricted by the requirements of 2-1.5.

4-1.2*

Any member who has skin or mucosal contact with body fluids shall thoroughly wash the exposed area immediately using water or saline on mucosal surfaces and soap and running water on skin surfaces. If soap and running water are not available, waterless soap, antiseptic wipe, alcohol, or other skin cleaning agents that do not need running water shall be used until soap and running water can be obtained.

A-4-1.2 If germicidal agents are readily available they can be used in lieu of soap when washing skin surfaces.

4-1.3

After removal of any personal protective equipment, including gloves, all members shall wash their hands immediately or as soon as feasible.

4-2 Personal Protective Equipment

4-2.1

Members engaging in any emergency patient care shall don emergency medical gloves prior to initiating such care to protect against the variety of diseases, modes of transmission, and unpredictable nature of the work environment. Emergency medical gloves shall be a standard component of emergency response equipment.

4-2.2

Emergency medical gloves shall be removed as soon as possible after the termination of patient care, taking care to avoid skin contact with the glove's exterior surface, and shall be disposed of in accordance with 5-5.2. Hands shall be washed as specified in 5-5.5 following removal of emergency medical gloves.

4-2.3

All personal protective equipment used in emergency medical care shall meet the requirements of NFPA 1999, *Standard on Protective Clothing for Emergency Medical Operations.*

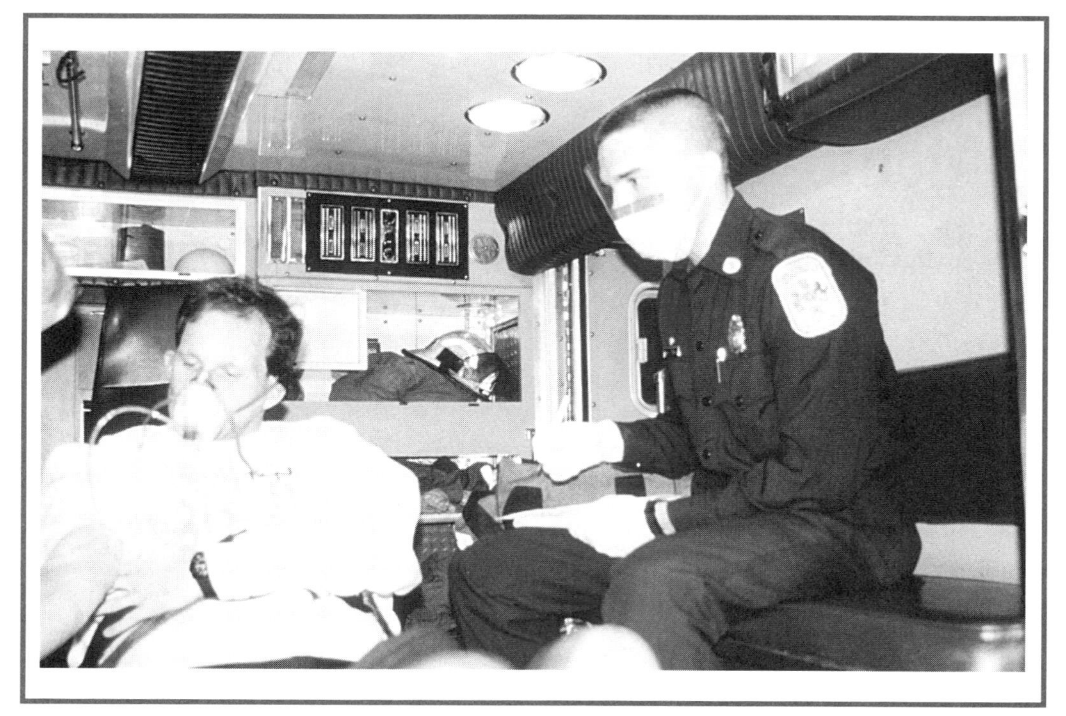

Figure 1581-4.1 *Members need to fully protect themselves while providing patient care. This includes protection from airborne and bloodborne pathogens. The use of EMS personal protective clothing that meets the requirements of NFPA 1999 (1997) affords the EMS provider a level of protection. (Photo courtesy of Fairfax County Fire and Rescue Dept., Fairfax, Virginia)*

4-2.4

Personal protective equipment used in emergency medical care, including masks, splash-resistant eyewear, gloves, and fluid-resistant clothing, shall be present on all fire department vehicles that provide emergency medical operations.

4-2.5

Prior to any patient situations during which large splashes of body fluids can occur, such as those involving spurting blood, trauma, or childbirth, masks, splash-resistant eyewear, emergency medical gloves, and fluid-resistant clothing shall be donned by those members who will be providing treatment.

4-2.6

Resuscitation equipment, including pocket masks, shall be available on all fire department vehicles that provide emergency medical operations. This equipment shall be used by members performing airway management.

4-2.7

Structural fire fighting gloves shall meet the requirements of NFPA 1973, *Standard on Gloves for Structural Fire Fighting.*

4-2.8

Structural fire fighting gloves shall be worn by members in any situation where sharp or rough surfaces or a potentially high heat exposure is likely to be encountered, such as patient extrication.

4-2.9*

Medical gloves shall not be worn under structural fire fighting gloves due to complications that exposure to heat might cause, such as burns, dripping, melting, or a combination thereof, to the skin.

A-4-2.9 The intent is to ensure that members are not unnecessarily injured by melting, dripping, or burning due to medical gloves being worn under structural fire fighting gloves. Gloves worn by members could be subjected to high heat and show no external signs of damage, but the medical gloves could degrade inside the fire fighting glove, causing injury to the fire fighter.

An area of potential controversy centers on the use of medical gloves in conjunction with structural fire fighting gloves. Structural fire fighting gloves must be used any time a member may come into contact with sharp, jagged, or rough edges (such as those at a vehicle crash). However, structural fire fighting gloves provide questionable body fluid barrier protection. Thus, many responders have opted to wear medical gloves under structural fire fighting gloves. NFPA 1581 prohibits this practice due to complications that exposure to heat (such as burns, dripping, melting, or a combination thereof) might cause to the skin. Structural fire fighting gloves worn by members could be subjected to high heat and sustain no external signs of damage, but the medical gloves could degrade inside the fire fighting glove and injure the fire fighter.

4-2.10

Cleaning gloves shall be reusable, heavy-duty, mid-forearm length, and designed to provide limited protection from abrasions, cuts, snags, and punctures, and they shall provide a barrier against body fluids, cleaning fluids, and disinfectants.

4-2.11

Cleaning gloves, splash-resistant eyewear, and fluid-resistant clothing shall be worn by members during cleaning or disinfecting of clothing or equipment potentially contaminated during emergency medical operations.

4-2.12

Members shall not eat, drink, smoke, apply cosmetics or lip balm, or handle contact lenses while wearing cleaning gloves.

Paragraphs 4-2.10, 4-2.11, and 4-2.12 address cleaning gloves. These are long gloves and must be worn with face/eye protection and fluid-resistant clothing (an apron, for example) when cleaning and disinfecting equipment. The combination of cleaning gloves and fluid-resistant clothing will help protect the member from incidental contamination by body fluids on the object being cleaned. To prevent accidental inhalation, ingestion, or contact with any contaminants on the gloves, while wearing any type of glove, or before washing hands after doffing gloves, members should avoid the following activities:

- Eating
- Drinking
- Smoking
- Applying cosmetics or lip balm
- Handling contact lenses

4-3 Handling of Sharp Objects

4-3.1

All members shall take precautions during procedures to prevent injuries caused by needles, scalpel blades, and other sharp instruments or devices.

4-3.2

All used sharp objects, such as needles, scalpels, catheter styles, and other contaminated sharp objects, shall be considered infectious and shall be handled with extraordinary care.

4-3.3

Needles shall not be manually recapped, bent, or broken. Following use, all sharp objects shall be placed immediately in sharps containers. These sharps containers shall be located in all patient transport vehicles and readily available in such areas as drug boxes, trauma kits, and IV kits.

Section 4-3 is part of NFPA 1581 for a very simple reason: Sharps protection is an essential part of infection control. Most fire and EMS departments that provide advanced life support services carry sharps boxes or sharps caddies in their drug boxes and trauma kits and have one readily accessible in or on the unit. An appropriately labeled impervious container kept within reach makes it easy for a responder to immediately and safely dispose of needles, syringes, lancets, and other sharp objects. Sharps should never be set down, jabbed in a cushion, recapped, bent, broken, or disposed of in any way other than in an approved sharps container. *All used sharps must be considered infectious. A needle stick with a contaminated sharp is considered a high-risk exposure.*

CHAPTER 5

Cleaning, Disinfecting, and Disposal

5-1 Skin Washing

5-1.1

Hands shall be washed after each emergency medical incident, immediately or as soon as possible after removal of gloves or other personal protective equipment, after cleaning and disinfecting emergency medical equipment, after cleaning personal protective equipment, after any cleaning function, after using the bathroom, and before and after handling food or cooking and food utensils.

5-1.2

Hands and contaminated skin surfaces shall be washed with nonabrasive soap and water by lathering the skin and vigorously rubbing together all lathered surfaces for at least 10 seconds, followed by thorough rinsing under running water.

5-1.3

Where provision of handwashing facilities is not feasible, appropriate antiseptic hand cleansers in conjunction with clean cloth, paper towels, or antiseptic towelettes shall be used. Where antiseptic hand cleansers or towelettes are used, hands shall be washed with nonabrasive soap and running water as soon as feasible.

Section 5-1 emphasizes the importance of skin washing to prevent the spread of infection. This section states when and how hands should be washed for maximum effectiveness.

All emergency response vehicles should have waterless antiseptic hand cleansers and some type of paper or cloth towel for immediate handwashing needs. When waterless hand cleanser is used, a rewash with regular soap and running water should follow as soon as possible.

5-2 Disinfectants

5-2.1

All disinfectants shall be approved by and registered with the U.S. Environmental Protection Agency and also shall be registered as tuberculocidal.

5-2.2

Care shall be taken in the use of all disinfectants. Members shall be aware of the flammability and reactivity of disinfectants and shall follow the manufacturer's instructions. Disinfectants shall be used only with adequate ventilation and while wearing appropriate infection control garments and equipment including, but not limited to, cleaning gloves, face protection devices, and aprons.

5-2.3

Disinfecting shall take place in the designated disinfecting facility as specified in Section 3-8.

As required by Section 5-2, disinfectants used should be appropriate for the item being disinfected. All precautions on the label should be followed, and, if appropriate, a material safety data sheet (MSDS) should be on file. Storage precautions are especially important: *Do not* store disinfectants in a furnace room, near food, or with incompatible chemicals. Disinfectants must be used only by members wearing appropriate personal protective equipment and working in a ventilated area. If any quantity of disinfectant is transferred to a smaller container for use, the new container must be labeled appropriately.

5-3 Emergency Medical Equipment

5-3.1

Where emergency medical equipment cleaning is performed by members, it shall take place in the designated disinfecting facility as specified in Section 3-8, and appropriate personal protective equipment including splash-resistant eyewear, cleaning gloves, and fluid-resistant clothing shall be available.

5-3.2

Dirty or contaminated emergency medical equipment shall not be cleaned or disinfected in fire station kitchen, living, sleeping, or personal hygiene areas.

5-3.3

Personal protective equipment shall be used wherever there is a potential for exposure to body fluids or potentially infectious materia l during cleaning or disinfecting.

5-3.4

Dirty or contaminated emergency medical equipment, prior to cleaning and disinfecting, shall be stored separately from cleaned and disinfected emergency medical equipment.

5-3.5

Disinfectants meeting the requirements specified in 5-2.1 shall be used. The disinfectant manufacturer's instructions for use shall be followed.

5-3.6

Dirty or contaminated runoff from emergency medical equipment and cleaning and disinfecting solutions shall be drained into a sanitary sewer system or septic system.

5-3.7

Emergency medical equipment, metal, and electronic equipment, shall be cleaned in a manner appropriate for the equipment and then disinfected. Only disinfectants that are chemically compatible with the equipment to be disinfected and that meet the requirements specified in 5-2.1 shall be used. The disinfectant manufacturer's instructions for use shall be followed.

5-3.8*

Reusable emergency medical equipment that comes in contact with mucous membranes shall require cleaning and a high-level disinfection or sterilization after each use. The medical equipment manufacturer's instructions shall be followed.

A-5-3.8 Disinfection and Sterilization Methods for Equipment Used in Emergency Medical Operations.

(a) **Sterilization.** Destroys all forms of microbial life, including high numbers of bacterial spores.

Methods. Steam under pressure (autoclave), gas (ethylene oxide), dry heat, or immersion in an EPA-approved chemical sterilant for a prolonged period of time (e.g., 6 hours to 10 hours) or according to manufacturer's instructions. Liquid chemical sterilants should be used only on those instruments that are impossible to sterilize or disinfect with heat.

Use. For those instruments or devices that penetrate skin or contact normally sterile areas of the body (e.g., scalpels, needles). Disposable invasive equipment eliminates the need to sterilize these types of items. Where indicated, however, arrangements should be made with a health care facility for sterilization of reusable invasive instruments.

(b) **High-Level Disinfection.** Destroys all forms of microbial life, except high numbers of bacterial spores.

Methods. Hot water pasteurization [176°F to 212°F (80°C to 100°C) for 30 min] or exposure to an EPA-regulated sterilant, as specified in A-5-3.8(a), except for a short exposure time (e.g., 10 min to 45 min) or according to manufacturer's instructions.

Use. For reusable instruments or devices that come into contact with mucous membranes (e.g., laryngoscope blades, endotracheal tubes).

(c) **Intermediate-Level Disinfection.** Destroys *Mycobacterium tuberculosis*, vegetative bacteria, most viruses, and most fungi, but does not kill bacterial spores.

Methods. EPA-registered hospital-disinfectant, chemical germicides that have a label claim for tuberculocidal activity; commercially available hard-surface germicides or solutions containing at least 500 ppm free available chlorine (a 1:100 dilution of common household chlorine bleach approximately $^1/_2$ cup of chlorine bleach per gallon of tap water).

Use. For those surfaces that come into contact only with intact skin (e.g., stethoscopes, blood pressure cuffs, splints) and have been visibly contaminated with body fluids. Surfaces should be precleaned of visible material before the germicidal chemical is applied for disinfection.

(d) **Low-Level Disinfection.** Destroys most bacteria, some viruses, some fungi, but not *Mycobacterium tuberculosis* or bacterial spores.

Methods. EPA-registered hospital disinfectants (no label claim for tuberculocidal activity).

Use. These agents are excellent cleaners and can be used for routine housekeeping or removal of soiling in the absence of visible body fluid contaminants.

(e) **Environmental Disinfection.** Environmental surfaces that have become soiled should be cleaned and disinfected.

(f) **Housekeeping.**

1. *General.* Employers should ensure that the worksite is maintained in a neat condition, free of any contamination. The employer should determine and implement an appropriate written schedule for cleaning and decontamination. The method of decontamination should be based upon the location within the facility, type of surface to be cleaned, type of contamination, and the tasks or procedures performed. For example:
   (i) Personal protective equipment and other clothing should be cleaned and/or laundered.
   (ii) Emergency medical equipment should be cleaned and disinfected.
   (iii) Invasive medical instruments should be cleaned and sterilized.
   (iv) Contaminated surfaces should be cleaned and disinfected with a disinfectant appropriate for the surface.
   (v) Contaminated work surfaces should be decontaminated immediately or as soon as feasible after completion of the emergency medical operation; and at the end of the work shift if the surface could have been contaminated since the last decontamination was performed.

IMPORTANT: To ensure the effectiveness of any sterilization or disinfection process, equipment and instruments first should be thoroughly cleaned of all visible soil.

5-3.9*

Environmental surfaces shall be cleaned in a manner appropriate for the surface and then disinfected. Only disinfectants that are chemically compatible with the surface to be disinfected and that meet the requirements specified in 5-2.1 shall be used. The disinfectant manufacturer's instructions for use shall be followed.

A-5-3.9 A 1:100 dilution of household chlorine bleach (5.25 percent sodium hypochlorite) to water may be permitted to be used as a general surface disinfectant; however, it is corrosive to metal and could interfere with the function of electronic equipment. (*See also A-5-3.8.*)

Much of the material in Section 5-3 has been covered in other sections, such as Sections 3-7 and 3-8. Many departments leave disinfection of emergency medical equipment to the appropriate hospital facility, thus reducing the department's risk and liability. Section 5-3 addresses those fire and EMS departments that do clean and disinfect their own equipment.

Personal protective equipment must be used while cleaning and disinfecting emergency medical equipment. All cleaning and disinfecting must be done in an appropriate location, that is, *not* in the kitchen, bathroom, or other hygiene areas. Temporary storage of contaminated equipment must be away from clean equipment and supplies, food, and hygiene and living areas.

Disinfectants must be appropriate for the equipment or environmental surface being disinfected. The equipment manual, if available, should provide guidance on disinfecting. If the emergency medical equipment is used for any invasive procedures (including mucosal procedures), high-level disinfection or sterilization must be performed. This is typically done at a hospital or other outside agency.

5-4 Clothing and Personal Protective Equipment

5-4.1*

The fire department shall clean, launder, and dispose of personal protective equipment at no cost to the member. The fire department also shall repair or replace personal protective equipment as needed to maintain its effectiveness, at no cost to the member.

A-5-4.1 Clean protective clothing reduces health and safety risks. It is recommended that clothing be cleaned frequently to reduce the level of, and bodily contact with, contaminants. User agencies should establish guidelines for frequency and situations for garment cleaning. For gross contamination with products of combustion, fire debris, or body fluids, removal of contaminants by flushing with water as soon as practical is necessary, followed by appropriate cleaning.

Decontamination might not be possible where personal protective clothing is contaminated with chemical, radiological, or biological agents. Where decontamination is not possible, garments should be discarded in accordance with local, state, and federal regulations.

5-4.2

If a garment(s) is penetrated by blood or other potentially infectious materials, the garment(s) shall be removed immediately or as soon as feasible.

5-4.3

All personal protective equipment shall be removed prior to leaving the work area.

5-4.4

Clothing that is contaminated with large amounts of body fluids shall be placed in leakproof bags, sealed, and transported for proper cleaning or disposal.

5-4.5

Cleaning or disinfecting of contaminated structural fire fighting clothing, personal protective garments, station/work uniforms, or other clothing shall take place in the proper area as specified in either Section 3-5 or Section 3-7. To avoid the possibility of spreading infectious diseases by cross-contamination, the cleaning of contaminated personal protective equipment, station/work uniforms, or other clothing shall not be done at home.

5-4.6*

Structural fire fighting protective clothing, gloves, station/work uniforms, and protective footwear shall be cleaned and dried according to the manufacturer's instructions as needed and at least every 6 months. Chlorine bleach or cleaning agents containing chlorine bleach shall not be used.

A-5-4.6 Some components of these garments are inherently flame resistant but lose their physical integrity on exposure to chlorine bleach. Other components will actually lose their flame-resistant properties and thermal insulation on exposure to chlorine bleach. In either case, the protection provided by the garment will be compromised.

There are industrial cleaning products and facilities available for protective clothing that the user might wish to investigate. The manufacturer of protective clothing should be contacted for additional information. Where not explicitly outlined by the manufacturer, the following procedures are recommended for cleaning and disinfecting these garments.

Cleaning or Disinfecting Procedures for Structural Fire Fighting Protective Clothing, Station/Work Uniforms, Personal Protective Garments, and Other Clothing

Section 1 Spot Cleaning. Precleaners can be used to clean light spots and stains on protective clothing. Precleaner should be squirted once or twice onto the soiled areas. The fabric should be rubbed together gently until a light foam appears on the surface and carefully rinsed off with cool water.

Section 2 Pretreating. Liquid detergent should be applied directly from the bottle onto the soiled areas. The fabric should be rubbed together gently until a light foam appears on the surface. The garments should be placed into the washing machine as specified in Section 3 and the remaining amount of the recommended detergent added. To clean garments that are heavily soiled, a liquid detergent or precleaner solution should be used in the following manner prior to laundering:

(a) The garment should be air-dried before applying product.
(b) The liquid detergent or precleaner should be squirted directly onto the stain and the surrounding areas (3 to 4 squirts). It should be made certain that the soiled area is soaked with the product.
(c) A soft bristle brush (toothbrush or fingernail-type brush dipped in water) should be used to scrub the soiled area gently for about 1 minute.
(d) The liquid detergent or precleaner should be reapplied to the soiled areas again (1 or 2 squirts).
(e) The garment should be placed into the washing machine as described in Section 3.

Section 3 Washing Instructions. Protective clothing should be washed separately from other garments. All hooks and eyes should be fastened, and the garment should be turned inside out or placed in a large laundry bag that can be tied shut to avoid damage to the washtub. A stainless steel tub should be utilized if available.

These instructions can be used for cleaning any of the following wash loads in a large capacity (16-gal) top-loading or front-loading washing machine.

(a) One protective coat and one protective trouser;
(b) Two protective coats;
(c) Two protective trousers;

Prior to washing, heavily soiled garments should be pretreated using the procedures outlined in Section 2.

1. While the washing machine is filling with hot water [120°F to 130°F (49°C to 55°C)], $^1/_2$ cup (4 oz) of liquid oxygenated bleach (chlorine bleach should not be used) and 1 cup (8 oz) of liquid detergent should be added. These products are readily available in supermarkets.
2. The washing machine should be filled to the highest water level.
3. The garments to be washed should be added.
4. The washing machine should be set for normal cycle, cotton/white, or similar setting.
5. The machine should be programmed for double rinse. If the machine will not automatically double rinse, a complete second cycle should be run without adding detergent or oxygenated bleach. Double rinsing helps remove any residual dirt and ensures detergent removal.
6. The garments should be removed from the washing machine and dried by hanging in a shaded area that receives a good cross ventilation, or they should be hung on a line and a fan used to circulate the air. A water extractor may be permitted to be utilized.

Section 4 Laundering and Cleaning Products. Some examples of products that may be permitted to be utilized for cleaning, spot cleaning, and pretreating include:

Cleaning:

Liquid Wisk®
Liquid Cheer®

Liquid Tide®
Liquid Fab®

Oxygenated Bleaches:

Liquid Clorox 2®
Liquid Vivid®

DO NOT USE CHLORINE BLEACH ON FIRE FIGHTER PROTECTIVE CLOTHING

Spot Cleaning and Pretreating:

Liquid Spray and Wash®
Liquid Tide®
Liquid Shout®

5-4.7

When a garment is contaminated, it shall be cleaned as soon as possible.

5-4.8

When personal protective equipment is removed, it shall be placed in an appropriately designated area or container for storage until cleaning or disposal.

The fire or EMS department is responsible for providing appropriate personal protective equipment and for cleaning, laundering, disposing of, repairing, and/or replacing PPE as appropriate. Section 5-4 describes requirements to accomplish these activities.

If a garment—station/work uniform or PPE—becomes wet from blood or other body fluids, it should be removed immediately, placed in a leakproof bag, sealed, and transported for proper cleaning and disinfecting. The immediate removal is to prevent the blood or body fluids from soaking through and contacting the member's skin. When the garment is cleaned, it should be done in accordance with manufacturer's instructions in the appropriate facility. Contaminated clothing or PPE must *not* be taken home.

Personal protective equipment, in particular structural fire fighting PPE, should be cleaned whenever necessary and at least every six months. In the past, the dirtier the gear the better. Now, it has been recognized that dirt on gear is not a badge of honor, but rather a myriad of contaminants that could lead to illness. Thus, regular cleaning of PPE is needed. Chlorine-containing products must *never* be used on structural fire fighting PPE. Proper laundering procedures for structural fire fighting protective clothing are outlined in paragraph A-5-4.6 of this standard.

5-5* Disposal of Materials

A-5-5 For information regarding management of medical waste or other regulated waste, the following publications are recommended: *EPA Guide for Infectious Waste Management*, U.S. Environmental Protection Agency, and *Guidelines for Handwashing and Hospital Environmental Control*, revised by Julia S. Garner, R.N., M.N., and Martin S. Favero, Ph.D., Hospital Infection Program, Centers for Disease Control and Prevention, Atlanta, Georgia.

5-5.1

Sharps containers shall be disposed of in accordance with applicable federal, state, and local regulations.

5-5.2

Contaminated sharps shall be discarded immediately or as soon as feasible in containers that are closable; puncture resistant; leakproof on sides and bottom; and labeled or color-coded in accordance with Section 5-8.

5-5.3

During use, containers for contaminated sharps shall be easily accessible to personnel and located as close as is feasible to the immediate area where sharps are used or can be reasonably anticipated to be found (e.g., laundries); maintained upright throughout use; and replaced routinely and not be allowed to overfill.

5-5.4

When moving containers of contaminated sharps from the area of use, the containers shall be closed immediately prior to removal or replacement to prevent spillage or protrusion of contents during handling, storage, transport, or shipping and shall be placed in a secondary container if leakage is possible.

5-5.5

Contaminated disposable medical supplies and equipment, contaminated disposable personal protective equipment, and contaminated wastes shall be placed in leakproof bags, sealed, and disposed of as medical waste.

5-5.6

Noncontaminated disposable medical supplies and equipment, noncontaminated disposable personal protective equipment, and noncontaminated wastes shall be permitted to be collected in closable waste containers and shall be disposed of properly. Such waste collection containers shall not be located in any fire station kitchen, living, or sleeping areas.

5-5.7

Where it has been determined by the infection control officer that normally nondisposable items cannot be disinfected, they shall be placed in leakproof bags, sealed, and disposed of as medical waste.

As discussed in Section 4-3, contaminated needles, lancets, and other sharps pose a significant risk to members, and they must be disposed of properly. Section 5-5 requires that a puncture-resistant, leakproof container that is color-coded or labeled (sharps container) must be placed anywhere sharps may be used or found so that a used sharp can be immediately and safely disposed of. *(See Figure 1581-5.1.)* The sharps container should be designed to prevent contact with used sharps inside while disposing of a sharp. Furthermore, there must be no chance of spilling. Such containers are commercially available in various shapes and sizes. Full sharps containers should be sealed and disposed of as medical waste.

Contaminated disposable medical supplies and equipment, as well as potentially contaminated disposable PPE, should be placed in a leakproof bag at the site where they have been used. The bag should be sealed and transported for proper disposal as medical waste. Reusable or nondisposable items that cannot be disinfected adequately should be packaged the same way and may need to be disposed of. The distributor or manufacturer of expensive items may be able to provide guidance about disinfecting, repairing, or replacing the item. Disposal of larger or more expensive items may present some departmental accountability or inventory-related concerns, as well.

Noncontaminated waste should be disposed of in a closable container that is located outside kitchen, living, or sleeping areas. Many fire departments place a large trash can with a lid and a plastic trash bag in the cleaning area specifically for this purpose. They also may place a smaller trash can with a lid and a color-coded leakproof bag for medical waste beside the larger trash can.

Many localities have specific criteria for the storage, transportation, and disposal of medical or biohazardous waste. The local health department can provide applicable regulations. Many departments depend on their local hospital(s) for disposal of waste and disinfection of larger items. Some departments contract with a hazardous waste disposal firm. Hazardous waste services can be expensive; it may be best to work with neighboring departments to ensure that the process is as safe, efficient, and affordable as possible.

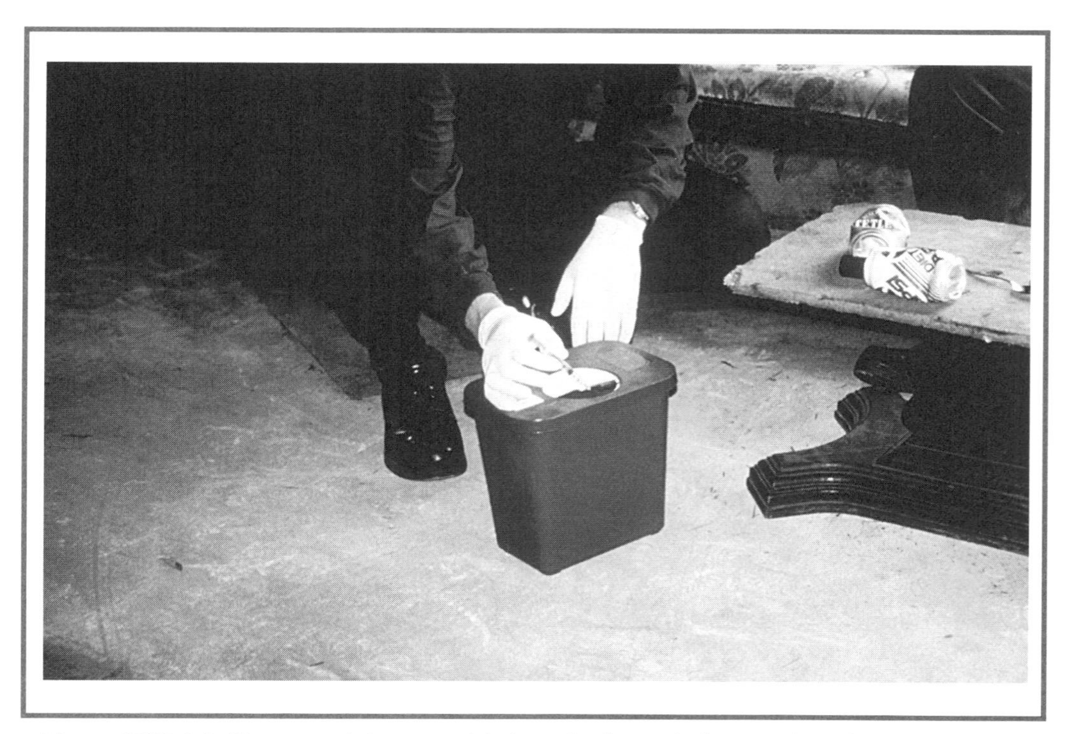

Figure 1581-5.1 Sharps containers provide for safe disposal of contaminated equipment. The proper use, storage, and disposal of containers should be done as part of the department's infection control program. (Photo courtesy of Fairfax County Fire and Rescue Dept., Fairfax, Virginia)

5-6 Linen

5-6.1

Contaminated laundry shall be handled as little as possible with a minimum of agitation. Contaminated laundry shall be bagged or put into containers at the location where it was used and shall not be sorted or rinsed at the location of use.

5-6.2

Contaminated laundry shall be placed and transported in bags or containers labeled or color-coded in accordance with Section 5-8.

5-6.3

Wherever contaminated laundry is wet and presents a reasonable likelihood of soaking through or leaking from the bag or container, the laundry shall be placed and transported in bags or containers that prevent soak-through or leakage, or both, of fluids to the exterior.

5-6.4

The employer shall ensure that employees who have contact with contaminated laundry wear appropriate personal protective equipment.

5-6.5

Where a fire department ships contaminated laundry to a facility that does not utilize universal precautions in the handling of all laundry, the facility generating the contaminated laundry shall place such laundry in bags or containers that are labeled or color-coded in accordance with 5-8.2.

Contaminated or potentially contaminated linen should be packaged just as contaminated waste is packaged—in a leakproof bag that is then sealed. If the linen is soaked with body fluids, the bag should be placed inside another leakproof bag or a leakproof container. This must all be done by someone wearing appropriate personal protective equipment. Leakproof bags that disintegrate in the laundry are available; typically these are a different color than biohazardous waste bags.

Many departments have a linen agreement with the local hospital. Contaminated linen (appropriately packaged) is deposited at the hospital, and clean linen is retrieved. Other departments contract with a linen service, temporarily storing properly packaged contaminated linen until it is picked up by the service. In this case, it is important that the fire or EMS department contract call for the linen service to use universal precautions when handling the linen; this will reduce the department's liability. If a department launders its own linen, members doing the laundering must wear proper PPE and remember that leakproof bags (if not the type that go directly in the laundry) are considered medical waste and must be disposed of appropriately.

5-7 Housekeeping

5-7.1

The fire department shall ensure that the worksite is maintained in a clean and sanitary condition. The fire department shall determine and implement an appropriate written schedule for cleaning and method of decontamination based upon the location within the facility, type of surface to be cleaned, type of soil present, and tasks or procedures being performed in the area.

5-7.2

All equipment and environmental and working surfaces shall be cleaned and decontaminated after contact with blood or other potentially infectious materials.

5-7.3

All equipment and environmental and working surfaces shall be cleaned and decontaminated after contact with blood or other potentially infectious materials using any cleaner or disinfectant agent that is intended for environmental use. Such surfaces include floors, woodwork, ambulance seats, and countertops.

5-7.4

Contaminated work surfaces shall be decontaminated with an appropriate disinfectant after completion of emergency medical operations; immediately or as soon as feasible where surfaces are overtly contaminated or after any spill of blood or other potentially infectious materials; and at the end of the workshift if the surface could have become contaminated since the last cleaning.

5-7.5

All bins, pails, cans, and similar receptacles intended for reuse that have a reasonable likelihood of becoming contaminated with blood or other potentially infectious materials shall be inspected and decontaminated on a regularly scheduled basis and cleaned and decontaminated immediately or as soon as feasible upon visible contamination.

The intent of Section 5-7 is to provide clean and sanitary equipment and environmental work surfaces, not only after overt contamination with blood or other potentially infectious materials, but at all times. This requires regularly scheduled cleaning and decontamination of all work surfaces, both at the station and on the apparatus. The schedule for such cleaning and decontamination should be written and posted, and should include the following:

- Floors, countertops, sinks, and other surfaces at the station
- Compartments, seats, interior floors, doorhandles, and other surfaces of the apparatus

Cleaning and disinfecting materials should be used according to manufacturer's instructions, and appropriate personal protective equipment should be used when cleaning/disinfecting.

Likely areas of contamination include trash cans and other containers used for contaminated linen or medical waste, even with a leakproof bag in the container. These containers should be inspected on a regular basis, and cleaned and disinfected regularly and whenever there is visible contamination.

5-8 Labeling

5-8.1

Warning labels shall be affixed to containers of regulated waste and other containers used to store, transport, or ship blood or other potentially infectious materials (e.g., sharps containers).

5-8.2

Labels required by this section shall include the following legend:

These labels shall be fluorescent orange or orange-red or predominantly so, with lettering or symbols in a contrasting color.

5-8.3

The labels required shall be affixed as closely as feasible to the container by string, wire, adhesive, or other method that prevents their loss or unintentional removal.

5-8.4

Red bags or red containers shall be permitted to be substituted for labels.

5-8.5

Labels required for contaminated equipment shall be in accordance with this paragraph and also shall specify which portions of the equipment remain contaminated.

5-8.6

Regulated waste that has been decontaminated shall not be required to be labeled or color-coded.

Section 5-8 sets out the labeling requirements for containers used to store or transport contaminated materials. Bags used for this purpose are typically red and often have the biohazard symbol (shown in paragraph 5-8.2) imprinted. Labels must be fluorescent orange or orange-red with black letters and biohazard symbol, or white with orange-red letters and biohazard symbol.

In the emergency services, "red bagging" is a term often used to refer to the proper packaging of contaminated materials, as this is the most common method used. Sharps containers are typically red, with an adhesive or imprinted label indicating the presence of biohazardous waste. Contaminated linens are often placed in a yellow bag or labeled (with a biohazard symbol) as contaminated material.

While not addressed specifically in NFPA 1581, OSHA regulations require all cleaning and disinfecting materials to be labeled to indicate what the product is. This is especially important when products have been transferred to other containers (e.g., spray bottles) for use. Labels on the new containers must include (1) the contents, (2) any necessary precautions to be taken, and (3) where to find the product's material safety data sheet (MSDS).

CHAPTER 6

Referenced Publications

6-1

The following documents or portions thereof are referenced within this standard and shall be considered part of the requirements of this document. The edition indicated for each reference shall be the current edition as of the date of the NFPA issuance of this document.

6-1.1 NFPA Publications.

National Fire Protection Association, 1 Batterymarch Park, P.O. Box 9101, Quincy, MA 02269-9101.

NFPA 1500, *Standard on Fire Department Occupational Safety and Health Program*, 1992 edition.

NFPA 1582, *Standard on Medical Requirements for Fire Fighters*, 1992 edition.

NFPA 1973, *Standard on Gloves for Structural Fire Fighting*, 1993 edition.

NFPA 1999, *Standard on Protective Clothing for Emergency Medical Operations*, 1992 edition.

6-1.2 Other Publications.

6-1.2.1 U.S. Government Publication. U.S. Government Printing Office, Superintendent of Documents, Washington, DC 20402.

Title 29, *Code of Federal Regulations*, Part 1910.20, "Access to Employee Exposure and Medical Records."

REFERENCES CITED IN COMMENTARY

Public Law 101-381, *The Ryan White Comprehensive AIDS Resources Emergency (CARE) Act of 1990*, Final Rule, U.S. Government Printing Office, Washington, DC, 20402.

Title 29, *CFR*, Part 1910.1030, "Bloodborne Pathogens," Final Rule, U.S. Government Printing Office, Washington, DC, 20402.

U.S. Fire Administration, Publication #FA-112, *Guide to Developing and Managing an Emergency Service Infection Control Program.*

U.S. Fire Administration, *Infection Control for Emergency Response Personnel: The Supervisor's Role*, February 1992.

APPENDIX A

Explanatory Material

The material contained in Appendix A of this standard is not part of the requirements of the code but is included with the code for informational purposes only. For the convenience of readers, in this handbook the Appendix A material is interspersed among the verbiage of Chapters 1 through 5 and, therefore, is not repeated here.

APPENDIX B

Referenced Publications

B-1

The following documents or portions thereof are referenced within this standard for informational purposes only and thus are not considered part of the requirements of this document. The edition indicated for each reference is the current edition as of the date of the NFPA issuance of this document.

B-1.1 NFPA Publication.

National Fire Protection Association, 1 Batterymarch Park, P.O. Box 9101, Quincy, MA 02269-9101.

NFPA 1500, *Standard on Fire Department Occupational Safety and Health Program*, 1992 edition.

B-1.2 Other Publications.

B-1.2.1 U.S. Centers for Disease Control Publications. These publications are available from the Superintendent of Documents, U.S. Government Printing Office, Washington, D.C. 20402 or the National Technical Information Service (NTIS), U.S. Department of Commerce, 5285 Port Royal Road, Springfield, VA 22161.

A Curriculum Guide for Public Safety and Emergency Response Workers, Prevention of Transmission of Human Immunodeficiency Virus and Hepatitis B Virus, February 1989.

Guidelines for Handwashing and Hospital Environmental Control, 1985.

Guidelines for Infection Control in Hospital Personnel, July 1983.

Guidelines for Prevention of Transmission of Human Immunodeficiency Virus and Hepatitis B Virus to Health Care and Public Safety Workers, February 1989.

EPA Guide for Infectious Waste Management, 1986.

"Public Health Service Guidelines for Counseling and Anti-Body Testing to Prevent HIV Infection and AIDS," *Morbidity and Mortality Weekly Review*, 1987, No. 36, pp. 509-515.

Title 29, *Code of Federal Regulations*, Part 1910.1030, "Bloodborne Pathogens," Final Rule; December 6, 1991.

Public Law 101-381, *The Ryan White Comprehensive AIDS Resources Emergency (CARE) Act of 1990*, Final Rule.

B-1.2.2 U.S. Fire Administration Publication. Publications Office, U.S. Fire Administration, 16825 South Seton Ave. Emmitsburg, MD 21727.

Publication #FA-112, *Guide to Developing and Managing an Emergency Service Infection Control Program*, Appendix A, pp. 105-113.

Infection Control for Emergency Response Personnel: The Supervisor's Role (Student Manual), February 1992.

PART FIVE

NFPA 1582
Standard on Medical Requirements for Fire Fighters and Commentary

Part Five of this handbook includes the complete text of the 1997 edition of NFPA 1582, *Medical Requirements for Fire Fighters.* The first edition of NFPA 1582, published in 1992, addressed the medical requirements for both candidate and incumbent fire fighters, with emphasis on the tools for determining "fit-for-duty" status. This second edition reflects the numerous changes in medical technology since that time.

The mandatory provisions found in Chapters 1 through 3 of NFPA 1582 were prepared by the Technical Committee on Fire Service Occupational Safety within the framework of NFPA's consensus codes- and standards-making system. Because these provisions are designed to be suitable for adoption into law, or for reference by other codes and standards, the text is concise, without extended explanation.

The material found in Appendix A of NFPA 1582 was also developed by the Technical Committee on Fire Service Occupational Safety within NFPA's codes- and standards-making system to assist users in understanding and interpreting the mandatory provisions of the standard. Appendix A is not considered part of the requirements of the standard; it is advisory or informational. An asterisk (*) following a paragraph number in the standard indicates that advisory appendix material pertaining to that paragraph appears in Appendix A. For the reader's convenience, in this handbook, Appendix A material has been repositioned to appear immediately following its base paragraph in the body of the standard. The text of the standard and the Appendix A material are printed in black in this handbook.

Explanatory commentary, which was prepared by Dr. M. S. "Sandy" Bogucki, immediately follows the standard text it discusses and is printed in blue for easy identification. The commentary is intended to provide the reader with a deeper understanding of the standard and to serve as a resource and reference for implementing its provisions. It is not a substitute for the actual wording of the standard or the text of any code or standard that may be incorporated by reference.

Bogucki, who holds a Ph.D. in microbiology as well as an M.D., is a member of the faculty of Emergency Medicine at Yale University and an attending physician in the Emergency Department at Yale–New Haven Hospital. In addition, she is the EMS medical adviser to three local fire departments, fire surgeon for the Branford, Connecticut, Fire Department, and medical director of the Connecticut Fire Academy in Windsor Locks. Dr. Bogucki has been an EMS/haz mat course developer and a member of the contract faculty for the National Fire Academy in Emmitsburg,

Maryland; the South Tech Fire Academy in Boynton Beach, Florida; and the Connecticut Fire Academy. In 1995, while on sabbatical leave from Yale as a visiting scholar to the U.S. Fire Administration, she developed and chaired the national symposium "Medical Support for the Fire Service." She presently serves on numerous state and national panels, including the Connecticut EMS Medical Advisory Council; NFPA Technical Committees for NFPA 1500, NFPA 1582, and NFPA 1583; and the Board of Directors of the National Registry of EMTs.

CHAPTER 1

Administration

The task group formed by the technical committee on Fire Service Occupational Safety and Health to review and revise the 1997 edition of NFPA 1582, *Standard on Medical Requirements for Fire Fighters,* was chaired by Richard D. Gerkin, Jr., MD.F.A.C.M.T. Richard has served, for the past 11 years, as the Medical Director for the Phoenix, Arizona, Fire Department Medical Center. In addition to these duties, Richard serves as the Assistant Director at the Samaritan Regional Poison Center in Phoenix. His contributions both to the original (1992) edition and to its 1997 revision were protean. Due to idiosyncrasies in the NFPA reappointment process, which coincided with the reorganization of the Occupational Safety and Health Committees, Dr. Gerkin's name does not appear in the published document. The leadership, insight, creativity, academic rigor, and enormous time commitment he brought to this project deserve proper recognition.

As subsequently described in the Americans with Disabilities Act (ADA), NFPA 1001, *Standard on Fire Fighter Professional Qualifications,* served as the "essential job function" analysis for the framers of NFPA 1582. The medical requirements, then, apply to anyone expected or required to perform these duties, regardless of whether they are currently employed or not. NFPA 1582 profiles the medical condition necessary to safely and effectively perform all of the anticipated tasks assigned to a fire fighter.

NFPA 1582 is not intended for use as a tool by which to stratify job applicants. The standard may, however, eliminate some candidates in whom medical conditions are identified that would or could render them unable to safely and effectively perform the tasks delineated in NFPA 1001. Obviously, then, it must apply to those already on the job.

The purpose of NFPA 1582 is to enhance the health, safety, and ultimate longevity of fire fighters and their fellow members. Although the standard may reduce liability for the department or jurisdiction, this should be considered a secondary effect of compliance.

1-1 Scope

1-1.1

This standard contains medical requirements for fire fighters, including full-time or part-time employees and paid or unpaid volunteers.

1-1.2

These requirements are applicable to organizations providing rescue, fire suppression, and other emergency services, including public, military, private, and industrial fire departments.

1-1.3

This standard does not apply to industrial fire brigades that also can be known as emergency brigades, emergency response teams, fire teams, plant emergency organizations, or mine emergency response teams.

1-2 Purpose

1-2.1

The purpose of this standard is to specify minimum medical requirements for candidates and current fire fighters.

1-2.2*

The implementation of the medical requirements outlined in this standard will help ensure that candidates and current fire fighters will be medically capable of performing their required duties and will help to reduce the risk of occupational injuries and illnesses.

A-1-2.2 There is a direct relationship between the medical requirements and the job description of fire fighters. The job description should include all essential job functions of fire fighters, both emergency and nonemergency. Fire fighters perform a variety of emergency operations including fire fighting, emergency medical care, hazardous materials mitigation, and special operations. Nonemergency duties can include and are not limited to training, station and vehicle maintenance, and physical fitness. Each fire department must identify and develop a written job description for fire fighters. Appendix C, Essential Fire-Fighting Functions, provides an example of essential job functions for fire fighters.

1-2.3

Nothing herein is intended to restrict any jurisdiction from exceeding these minimum requirements.

1-3 Implementation

1-3.1

For candidates, the medical requirements of this standard shall be implemented when this standard is adopted by an authority having jurisdiction on an effective date specified by the authority having jurisdiction.

1-3.2*

When this standard is adopted by a jurisdiction, the authority having jurisdiction shall set a date or dates for current fire fighters to achieve compliance with the requirements of this standard and shall be permitted to establish a phase-in schedule for compliance with specific requirements of this standard in order to minimize personal and departmental disruption.

A-1-3.2 The specific determination of the authority having jurisdiction depends on the mechanism under which this standard is adopted and enforced. Where this standard is adopted voluntarily by a particular fire department for its own use, the authority having jurisdiction should be the fire chief or the political entity that is responsible for the operation of the fire department. Where this standard is legally adopted and enforced by a body having regulatory authority over a fire department, such as federal, state, or local government or political subdivision, this body is responsible for making those determinations as the authority having jurisdiction. The compliance program should take into account the services the fire department is required to provide, the financial resources available to the fire department, the availability of personnel, the availability of trainers, and such other factors as will affect the fire department's ability to achieve compliance.

1-4 Definitions

Approved.* Acceptable to the authority having jurisdiction.

A-1-4 Approved. The National Fire Protection Association does not approve, inspect, or certify any installations, procedures, equipment, or materials; nor does it approve or evaluate testing laboratories. In determining the acceptability of installations, procedures, equipment, or materials, the authority having jurisdiction may base acceptance on compliance with NFPA or other appropriate standards. In the absence of such standards, said authority may require evidence of proper installation, procedure, or use. The authority having jurisdiction may also refer to the listings or labeling practices of an organization that is concerned with product evaluations and is thus in a position to determine compliance with appropriate standards for the current production of listed items.

Authority Having Jurisdiction.* The organization, office, or individual responsible for approving equipment, an installation, or a procedure.

A-1-4 Authority Having Jurisdiction. The phrase "authority having jurisdiction" is used in NFPA documents in a broad manner, since jurisdictions and approval agencies vary, as do their responsibilities. Where public safety is primary, the authority having jurisdiction may be a federal, state, local, or other regional department or individual such as a fire chief; fire marshal; chief of a fire prevention bureau, labor department, or health department; building official; electrical inspector; or others having statutory authority. For insurance purposes, an insurance inspection department, rating bureau, or other insurance company representative may be the authority having jurisdiction. In many circumstances, the property owner or his or her designated agent assumes the role of the authority having jurisdiction; at government installations, the commanding officer or departmental official may be the authority having jurisdiction.

Candidate.* A person who has made application to commence performance as a fire fighter.

A-1-4 Candidate. In an employment context, the Americans with Disabilities Act (discussed in further detail in Appendix D) requires that any medical examination to be conducted take place after an offer of employment is made and prior to the commencement of duties. Therefore, in the employment context, the definition of "candidate" should be applied so as to be consistent with that requirement.

Volunteer fire fighters have been deemed to be "employees" in some states or jurisdictions. Volunteer fire departments should seek legal counsel as to their legal responsibilities in these matters.

Category A Medical Condition. A medical condition that would preclude a person from performing as a fire fighter in a training or emergency operational environment by presenting a significant risk to the safety and health of the person or others.

Category B Medical Condition. A medical condition that, based on its severity or degree, could preclude a person from performing as a fire fighter in a training or emergency operational environment by presenting a significant risk to the safety and health of the person or others.

An individual may, in some cases, successfully perform the full spectrum of fire-fighting duties while having a disqualifying or potentially disqualifying (Category A or B) condition. Members often point out that they have been serving as fire fighters without difficulty for some time despite the presence of one of these conditions and should therefore be permitted to continue doing so. In many of these cases, the condition was considered grounds for disqualification by this standard because of the risk of sudden or unexpected incapacitation during emergency responses or operations, rather than physical inability to complete certain critical tasks. Such sudden incapacitation could jeopardize the life and health of both the member and others responding to, or operating in, a hazardous environment. Therefore, if episodes of sudden incapacitation are intrinsic to a medical condition, even if these episodes occur only rarely, the condition is generally given Category A status.

In many instances, a situation in which a disqualifying condition compromises the fire fighter's health or safety hasn't been confronted yet. A common example of this is hearing impairment. A hearing-impaired fire fighter's compensatory mechanisms may be adequate for the vast majority of situations. Occasionally, however, hearing may be critical, as for radio transmissions ordering abandonment of an interior attack or the accompanying air horns signaling emergency evacuation of an untenable structure.

Medical conditions are therefore assigned to Category A or B, not just on the basis of test results obtained in the controlled (medical) environment, but also on the risks that may be incurred by the individual under the extreme stress and unpredictable demands of the emergency environment. For further discussion, see Appendix B3.1.

Current Fire Fighter. A person who is already a member and whose duties require the performance of essential fire-fighting functions.

Drug. Any substance, chemical, over-the-counter medication, or prescribed medication that could affect the performance of the fire fighter.

Emergency Operations. Activities of the fire department relating to rescue, fire suppression, and special operations, including response to the scene of the incident and all functions performed at the scene.

Essential Job Function. Task or assigned duty that is critical to successful performance of the job.

Evaluation. See Medical Evaluation.

Fire Department Physician. The licensed doctor of medicine or osteopathy who has been designated by the fire department to provide professional expertise in the areas of occupational safety and health as they relate to emergency services.

Fire Fighter.* A member of a fire department whose duties require the performance of essential fire-fighting functions or substantially similar functions.

A-1-4 Fire Fighter. See Appendix C, Essential Fire-Fighting Functions.

Functional Capacity Evaluation. An assessment of the correlation between that individual's capabilities and the essential job functions.

Medical Evaluation. The analysis of information for the purpose of making a determination of medical certification. Medical evaluation can include a medical examination.

Medical Examination. An examination performed or directed by the fire department physician that incorporates the components described in 2-4.1.4.

Medically Certified. A determination by the fire department physician that the candidate or current fire fighter meets the medical requirements of this standard.

Member. A person involved in performing the duties and responsibilities of a fire department, under the auspices of the organization. A fire department member can be a full-time or part-time employee or a paid or unpaid volunteer, can occupy any position or rank within the fire department, and can engage in emergency operations.

Shall. Indicates a mandatory requirement.

Should. Indicates a recommendation or that which is advised but not required.

CHAPTER 2

Medical Process

2-1 Medical Evaluation Process

2-1.1*

The fire department shall establish and implement a medical evaluation process for candidates and current fire fighters.

A-2-1.1 See Appendix D, "Guide for Fire Department Administrators."

2-1.2

The medical evaluation process shall include preplacement medical evaluations, periodic medical evaluations, and return-to-duty medical evaluations.

2-1.3

The fire department shall ensure that the medical evaluation process and all medical evaluations meet all of the requirements of this section.

2-1.4

Each candidate or current fire fighter shall cooperate, participate, and comply with the medical evaluation process and shall provide complete and accurate information to the fire department physician.

2-1.5*

Each candidate or current fire fighter shall, on a timely basis, report to the fire department physician any exposure or medical condition that could interfere with the ability of the individual to perform as a fire fighter.

A-2-1.5 Exposures and medical conditions that should be reported if they can interfere with the ability of the individual to perform as a fire fighter include, but are not limited to, the following:

(a) Exposures to hazardous materials or toxic substances
(b) Exposure to infectious or contagious diseases
(c) Illness or injury
(d) Use of prescription or nonprescription drugs
(e) Pregnancy

Paragraph A-2-1.5 cites several examples of reportable conditions, but is certainly not exhaustive. The fire department cannot reasonably expect members to know intuitively all possible conditions that need to be reported to the department physician.

Reliable member reporting of potentially significant medical conditions must therefore be accomplished through several different mechanisms. In some cases, departmental standard operating procedures (SOPs) require reporting of conditions or exposures by members. Obvious examples are pregnancy or infectious exposure. See NFPA 1581, *Standard on Fire Department Infection Control Program* (1995) (Part Four of this handbook), for further discussion.

Other exposures or potential exposures may be reported by supervisory staff or retrieved from administrative records of members' activities during emergency operations. Such reporting is frequently seen following hazardous materials incidents or EMS incidents, where a comprehensive list of involved products or exposures may only become available retrospectively.

Some conditions or exposures may only be elicited by the department physician's questioning or examination at the time of routine medical evaluation, underscoring the importance of regular evaluation. In addition, the fire department physician must maintain a good working relationship with the staff of the department's member assistance plan [as required by Section 9-1 of NFPA 1500, *Standard on Fire Department Occupational Safety and Health Program* (1997) (Part One of this handbook) so that information derived by one is appropriately forwarded to the other when necessary. This exchange of information must, of course, take place with knowledge and consent of the member, and with full cognizance of the requirements of medical confidentiality. Thus, it is clear that the member, the department, the fire department physician, and certain ancillary staff all share responsibility for the "timely reporting" required by NFPA 1582.

2-1.6

If the candidate or current fire fighter presents with an acute medical problem or newly acquired chronic medical condition, the medical evaluation shall be postponed until that person has recovered from this condition and presents to the fire department for review.

Paragraph 2-1.6 allows the department to delay the medical evaluation determining fitness for duty until an individual is considered to be "at baseline." If a member is currently ill or injured and the condition is thought to be reversible—that is, that it will improve with time and/or therapy—it is appropriate to postpone the evaluation for medical certification. In most cases where it is deemed necessary or advantageous to postpone such evaluation, the individual will not be performing full fire-fighting duties as described in NFPA 1001, *Standard on Fire Fighter Professional Qualifications* (1997). The member whose evaluation is postponed for illness or injury will generally be on light duty or temporarily off duty, at the discretion of the fire department physician and/or departmental administration.

2-2 Fire Department Physician

2-2.1*

The fire department physician shall be a licensed doctor of medicine or osteopathy.

A-2-2.1 See Appendix D, Section D-2, Choosing a Fire Department Physician.

2-2.2*

The fire department physician shall be qualified to provide professional expertise in the areas of occupational safety and health as they relate to emergency services.

A-2-2.2 See Appendix B, "Guide for Fire Department Physicians."

2-2.3*

For the purpose of conducting medical evaluations, the fire department physician shall understand the physiological and psychological demands placed on fire fighters and shall understand the environmental conditions under which fire fighters must perform.

A-2-2.3 See Appendix B, Section B-2, Occupational Safety and Health Problems for Fire Fighters, and Appendix C, "Essential Fire-Fighting Functions."

NFPA 1582 does not delineate all medical conditions that disqualify a person from fire fighting. The professional judgment of the fire department physician is key to a fire department occupational safety and health program. This judgment is enhanced by an understanding of fire fighting, as required by paragraph 2-2.3. After the list of Category A and Category B conditions found under each physiological system in Chapter 3 of NFPA 1582, the statement "Any other . . . condition that results in a person not being able to perform as a fire fighter" appears. The evaluating physician must be sufficiently familiar with the demands of fire fighting to analyze any unlisted medical findings or conditions discovered in light of the occupation. Furthermore, the severity and consequences of all Category B conditions must be evaluated for each individual member with respect to the functional job analysis. In other words, the apparently comprehensive list of potentially disqualifying medical conditions included in this standard does not diminish the importance of the fire department physician's intimate understanding of fire fighting as an occupation.

The committee also intended that the fire department physician would counsel individuals regarding the potential risk(s) posed by Category A and Category B conditions. Following such counseling, it should be clear to the fire fighter or candidate why alternative occupations should be considered. Regardless of whether an individual is medically disqualified, he or she should fully understand all of the implications of engaging in fire fighting in the presence of the identified medical condition.

2-2.4 Fire Department Physician Roles.

2-2.4.1 The fire department physician shall evaluate the person to ascertain the presence of any medical conditions listed in this standard.

2-2.4.2 When medical evaluations are conducted by a physician other than the fire department physician, the evaluation shall be reviewed and approved by the fire department physician.

2-3* Preplacement Medical Evaluation

A-2-3 See Appendix B, Section B-3, Guidance for Medical Evaluations.

2-3.1

The candidate shall be certified by the fire department physician as meeting the medical requirements of Chapter 3 of this standard prior to entering into a training program to become a fire fighter or performing in an emergency operational environment as a fire fighter.

2-3.2

The candidate shall be evaluated according to the medical requirements of Chapter 3 of this standard to assess the effect of medical conditions on the candidate's ability to perform as a fire fighter.

2-3.3

A candidate shall not be certified as meeting the medical requirements of this standard if the fire department physician determines that the candidate has any Category A medical condition specified in Chapter 3 of this standard.

2-3.4*

A candidate shall not be certified as meeting the medical requirements of this standard if the fire department physician determines that the candidate has a Category B medical condition specified in Chapter 3 of this standard that is of sufficient severity to prevent the candidate from performing, with or without reasonable accommodation, the essential functions of a fire fighter without posing a significant risk to the safety and health of the candidate or others.

A-2-3.4 See Appendix D, Section D-1, Legal Considerations in Applying the Standard.

2-3.4.1 The determination of whether there is reasonable accommodation shall be made by the authority having jurisdiction in conjunction with the fire department physician.

Appendix D, Section D-2, of NFPA 1582 includes materials intended to familiarize fire department administrators and physicians with some of the relevant provisions of the Americans with Disabilities Act of 1990. Physicians with training and expertise in occupational medicine will already be well acquainted with these provisions and with the concept of "reasonable accommodation."

A department's capacity for reasonable accommodation is generally determined by its own administration, and not by the fire department physician. It is the physician's responsibility to notify the department of the presence of a condition that compromises a candidate's or member's ability to perform the essential job functions. The physician may also be asked to evaluate the adequacy of accommodations that can be offered by the department to allow the individual to do the job. It is the department's responsibility to determine its ability to accommodate the candidate or member with a disability.

Limitations to a department's responsibility for reasonable accommodation include the size and configuration of the department, fiscal constraints, and others. Different departments, of different sizes, in different financial circumstances and in different geographical areas will likely be held to different standards of reasonable accommodation by federal enforcement officials. Furthermore, the law requires that each case be considered individually.

A ready example of an accommodation that might be expected of many (though not necessarily all) departments is providing self-contained breathing apparatus masks with integrated corrective lenses for fire fighters whose visual acuity would not otherwise meet the requirements of paragraph 3-2.1.

2-3.5

If the candidate presents with an acute medical problem or newly acquired chronic medical condition that interferes with the candidate's ability to perform the functions of a fire fighter, medical certification shall be postponed until that person has recovered from this condition and presents to the fire department for review.

2-4* Periodic Medical Evaluation

A-2-4 See Appendix B, Section B-3, Guidance for Medical Evaluations.

2-4.1

The current fire fighter shall be annually certified by the fire department physician as meeting the medical requirements of Chapter 3 of this standard to determine that fire fighter's medical ability to continue participating in a training or emergency operational environment as a fire fighter.

2-4.1.1 The components of the annual medical evaluation specified in 2-4.1.2 of this section shall be permitted to be performed by qualified personnel as authorized by the fire department physician. When other qualified personnel are used, the fire department physician shall review the data gathered during the evaluation.

2-4.1.2 The annual medical evaluation shall consist of the following:

(a) An interval medical history
(b) An interval occupational history, including significant exposures
(c) Height and weight
(d) Blood pressure

2-4.1.3* The annual medical evaluation shall include a medical examination according to the following schedule:

(a) Ages 29 and under—every 3 years
(b) Ages 30 to 39—every 2 years
(c) Ages 40 and above—every year

A-2-4.1.3 At the discretion of the fire department physician an examination can be performed sooner than would be expected from the schedule given in 2-4.1.3. Current medical conditions and coronary risk factors could mandate more frequent medical examinations.

2-4.1.4* The medical examination shall include examination of the following components:

(a) Vital signs, namely, pulse, respiration, blood pressure, and, if indicated, temperature
(b) Dermatological system
(c) Ears, eyes, nose, mouth, throat
(d) Cardiovascular system
(e) Respiratory system
(f) Gastrointestinal system
(g) Genitourinary system
(h) Endocrine and metabolic systems
(i) Musculoskeletal system
(j) Neurological system
(k) Audiometry
(l) Visual acuity and peripheral vision testing
(m) Pulmonary function testing
(n) Laboratory testing, if indicated
(o) Diagnostic imaging, if indicated
(p) Electrocardiography, if indicated

A-2-4.1.4 See Appendix B, "Guide for Fire Department Physicians."

Paragraph 2-4.1.4 provides a protocol for medical examination. The elements of the evaluation and examination screen for conditions that presently or potentially compromise a member's ability to wear protective equipment and/or perform as a fire fighter. In addition, the examination is an attempt at earlier detection of conditions for which fire fighters are known or thought to be at increased risk. This protocol represents the preventive health or "surveillance" aspect of occupational medicine. For further discussion of specific examples of such conditions, see Appendix B, Section B-2, of this standard.

An additional concern of the comprehensive health program for a department includes mechanism(s) through which relevant baseline data from the occupational health program can be made available as needed during emergencies. For example, the hospital emergency department staff needs access to baseline electrocardiographic tracings when evaluating a fire fighter for chest pain or following carbon monoxide exposure. How access to baseline information will be provided will depend upon cooperative interfaces among those providing emergency and occupational medical services for the department.

2-4.2

A current fire fighter shall not be certified as meeting the medical requirements of this standard if the fire department physician determines that the fire fighter has any Category A medical condition specified in Chapter 3 of this standard.

2-4.3*

A current fire fighter shall not be certified as meeting the medical requirements of this standard if the fire department physician determines that the fire fighter has a Category B condition specified in Chapter 3 of this standard that is of sufficient severity to prevent the fire fighter from performing, with or without reasonable accommodation, the essential functions of a fire fighter without posing a significant risk to the safety and health of the fire fighter or others.

A-2-4.3 See Appendix D, Section D-1, Legal Considerations in Applying the Standard.

2-4.3.1 The determination of reasonable accommodation shall be made by the authority having jurisdiction in conjunction with the fire department physician.

2-4.4

If the current fire fighter presents with an acute illness or recently acquired chronic medical condition, the evaluation shall be deferred until the fire fighter has recovered from the condition and presents to the fire department to return to duty.

2-5 Return-to-Duty Medical Evaluation

2-5.1

A current fire fighter who has been absent from duty for a medical condition of a nature or duration that could affect performance as a fire fighter shall be evaluated by the fire department physician before returning to duty.

2-5.2

The fire department physician shall not medically certify the current fire fighter for return to duty if any Category A medical condition specified in Chapter 3 of this standard is present.

2-5.3*

The fire department physician shall not medically certify the current fire fighter for return to duty if any Category B medical condition specified in Chapter 3 of this standard is present that is determined to be severe enough to affect the fire fighter's performance as a fire fighter. The fire department physician, in conjunction with the authority having jurisdiction, shall take into account the fire fighter's current duty assignment and alternative duty assignments or other programs that would allow a fire fighter to gradually return to full duty.

A-2-5.3 See Appendix D, Section D-1, Legal Considerations in Applying the Standard.

2-6 Medical Evaluation Records, Results, Reporting, and Confidentiality

2-6.1

All medical information collected as part of a medical evaluation shall be considered confidential medical information and shall be released by the fire department physician only with the specific written consent of the candidate or current fire fighter.

2-6.2

The fire department physician shall report the results of the medical evaluation to the candidate or current fire fighter, including any medical condition(s) disclosed during the medical evaluation, and the recommendation as to whether the candidate or current fire fighter is medically certified to perform as a fire fighter.

2-6.3

The fire department physician shall inform the fire department only as to whether or not the candidate or current fire fighter is medically certified to perform as a fire fighter. The specific written consent of the candidate or current fire fighter shall be required in order to release confidential medical information regarding this condition to the fire department.

The requirement of medical confidentiality ranges from the report of results of any given medical evaluation to all medical records kept by the department. If evaluations are performed within the department and/or records are maintained on the premises, the department must ensure that unauthorized personnel do not have access to them. Furthermore, the number of authorized personnel should be severely restricted, and members should be aware of who has access to the medical records. Any breach in the security of these files or the information within them may expose a department, its leadership, and the municipal government to enormous liability.

CHAPTER 3*

Category A and Category B Medical Conditions

A-3 The medical conditions listed are organized by organ system. In the corresponding Appendix A explanatory material, a diagnostic example is often included with the list to help the examiner understand the type of condition that might result in rejection or acceptance. In addition, the rationale for the exclusion is presented in terms of the effect of the medical condition on the capability of the person to perform as a fire fighter.

3-1 Head and Neck

3-1.1 Head.

3-1.1.1 There shall be no Category A medical conditions.

3-1.1.2* Category B medical conditions shall include the following:

(a) Deformities of the skull such as depressions or exostoses
(b) Deformities of the skull associated with evidence of disease of the brain, spinal cord, or peripheral nerves
(c) Loss or congenital absence of the bony substance of the skull
(d) Any other head condition that results in a person not being able to perform as a fire fighter

A-3-1.1.2 Category B medical conditions of the head include the following:

(a) Deformities of the skull, such as depressions or exostoses, of a degree that interferes with the use of protective equipment. Deformities of the skull can result in the fire fighter's inability to properly wear protective equipment.

(b) Deformities of the skull associated with evidence of disease of the brain, spinal cord, or peripheral nerves. These deformities can result in the potential for sudden incapacitation; the inability to properly wear protective equipment; and the inability to communicate effectively due to oropharyngeal dysfunction.

(c) Loss or congenital absence of the bony substance of the skull (if associated with disease interfering with performance or if appropriate protection cannot be provided for area without interfering with protective equipment and vision). Loss or congenital absence of the bony substance of the skull can result in the inability to properly wear protective equipment, and the inability to communicate effectively due to oropharyngeal dysfunction.

(d) Any other head condition that results in a person not being able to perform as a fire fighter

3-1.2 Neck.

3-1.2.1 There shall be no Category A medical conditions.

3-1.2.2* Category B medical conditions shall include the following:

(a) Thoracic outlet syndrome
(b) Congenital cysts, chronic draining fistulas, or similar lesions
(c) Contraction of neck muscles
(d) Any other neck condition that results in a person not being able to perform as a fire fighter

A-3-1.2.2 Category B medical conditions of the neck include the following:

(a) Thoracic outlet syndrome (symptomatic). Thoracic outlet syndrome can result in frequent episodes of pain or inability to perform work.

(b) Congenital cysts, chronic draining fistulas, or similar lesions (if lesions or underlying disease interferes with performance). Congenital cysts, chronic draining fistulas, or similar lesions can result in the inability to properly wear protective equipment, and the inability to communicate effectively due to oropharyngeal dysfunction.

(c) Contraction of neck muscles (if it interferes with wearing of protective equipment or ability to perform duties). The contraction of neck muscles may result in the inability to properly wear protective equipment, and the inability to perform functions as a fire fighter due to limitation of flexibility.

(d) Any other neck condition that results in a person not being able to perform as a fire fighter

3-2 Eyes and Vision

3-2.1*

Category A medical conditions shall include the following:

(a) Far visual acuity. Far visual acuity shall be at least 20/30 binocular corrected with contact lenses or spectacles. Far visual acuity uncorrected shall be at least 20/100 binocular for wearers of hard contacts or spectacles. Successful long-term soft contact lens wearers shall not be subject to the uncorrected criterion.

(b) Peripheral vision. Visual field performance without correction shall be 140 degrees in the horizontal meridian in each eye.

A-3-2.1 Category A medical conditions of the eyes and vision include the following:

(a) Far visual acuity. Far visual acuity is at least 20/30 binocular corrected with contact lenses or spectacles. Far visual acuity uncorrected is at least 20/100 binocular for wearers of hard contacts or spectacles. Successful long-term soft contact lens wearers (that is, six months without a problem) are not subject to the uncorrected standard. Inadequate far visual acuity can result in the failure to be able to read placards and street signs or to see and respond to imminently hazardous situations.

Paragraph 3-2.1(a) intends to provide adequate vision for safe job performance while wearing self-contained breathing apparatus. Based upon the job task analysis and the resources available in any given department, reasonable accommodation of myopic fire fighters might include supplying SCBA facepieces that support prescription lenses or have the prescription ground into the mask. Where the job analysis identifies job functions in addition to wearing SCBA during which spectacles might become dislodged, the accommodation of SCBA with prescription lenses still may not be adequate to allow individuals who do not meet the vision requirements of NFPA 1582 to function as fire fighters.

Soft contact lens wearers must also demonstrate that the lenses remain comfortable and corrective during use of positive-pressure SCBA.

(b) Peripheral vision. Visual field performance without correction is 140 degrees in the horizontal meridian in each eye. (Fire fighters must not have just monocular vision.) Inadequate peripheral vision can result in the failure to be able to read placards and street signs or to see and respond to imminently hazardous situations.

The minimal acceptable peripheral vision required by paragraph 3-2.1(b) was selected with the knowledge that wearing an SCBA facepiece significantly compromises peripheral vision for most individuals. It was felt that any further restriction of the visual field beyond that imposed by the SCBA presents an unacceptable added risk for personnel operating in hazardous environments.

3-2.2*

Category B medical conditions shall include the following:

(a) Diseases of the eye such as retinal detachment, progressive retinopathy, or optic neuritis
(b) Ophthalmological procedures such as radial keratotomy or repair of retinal detachment
(c) Any other eye condition that results in a person not being able to perform as a fire fighter

A-3-2.2 Category B medical conditions of the eyes and vision include the following:

(a) Diseases of the eye such as retinal detachment, progressive retinopathy, or optic neuritis (severe or progressive). These diseases of the eye can result in the failure to read placards and street signs or to see and respond to imminently hazardous situations.

(b) Ophthalmological procedures such as radial keratotomy and repair of retinal detachment. Sufficient time (that is, six months) must have passed to allow stabilization of visual acuity and to ensure that there are no postsurgical complications. These ophthalmological procedures may result in the failure to be able to read placards and street signs or to see and respond to imminently hazardous situations.

(c) Any other eye condition that results in a person not being able to perform as a fire fighter

Formerly, color vision deficiency was listed as a Category B medical condition. However, it is felt that in most cases this condition will not affect the ability of a fire fighter to perform the essential functions of his or her job. The fire service physician should consider the color vision deficiency of the individual and consider the color vision requirements of the fire fighter's job and reach an individual determination.

3-3 Ears and Hearing

3-3.1

There shall be no Category A medical conditions.

3-3.2*

Category B medical conditions shall include the following:

(a) Hearing deficit in the pure tone thresholds in the unaided worst ear

EITHER

1. Greater than 25 dB in three of the four frequencies

a. 500 Hz
b. 1000 Hz
c. 2000 Hz
d. 3000 Hz

OR

2. Greater than 30 dB in any one of the three frequencies

a. 500 Hz
b. 1000 Hz
c. 2000 Hz

AND

an average greater than 30 dB for the four frequencies

a. 500 Hz
b. 1000 Hz
c. 2000 Hz
d. 3000 Hz

(b) Atresia, severe stenosis, or tumor of the auditory canal
(c) Severe external otitis
(d) Severe agenesis or traumatic deformity of the auricle
(e) Severe mastoiditis or surgical deformity of the mastoid
(f) Meniere's syndrome or labyrinthitis
(g) Otitis media
(h) Any other ear condition that results in a person not being able to perform as a fire fighter; AND, in addition to the above conditions, is unable to pass a job-specific functional hearing task test OR a Hearing in Noise Test.

A-3-3.2 Category B medical conditions of hearing include the following:

(a) Hearing deficit in pure tone thresholds in the unaided worst ear

EITHER

1. Greater than 25 dB in three of the four frequencies

a. 500 Hz
b. 1000 Hz
c. 2000 Hz
d. 3000 Hz

OR

2. Greater than 30 dB in any one of the three frequencies

a. 500 Hz
b. 1000 Hz
c. 2000 Hz

AND

an average greater than 30 dB for the four frequencies

a. 500 Hz
b. 1000 Hz
c. 2000 Hz
d. 3000 Hz

The inability to hear sounds of low intensity or to distinguish voice from background noise can lead to a failure to respond to imminently hazardous situations.

The values in paragraph 3-3.2(a) were set with the understanding that they imperfectly test an individual's functional hearing capacity under emergency conditions. To date, however, there is no widely accepted or adequately validated test of hearing radio transmissions, voices muffled by personal protective equipment, or alarms sounding at a variety of different frequencies in environments with tremendous background noise (with or without accompanying visual cues).

(b) Atresia, severe stenosis, or tumor of the auditory canal. These conditions can result in the inability to hear sounds of low intensity or to distinguish voice from background noise, leading to failure to respond to imminently hazardous situations.

(c) Severe external otitis (that is recurrent loss of hearing). Severe external otitis can result in the inability to hear sounds of low intensity or to distinguish voice from background noise, leading to failure to respond to imminently hazardous situations.

(d) Severe agenesis or traumatic deformity of the auricle to the degree that interferes with ability to wear protective equipment or with hearing acuity. Severe agenesis or traumatic deformity of the auricle can result in the inability to properly wear protective equipment, and the inability to hear sounds of low intensity or to distinguish voice from background noise, leading to failure to respond to imminently hazardous situations.

(e) Severe mastoiditis or surgical deformity of the mastoid. Severe mastoiditis or surgical deformity of the mastoid can result in the inability to properly wear protective equipment, and the inability to hear sounds of low intensity or to distinguish voice from background noise, leading to failure to respond to imminently hazardous situations.

(f) Meniere's syndrome or labyrinthitis (severe). Meniere's syndrome or severe labyrinthitis may result in the potential for sudden incapacitation and the inability to perform job functions due to limitations of balance.

The requirement of 3-3.2(f) should be understood to include *any* condition producing episodes of true vertigo, with or without tinnitus or vomiting. If the condition is transient and the member is not thought to be at higher risk than the rest of the population for a recurrence of symptoms, the member may be cleared for duty. Any relapsing syndromes producing recurrent episodes of vertigo should be seriously considered by the fire department physician since ladder work and roof operations, common tasks for structural fire fighters, may have been done under hostile conditions.

(g) Otitis media (chronic). Otitis media can result in frequent episodes of pain or the inability to perform work and the inability to hear sounds of low intensity or to distinguish voice from background noise, leading to failure to respond to imminently hazardous situations.

(h) Any other ear condition that results in a person not being able to perform as a fire fighter

3-4 Dental

3-4.1

There shall be no Category A medical conditions.

3-4.2*

Category B medical conditions shall include the following:

(a) Diseases of the jaws or associated tissues
(b) Orthodontic appliances
(c) Oral tissues, extensive loss
(d) Relationship between the mandible and maxilla that precludes satisfactory postorthodontic replacement or ability to use protective equipment
(e) Any other dental condition that results in a person not being able to perform as a fire fighter

A-3-4.2 Category B dental medical conditions include the following:

(a) Diseases of the jaws or associated tissues (those that are incapacitating or preclude ability to use protective equipment). Diseases of the jaws or associated tissues can result in the inability to properly wear protective equipment.

(b) Orthodontic appliances (those that preclude the ability to use protective equipment). The wearing of orthodontic appliances can result in the inability to properly wear protective equipment.

(c) Oral tissues, extensive loss (that which precludes satisfactory postorthodontic replacement or ability to use protective equipment). Extensive loss of oral tissues may result in the inability to properly wear protective equipment and the inability to communicate effectively due to oropharyngeal dysfunction.

(d) Relationship between the mandible and maxilla that precludes satisfactory postorthodontic replacement or ability to use protective equipment. This condition can result in the inability to properly wear protective equipment and the inability to communicate effectively due to oropharyngeal dysfunction.

(e) Any other dental condition that results in a person not being able to perform as a fire fighter

3-5 Nose, Oropharynx, Trachea, Esophagus, and Larynx

3-5.1*

Category A medical conditions shall include the following:

(a) Tracheostomy
(b) Aphonia
(c) Anosmia

A-3-5.1 Category A medical conditions of the nose, oropharynx, trachea, esophagus, and larynx include the following:

(a) Tracheostomy. A tracheostomy can result in the inability to properly wear protective equipment, the inability to perform job functions due to limitations of endurance, and the inability to communicate effectively due to oropharyngeal dysfunction.

(b) Aphonia, regardless of cause. Aphonia can result in the inability to communicate effectively due to oropharyngeal dysfunction.

(c) Anosmia. Anosmia can result in the inability to smell smoke or hazardous materials, resulting in failure to respond to imminently hazardous situations.

3-5.2*

Category B medical conditions shall include the following:

(a) Congenital or acquired deformity
(b) Allergic respiratory disorder
(c) Sinusitis, recurrent
(d) Dysphonia
(e) Any other nose, oropharynx, trachea, esophagus, or larynx condition that results in a person not being able to perform as a fire fighter or to communicate effectively

A-3-5.2 Category B medical conditions of the nose, oropharynx, trachea, esophagus, and larynx include the following:

(a) Congenital or acquired deformity that interferes with the ability to use protective equipment. A congenital or acquired deformity can result in the inability to properly wear protective equipment.

(b) Allergic respiratory disorder (uncontrolled). Allergic respiratory disorder can result in frequent episodes of pain or the inability to perform work and the inability to perform functions as a fire fighter due to limitations of endurance.

As is the case with many Category A or B conditions, the medications used to control the symptoms may significantly degrade the fire fighter's ability to function safely on the job. In many cases, it may be necessary to relieve personnel of duty while they require medication for acute cases of conditions such as severe allergic rhinitis or asthmatic bronchitis.

(c) Sinusitis, recurrent (severe, requiring repeated hospitalizations or causing impairment). Recurrent sinusitis can result in frequent episodes of pain and the inability to perform work.

(d) Dysphonia (severe). Severe dysphonia can result in the inability to communicate effectively due to oropharyngeal dysfunction.

(e) Any other nose, oropharynx, trachea, esophagus, or larynx condition that results in a person not being able to perform as a fire fighter or to communicate effectively.

3-6 Lungs and Chest Wall

3-6.1*

Category A medical conditions shall include the following:

(a) Active hemoptysis
(b) Empyema
(c) Current pneumonia
(d) Pulmonary hypertension
(e) Active tuberculosis
(f) Infectious diseases of the lungs or pleural space

A-3-6.1 Category A medical conditions of the lungs and chest wall include active hemoptysis, empyema, current pneumonia, pulmonary hypertension, active tuberculosis, or infectious diseases of the lungs or pleural space. These conditions can result in the inability to perform functions as a fire fighter due to limitations of endurance.

Some of the conditions identified in paragraph A-3-6.1 may call for the fire department to consult with local public health authorities before returning fire fighters to full duty. Significant additional considerations include housing arrangements for on-duty personnel and the range of duties fire fighters may be asked to perform; for example, is EMS patient care part of the job description?

3-6.2*

Category B medical conditions shall include the following:

(a) Pulmonary resectional surgery, chest wall surgery, pneumothorax
(b) Bronchial asthma or reactive airways disease
(c) Fibrothorax, chest wall deformity, diaphragm abnormalities
(d) Chronic obstructive airways disease
(e) Hypoxemic disorders
(f) Interstitial lung diseases
(g) Pulmonary vascular diseases, pulmonary embolism
(h) Bronchiectasis

A-3-6.2 Category B medical conditions of the lungs and chest wall include the following:

(a) Pulmonary resectional surgery, chest wall surgery, pneumothorax (that is history of recurrent spontaneous pneumothorax). These conditions can result in the inability to perform functions as a fire fighter due to limitations of strength or endurance and may result in the potential for sudden incapacitation.

(b) Bronchial asthma or reactive airways disease (frequent medication use or symptoms caused by exposures to exertion, heat and cold, or products of combustion and other irritant inhalation). Bronchial asthma or reactive airways disease can result in frequent episodes of pain or the inability to perform work, the potential for sudden incapacitation, and the inability to perform functions as a fire fighter due to limitations of endurance.

(c) Fibrothorax, chest wall deformity, diaphragm abnormalities. Fibrothorax, chest wall deformity, and diaphragm abnormalities can result in the inability to perform functions as a fire fighter due to limitations of endurance.

(d) Chronic obstructive airways disease. Chronic obstructive airways disease can result in the inability to perform functions as a fire fighter due to limitations of endurance.

(e) Hypoxemic disorders. Hypoxemic disorders can result in the inability to perform functions as a fire fighter due to limitations of endurance.

(f) Interstitial lung diseases. Interstitial lung diseases can result in the inability to perform functions as a fire fighter due to limitations of endurance.

(g) Pulmonary vascular diseases, pulmonary embolism. Pulmonary vascular diseases and pulmonary embolism can result in frequent episodes of pain and the inability to perform functions as a fire fighter due to limitations of endurance.

(h) Bronchiectasis with significant residual impairment of pulmonary function or requiring frequent therapy.

Bronchiectasis can result in the inability to perform functions as a fire fighter due to limitations of endurance.

(i) Any other pulmonary or chest wall condition that results in a person not being able to perform as a fire fighter

3-7 Heart and Vascular System

3-7.1 Heart.

3-7.1.1* Category A medical conditions shall include the following:

(a) Angina pectoris, current
(b) Left bundle branch block or second-degree Type II atrioventricular block
(c) Heart failure, current
(d) Acute pericarditis, endocarditis, or myocarditis
(e) Syncope, recurrent
(f) Automatic implantable cardiac defibrillator

A-3-7.1.1 Category A medical conditions of the heart and vascular system include the following:

(a) Angina pectoris, current. Angina pectoris can result in frequent episodes of pain or inability to perform work, progressive illness leading to functional impairment, and the potential for sudden incapacitation.

(b) Left bundle branch block or second-degree Type II artioventricular block. This condition can result in the potential for sudden incapacitation.

(c) Heart failure, current. Heart failure can result in frequent episodes of pain or inability to perform work, progressive illness leading to functional impairment, and the potential for sudden incapacitation.

(d) Acute pericarditis, endocarditis, or myocarditis. These conditions can result in frequent episodes of pain or the inability to perform work.

(e) Syncope, recurrent. Recurrent syncope can result in the potential for sudden incapacitation.

(f) Automatic implantable cardiac defibrillator. An automatic implantable cardiac defibrillator can result in the potential for sudden incapacitation.

Paragraph A-3-7.1.1 is intended to include any condition for which an automatic implantable cardiac defibrillator (AICD) is indicated. A history of "sudden cardiac death" due to ventricular arrhythmia without a clear, non-cardiac precipitant (whether actually treated with anti-arrhythmic medications alone or with an AICD) is considered a disqualifying condition.

3-7.1.2* Category B medical conditions shall include the following:

(a) Significant valvular lesions of the heart, including prosthetic valves
(b) Coronary artery disease, including history of myocardial infarction, coronary artery bypass surgery, or coronary angioplasty, and similiar procedures
(c) Atrial tachycardia, flutter, or fibrillation
(d) Third-degree atrioventricular block
(e) Ventricular tachycardia
(f) Hypertrophy of the heart
(g) Recurrent paroxysmal tachycardia
(h) History of a congenital abnormality
(i) Chronic pericarditis, endocarditis, or myocarditis
(j) Cardiac pacemaker
(k) Coronary artery vasospasm
(l) Any other cardiac condition that results in a person not being able to perform as a fire fighter

A-3-7.1.2 Category B medical conditions of the heart and vascular system include the following:

(a) Significant valvular lesions of the heart, including prosthetic valves. Specific recommendations include the following:

Mitral stenosis. Mitral stenosis is acceptable if in sinus rhythm and stenosis is mild, that is, valve area $>1.5\ cm^2$ or pulmonary artery systolic pressure <35 mm Hg.

Mitral insufficiency. Mitral insufficiency is acceptable if in sinus rhythm with normal left ventricular size and function.

Aortic stenosis. Aortic stenosis is acceptable if stenosis is mild, that is, mean aortic valvular pressure gradient <20 mm Hg.

Aortic regurgitation. Aortic regurgitation is acceptable if left ventricular size is normal or slightly increased and systolic function is normal.

Prosthetic valves. Prosthetic valves are acceptable unless full anticoagulation is in effect.

In this edition of NFPA 1582, therapeutic anticoagulation has been changed from Category A to Category B. *(See paragraph A-3-19.2 for information about anticoagulation.)*

(b) Coronary artery disease, including history of myocardial infarction, coronary artery bypass surgery, coronary angioplasty, and similiar procedures. Persons at mildly increased risk for sudden incapacitation are acceptable for fire fighting. Mildly increased risk is defined by the presence of each of the following:

1. Normal left ventricular ejection fraction
2. Normal exercise tolerance, >10 metabolic equivalents (METS)
3. Absence of exercise-induced ischemia by exercise testing

4. Absence of exercise-induced complex ventricular arrhythmias
5. Absence of hemodynamically significant stenosis on all major coronary arteries (> or = 70 percent lumen diameter narrowing), or successful myocardial revascularization

The changes in this area from the previous edition reflect improved cardiac care available to fire fighters. Most notably, these improvements include the widespread availability of percutaneous translumenal coronary angioplasty, with or without stenting. More improvements are expected as minimally invasive techniques for coronary artery bypass grafting are developed.

These improvements in cardiac care should serve as strong, added incentive to members to reduce their cardiac risk factors. At the same time, members will hopefully be aggressive in evaluating and treating the earliest signs of impending ischemic heart disease. Recognition and treatment of coronary artery stenosis before a myocardial infarction vastly improve the likelihood of conserving left ventricular function.

Many departments routinely subject all members and candidates to exercise tolerance testing. However, NFPA 1582 only requires stress testing when medically indicated by risk factors, symptoms, or signs. This is an unclear area in the medical literature, as well. The sensitivity and specificity of cardiac stress testing have not, thus far, supported its use as a screening tool. For certain populations, such as fire fighters, it is not reasonable to continue stress testing where it has not been established that this type of testing is indicated. Further study of its potential application and benefits is being conducted.

Members or candidates who have successfully undergone procedures to correct coronary artery stenosis or obstruction, and who satisfy the other requirements above, are acceptable for duty. These individuals require close follow-up and periodic clearance by a qualified cardiologist who understands the demands of the job.

(c) Atrial tachycardia, flutter, or fibrillation

(d) Third-degree atrioventricular block (will result in disqualification unless exercise can be performed with an adequate heart rate response). A third-degree atrioventricular block can result in frequent episodes of pain or the inability to perform work, and the potential for sudden incapacitation.

(e) Ventricular tachycardia. Ventricular tachycardia can result in the potential for sudden incapacitation and the inability to perform job functions due to limitations of strength or endurance.

(f) Hypertrophy of the heart. Hypertrophy of the heart can result in the potential for sudden incapacitation and the inability to perform job functions due to limitations of endurance.

(g) Recurrent paroxysmal tachycardia. Recurrent paroxysmal tachycardia can result in the potential for sudden incapacitation and the inability to perform job functions due to limitations of strength or endurance.

(h) History of a congenital abnormality that has been treated by surgery but with residual complications or that has not been treated by surgery, leaving residuals or complications. A congenital abnormality can result in frequent episodes of pain or inability to perform work and the potential for sudden incapacitation.

(i) Chronic pericarditis, endocarditis, or myocarditis. These conditions can result in the inability to perform job functions due to limitations of endurance.

(j) Cardiac pacemaker. If the person is pacemaker-dependent, then the risk for sudden failure due to trauma is not acceptable. Those with cardiac pacemakers can have the potential for sudden incapacitation.

(k) Coronary artery vasospasm. Those with cardiac artery vasospasm can have the potential for sudden incapacitation.

(l) Any other cardiac condition that results in a person not being able to perform as a fire fighter

3-7.2 Vascular System.

3-7.2.1 There shall be no Category A medical conditions.

3-7.2.2* Category B medical conditions shall include the following:

(a) Hypertension
(b) Peripheral vascular disease such as Raynaud's phenomenon
(c) Recurrent thrombophlebitis
(d) Chronic lymphedema due to lymphadenopathy or severe venous valvular incompetency
(e) Congenital or acquired lesions of the aorta or major vessels
(f) Marked circulatory instability as indicated by orthostatic hypotension, persistent tachycardia, and severe peripheral vasomotor disturbances
(g) Aneurysm of the heart or major vessel
(h) Any other vascular condition that results in a person not being able to perform as a fire fighter

A-3-7.2.2 Category B medical conditions of the vascular system include the following:

(a) Hypertension that is uncontrolled or poorly controlled, or requires medication likely to interfere with the performance of duties. Acceptable hypertension is a blood pressure less than 180/100 and no target organ damage. Hypertension is a progressive illness leading to functional impairment with the potential for sudden incapacitation.

(b) Peripheral vascular disease, such as Raynaud's phenomenon that interferes with performance of duties or makes the individual likely to have significant risk of severe injury. Peripheral vascular disease can result in frequent episodes of pain or the inability to perform work and the inability to perform functions as a fire fighter due to limitations of endurance.

(c) Recurrent thrombophlebitis. Recurrent thrombophlebitis can result in frequent episodes of pain or the inability to perform work and the inability to perform functions as a fire fighter due to limitations of endurance.

(d) Chronic lymphedema due to lymphopathy or severe venous valvular incompetency. Chronic lymphedema can result in the inability to perform functions as a fire fighter due to limitations of endurance.

(e) Congenital or acquired lesions of the aorta or major vessels, for example, syphilitic aortitis, demonstrable atherosclerosis that interferes with circulation, and congenital acquired dilatation of the aorta. Congenital or acquired lesions of the aorta or major vessels can result in the potential for sudden incapacitation and the inability to perform job functions due to limitations of endurance.

(f) Marked circulatory instability as indicated by orthostatic hypotension, persistent tachycardia, and severe peripheral vasomotor disturbances. Marked circulatory instability can result in the inability to perform job functions due to limitations of endurance and the inability to perform job functions due to limitations of balance.

(g) Aneurysm of the heart or major vessel, congenital or acquired. An aneurysm of the heart or major vessel can result in frequent episodes of pain or inability to perform work and the potential for sudden incapacitation.

(h) Any other vascular condition that results in a person not being able to perform as a fire fighter

3-8 Abdominal Organs and Gastrointestinal System

3-8.1*

Chronic active hepatitis shall be a Category A medical condition.

A-3-8.1 Chronic, active hepatitis is a Category A medical condition of the abdominal organs and gastrointestinal system. Chronic, active hepatitis can result in frequent episodes of pain or the inability to perform work.

3-8.2*

Category B medical conditions shall include the following:

(a) Cholecystitis
(b) Gastritis
(c) Hemorrhoids
(d) Acute hepatitis
(e) Hernia
(f) Inflammatory bowel disease
(g) Intestinal obstruction
(h) Pancreatitis
(i) Resection, bowel
(j) Ulcer, gastrointestinal
(k) Cirrhosis, hepatic or biliary
(l) Any other gastrointestinal condition that results in a person not being able to perform the duties of fire fighter

A-3-8.2 Category B medical conditions of the abdominal organs and gastrointestinal system include the following:

(a) Cholecystitis (that which causes frequent pain due to stones or infection). Cholecystitis can result in frequent episodes of pain or the inability to perform work.

(b) Gastritis (that which causes recurrent pain and impairment). Gastritis can result in frequent episodes of pain or the inability to perform work.

(c) Hemorrhoids (where severe symptoms lead to impairment). Hemorrhoids can result in frequent episodes of pain or the inability to perform work.

(d) Acute hepatitis (until resolution of acute hepatitis as determined by clinical examination and appropriate laboratory testing). Acute hepatitis can result in frequent episodes of pain or the inability to perform work.

(e) Hernia (unrepaired inguinal or abdominal hernia that could obstruct during duty). A hernia can result in the potential for sudden incapacitation.

(f) Inflammatory bowel disease (that which causes disabling pain or diarrhea). Inflammatory bowel disease can result in frequent episodes of pain or the inability to perform work. It is a progressive illness leading to functional impairment.

(g) Intestinal obstruction (that is, recent obstruction with impairment). An intestinal obstruction can result in frequent episodes of pain or the inability to perform work and the potential for sudden incapacitation.

(h) Pancreatitis (that is, chronic or recurrent with impairment). Pancreatitis can result in frequent episodes of pain or the inability to perform work.

(i) Resection, bowel (if frequent diarrhea precludes performance of duty). A bowel resection can result in frequent episodes of pain or the inability to perform work.

(j) Ulcer, gastrointestinal (where symptoms are uncontrolled by drugs or surgery). A gastrointestinal ulcer can result in frequent episodes of pain or the inability to perform work.

(k) Cirrhosis, hepatic or biliary (that which is symptomatic or in danger of bleeding). Cirrhosis can result in frequent episodes of pain or the inability to perform work.

(l) Any other gastrointestinal condition that results in a person not being able to perform as a fire fighter

3-9 Genitourinary System

3-9.1 Reproductive.

3-9.1.1 There shall be no Category A medical conditions.

3-9.1.2* Category B medical conditions shall include the following:

(a) Pregnancy, for its duration
(b) Dysmenorrhea
(c) Endometriosis, ovarian cysts, or other gynecologic conditions
(d) Testicular or epididymal mass
(e) Any other genital condition that results in a person not being able to perform as a fire fighter

A-3-9.1.2 Category B medical conditions of the reproductive organs include the following:

(a) Pregnancy. Pregnancy can result in frequent episodes of pain or the inability to perform work; progressive inability to perform work due to limitations of endurance, flexibility, or strength; and the inability to properly wear protective equipment. See Section B-4.4, Reproductive.

(b) Dysmenorrhea that leads to recurrent incapacitation. Dysmenorrhea can result in frequent episodes of pain or the inability to perform work.

(c) Endometriosis, ovarian cysts, or other gynecologic conditions (severe, leading to recurrent incapacitation). Endometriosis, ovarian cysts, and other gynecologic conditions can result in frequent episodes of pain or the inability to perform work.

(d) Testicular or epididymal mass (that which requires medical evaluation). A testicular or epididymal mass can result in frequent episodes of pain or the inability to perform work. This is a progressive illness leading to functional impairment.

(e) Any other genital condition that results in a person not being able to perform as a fire fighter

3-9.2 Urinary System.

3-9.2.1 There shall be no Category A medical conditions.

3-9.2.2* Category B medical conditions shall include the following:

(a) Diseases of the kidney
(b) Diseases of the ureter, bladder, or prostate
(c) Any other urinary condition that results in a person not being able to perform as a fire fighter

A-3-9.2.2 Category B medical conditions of the urinary system include the following:

(a) Diseases of the kidney requiring dialysis. Diseases of the kidney can result in frequent episodes of pain or the inability to perform work. Kidney disease is a progressive illness leading to functional impairment.

(b) Diseases of the ureter, bladder, or prostate that require frequent or prolonged treatment. These diseases can result in frequent episodes of pain or the inability to perform work.

(c) Any other urinary condition that results in a person not being able to perform as a fire fighter

3-10 Spine, Scapulae, Ribs, and Sacroiliac Joints

3-10.1

There shall be no Category A medical conditions.

3-10.2*

Category B medical conditions shall include the following:

(a) Arthritis
(b) Structural abnormality, fracture, or dislocation
(c) Nucleus pulposus, herniation of or history of laminectomy
(d) Any other spinal condition that results in a person not being able to perform as a fire fighter

A-3-10.2 Category B medical conditions of the spine, scapulae, ribs, and sacroiliac joints include the following:

(a) Arthritis that results in progressive impairment or limitation of movement. Arthritis is a progressive illness that leads to functional impairment. Arthritis can result in the inability to perform functions as a fire fighter due to limitations of endurance or flexibility.

(b) Structural abnormality, fracture, or dislocation that is a progressive or recurrent impairment. These conditions are progressive illnesses leading to functional impairment. These illnesses can result in the inability to perform functions as a fire fighter due to limitations of strength or flexibility.

(c) Nucleus pulposus, herniation of or history of laminectomy (if symptomatic within the last three years). These conditions are progressive illnesses leading to functional impairment and the inability to properly wear protective equipment.

(d) Any other spinal condition that results in a person not being able to perform as a fire fighter

3-11 Extremities

3-11.1

There shall be no Category A medical conditions.

3-11.2*

Category B medical conditions shall include the following:

(a) Limitation of motion of a joint
(b) Amputation or deformity of a joint or limb
(c) Dislocation of a joint
(d) Joint reconstruction, ligamentous instability, or joint replacement
(e) Chronic osteoarthritis or traumatic arthritis
(f) Inflammatory arthritis
(g) Any other extremity condition that results in a person not being able to perform as a fire fighter

A-3-11.2 Category B medical conditions of the extremities include the following:

(a) Limitation of motion of a joint of a degree to interfere with successful and safe performance of fire-fighting duties. The limitation of motion of a joint can result in the inability to perform functions as a fire fighter due to limitation of flexibility.

(b) Amputation or deformity of a joint or limb of a degree to interfere with successful and safe performance of fire-fighting duties. The amputation or deformity of a joint or limb can result in the inability to perform functions as a fire fighter due to limitations of strength and/or balance.

(c) Dislocation of a joint (that is, recurrent or with residual limitation of motion of a degree to interfere with successful and safe performance of fire-fighting duties; successful surgery for recurrent shoulder dislocation, if range of motion is intact, would not exclude a person). Dislocation of a joint can result in the inability to perform functions as a fire fighter due to limitations of strength or flexibility.

(d) Joint reconstruction, ligamentous instability, or joint replacement (in cases where recurrent or with residual limitation of motion of a degree to interfere with successful and safe performance of fire-fighting duties; surgery for a torn anterior cruciate ligament could disqualify if quadriceps strength is not normal or if the knee is lax or develops pain or swelling when stressed.) These conditions of the joint can result in the inability to perform functions as a fire fighter due to limitations of strength or flexibility.

(e) Chronic osteoarthritis or traumatic arthritis (in cases where recurrent exacerbations leads to impairment). Chronic osteoarthritis or traumatic arthritis can result in frequent episodes of pain or the inability to perform work and the inability to perform functions as a fire fighter due to limitations of strength, endurance, or flexibility.

(f) Inflammatory arthritis (in cases where severe recurrent or progressive illness or with deformity or limitation of range of motion of a degree to interfere with successful and safe performance of fire-fighting duties). Inflammatory arthritis can result in frequent episodes of pain or the inability to perform work and the inability to perform functions as a fire fighter due to limitations of strength, endurance, or flexibility.

(g) Any other extremity condition that results in a person not being able to perform as a fire fighter

3-12 Neurological Disorders

3-12.1*

Category A medical conditions shall include the following:

(a) Ataxias of heredo-degenerative type
(b) Cerebral arteriosclerosis as evidenced by documented episodes of neurological impairment
(c) Multiple sclerosis with activity or evidence of progression within previous three years
(d) Progressive muscular dystrophy or atrophy
(e) All epileptic conditions to include simple partial, complex partial, generalized, and psychomotor seizure disorders other than those with complete control during previous five years, normal neurological examination, and definitive statement from qualified neurological specialist. If a change is made in the medical regimen that has provided a five-year seizure-free interval of an epileptic fire fighter, that individual shall not be cleared for return to fire-fighting duty until he or she has completed five years without a seizure on the new regimen.

A-3-12.1 Category A medical conditions of neurological nature include the following:

(a) Ataxias of heredo-degenerative type. Ataxias of heredo-degenerative type can result in the inability to perform functions as a fire fighter due to limitations of balance.

(b) Cerebral arteriosclerosis as evidenced by documented episodes of neurological impairment. Cerebral arteriosclerosis can result in the inability to perform functions as a fire fighter due to limitations of strength and/or balance.

(c) Multiple sclerosis with activity or evidence of progression within previous three years. Multiple sclerosis can result in the inability to perform functions as a fire fighter due to limitations of strength or flexibility.

(d) Progressive muscular dystrophy or atrophy. This condition can result in the inability to perform functions as a fire fighter due to limitations of strength and/or balance.

(e) Epileptic conditions. After a provoked seizure, with the precipitant identified and alleviated, with subsequent normal CT or MRI scan, normal EEG, normal neurological exam, free of recurrence without medication for one year, and with definitive statement from a qualified neurological specialist, a fire fighter can be cleared to return to duty.

3-12.2*

Category B medical conditions shall include the following:

(a) Congenital malformations
(b) Migraine
(c) Clinical disorders with paresis, paralysis, dyscoordination, deformity, abnormal motor activity, abnormality of sensation, or complaint of pain
(d) Subarachnoid or intracerebral hemorrhage
(e) Abnormalities from recent head injury such as severe cerebral contusion or concussion
(f) Any other neurological condition that results in a person not being able to perform as a fire fighter

A-3-12.2 Category B medical conditions of neurological nature include the following:

(a) Congenital malformations (that is, severe vascular malformations that interfere with the ability to wear protective equipment). Congenital malformations can result in the inability to properly wear protective equipment.

(b) Migraine (that is, recurrent, with impairment uncontrolled). Migraines can result in frequent episodes of pain or the inability to perform work.

(c) Clinical disorders with paresis, paralysis, dyscoordination, deformity, abnormal motor activity, abnormality of sensation, or complaint of pain (progressive or severe). These disorders are progressive illnesses leading to functional impairment. They can result in the inability to perform functions as a fire fighter due to limitations of strength, flexibility, or balance.

(d) Subarachnoid or intracerebral hemorrhage, verified either clinically or by laboratory studies, except for those corrected with verification by laboratory studies and report of treating physician. Subarachnoid or intracerebral hemorrhage is a progressive illness leading to functional impairment. This illness can result in the potential for sudden incapacitation.

(e) Abnormalities from recent head injury such as severe cerebral contusion or concussion. The abnormalities can result in the potential for sudden incapacitation.

(f) Any other neurological condition that results in a person not being able to perform as a fire fighter

3-13 Skin

3-13.1

There shall be no Category A medical conditions.

3-13.2*

Category B medical conditions shall include the following:

(a) Acne or inflammatory skin disease
(b) Eczema
(c) Any other dermatologic condition that results in the person not being able to perform as a fire fighter

A-3-13.2 Category B medical conditions of the skin include the following:

(a) Acne or inflammatory skin disease (if condition precludes good fit of protective equipment such as SCBA facepiece or prevents shaving). Acne or inflammatory skin disease can result in the inability to properly wear protective equipment.

(b) Eczema (if broken skin results in impairment from infections or pain or interferes with seal between skin and personal protective equipment). Eczema can result in frequent episodes of pain or the inability to perform work.

(c) Any other dermatologic condition that results in the person not being able to perform as a fire fighter

3-14 Blood and Blood-Forming Organs

3-14.1*

Category A medical conditions shall include the following:

(a) Hemorrhagic states requiring replacement therapy
(b) Sickle cell disease (homozygous)

A-3-14.1 Category A medical conditions of blood and blood-forming organs include the following:

(a) Hemorrhagic states requiring replacement therapy (for example, von Willebrand's disease, thrombocytopenia, hemophilia). These hemorrhagic states can result in frequent episodes of pain or the inability to perform work.

(b) Sickle cell disease (homozygous). Sickle cell disease can result in frequent episodes of pain or the inability to perform work and the potential for sudden incapacitation.

3-14.2*

Category B medical conditions shall include the following:

(a) Anemia
(b) Leukopenia
(c) Polycythemia vera
(d) Splenomegaly
(e) History of thromboembolic disease
(f) Any other hematological condition that results in a person not being able to perform as a fire fighter

A-3-14.2 Category B medical conditions of blood and blood-forming organs include the following:

(a) Anemia (in cases that require regular transfusions). Anemia can result in frequent episodes of pain or the inability to perform work. Anemia is a progressive illness leading to functional impairment.

(b) Leukopenia (where chronic and indicative of serious illness). Leukopenia is a progressive illness leading to functional impairment.

(c) Polycythemia vera (where severe, requiring treatment). Polycythemia vera can result in frequent episodes of pain or the inability to perform work and the potential for sudden incapacitation.

(d) Splenomegaly (where the spleen is susceptible to rupture from blunt trauma). Splenomegaly can result in the potential for sudden incapacitation.

(e) History of thromboembolic disease (that is, more than one episode, underlying condition). A history of thromboembolic disease can result in the potential for sudden incapacitation.

(f) Any other hematological condition that results in a person not being able to perform as a fire fighter

3-15 Endocrine and Metabolic Disorders

3-15.1*

Diabetes mellitus, which is treated with insulin or an oral hypoglycemic agent and where an individual has a history of one or more episodes of incapacitating hypoglycemia, shall be a Category A medical condition.

A-3-15.1 Category A medical conditions of endocrine and metabolic disorders include diabetes mellitus that is treated with insulin or an oral hypoglycemic agent and with a history of one or more episodes of incapacitating hypoglycemia. Diabetes mellitus can result in the potential for sudden incapacitation.

3-15.2*

Category B medical conditions shall include the following:

(a) Diseases of the adrenal gland, pituitary gland, parathyroid gland, or thyroid gland of clinical significance
(b) Nutritional deficiency disease or metabolic disorder
(c) Diabetes mellitus requiring treatment with insulin or oral hypoglycemic agent without a history of incapacitating hypoglycemia
(d) Any other endocrine or metabolic condition that results in a person not being able to perform as a fire fighter

A-3-15.2 Category B medical conditions of endocrine and metabolic disorders includes the following:

(a) Diseases of the adrenal gland, pituitary gland, parathyroid gland, or thyroid gland of clinical significance (that is, symptomatic and poorly controlled). These diseases can result in frequent episodes of pain or the inability to perform work, and the potential for sudden incapacitation.

(b) Nutritional deficiency disease or metabolic disorder (where clinically significant and not correctable by replacement therapy or other medication). Nutritional deficiency disease or metabolic disorder can result in frequent episodes of pain or the inability to perform work.

(c) Diabetes mellitus requiring treatment with insulin or oral hypoglycemic agent. Diabetes mellitus can result in episodes of pain or inability to perform work. It is a progressive illness leading to functional impairment and can result in the potential for sudden incapacitation.

(d) Any other endocrine or metabolic condition that results in a person not being able to perform as a fire fighter

3-16 Systemic Diseases and Miscellaneous Conditions

3-16.1

There shall be no Category A medical conditions.

3-16.2*

Category B medical conditions shall include the following:

(a) Connective tissue disease, such as dermatomyositis, lupus erythematosus, scleroderma, and rheumatoid arthritis
(b) Residuals from past thermal injury

(c) Documented evidence of a predisposition to heat stress with recurrent episodes or resulting residual injury
(d) Any other systemic condition that results in a person not being able to perform as a fire fighter

A-3-16.2 Category B medical conditions of systemic diseases and miscellaneous conditions include the following:

(a) Connective tissue disease, such as dermatomyositis, lupus erythematosus, scleroderma, and rheumatoid arthritis (where manifested by systemic impairment or limitations of motion). These connective tissue diseases are progressive illnesses leading to functional impairment and the inability to function as a fire fighter due to limitations of strength or flexibility.

(b) Residuals from past thermal injury (for example, frostbite resulting in significant symptomatic discomfort). Residuals from past thermal injury may result in the inability to perform functions as a fire fighter due to limitations of strength, endurance, or flexibility.

(c) Documented evidence of a predisposition to heat stress with recurrent episodes or resulting residual injury. A predisposition to heat stress can result in the potential for sudden incapacitation and the inability to perform functions as a fire fighter due to limitations of endurance.

(d) Any other systemic condition that results in a person not being able to perform as a fire fighter

3-17 Tumors and Malignant Diseases

3-17.1

There shall be no Category A medical conditions.

3-17.2*

Category B medical conditions shall include the following:

(a) Malignant disease that is newly diagnosed, untreated, or currently being treated. Candidates shall be subject to the provisions of 2-3.5 of this standard. Current fire fighters shall be subject to the provisions of 2-4.4 of this standard.

(b) Treated malignant disease shall be evaluated based on that person's current physical condition and on the likelihood of that person's disease to recur or progress.

(c) Any other tumor or similar condition that results in a person not being able to perform as a fire fighter

A-3-17.2 Category B medical conditions of tumors and malignant diseases can include the following:

(a) The medical evaluation of any person with malignant disease that is newly diagnosed, untreated, or currently being treated will be deferred.

Any person with treated malignant disease should be evaluated based on that person's current physical condition and on the likelihood of that person's disease to recur or progress.

(b) Any other tumor or similar condition that results in a person not being able to perform as a fire fighter

3-18 Psychiatric Conditions

3-18.1

There shall be no Category A medical conditions.

3-18.2*

Category B medical conditions shall include the following:

(a) A history of psychiatric condition or substance abuse problem. Candidates and current fire fighters shall be evaluated based on the individual's current condition.

(b) Any other psychiatric condition that results in a person not being able to perform as a fire fighter

A-3-18.2 Category B medical conditions of a psychiatric nature include the following:

(a) Any person with a history of a psychiatric condition or substance abuse problem should be evaluated based on that person's current condition. Psychiatric conditions and substance abuse problems can result in frequent episodes of pain or the inability to perform work and the potential for sudden incapacitation. These conditions are progressive illnesses leading to functional impairment.

(b) Any other psychiatric condition that results in a person not being able to perform as a fire fighter

3-19 Chemicals, Drugs, and Medications

3-19.1

There shall be no Category A medical conditions.

3-19.2*

Category B medical conditions shall include the use of the following:

(a) Anticoagulant agents
(b) Cardiovascular agents
(c) Narcotics
(d) Sedative-hypnotics
(e) Stimulants
(f) Psychoactive agents
(g) Steroids
(h) Any other chemical, drug, or medication that results in a person not being able to perform as a fire fighter

A-3-19.2 Category B medical conditions concerning chemicals, drugs, and medications include the following:

(a) Anticoagulant agents—for example, coumadin—if the anticoagulated state is controlled such that the prothrombin time or INR has been in the therapeutic range for at least one month and that no other coexisting conditions would either contribute to a bleeding diathesis or by themselves preclude certification for full duty. Anticoagulant agents can result in frequent episodes of pain or the inability to perform work as well as the potential for sudden incapacitation.

(b) Cardiovascular agents (for example, antihypertensives). Cardiovascular agents can result in frequent episodes of pain or the inability to perform work as well as the potential for sudden incapacitation.

(c) Narcotics. The use of narcotics can result in frequent episodes of pain or the inability to perform work as well as the potential for sudden incapacitation.

(d) Sedative-hypnotics. The use of sedative-hypnotics can result in frequent episodes of pain or the inability to perform work as well as the potential for sudden incapacitation.

(e) Stimulants. The use of stimulants can result in frequent episodes of pain or the inability to perform work as well as the potential for sudden incapacitation.

(f) Psychoactive agents. The use of psychoactive agents can result in frequent episodes of pain or the inability to perform work as well as the potential for sudden incapacitation.

(g) Steroids. The use of steroids can result in frequent episodes of pain or the inability to perform work.

(h) Any other chemical, drug, or medication that results in a person not being able to perform as a fire fighter

APPENDIX A

Explanatory Material

The material contained in Appendix A of this standard is not part of the requirements of the code but is included for informational purposes only. For the convenience of readers, in this handbook the Appendix A material is interspersed among the verbiage of Chapters 1 through 3 and, therefore, is not repeated here.

APPENDIX B

Guide for Fire Department Physicians

This appendix is not a part of the requirements of this NFPA document but is included for informational purposes only.

B-1 Introduction

This information is designed to help physicians implement the requirements of this standard. The appendix includes sections on the occupational health risks for fire fighters, organization of a medical program for fire fighters, guidance for conducting the examinations, and further information on medical conditions that might cause difficulties when implementing this standard.

The medical conditions outlined in Chapter 2 apply to individuals conducting essential fire-fighting functions. *(See Appendix C.)* The application of these guidelines to individuals with other fire department jobs requires a careful consideration of the job duties of these other individuals and the medical conditions that might affect a person's ability to conduct those duties.

B-2 Occupational Safety and Health Problems for Fire Fighters

Fire fighting and emergency response are very difficult jobs. People in these jobs perform functions that are physically and psychologically very demanding. These functions are often performed under very difficult conditions. *(See Appendix C.)* Studies have shown that fire-fighting functions require working at near maximal heart rates for prolonged periods of time. Heavy protective equipment (including respirators) and the heat from the fire contribute to this physical load.

Fire fighters and emergency response personnel also are exposed to many toxic substances during their work. Carbon monoxide is the most common contaminant; studies have shown individual exposures as high as 5000 ppm in actual fires. Other significant exposures common in fires include cyanide, acrolein, hydrogen chloride, nitrogen dioxide, and benzene. The burning of plastics and other synthetic materials can expose fire fighters to other toxic materials such as isocyanates and nitrosamines. Hazardous materials incidents can involve exposures to many other toxic materials. While the use of respirators helps to reduce exposures, mechanical, environmental, and behavioral factors can limit their use during all phases of a fire.

The available health data on fire fighters are limited. While the protection for fire fighters has improved over the last several years, exposures might be changing due to the introduction of more synthetic materials. Given the delay between exposure and onset, that is latency, of many occupational illnesses, current or past health studies of fire fighters might not reflect future health risks. These limitations should be recognized when reviewing the available studies.

Available data indicate that fire fighters have increased risk for injuries, pulmonary disease, cardiovascular disease, cancer, and noise-induced hearing loss. The increased risk for injuries is expected, given the demands and circumstances for this work. Fatalities and serious injuries from burns or other fire scene hazards can occur.

The risk for respiratory disease occurs due to the respiratory damage caused by many of the components of fire smoke, for example, particulate, acrolein, nitrogen oxides, and so on. Acute reductions in pulmonary function and even hypoxemia are not uncommon after fires, even in asymptomatic fire fighters. Permanent damage from smoke inhalation has also been reported. Studies of chronic pulmonary changes from fire fighting have not had consistent results. Some follow-up studies have shown a greater rate of decline in pulmonary function among fire fighters over time while others have not been able to detect this change. Increased use of protective equipment and job selection factors (ill fire fighters transferring to other duties) could account for these inconsistent findings.

The strenuous work demands of fire fighting combined with exposures to carbon monoxide and other toxic substances can increase the risk for cardiovascular disease among fire fighters. Acute respiratory changes also can stress the cardiovascular system. This increased cardiovascular disease risk has been documented even in some mortality studies despite the job selection factors that tend to mask any increase when compared to the general population. Other studies have not detected this risk. Certainly, the combination of the physical stress of fire fighting and exposures for a person with preexisting coronary heart disease would be expected to increase the risk of a myocardial infarction or other acute event. However, the degree of this acute risk and whether fire fighting also contributes to the development of coronary heart disease is uncertain.

Increased cancer risk for fire fighters has been found in several recent studies. While not totally consistent, these studies generally show an increased risk of brain cancer, gastrointestinal cancers, and leukemia among fire fighters in many different parts of the world. Increased incidence of other cancer sites has also been shown in some studies. Several studies are currently under way to further evaluate this risk.

Noise-induced hearing loss has now been documented in several studies of fire fighters. Fire fighters might also be at risk from other specific exposures including infectious diseases and liver, kidney, or neurological damage from exposure to specific chemicals.

B-3 Guidance for Medical Evaluations

B-3.1 Preplacement and Baseline Medical Evaluations.

Preplacement medical evaluations assess an individual's health status before assignment to a position. The purpose of the evaluation is to ascertain whether the individual has any health condition that prevents him or her from performing the job, including the ability to wear protective equipment required for the job. The evaluation should also identify any health problems that could be substantially aggravated by the physical demands and working conditions. Baseline medical information concerning the applicant's health status can then be compared to subsequent evaluation results for the purpose of determining whether the individual has any significant health trends that can be occupationally related.

Two types of information are essential for a medical preplacement evaluation for those performing fire fighter duties. First, the physician must understand the working conditions and physical demands of this occupation. Appendix C provides a list of the environmental factors encountered in fire fighting and emergency response. The physician also should obtain additional information from the fire department regarding specific job duties and task lists, if the fire department has conducted a validation study or job analysis, and should be familiar with the organization of the fire department. For the evaluation of some medical conditions, the physician will need to obtain further information about specific job duties in order to make a determination. This might require on-site inspections and consultation with fire department personnel.

Second, the physician needs to have accurate information about the person's disease or medical condition, the functional limitations associated with that condition, and an understanding of how physical demands and working conditions would impact on that condition. An accurate diagnosis is often the key factor in determining the person's capability. For example, different skin diseases can have similar clinical appearances but can markedly differ in their response to environmental exposures. The physician should also recognize that individual variability can exist between persons with the same clinical condition.

Upon completion of the examination, the physician should inform the authority having jurisdiction if the applicant is medically qualified to perform as a fire fighter.

B-3.2 Periodic Medical Evaluations.

The periodic medical evaluation is designed to evaluate the person's continued ability to perform his or her duties and to detect any other significant changes in the condition of his or her health. The latter includes possible job-related changes or abnormalities.

Every year, each fire fighter will be medically evaluated by the fire department physician. This medical evaluation includes an update on the fire fighter's medical history, including any significant changes, a brief review of symptoms, and a report on any significant job-related exposures experienced during the past year. Height, weight, visual acuity, and blood pressure are measured and recorded. The extent of the medical evaluation and additional testing will depend on the fire fighter's medical condition.

A more thorough evaluation, including a medical examination, is conducted on a periodic basis. For individuals less than 30 years of age, the medical evaluation and examination is conducted every three years; for those 30 to 39, every two years; and for those 40 or over, every year. This evaluation should include an updated medical and interval history, complete physical examination, vision testing, audiometry, pulmonary function testing, and a CBC, urinalysis, and blood biochemistry (SMA).

The use of chest X-rays in surveillance activities in the absence of significant exposures, symptoms, or medical findings has not been shown to reduce respiratory or other health impairment. Therefore, only preplacement chest X-rays are recommended.

No firm guidelines for stress electrocardiography in asymptomatic individuals have been developed. There have been problems with false-positive results from this testing, especially in younger age groups and in women. In those with one or more risk factors for coronary artery disease, there is probably justification for performing the testing. As well, stress tests are more important in those whose work deals with public safety.

A reasonable approach is to start periodic treadmill testing on fire fighters at age 40. In those with one or more coronary artery disease risk factors [premature family history (less than age 55), hypertension, diabetes mellitus, cigarette smoking, and hypercholesterolemia (total cholesterol greater than 240 or HDL cholesterol less than 35)], testing should be started by age 35. The frequency of testing should increase with age, but at the minimum the test should be done at least every two years. Testing can also be done as indicated for those with symptoms suggestive of coronary artery disease as reported in their yearly medical histories or interim reports.

B-3.3 Content of the Medical Evaluation.

B-3.3.1 Medical and Occupational History. The medical history should cover the person's known health problems, such as major illnesses, surgeries, medication use, allergies, etc. Symptom review is also important for detecting early signs of illness. In addition, a comprehensive medical history should include a personal health history, a family health history, a health habit history, an immunization history, and a reproductive history. An occupational history should also be obtained to collect information about the person's past occupational and environmental exposures.

B-3.3.2 Medical Examination. The medical examination includes the following organ systems and tests:

(a) Vital signs, such as pulse, respiration, blood pressure, and, if indicated, temperature
(b) Dermatological
(c) Ears, eyes, nose, mouth, throat
(d) Cardiovascular
(e) Respiratory
(f) Gastrointestinal
(g) Genitourinary
(h) Endocrine and metabolic
(i) Musculoskeletal
(j) Neurological
(k) Audiometry
(l) Visual acuity and peripheral vision testing
(m) Pulmonary function testing
(n) Laboratory testing, if indicated
(o) Diagnostic imaging, if indicated
(p) Electrocardiography, if indicated

B-3-3.2.1 Laboratory Tests. CBC, biochemical test battery (SMA), and urinalysis should be conducted for detecting specific illnesses as well as developing a baseline for later comparison.

B-3-3.2.2 X-rays. A baseline chest X-ray can be helpful for individuals with a history of respiratory health problems or symptoms. For others, it can be useful for later comparison.

B-3-3.2.3 Pulmonary Function Testing. Pulmonary function testing can be helpful for individuals with a history of respiratory health problems and as a baseline for later comparison. A baseline test should be administered by an experienced person. Only a spirogram that is technically acceptable and demonstrates the best efforts by an individual should be used to calculate the forced vital capacity (FVC) and forced expiratory volume in one second (FEV1).

B-3-3.2.4 Audiometry. Audiograms should be performed in an ANSI-approved "soundproof" booth (ANSI S3.1-1977) with equipment calibrated to ANSI standards (ANSI S3.6-1973). If a booth is unavailable, the test room sound pressure levels should not exceed those specified in the federal OSHA noise regulations (29 CFR 1910.95).

B-3-3.2.5 Electrocardiography. Baseline electrocardiography should be conducted.

B-3.4 Reporting the Results of the Medical Evaluation.

All individuals participating in a medical evaluation should be informed ahead of time about the purpose of the medical evaluation and the content of the exam. The results of any medical evaluation are considered to be confidential medical information subject to customary patient-physician confidentiality restrictions. Under most circumstances, results and recommendations arising from the evaluation should be expressed in general terms without specific diagnostic information. In cases where more specific information is needed in order to make a decision on the status of a candidate or fire fighter, a specific consent form releasing that information should be obtained from the candidate or fire fighter. Blanket or general "release of medical information" forms should not be used.

In most cases, a simple statement will suffice:

> Based on the results of the preplacement medical evaluation of December 10, 1996, Jane Doe is (or is NOT) medically certified to engage in training and emergency operations for Anytown Fire Department.
>
> OR
>
> Based on the results of the preplacement medical evaluation of December 10, 1996, John Doe is NOT medically certified to engage in training and emergency operations for Anytown Fire Department. He has been advised of the

medical reasons for this recommendation and of the policies and procedures available to him if he disagrees with the results of the medical evaluation.

B-3.5 Second Opinions.

Fire department policies and procedures should allow for a medical "second opinion" when a candidate or fire fighter disagrees with the results or recommendations of a medical examination conducted by the fire department physician or when the fire department physician is uncertain about the limitations or prognosis of the individual's condition. Often other physicians will not be familiar with the duties and demands of fire fighting and emergency response. When possible, the fire department physician should help educate the other physician about how the individual's condition could affect or be affected by fire fighting. If there is still disagreement about the condition or placement recommendation, a third physician (acceptable to both the fire department and the candidate) can be consulted.

B-3.6 Musculoskeletal System.

Some of the injuries or problems encountered in this system will need functional capacity evaluation to determine fitness for duty. Physical therapy providers often design tests for employers to determine ability to perform tasks similiar to those required as part of their essential job functions. These tests should be based on direct measurements of the actual job functions. These functional capacity evaluations can be especially useful when a fire fighter has been cleared for full duty by a physician who is not familiar with the essential job functions of a fire fighter.

B-4 Specific Medical Conditions

B-4.1 Diabetes Mellitus.

The major concern for diabetic fire fighters is the risk of becoming hypoglycemic during fireground operations or other emergency responses. Both exogenous insulin and oral hypoglycemic agents can be associated with episodes of hypoglycemia that can rapidly progress from impaired judgment to unconsciousness. The most reliable predictor of hypoglycemia is a history of it. In one study of insulin-dependent adolescents conducted at the Joslin Clinic (Bhatia and Wolfsdorf 1991), all 196 patients experienced hypoglycemia at least once during the two-year observation period. Of these, 15 percent were classified as severe, based on loss of consciousness, seizure, or the clinical need for therapeutic glucagon or intravenous glucose. It was particularly concerning that 24 percent of hypoglycemic episodes detected by blood glucose monitoring were inapparent to the patients. The probable causes of hypoglycemia were identified in 71 percent of cases, and the most common were strenuous exercise and skipped meals or snacks. Both of these precipitants are likely to occur in emergency responders, especially fire service personnel. In addition to accelerating glucose utilization, strenuous exercise increases insulin sensitivity (Wasserman and Sinman 1994). With the tighter glycemic control that is now known to decrease and delay onset of diabetic complications, there is a concomitantly increased likelihood of exercise-induced hypoglycemia (Wasserman and Sinman 1994).

Insulin is clearly associated with a much higher risk of symptomatic hypoglycemia than are oral agents. In the absence of a history of incapacitating hypoglycemic episodes, and with close medical monitoring, there is probably no reason to exclude fire fighters who are taking oral hypoglycemic agents, as long as they have stable weights, diets, and renal function. Although the Americans with Disabilities Act (Public Law 101-336 1990) does not appear to require each diabetic patient to be evaluated for fitness for duty individually, there is some case law that disallowed blanket exclusion of insulin-dependent diabetics from public safety positions (*Fire & Police Personnel Reporter* 1994). The Federal Aviation Administration (14 *CFR* 67.13–16 1995) does not grant medical certificates to diabetics treated with insulin and severely limits those on oral hypoglycemic agents.

References

1. Bhatia, V., and J. I. Wolfsdorf. 1991. "Severe Hypoglycemia in Youth with Insulin-Dependent Diabetes Mellitus: Frequency and Causative Factors." *Pediatrics* 88:1187.
2. Wasserman, D. H., and B. Sinman. 1991. "Exercise in Individuals with IDDM." *Diabetic Care* 17:924.
3. Public Law 101-336. 1990. Title I—Employment.
4. *Fire & Police Personnel Reporter*. November 1994, 169.
5. 14 *CFR* 67.13-16. January 1995.

B-4.2 Asthma and Reactive Airways Disease.

The diagnosis of asthma and related airway hyperactivity disorders is often confounded by definitional issues. For the purposes of fire fighter certification, a variety of airway disorders that meet the following criteria can be included. "Asthma is a chronic inflammatory disorder of the airways. In susceptible individuals, this inflammation causes symptoms that are usually associated with widespread but variable airflow obstruction that is often reversible, either spontaneously or with treatment, and causes an associated increase in airway responsiveness to a variety of stimuli."

Since asthma is a highly prevalent disease, a number of fire fighter applicants will require special evaluation. Combustion products, exercise, and cold air are all potent provokers of an asthma attack. Some of these exposures are unavoidable, even with SCBA use. If a candidate has a diagnosis or symptoms consistent with an asthma-like disease, many factors will need to be considered. An asthma attack during a suppression activity could harm the fire fighter, his fellow fire fighters, or a member of the public.

The following factors can be used to help in certification: The persistence of airway obstruction between attacks (as measured by spirometry); the need and frequency of steroid and bronchodilator use (frequent bronchodilator use suggests persistent airway hyperactivity); the usual type of triggers in the applicant (allergic, infectious, exercise induced, etc.); the history of hospitalization, emergency room, or urgent treatment; the length of time between attacks; nocturnal symptoms and other estimates of airway instability.

Moderate asthma or worse could disqualify an individual for fire fighter duties. Unknown factors such as the suppression of airway hyperactivity with anti-inflammatory medications to reduce the possibility of a sudden or severe attack are under investigation and could modify current suggestions.

B-4.3 Heart Disease.

The medical conditions relating to the cardiovascular system have been reviewed since the previous edition (1992) of this document. The task forces at the Bethesda Conference published recommendations for athletes competing with cardiovascular disease in the *Journal of American Cardiac Care* in October 1994. The analysis used by the task force has relevance to the evaluation of fire fighters with cardiovascular disease. Fire-fighting activities have a high static component (i.e., inducing predominantly an increase in blood pressure) and a moderate to high dynamic component (i.e., inducing predominantly an increase in heart rate). Sports having a similar set of demands include wrestling, body building, and boxing. Recommendations made by the task force with respect to athletic activities that have these physical demands (high static, moderate dynamic) have been followed in this document.

B-4.4 Reproductive.

Exposures in the fire-fighting environment can cause adverse reproductive effects for both males and females. Medical evidence exists to indicate that chemical exposure, heat, noise, and physical exertion can affect various endpoints of reproductive health including fertility, fetal loss, and growth parameters of the offspring. All candidates and fire fighters should be educated about these risks and about the need to take appropriate steps to limit their exposures.

Also, there could be some situations where a male or female fire fighter is attempting to conceive a child and is having difficulty. In these situations, where a complete medical evaluation has not identified another cause for this infertility, temporary assignment on a voluntary basis to alternative duty or a leave of absence should be considered.

Medical evidence exists that certain toxic substances or conditions that are present in the fire-fighting environment are dangerous to the safety and well-being of the fetus. Therefore, it is important to educate all fire fighters about these risks and the reasons for recommending that pregnant fire fighters restrict their fire-suppression activities. For example, there is good evidence that the fetus is especially sensitive to carbon monoxide, a known significant component of fire smoke. Although the use of SCBA is assumed to be protective, sometimes such equipment is not used throughout a fire suppression or hazardous materials incident. The use of such equipment also increases other fetal stressors, such as exertion and heat. Other concerns are those involving physical work. Prolonged standing, heavy lifting, and exposures to temperature extremes and humidity have been related to an increase of preterm and low birth weight infants. Because the fetus should be protected from these exposures at the earliest possible time, the fire fighter who might be pregnant should obtain early pregnancy testing. Recognizing potential risks to the fetus from the fire-fighting environment is a relatively recent event, and many fire fighters might not be aware of these risks.

Based on a recent U.S. Supreme Court decision (*International Union et al. v. Johnson Controls, Inc.*, 59 U.S.L.W. 4209, March 20, 1991), the ability to perform as a fire fighter is to be the basis for the medical certification without consideration of health risks to the fetus. However, the pregnant fire fighter should be counseled of the potential risks to her fetus due to her exposures during fire-fighting duties.

Any fire fighter who becomes pregnant should be offered the opportunity at any time during the pregnancy to be voluntarily removed from fire-fighting duties and from other duties involving the hazards or physical stress that might endanger the fetus. If practical, the fire fighter should be offered voluntary reassignment to an alternative position. At such time as the pregnant fire fighter can no longer be medically certified as being capable of performing fire-fighting duties, the fire fighter should be reassigned to other duties. At such time as the fire fighter is no longer pregnant, the fire fighter should be reinstated to the position held prior to being pregnant. Nursing fire fighters should also be advised about the potential exposures to their infants.

B-4.5 Noise-Induced Hearing Loss.

This category can pose difficulties because a high percentage of current fire fighters have noise-induced hearing loss due to their exposures as fire fighters. Implementation of hearing conservation programs and programs to reduce noise exposures should lead to a decrease in the prevalence of this condition in the future.

B-4.6 Seizures and Epilepsy.

It is important to distinguish between a history of seizures and epilepsy. As much as 10 percent of the population will experience at least one seizure in a lifetime, whereas less than 1 percent of the population qualifies for a diagnosis of epilepsy (Hauser and Hesdorffer 1990). Many conditions producing seizures in the pediatric age group are known to remit prior to adulthood, and many adults sustain a reactive seizure that can be attributed to a reversible, underlying precipitant. These circumstances do not necessarily represent an ongoing risk of sudden, unpredictable incapacitation of a fire fighter. If a fire fighter has a single seizure, a clear precipitant not associated with central nervous system damage is identified and eliminated, and the individual has no recurrence over the ensuing year, then he or she is probably not more likely to have another seizure than the rest of the general population (Spencer 1995). Most fire department physicians will want a qualified neurologist to verify that an individual with a history of seizures does not, in fact, have epilepsy.

Epilepsy is diagnosed by the presence of "unprovoked, recurrent seizures—paroxysmal disorders of the central nervous system characterized by an abnormal cerebral neuronal discharge with or without loss of consciousness" (Cascino 1994). Treatment of patients with epilepsy is only variably successful, with roughly 40 percent of patients attaining remission on anti-convulsant therapy (Hauser and Hesdorffer 1990; Spencer 1995). Remission is defined as five years without recurrence of seizure activity (Annegers, Hauser, and Elveback 1979). Further complicating the fitness-for-duty issue is the fact that only 50 percent of patients who achieve remission do so without toxic side effects of the anti-convulsant drug (Cascino 1994).

Partial, simple epilepsy, or recurrent seizures that do not impair consciousness, are felt to be a disqualifying condition because of the uncertainty regarding how much of the brain might be involved, and the risk of propagation to other regions of the brain, particularly in the highly epileptogenic environment of the fireground (Spencer 1995).

This standard is somewhat more liberal than that promulgated by the Federal Aviation Administration of the U.S. Department of Transportation for aircraft pilots (14 *CFR* 67.13–16 1995). All epileptics, regardless of therapeutic success are denied First, Second, or Third class medical certificates, except under the provisions of 14 CFR 67.19, *Special Issue of Medical Certificates.*

References

1. Hauser, W. A., and D. C. Hesdorffer. 1990. *Epilepsy: Frequency, Causes and Consequences.* New York: Demos.
2. Spencer, S., personal communication, 1995. (Spencer is professor of neurology and director of the Clinical Epilepsy and Electrophysiologic Monitoring Services at Yale University School of Medicine.)
3. Cascino, G. D. 1994. "Epilepsy: Contemporary Perspectives on Evaluation and Treatment." *Mayo Clinic Proceedings* 69:1199.
4. Annegers, J. F., W. A. Hauser, and L. R. Elveback. 1979. "Remission of Seizures and Relapse in Patients with Epilepsy." *Epilepsia* 20:729.
5. 14 *CFR* 67.13-16. January 1995.

APPENDIX C

Essential Fire-Fighting Functions

This appendix is not a part of the requirements of this NFPA document but is included for informational purposes only.

The medical requirements in this standard were based on in-depth consideration of essential fire-fighting functions. These essential functions are what fire fighters are expected to perform at emergency incidents and are derived from the performance objectives stated in NFPA 1001, *Standard on Fire Fighter Professional Qualifications*.

Such essential functions are performed in and affected by the following environmental factors:

(a) Operate both as a member of a team and independently at incidents of uncertain duration
(b) Spend extensive time outside exposed to the elements
(c) Tolerate extreme fluctuations in temperature while performing duties. Must perform physically demanding work in hot (up to 400°F), humid (up to 100 percent) atmospheres while wearing equipment that significantly impairs body-cooling mechanisms.
(d) Experience frequent transition from hot to cold and from humid to dry atmospheres
(e) Work in wet, icy, or muddy areas
(f) Perform a variety of tasks on slippery, hazardous surfaces such as on rooftops or from ladders
(g) Work in areas where sustaining traumatic or thermal injuries is possible
(h) Face exposure to carcinogenic dusts such as asbestos, toxic substances such as hydrogen cyanide, acids, carbon monoxide, or organic solvents either through inhalation or skin contact
(i) Face exposure to infectious agents such as hepatitis B or HIV
(j) Wear personal protective equipment that weighs approximately 50 lb while performing fire-fighting tasks
(k) Perform physically demanding work while wearing positive pressure breathing equipment with 1.5 in. of water column resistance to exhalation at a flow of 40 l/min
(l) Perform complex tasks during life-threatening emergencies
(m) Work for long periods of time, requiring sustained physical activity and intense concentration
(n) Face life-or-death decisions during emergency conditions
(o) Be exposed to grotesque sights and smells associated with major trauma and burn victims
(p) Make rapid transitions from rest to near-maximal exertion without warm-up periods
(q) Operate in environments of high noise, poor visibility, limited mobility, at heights, and in enclosed or confined spaces
(r) Use manual and power tools in the performance of duties
(s) Rely on senses of sight, hearing, smell, and touch to help determine the nature of the emergency, maintain personal safety, and make critical decisions in a confused, chaotic, and potentially life-threatening environment throughout the duration of the operation

APPENDIX D

Guide for Fire Department Administrators

This appendix is not a part of the requirements of this NFPA document but is included for informational purposes only.

D-1 Legal Considerations in Applying the Standard

The consideration of an application or continued employment of a fire fighter based on medical or physical performance evaluations involves a determination that is not without legal implications. To this end, prior to making an adverse employment decision based on the foregoing standard, the authority having jurisdiction might wish to consult with counsel.

(a) *Individuals with Handicaps or Disabilities.* The Rehabilitation Act of 1973, as amended, 29 U.S.C. 791 et seq., and implementing regulations, prohibit discrimination against those with handicaps or disabilities under any program receiving financial assistance from the federal government. The Americans with Disabilities Act of 1990, 42 U.S.C. § 12101, et seq., also prohibits employment discrimination by certain private employers against individuals with disabilities. In addition, many states have enacted legislation prohibiting discrimination against those with handicaps or disabilities. These laws prevent the exclusion, denial of benefits, refusal to hire or promote, or other discriminatory conduct against an individual based on a handicap or disability, where the individual involved can, with or without reasonable accommodation, perform the essential functions of the job without creating undue hardship on the employer or program involved. Application of this standard should be undertaken with these issues in mind.

The medical requirements of the 1992 edition of this standard were initially developed and found to be job-related by a subcommittee comprised of medical doctors, physiological specialists, and fire service professionals, as processed through the NFPA consensus standards-making system. Changes for the current edition have been proposed by a task group comprised of similar expertise. The standard provides, to the extent feasible, that decisions concerning those with medical ailments, handicaps, or disabilities be made after case-by-case medical evaluations. Thus, most medical conditions have been assigned to Category B.

The medical requirements in this edition of the standard were revised based on the critical core fire-fighting functions contained in Appendix C. It is recognized that some fire-fighting functions and tasks can vary from location to location due to differences in department size, functional and organizational differences, geography, level of urbanization, equipment utilized, and other factors. Therefore, it is the responsibility of each individual fire department to document, through job analysis, that the critical core fire-fighting functions performed in the local jurisdiction are substantially similar to those contained in Appendix C.

There are a wide variety of job analytic techniques available to document the essential functions of the job of fire fighter. However, at a minimum, any method utilized should be current, in writing, and meet the provisions of the Americans with Disabilities Act [29 *CFR* 1630.2(n)(3)]. Job descriptions should focus on critical and important work behaviors and specific tasks and functions. The frequency and/or duration of task performance, and the consequences of failure to perform the task should be specified. The working conditions and environmental hazards in which the work is performed should be described.

The job description (examples found in Appendix E) should be made available to the fire service physician for use during the preplacement medical examination for the individual determination of the medical suitability of applicants for fire fighter.

(b) *Anti-Discrimination Laws.* Finally, the user of this standard should be aware that, while courts are likely to give considerable weight to the existence of a nationally recognized standard such as NFPA 1582, *Standard on Medical*

Requirements for Fire Fighters [e.g., *Miller v. Sioux Gateway Fire Department,* 497 N.W.2d 838 (1993)], reliance on the standard might not alone be sufficient to withstand a challenge under the anti-discrimination laws. Even in the case of category A medical conditions, courts can still require additional expert evidence concerning an individual candidate or fire fighter's inability to perform the essential functions of the job. Until the courts provide further guidance in this developing area of law, some uncertainty as to the degree and nature of the evidence required to establish compliance with the anti-discrimination laws will remain.

(c) *Individuals Who Are Members of Protected Classes (Race, Sex, Color, Religion, or National Origin).* Title VII of the Civil Rights Act of 1964, as amended, 42 U.S.C. 2000e, and implementing regulations by the Equal Employment Opportunity Commission (EEOC) prohibit discrimination in employment on the basis of race, sex, color, religion, or national origin (i.e., protected classes).* Additionally, many states, cities, and localities have adopted similar legislation. Generally, physical performance or other requirements that result in "adverse impact" on members of a protected class (e.g., on the basis of gender) are required to be validated through a study in accordance with EEOC guidelines, if such requirements are to be relied on in making employment decisions. Under EEOC guidelines, a study validating employment standards in one jurisdiction can be transportable to another jurisdiction (and therefore used in lieu of conducting a separate study). However, specific preconditions must be met in this regard, and the authority having jurisdiction should seek the advice of counsel before relying on a transported validation study.

(d) *Pregnancy and Reproductive.* Federal regulations, as well as many court decisions (including the U.S. Supreme Court's decision in *International Union, et al. v. Johnson Controls, Inc.,* 499 U.S. 187, 111 S.Ct. 1196 (1991), have interpreted the requirements of Title VII with respect to pregnancy and reproduction. The authority having jurisdiction should seek the advice of counsel in resolving specific questions concerning these requirements as well as other requirements that can be imposed by state or local laws.

D-2 Choosing a Fire Department Physician

Several factors should be considered in choosing a fire department physician. There are relatively few physicians with formal residency training and certification in occupational medicine. The fire department physician shall be qualified to provide professional expertise in the areas of occupational safety and health as they relate to emergency services. For the purpose of conducting medical evaluations, the fire department physician shall understand the physiological and psychological demands placed on fire fighters and shall understand the environmental conditions under which fire fighters must perform.

Therefore, physicians with other specialties need to be considered. The background and experience of the physician should be considered. Knowledge of occupational medicine and experience with occupational health programs obviously would be helpful.

The physician must be committed to meeting the requirements of the program including appropriate record keeping. His/her willingness to work with the department to continually improve the program is also important. Finally, his/her concern and interest in the program and in the individuals in the department is vital.

There are many options for obtaining physician services. They could be paid on a service basis or through a contractual arrangement. For volunteer departments, local physicians might be willing to volunteer their services for the program with additional arrangements to pay for laboratory testing, X-rays, etc. Some departments might want to utilize a local health care facility for their care. However, in that case, the department should be sure to have one individual physician responsible for the program, record keeping, etc. In some cases it could be possible to have the medical examination by the fire department physician, yet have some of the associated costs defrayed by the fire fighter's own health insurance. For example, the health insurance provider might allow the fire fighter to have a yearly physical, normally performed by the fire fighter's personal physician. The health care insurance provider can allow that physical to be performed by the fire department physician with some degree of reimbursement.

D-3 Coordinating the Medical Evaluation Program

An individual from within the department should be assigned the responsibility for managing the health and fitness program, including the coordination and scheduling of evaluations and examinations. This person should also act as liaison between the department and the physician to make sure that each has the information necessary for decisions about placement, scheduling appointments, etc.

Confidentiality of all medical data is critical to the success of the program. Members must feel assured that the information provided to the physician will not be inappro-

*Under Title VII, an "employer" is defined, generally, to mean a person with "15 or more employees for each working day in each of 20 or more calendar weeks in the current or preceding calendar year." See 42 U.S.C. 2000e. Several federal jurisdictions have held that unpaid volunteers are not considered to be "employees" under Title VII.

priately shared. No fire department supervisor or manager should have access to medical records without the express written consent of the member. There are occasions when specific medical information is needed to make a decision about placement, return to work, and so forth, and a fire department manager must have more medical information. In that situation, written medical consent should be obtained from the individual to release the specific information necessary for that decision.

Budgetary constraints can affect the medical program. Therefore, it is important that components of the program be prioritized such that essential elements are not lost. With additional funding, other programs or testing can be added to enhance the program.

APPENDIX E

Sample Forms

The Physical Exam Summary and the Medical Examination forms (Sections E-1 and E-2) in Appendix E of the 1997 edition of *Standard on Medical Requirements for Fire Fighters* are not part of the requirements of the standard, but are included with the standard for informational purposes only. For the convenience of readers, in this handbook the forms are included in Supplement 12 as Forms S12-5 and S12-6 in full-size versions suitable for reproduction. *(See Part Six of this handbook.)*

E-3 Entry-Level Fire Fighter Job Description

General Overview

Fire fighters play a major role in the protection of life and property. Therefore, a fire fighter must possess the knowledge, skills, abilities, and other characteristics (KSAOs) necessary to be ready to react instantaneously and effectively in all emergency situations.

A fire fighter must be familiar with safety policies and procedures, fire-fighting equipment and methods, and first aid techniques. In addition, a fire fighter must be able to carry, secure, and climb ladders; carry and/or drag victims; and use equipment to gain access and ventilate buildings. Therefore, physical strength, endurance, and agility are also required. Finally, a fire fighter must be able to interact and communicate with the public during periods of crisis and in standard community settings.

Educational Requirements

Must meet the minimum educational requirements established by the authority having jurisdiction.

Age Requirements

Must meet the age requirements established by the authority having jurisdiction.

Medical Requirements

Must meet requirements for entry-level personnel developed and validated by the authority having jurisdiction and in compliance with applicable legal requirements (e.g., Equal Opportunity and Americans with Disabilities Act regulations).

Work Behaviors

What follows is a list of work behaviors required for success as a fire fighter:

(a) Understands the organization and mission of the fire department as well as the applicable rules and regulations of the position
(b) Performs hose evolutions; controls fire with water, maintaining orientation in fire building
(c) Operates pump, determining appropriate water pressure to adjust equipment properly
(d) Recognizes hazardous conditions such as backdraft, presence of noxious fumes, or possible structural collapse of building
(e) Raises and secures appropriate ladders in safe areas and manner
(f) Performs lifesaving and rescue operations applying proper search and rescue techniques
(g) Performs overhaul and salvage of buildings
(h) Drives or tillers fire apparatus safely and properly, adapting to changing conditions while en route (blocked streets, etc.)
(i) Stands station watch using all equipment appropriately, receiving and transmitting information clearly and accurately
(j) Inspects residences or structures for possible safety hazards
(k) Participates in drills, fire strategy sessions, and hydrant inspection
(l) Maintains all fire department tools and equipment, inspecting these for defects and performing proper maintenance procedures.

NOTE: This list must be tailored to each jurisdiction. Some behaviors might or might not be required in all jurisdictions.

APPENDIX F

Referenced Publications

F-1

The following documents or portions thereof are referenced within this standard for informational purposes only and are thus not considered part of the requirements of this standard. The edition indicated here for each reference is the current edition as of the date of the NFPA issuance of this standard.

F-1.1 NFPA Publications.

National Fire Protection Association, 1 Batterymarch Park, P.O. Box 9101, Quincy, MA 02269-9101.

NFPA 1001, *Standard on Fire Fighter Professional Qualifications,* 1997 edition.

NFPA 1581, *Standard on Fire Department Infection Control Program,* 1995 edition.

NFPA 1582, *Standard on Medical Requirements for Fire Fighters,* 1997 edition.

F-1.2 ANSI Publications.

American National Standards Institute, 11 West 42nd Street, New York, NY 10036.

ANSI S3.1-1991, *Maximum Permissible Ambient Noise Levels for Audiometric Test Rooms.*

ANSI S3.6-1989, *Specifications for Audiometers.*

F-1.3 U.S. Government Publications.

U.S. Government Printing Office, Washington, DC 20402.

14 *CFR* 67.13-16, January 1995, Federal Aviation Administration Department of Transportation, Aeronautics, and Space, *Medical Standards and Certification.*

14 *CFR* 67.19, January 1995, Federal Aviation Administration, Department of Transportation, Aeronautics, and Space, *Special Issue of Medical Certificates.*

29 *CFR* 1630.2(n)(3), July 1995, Chapter XIV, Equal Employment Opportunity Command, *Regulations to Implement the Equal Employment Provisions of ADA.*

29 *CFR* 1910.95, July 1995, *Occupational Noise Exposure,* OSHA, Department of Labor.

29 U.S.C. 791 et seq., The Rehabilitation Act of 1973, as amended.

42 U.S.C. 2000e, Title VII of the Civil Rights Act of 1964, as amended.

42 U.S.C. § 12101 et seq., The Americans with Disabilities Act of 1990.

F-1.4 Other Publications.

Annegers, J. F., W. A. Hauser, and L. R. Elveback. 1979. "Remission of Seizures and Relapse in Patients with Epilepsy." *Epilepsia* 20:729.

Bhatia, V., and J. I. Wolfsdorf. 1991. "Severe Hypoglycemia in Youth with Insulin-Dependent Diabetes Mellitus: Frequency and Causative Factors." *Pediatrics* 88:1187.

Cascino, G. D., "Epilepsy: Contemporary Perspectives on Evaluation and Treatment." *Mayo Clinic Proceedings.* 69:1199.

Fire & Police Personnel Reporter, November 1994, 169.

Hauser, W. A., and D. C. Hesdorffer. 1990 *Epilepsy: Frequent Causes and Consequences.* New York, Demos.

Journal of American Cardiac Care, October, 1994.

Public Law 101-336, 1990 Title I—Employment.

Spencer, S., personal communication, 1995. (Spencer is professor of neurology and director of the Clinical Epilepsy and Electrophysiologic Monitoring Services at Yale University School of Medicine.)

Wasserman, D. H., and B. Sinman. 1994. "Exercise in Individuals with IDDM." *Diabetic Care* 17:924.

REFERENCE CITED IN COMMENTARY

The Americans with Disabilities Act of 1990, 42 U.S.C. §12101 et seq., U.S. Government Printing Office, Washington, DC 20402.

PART SIX

Supplements

The thirteen supplements included in this section of the *Fire Department Occupational Health and Safety Standards Handbook* provide additional information about key areas of concern for fire fighter safety. They are not part of the official NFPA documents or the commentary presented in the previous sections of this book. A number of these supplements have been written by recognized experts in the fields they cover, and all provide in-depth coverage of various specialized areas.

SUPPLEMENT 1

1996 Fire Fighter Fatalities

Arthur E. Washburn, Paul R. LeBlanc, and Rita F. Fahy

Editor's Note: Each year NFPA publishes its "Annual Fire Fighter Fatality" report in Fire Journal. The following report is reprinted from the July/August 1997 issue. There's good news and there's bad news. The good news is that over the last 20 years, there's been a 40 percent decrease in the average number of fire fighter deaths each year.

Over the past 20 years, remarkable progress has been made in reducing the annual fire fighter death toll in the United States. In fact, there has been a decrease of approximately 40 percent in the average number of deaths each year, from the first five-year period to the most recent. Figure S1-1 shows fire fighter deaths for the years 1977 through 1996.

In 1996, for the fourth time in five years, fewer than 100 fire fighters died while on duty in the United States. The 95 who died represent no change from the 95 who died on duty in 1995.[1]

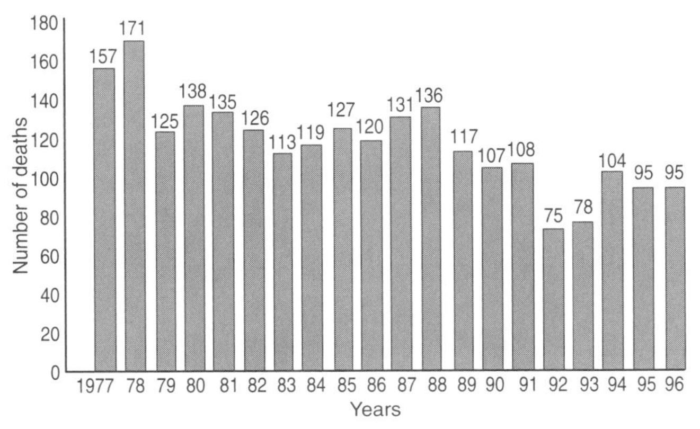

Figure S1-1 *Fire fighter deaths—1977 through 1996.*

In 1996, there were three incidents in which more than one fire fighter died, one a four-fatality incident and the remainder two-fatality incidents. In the four-fatality incident, the four victims were murdered, while two additional fire fighters were injured, by an off-duty fire fighter while they attended an administrative meeting. In the first two-fatality incident, the victims were fighting a fire with a hose line inside an auto parts store when the lightweight truss roof collapsed. They died as a result of burns and smoke inhalation. In the other two-fatality incident, the victims were killed in a fire department apparatus crash while responding to a false alarm.

Along with the four fire fighters who were shot during a meeting, two other fire fighters were murdered last year.

Type of Duty

Figure S1-2 shows the distribution of the 95 deaths in 1996 by type of duty. The largest proportion of deaths, 32 or 33.7 percent, occurred on the fireground. Another 31 deaths occurred while fire fighters were responding to or returning from alarms.

Of the 32 fire fighters who died on the fireground, 18 succumbed to heart attacks, 6 were asphyxiated, 3

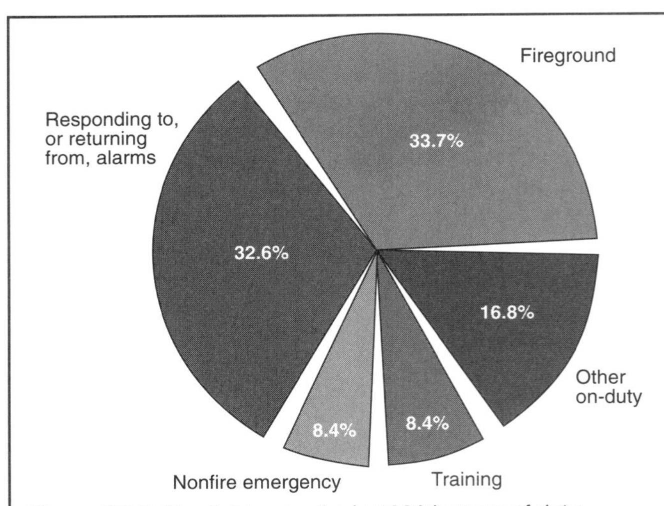

Figure S1-2 *Fire fighter deaths in 1996 by type of duty.*

died of burns, 2 died of crushing injuries, 2 were electrocuted, and 1 died of internal trauma. Twenty of the victims were volunteer fire fighters, and 12 were career fire fighters.[2]

Whether occurring in structures or elsewhere, injuries sustained on the fireground in the past decade have typically resulted in less than half the annual number of fire fighter deaths, and the number and proportion of 1996 fireground deaths are the lowest reported in the 20 years that NFPA has published these figures. Overall, the number of fireground deaths has dropped by more than half since the first six years of the study.

In contrast, the number of deaths that occurred while fire fighters were responding to or returning from alarms is higher, for the second consecutive year, than it has been since the late 1980s, accounting for almost one-third of the deaths. Generally, a quarter of the annual number of fire fighter deaths result from injuries sustained while responding to or returning from alarms.

Last year, 31 fire fighters died on the way to or from alarms. Fourteen were killed in collisions and rollovers—two of these accidents occurred while fire fighters were responding to false alarms. Another 12 died of heart attacks—one suffered after returning to the station from a false alarm. Over the past 10 years, 23 fire fighters have died while responding to or returning from false alarms, whether malicious or the result of alarm malfunctions.

Of the remaining five fire fighters who died while responding to or returning from alarms, one fell from the station sliding pole as he responded to an alarm. Another was killed and his partner was injured when the cab of their brush unit was hit by a falling tree during a hurricane. The third fire fighter was crushed between two pieces of apparatus as he tried to start the rear-mounted pump before responding to an incident. The remaining two fire fighters were murdered: one by beating and stabbing while walking to the fire station for a snow emergency standby, and the other by gunfire as his car approached the scene of a motor vehicle accident, by one of the motorists involved in the accident. Thirty of the 31 victims were volunteer fire fighters.

Sixteen fire fighters died on duty while performing non-emergency-related activities last year. Eight suffered fatal heart attacks—five during normal station duty, two at fire department fund-raisers, and one while performing vehicle maintenance. Four fire fighters were shot to death by an off-duty colleague when they attended an administrative meeting. Two were killed in motor vehicle crashes—one while traveling between two fire stations on fire department business, and the other while returning from a fund-raiser. One fire fighter suffered a fatal stroke while performing vehicle maintenance, and another died when fireworks at a fire department-sponsored display detonated prematurely.

Eight fire fighters died in 1996 during training activities. Six suffered fatal heart attacks—two during fitness activities, one at motor vehicle extrication training, one training in wildland fire operations, one at an EMT certification class, and one while acting as safety officer at a live fire training exercise. Another died as a result of heat stroke during a training run, and the eighth collapsed during fitness training and later died as the result of a disease associated with sickle cell anemia.

Eight fire fighters also died at nonfire emergencies—three as a result of heart attacks. Two of the heart attacks occurred at EMS calls and one at a smoke investigation call. A fourth fire fighter, who was also an EMT, was killed in a highway crash while driving an ambulance that was transporting a patient to a hospital. Another died as a result of complications suffered when his ambulance crashed several months earlier. The remaining three deaths occurred at the scenes of motor vehicle crashes. In separate incidents, while trying to extricate the victims of crashes, one fire fighter was electrocuted when he came into contact with a downed power line and another was struck by a vehicle. The third fire fighter was hit by a vehicle while directing traffic at the scene of a crash.

Cause of Fatal Injury or Illness

When looking at fire fighter deaths, we distinguish between the cause of the injury or illness that led to death and the nature of that injury or illness. The cause of a fatal injury or illness is the action, lack of action, or circumstances that resulted directly in that injury or illness, while the nature of the injury or illness refers to the medical process by which death occurs. In other words, the cause of a fire fighter's fatal injury or illness might be falling through a floor, which could result in asphyxiation. This asphyxiation would then be described here as the nature of the fire fighter's injury or illness. What we call the nature of injury is often referred to on death certificates and in autopsy reports as the "cause of death" *(see Figure S1-3)*.[3]

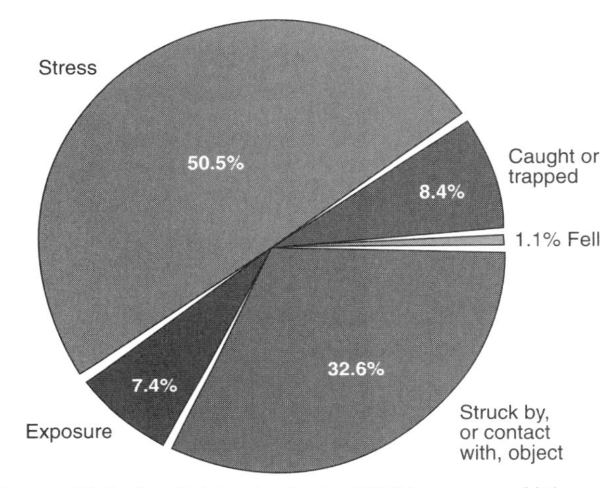

Figure S1-3 *Fire fighter deaths in 1996 by cause of injury.*

Let's first concentrate on the cause of injury or illness that led to the 95 fire fighter deaths last year. The leading cause of fatal injury for on-duty fire fighters in 1996 was, in fact, stress, as it has been in almost every year of this 20-year study, and this stress usually resulted in heart attacks. Forty-five of the 48 stress-related deaths resulted from heart attacks. Of the three remaining fatalities, one resulted in a stroke, one from an asthma attack, and the other from a disease associated with sickle cell anemia.

The second leading cause of injury was being struck by, or coming into contact with, an object, which resulted in 31 fire fighter deaths, or 32.6 percent of the fatalities. Eighteen of these fire fighters were killed in motor vehicle crashes, and three were hit by motor vehicles. Of the remaining nine fire fighters, six were murdered while on duty—five were shot, and one was stabbed. One fire fighter was hit by a falling tree; one was struck by power lines from a collapsing utility pole, electrocuting him; and another died when a wall collapsed. And one fire fighter was killed when a pyrotechnic device exploded prematurely.

Being caught or trapped was the third leading cause of fire fighter injury in 1996, resulting in eight, or 8.4 percent, of the total fatalities. Of the eight victims, four were killed when the roofs of the structures in which they were working collapsed.

Of the other four fire fighters who died as a result of being caught or trapped, one was trapped by a floor collapse, one was trapped by a ceiling collapse, and a third was trapped by rapid fire progress in a structure fire. The fourth was trapped and crushed between two pieces of fire apparatus while preparing to respond to an emergency call.

Seven fire fighters also died as a result of exposure to a variety of elements. Three of them succumbed to smoke inhalation, which caused two to asphyxiate and one to suffer a fatal heart attack. Another was asphyxiated while trying to rescue someone trapped in a grain elevator. Two were touched by downed power lines and were electrocuted—one while trying to extricate an accident victim, and the other during overhaul at a structure fire. And the seventh died of heat stroke while exercising in hot weather.

One fire fighter fell from the station sliding pole while responding to an alarm.

Nature of Fatal Injury or Illness

As noted, the nature of an injury or illness refers to the medical process by which death occurs. Figure S1-4 shows the distribution of deaths by nature of fatal injury or illness.

Heart attacks are typically the leading nature of injury in on-duty fire fighter deaths and usually

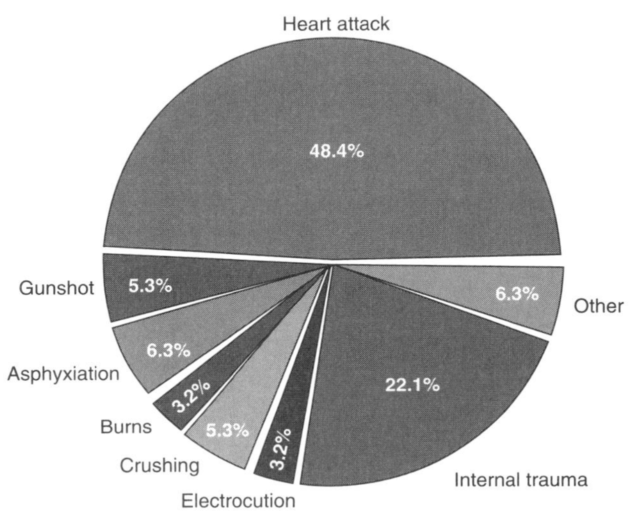

Figure S1-4 *Fire fighter deaths in 1996 by nature of injury.*

account for approximately half the total fatalities. Last year was no exception. Forty-six fire fighters died of heart attacks while on duty, which—at 48.4 percent—was the largest proportion of on-duty fire fighter deaths in 1996. The average number of heart attack deaths for the last five years was 42.0, compared to 54.5 per year for the 10-year period before that and 64.8 per year from 1977 through 1981, the first five years NFPA conducted this study.

Forty-five of the 46 heart attacks in 1996 were attributed to stress or overexertion. One heart attack resulted from exposure to smoke. Of the 46 heart attack victims, 10 were known to have had prior heart problems—usually previous heart attacks or bypass surgery—and medical documentation showed that 5 others had severe arteriosclerotic heart disease. Two fire fighters were suffering from hypertension, one had sickle cell anemia, and two were diabetic. No medical documentation was available for the remaining victims.

Over the past 20 years, medical documentation has been available for 535 of the 1079 heart attack victims. Of those 535 deaths, 49.5 percent had had previous heart attacks or bypass surgery, and another 32.5 percent had severe arteriosclerotic heart disease. Another 12.0 percent had hypertension or diabetes.

Of the 49 fire fighters who didn't die of heart attacks in 1996, 21 died of internal trauma, 6 were asphyxiated, 5 died of gunshot wounds, another 5 died of crushing injuries, 3 died of burns, and another 3 were electrocuted. Of the remaining six fire fighters, one drowned, one died of heat stroke, one of an asthma attack, one hemorrhaged to death, one died of a stroke, and one succumbed to a disease related to sickle cell anemia.

Ages of Fire Fighters

The median age of the fire fighters who died in 1996 was 43. The youngest was a 16-year-old boy, who was killed when his own vehicle overturned on an icy road as he was responding to the fire station, and the oldest was 79.

As might be expected, heart attacks account for a higher proportion of deaths among older fire fighters than anything else *(see Figure S1-5)*. Three-quarters of the fire fighters over age 45 who died in 1996 died of heart attacks. The youngest heart attack victim was a 29-year-old man who was participating in physical fitness training at the fire station.

More than one-third of all fire fighters who died during the five-year period from 1992 through 1996 were age 50 and over, although fire fighters in that age group

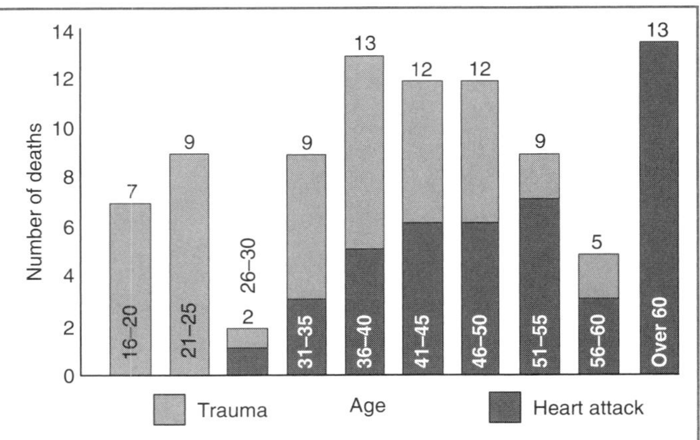

Figure S1-5 *Fire fighter deaths in 1996 by age and cause of death.*

account for only one-seventh of all fire fighters *(see Figure S1-6)*.[4] The death rate for fire fighters in their 50s is almost twice the average, and for fire fighters age 60 and over, it is four times the average. Fire fighters ages 30 through 39 had a death rate 35 percent lower than the average, the lowest death rate for fire fighters of all ages.

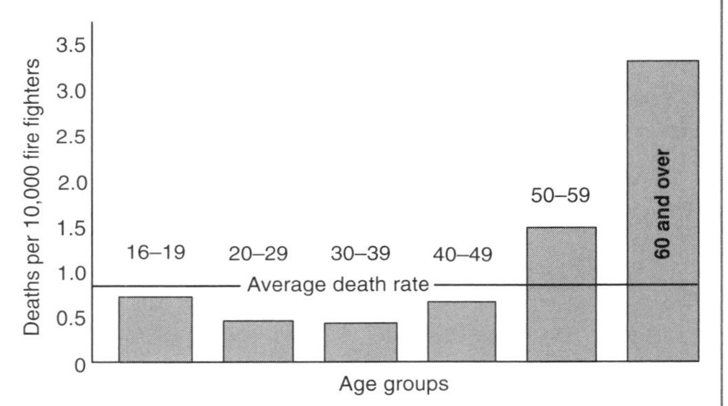

Figure S1-6 *On-duty death rates per 10,000 fire fighters between 1992 and 1996.*

Fireground Deaths

The largest proportion of the 32 fire fighters killed on the fireground to die in any one type of property—12 of the 32, or 37.5 percent—died in residential structures *(see Figure S1-7)*. Nine of the 12 died in one- and two-family dwellings, and 3 were killed in apartment buildings. Another 7 fire fighters died in stores, 4 died in wildland fires, 3 were killed in storage properties, and three died in vacant buildings. Another fire fighter died at a restaurant, another was killed at a chemical manufacturing plant, and the last died at an electrical distribution plant. There were no vehicle fire deaths in 1996.

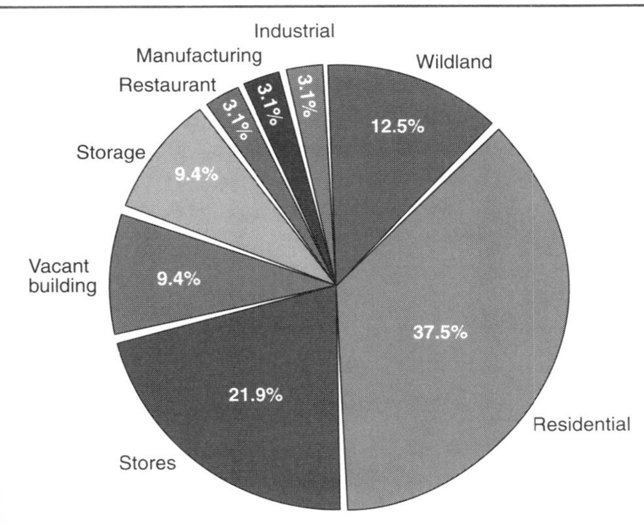

Figure S1-7 *Fireground deaths in 1996 by fixed property use.*

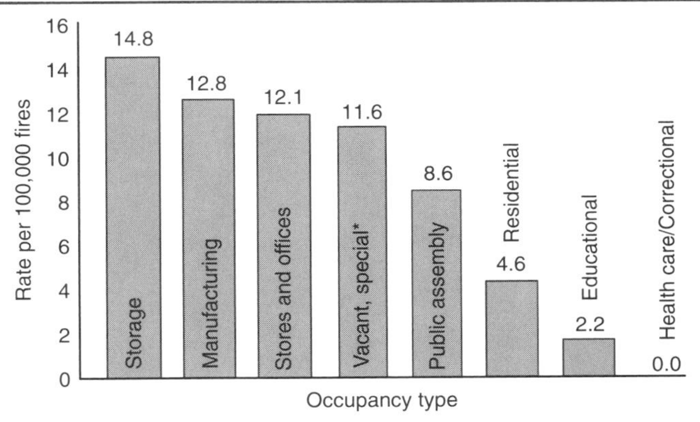

Figure S1-8 *On-duty fireground deaths per 100,000 structural fires between 1992 and 1996.*

To put the hazards of structural fire fighting in perspective, we examined the number of fireground deaths per 100,000 structure fires by property use using estimates of the fire experience in each type of property found in NFPA's annual fire loss studies from 1992 through 1996 and in the updated fire fighter fatality data for the corresponding years *(see Figure S1-8)*. Although more fire fighters die in residential structures than in any other type of structure, fires in nonresidential structures, other than educational or health-care and correctional properties, are, on average, more hazardous. There were 10.9 fireground deaths per 100,000 nonresidential structure fires from 1992 through 1996, compared to 4.6 deaths per 100,000 residential structure fires. The highest death rates over the five-year period actually occurred in storage properties. The low rate in health-care and correctional buildings and in educational buildings may reflect the fact that these occupancies are well regulated and inspected and that their occupants are likely to report fires in their early stages.

Motor Vehicle–Related Incidents

Twenty-two fire fighters, all of whom were volunteers, died in motor vehicle–related incidents.[5] Of these 22, 18 died in motor vehicle crashes, 3 were hit by vehicles, and 1 was crushed between two pieces of apparatus.

Twelve of the 18 fire fighters killed in collisions and rollovers were responding to alarms when the crashes occurred. Six of the 12 were driving their own vehicles. Two of these six had a history of seizure disorders, which might have played a role in the accidents. The other six fire fighters were killed in five incidents in which drivers of the responding apparatus in which they were riding lost control of their vehicles.

Another two fire fighters, both driving their own vehicles, were killed in crashes while returning from fires.

The remaining four crashes occurred while fire fighters were participating in other duty-related activities. In one instance, a vehicle hit an ambulance transporting a patient to a hospital, killing the fire fighter/EMT driving the ambulance and a county paramedic in the back of the vehicle. In another incident, a fire fighter died of complications suffered when his ambulance swerved to avoid a collision and overturned while he was tending to the patient en route to the hospital. In the third, a fire fighter returning to the station after filling a swimming pool—a fire department service offered to the community as a fund-raiser—lost control of his vehicle on a pothole-filled road. And in the fourth, a fire fighter traveling from one fire station to another on fire department business crashed into a tree.

Failure to wear seat belts, excessive speed, poor road conditions, and failure to obey traffic rules were factors in several of the crashes, although details were often incomplete. One driver was reportedly intoxicated at the time of his crash.

The three fire fighters struck by motor vehicles were all working at emergency scenes. One was working at a fire hydrant when he was hit by a passing vehicle. Another fire fighter, who was helping an injured person at the scene of a motor vehicle crash, was killed when a passing vehicle trying to avoid the accident overturned onto them. And finally, a fire fighter directing traffic at a crash scene was struck and killed by a passing vehicle.

Other Findings

In 1996, five fire fighters, or 5.3 percent, died as a result of incendiary and suspicious fires—three at structure fires, one at a wildland fire, and one while returning from a structure. They bring the number of fire fighters killed in incendiary or suspicious fires from 1987 through 1996 to 153, a figure that represents 14.7 percent of all on-duty deaths during that period. This is a drop of approximately one-third from the first 10 years that NFPA conducted this study and is, in part, a reflection of the decline in incendiary and suspicious fires over the same period.

In 1996, 5 fire fighters died as a result of false alarms—3 in two separate motor vehicle crashes while responding and 2 of heart attacks after returning to the station. Over the past 10 years, 24 fire fighters have died while responding to, or returning from, false alarms, whether malicious or the result of alarm malfunctions.

Of the 95 fire fighters who died while on duty in 1996, 92 were members of local career and volunteer fire departments, 2 were seasonal employees of federal forestry agencies, and 1 was an employee of a state forestry agency.

The distribution of deaths of career and volunteer fire fighters from local fire departments is shown in Figure S1-9. In general, the trend in career fire fighter deaths has continued downward since 1977. The downward trend since 1988 for volunteer fire fighters, however, seems to have reversed.

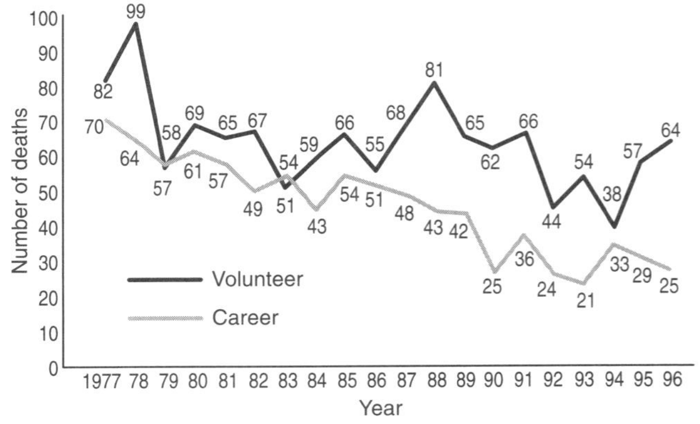

Figure S1-9 *Comparison of local career and local volunteer fire fighter deaths between 1977 and 1996.*

Conclusions

In the late 1970s, an average of 151 fire fighters died while on duty every year. In the 1980s, the annual average death toll dropped to 126. And so far in the 1990s, the annual average has dropped even further, to 95 deaths per year.

Much of this remarkable improvement can be attributed to a combination of better protective clothing and equipment, safer fire apparatus, better training, and better incident management. From 1977 through 1981, for example, an average of almost five fire fighters were killed each year in falls from emergency apparatus. Only two such deaths were reported from 1992 through 1996. From 1977 through 1981, an average of more than five fire fighters who weren't wearing SCBA died of smoke inhalation at structure fires each year. In 1977 alone, twelve fire fighters died from smoke exposure at structure fires, and of those twelve, ten weren't wearing SCBA. In the last five years, there's been an average of one such death per year.

Even though the total number of heart attack deaths has dropped over the 20-year period, heart attacks still account for approximately half the deaths that occur each year. In fact, they account for a slightly higher percentage of the deaths in the last five years of the study than in the first five years. And we know that more than 80 percent of the heart attack victims for whom medical documentation was available had already had heart attacks, bypass surgery, or severe arteriosclerotic heart disease.

Additional reductions in fire fighter deaths should be possible if we continue to pay attention to health and safety issues, placing particular emphasis on cardiovascular health and safe driving. Using NFPA 1582, *Medical Requirements for Fire Fighters,* to screen fire service applicants is also a step in the right direction. Properly screening fire service applicants, making sure they meet fitness requirements throughout their careers, and testing their health annually are essential if they are to be ready for the stress of duty—and if we are to reduce the number of fatal heart attacks that fire fighters continue to suffer on duty each year.

We must also pay more attention to safe driving. Motor vehicle–related incidents, many of which involve fire fighters' own vehicles and tankers, account for more than half of the large and growing difference in the death tolls among volunteer and career fire fighters, since nearly all such incidents involve volunteers. Excessive speed, disregard of traffic rules, and failure to use safety equipment repeatedly combine in tragic and unnecessary waste of life. Tankers/tenders[6] are essential in rural fire fighting, but they present special problems, and special care must be taken in driving them. Tanker/driver operators who have limited or no experience driving them and who drive too fast for road conditions are often factors in tanker crashes. Fire department tankers are often converted military vehicles and fuel tankers, not vehicles originally designed for fire department use.

Requiring operators of fire apparatus over a certain gross weight to hold commercial driver's licenses (CDLs) could help reduce accidents involving all types of apparatus, particularly if this were combined with more restrictive construction practices and training. Many jurisdictions require CDLs, which better prepare drivers to handle apparatus. The new standard, NFPA 1451, *Fire Service Vehicle Operations Training Program,* helps develop good driver training programs.

Health and safety issues should be our first priorities in the battle to reduce on-duty fire fighter deaths. A comprehensive safety and health program that is designed according to NFPA 1500, *Fire Department Occupational Safety and Health Program,* is an important step in achieving this goal.

References

1. NFPA's files on fatal injuries to on-duty fire fighters are updated continually for all years. The 95 deaths for 1995 are 7 more than the number identified in the July/August 1996 issue of *NFPA Journal*. The 95 deaths for 1996 are 3 more than the number identified in the July/August 1997 issue in the "Fire Fighter Fatalities" report.
2. For this report, the term *volunteer* refers to any fire fighter who isn't a full-time, paid member of a fire department. The term *career* refers to full-time, paid fire department members or employees of career organizations whose assigned duties include fire fighting.
3. These categories are based on the 1981 edition of NFPA 901, *Uniform Coding for Fire Protection.*
4. Michael J. Karter, Jr., "U.S. Fire Department Profile Through 1994," NFPA Fire Analysis and Research Division, Quincy, Massachusetts, November 1995, unpublished. The analysis shown here assumes that the number of fire fighters adequately estimates exposure and that the age distributions of career and volunteer fire fighters are similar.
5. For this report, the term *motor vehicle–related incident* refers to collisions and rollovers involving motor vehicles (including aircraft and boats) and incidents in which fire fighters fall from, or are struck by, vehicles where the involvement of the vehicle played an integral role in the incident.
6. The term *tanker* is used to describe a piece of fire apparatus used primarily for transporting water to an incident scene. Departments or agencies that use the Incident Command System refer to this type of apparatus as a water tender.

Credits

This study is made possible by the cooperation and assistance of the U.S. fire service, the Public Safety Officers' Benefits Program of the Department of Justice, the U.S. Fire Administration, the Forest Service of the U.S. Department of Agriculture, and the Bureau of Indian Affairs and the Bureau of Land Management of the U.S. Department of the Interior.

U.S. DEPARTMENT OF JUSTICE DEATH AND DISABILITY BENEFITS FOR PUBLIC SAFETY OFFICERS

The Public Safety Officers' Benefits (PSOB) Act, signed into law in 1976, provides a federal death benefit to the survivors of the nation's federal, state, and local law enforcement officers, fire fighters, and rescue and ambulance squad members, both career and volunteer, whose deaths are the direct and proximate result of a traumatic injury sustained in the line of duty.

In 1988, the Act was amended, increasing the amount of the benefit from $50,000 to $100,000. To help keep inflation from eroding the benefit's effectiveness, the 1988 amendment included an annual cost-of-living escalator. As a result, the benefit increases on October 1 of each year. The current benefit is $141,556, tax free (as of 10/1/97).

PSOB covers all federal, state, and local public safety officers, although its principal focus is on fire fighters, including volunteers, and law enforcement officers. A decedent's spouse and minor children usually are the eligible beneficiaries, although parents become eligible for the death benefit if a decedent wasn't married and there are no eligible children.

Congress amended the PSOB benefits program in 1990 to include permanent and total disabilities that occurred on or after November 29, 1990. PSOB is reserved for those few tragic cases in which an individual barely survives a traumatic, line-of-duty injury and is permanently unable to perform any gainful employment. Only then, in the presence of the program's statutory and regulatory qualifying criteria, will PSOB's disability benefit be awarded. The bill's supporters anticipated that PSOB wouldn't approve more than a small number of cases annually.

To initiate a claim for death benefits, to receive additional information on filing a disability claim, or to receive additional information about coverage, call or write the Public Safety Officers' Benefits Program, Bureau of Justice Assistance, U.S. Department of Justice, Washington, DC 20531; telephone (202) 307-0635.

INCIDENTS

Structural Collapse

A 31-year-old paid-on-call fire fighter died of severe head trauma when he was buried by an exterior wall that collapsed while he fought a fire in a vacant commercial building in Illinois. The fire fighter had responded to a mutual-aid call from a neighboring community.

The vacant building, which at one time had housed stores and a hotel, was a 70 by 73 foot, two-story structure of ordinary construction. It had been vacant for several years, and the storefront windows on the ground floor were covered with plywood to discourage vandalism. There had been a fire in the structure about 10 years earlier, but the damage had been repaired.

At 9:55 p.m., the fire chief received a telephone call from a bartender in a nearby tavern informing him that a passerby had discovered a fire in the vacant structure. The fire chief, who was the first to arrive on the scene, found heavy smoke coming from the second-story windows on all sides of the building and requested mutual aid from several neighboring communities. One of these departments responded with a pumper and an aerial ladder.

When the apparatus arrived on the scene, heavy fire was visible from the roof on one side of the building. The pumper crew was instructed to hook up to a hydrant approximately 500 feet from the building and to prepare to supply an aerial ladder master stream to protect the exposed structure—which happened to be city hall—behind the fire building. After setting up, they reported to the chief, who told them to advance a 2½-inch handline about 3 feet into the building through a doorway and begin to extinguish the visible fire. Fire fighters in full protective gear, including operating SCBA, were working their way into the building when a section of the ceiling suddenly collapsed, forcing the crew to back out. At this point, the fireground commander ordered the fire fighters to abandon their offensive attack and begin defensive operations using master streams and handlines from outside.

Four fire fighters were directed to remove a sheet of plywood from a storefront window to allow the heavy stream operations better access. One fire fighter was using a 1½-inch handline to protect the other three as they removed the plywood. They had just finished and were moving away from the building when a section of the roof collapsed, causing a large section of the building's exterior wall to collapse. In what is referred to as an *inward/outward* collapse, the top of the wall collapsed inward while the middle of the wall collapsed outward.

Three of the fire fighters, including the man on the handline, were able to run clear of the collapse, although one later had to be treated for cuts and bruises. However, one fire fighter was buried under the bricks of the collapsing wall. His fellow fire fighters immediately moved in and began digging him out by hand. They removed him within minutes and rushed him to a local hospital, where he was pronounced dead from crushing head injuries.

Investigators were unable to determine the cause of the fire, which destroyed the building. The collapse occurred approximately an hour after the fire was reported.

Tanker/Tender Crash

A 19-year-old volunteer fire fighter driving a tanker died and his 19-year-old passenger was injured when their vehicle overturned while responding to a fire in a clothes dryer in a manufactured home in Washington State. The tanker consisted of a 1982 three-axle chassis to which a 3000-gallon water tank had been added when it was converted to a fire department tanker, resulting in a total vehicle weight of 48,200 pounds.

The tanker and other apparatus responding to the 9:39 p.m. alarm passed a sign warning of an upcoming curve in the paved, two-lane road. Beyond the sign, the road had a 7 percent downgrade and curved to the left. The posted speed limit was 35 miles per hour (mph). A fire fighter in a piece of apparatus behind the tanker, which was reportedly traveling 50 to 60 mph, radioed the tanker driver to slow down as he approached the curve.

Unfortunately, the warning came too late. The front right wheel of the tanker went off the pavement onto the gravel shoulder of the curve, causing the tanker to overturn onto its right side. It continued to roll while skidding forward, crushing the cab, before it came to rest on its left side. The two occupants remained inside the cab the whole time, although neither was wearing a seat belt. A fire fighter in the apparatus following the tanker radioed for help, then removed the two young men from the crushed cab. They were transported to an area hospital where the driver was pronounced dead shortly after arrival. The passenger was treated and released.

An inspection of the tanker following the crash failed to identify any mechanical problems. The baffled, semi-elliptical tank didn't separate from the chassis.

Tanker/Tender Crash

A 55-year-old volunteer fire fighter died of multiple head trauma after he was thrown from the tanker he was driving to a fire in a single-family home in Arkansas.

The 1980 tanker, formerly used by a state forestry agency, wasn't originally designed or built to be a piece of fire apparatus. When it was converted, the original 750-gallon water tank was replaced by a square, 1000-gallon tank mounted over the single rear axle. The unit was equipped with air-assisted hydraulic brakes and had an automatic transmission.

At approximately 1:00 p.m., volunteer fire fighters received a report of a house fire. One fire fighter, who was working nearby, responded to the fire station and left driving the tanker. He was its only occupant. Approximately a mile and a half from the station, he stopped at an intersection, then proceeded onto a two-lane state highway. While descending a slight hill, the tanker gained speed, until it was traveling 50 to 55 mph. The road then began to rise slightly before it made a sharp left turn. At the curve, a gravel road entered the highway from the right. Just before he reached this gravel road, the driver apparently lost control of the tanker.

The vehicle went off the road onto a gravel shoulder and kept going 118 feet to the intersection of the gravel road, where the driver managed to bring the tanker back onto the highway. The tanker then crossed the center line, traveling about 100 feet down the road as the driver tried to bring it back into the travel lane. At this point, the tanker began to rock from side to side as it traveled more than 60 feet back over the center line. Turning to the left, the driver tried to keep the tanker from going off the right side of the road. He skidded on the road for another 98 feet as he again approached the center line. At this point, the tanker rolled over at least twice, coming to rest on its right side on the right side of the roadway.

The driver, who wasn't wearing a seat belt, was thrown through the windshield. Another volunteer fire fighter responding to the same call found him lying 53 feet from the tanker and called an ambulance. The injured fire fighter was taken to an area hospital and pronounced dead within an hour of the crash.

Factors contributing to this crash include the design and construction of the apparatus; excessive speed, particularly at a curve in the roadway; and failure to control the vehicle after it left the road. In addition, gravel spilling onto the paved road from the gravel road hindered the driver's efforts to bring the tanker back onto the road after he first lost control. Had the driver been wearing his seat belt, he might not have been thrown from the cab, improving his chance for survival.

The fire to which the fire fighter was responding was extinguished by the occupant.

Electrocution

An electrical arc from a 23,000-volt power line downed during a blizzard claimed the life of a 23-year-old volunteer fire fighter in Connecticut. The severe storm had blanketed the area with heavy, wet snow that snapped power lines, cutting off electrical power to a large area.

During the storm, a state police officer on patrol discovered that a power line arcing near the front of an occupied single-family house had ignited the exterior of the unprotected, wood-frame structure at the bottom of the roof line. The officer called in the alarm at 12:48 a.m., and responding fire fighters found the front of the house heavily involved and fire spreading inside. The occupants had safely evacuated. The fire chief asked the power company to shut the electricity off immediately and ordered fire fighters preparing to make their attack to wait for confirmation that it was safe to proceed.

While the fire fighters were waiting, two more arcs occurred, and the fire in the front of the dwelling intensified. At this point, all of the electrical power in the area apparently ceased—the streetlights went out, power to the other houses in the neighborhood went out, and the arcing stopped. Believing that the power company had shut off all power in the vicinity, fire fighters proceeded to knock down the fire on the outside of the house and moved inside, where they soon contained the blaze and began overhaul.

At approximately 1:30 a.m., a fire fighter removing shingles from the front exterior wall at grade level stepped back to check the damaged area. Apparently, he slipped, and his SCBA air cylinder touched a hanging 23,000-volt power line. Other fire fighters, unable to help, watched in horror as he was electrocuted.

The power line, which was hanging through the trees about 8 feet from the front steps of the house, near the edge of the road, is believed to have been energized during the entire operation. During the fire, it evidently dropped slowly from roof level until it reached the point at which the victim came into contact with it.

Crushing Between Apparatus

A 32-year-old volunteer fire fighter responding to a radio page for a large grass fire in Oklahoma was crushed to death when he was caught between two pieces of apparatus at the fire station. The man had arrived at the fire station at 6:42 p.m. with two other fire fighters, one of whom unlocked the pass door and went to the radio to acknowledge receipt of the report. A second fire fighter got into the brush unit, which was parked in front of another vehicle, to start it. At the same time, the victim went around the back of the brush unit to test start the auxiliary pump motor. The driver, who reportedly didn't realize that the other man was behind the vehicle, started the unit, apparently thinking that the manual transmission was in neutral. However, the apparatus lurched backward, crushing the fire fighter at the pump between the two vehicles.

An ambulance was requested immediately, and the fire fighter was taken to an area hospital. Over the next two days, his condition deteriorated, and he succumbed to abdominal injuries.

Fire department reports indicate that the department will take steps to prevent such accidents, including new and larger wheel blocks, a clutch safety switch, and backup alarms.

Tree Collapse

When Hurricane Fran struck North Carolina, the fatalities resulting from the storm included a 19-year-old volunteer fire fighter, who died of blunt head trauma when a tree fell on the cab of the apparatus he was driving.

At approximately 11:30 p.m., two fire fighters were dispatched in a brush fire unit to check a vehicle on which a tree had fallen. The two men left the station and were reportedly traveling at a cautious 20 mph when a falling tree hit the windshield and crushed the cab.

The 19-year-old fire fighter riding in the passenger seat survived and was able to bring the unit to a stop. A passerby helped him from the crushed cab after he radioed for assistance, and he was taken to a local hospital where he was treated for injuries to his left arm and shoulder.

The fire fighter who was driving the apparatus died of his injuries.

Apparatus Crash

Two volunteer fire fighters died of head and body trauma when they were involved in a single vehicle apparatus crash while responding to a false alarm in South Carolina. The accident occurred during the department's third response to the same single-family house after the occupants reported that their combination fire/burglar alarm system had activated. On the first two responses, fire fighters couldn't identify the cause of the activation.

The third call came in at 11:02 p.m., and part of this response included a 1984 brush fire unit equipped with a 260-gallon water tank driven by a 22-year-old fire fighter. A 19-year-old fire fighter rode in the passenger seat.

According to the investigation, the apparatus was traveling along a fairly straight section of a paved, two-lane road when the driver apparently lost control, sending the right front wheel of the apparatus off the road onto the low shoulder. He managed to get the vehicle back onto the roadway but overcompensated in his steering, sending the rig across the center line, rocking from side to side as he tried to bring it back to the right side of the road. The unit then rolled over, and the cab hit a tree on the opposite side of the road. Both young men, neither of whom was wearing a seat belt, died from their traumatic injuries. Police reports indicate that excessive speed was the major factor in the accident.

Structural Collapse

In Nebraska, a 43-year-old career fire captain died of asphyxiation when he was trapped under a section of roof and heavy plaster ceiling that collapsed during an arson fire in a large variety store.

The L-shaped, one-story store, which covered 10,574 square feet, was composed of two interconnected structures with different construction features. The older, larger section had masonry walls of both brick and concrete block. Its roof was a wood-frame assembly with a slight peak at the center line from front to back. This structure had been altered many times. The smaller, newer building had concrete block walls and a steel bowstring truss-supported roof. The two structures were built on concrete slabs and had neither fire detection nor suppression equipment.

An engine company was dispatched to the store at 5:00 p.m. after a neighbor reported a fire involving a wood fence near a rear corner of the older section of the building. The fence, which was very close to the building, extended above the wood facia overhang. At 5:06 p.m., the engine company officer requested additional units, since he feared that the fire had spread into the store's attic.

The first engine company to arrive at the front of the building advanced a 300-foot, preconnected, 1¾-inch handline into the main entrance of the store, which was in the newer section opposite the corner at which the fire fighters were operating. The three fire fighters entering through the front were wearing full protective clothing with SCBA, but their facepieces weren't in place.

The three fire fighters' initial search of the older section didn't uncover any fire or smoke. However, one of them noticed a red glow through an opening in the heavy plaster ceiling of a storeroom in the rear of the section. The fire fighters quickly began to don their SCBA facepieces and asked for their line to be charged. One of the fire fighters, a captain, took over the handline, and the other two began to pull down a section of the ceiling. Suddenly, a large section collapsed, separating the captain from the two fire fighters.

The fire fighters fought their way out of the debris that covered them, escaped through a door to the outside, and reported that the captain was trapped. Other crew members tried to enter through this same door, but they were driven back by the rapidly intensifying fire. They tried again through the front main entrance and followed the handline the captain and his crew had taken in earlier. When the rescuers reached the collapsed area, they couldn't find the captain. They kept searching until they heard the sound of his operating PASS device and saw the reflective material on his turnout clothing. He had collapsed a short distance from the front main entrance while trying to escape, his SCBA facepiece still in place. His rescuers moved him outside, where paramedics immediately began resuscitation efforts. He was taken to a local hospital where he was pronounced dead of asphyxiation after his SCBA air supply had depleted.

After examining all possible causes, investigators determined that the fire was incendiary. Authorities later arrested a 15-year-old for igniting combustibles at the base of the privacy fence. The structure and its contents were completely destroyed, for an estimated loss of $750,000.

As a result of this incident, the fire department reportedly plans to establish a red flag system to identify buildings with construction features that may be dangerous to fire fighters. A city ordinance may also be proposed requiring that structures with truss roof construction be identified with a placard as a warning to fire fighters.

Electrocution

A 38-year-old volunteer fire fighter was electrocuted in a seaside Texas community when he was struck by a falling power line.

The fire department had reportedly responded to a number of fires involving power poles during the summer. Apparently, drought conditions allowed salt to build up on the poles' insulators, resulting in arcing that ignited the fires.

The volunteer fire fighter was alone at the station at 11:56 a.m. when he received a call reporting another power pole fire. Jumping into a pumper, he was the first to arrive on the scene, where he noted that the fire involved the top of the pole near a transformer. He was putting his pumper in gear with his back to the power pole when the top part of the pole collapsed, bringing with it the attached power lines. One of the lines electrocuted him before he had a chance to escape.

Ambulance Crash

A tragic accident in Indiana involving a fire department ambulance and another vehicle killed a 25-year-old volunteer fire fighter, a 30-year-old county paramedic, and the patient they were transporting. The fire fighter and the paramedic died at the scene, and the patient died the following day. Both occupants of the other vehicle were also killed. Two other fire fighters were injured.

The fire department ambulance had been called at 3:40 a.m. to transport a person who had been seriously injured in a single-vehicle crash. EMS personnel staffing the ambulance during transport included two county paramedics assisted by two fire fighters/EMTs in the back, or patient-care area, of the ambulance. The ambulance was driven by a 25-year-old fire fighter/EMT. The county paramedic unit followed the ambulance during transport.

The ambulance was traveling at 50 mph along a straight, two-lane road at 4:24 a.m. when an oncoming vehicle crossed the center line and collided with it head-on. The paramedic driving the unit following the ambulance immediately radioed for help. He then pulled his ambulance up to illuminate the area and went to the driver's sides of both vehicles to assess their conditions. He found the 25-year-old driver of the ambulance and the driver and passenger of the other vehicle dead. A paramedic who had been riding in the back of the ambulance emerged, having suffered only minor injuries, and emptied the contents of a portable fire extinguisher on the smoldering engine. The second paramedic in the back of the ambulance died of traumatic injuries at the scene shortly after the crash. The two fire fighters who had been helping the paramedics were airlifted to a trauma center. One of them was hospitalized in serious condition, and the other, who was six months pregnant, delivered a stillborn baby the following day.

Toxicology reports on the 17-year-old driver of the car that crossed the center line of the road noted that she had a blood alcohol level of 0.0523 percent, which would have been considered relevant during a trial. Road conditions weren't a factor in the crash. The fire fighter who was killed was not wearing a seat belt.

Exposure to Fire Products

A fire in a 13-story, T-shaped apartment building of fire-resistive construction in New York resulted in the death of a 38-year-old career fire fighter who got lost in a third-story hallway while trying to escape intensifying fire conditions.

The fire was reported at 10:10 p.m. by the occupants of the third-story apartment, who wasted several minutes trying to extinguish it. After calling the fire department, they left the apartment, closing the door to the hallway. Members of the first-arriving ladder company took the stairs to the fire floor and began a primary search to locate anyone who might be trapped and to determine the location of the fire. One member of the ladder company crew had a portable, pressurized water extinguisher to make a possible initial attack.

The first-arriving engine company crew brought in a standpipe line consisting of two lengths of $2\frac{1}{2}$-inch hose and one length of $1\frac{3}{4}$-inch hose with a nozzle and connected them to the wet standpipe connection on the fire floor. However, they reportedly couldn't operate the handline because there was no operating wheel on the standpipe gate.

By this time, the ladder company crew had identified the apartment of origin, finding the door closed but unlocked. When fire fighters opened the door, the fire rapidly intensified, pushing heavy smoke and heat into the hallway. Because they were without water, the engine company was unable to protect the ladder crew.

During the next few moments, fire fighters tried to escape the untenable conditions. Although some became separated from the group, others were able to help each other find the door to the stairwell as an officer on the fire floor radioed a distress message. An engine company brought in another standpipe line, connected it to a second-story standpipe, and advanced to the fire floor to help the trapped fire fighters.

As the members of the ladder crew escaped from the fire floor, a head count was conducted, revealing that one fire fighter was missing. Crews forced their way back onto the fire floor and managed to locate the missing fire fighter only a few feet from the door to the involved apartment. His SCBA air supply had been depleted, his facepiece was not in place, and his PASS device had not been activated. The fire fighter was removed from the building and taken to an area hospital, where he was pronounced dead from serious burns and inhalation injuries.

The fire was confined to the third floor of the building, where investigators found that children playing with matches in a bedroom had ignited ordinary combustibles. Before fire fighters even arrived, the fire had become so intense that it broke a window in the room of origin. Gusting winds helped to intensify the fire further.

Six fire fighters were treated for burns to their hands and ears.

Asphyxiation

While rescuing a salvage company worker from a grain bin in Illinois, a 40-year-old volunteer fire chief was overcome by carbon monoxide and carbon dioxide fumes and asphyxiated before he could be rescued.

A month earlier, an explosion in the 500,000-bushel grain bin had produced numerous spot fires, which a salvage company was trying to suffocate by pumping carbon dioxide into the bin so that it could recover the undamaged corn. Local fire officials asked to be notified when the company did anything else to extinguish the fires and remove the product. Fire officials were also concerned about another grain bin of similar size that was connected by a tunnel to the involved bin.

On the day of the chief's death, representatives of the salvage company and an insurance company were at the site overseeing the removal of the corn from the bin—without notifying local fire officials. During the operation, the flow of corn from the bin stopped, and the representatives decided that someone had to enter the bin to see what had caused the interruption. A salvage company worker and a grain company employee climbed the exterior ladder to the top of the bin, which the salvage company employee entered by climbing down an interior ladder. Once inside, he began to experience difficulty breathing. The grain company worker descended the ladder after him and found the other man in a lethargic condition. He moved the semiconscious victim to a spot in the bin where the air was better and began CPR. Neither of the men wore protective breathing apparatus.

The fire department received a 911 call from the facility at 2:06 p.m., and the volunteer fire chief arrived at the scene with other fire fighters and emergency medical personnel minutes later. The chief, wearing street clothes and an SCBA unit, climbed the ladder to the top of the bin to assess the situation. He was accompanied by a fire fighter wearing full protective equipment, including SCBA. At the same time, other fire fighters entered the adjacent bin and used the connecting tunnel to bring oxygen units to the two victims. The grain company employee was able to place the medical oxygen bottles on himself and the other man, and the bin's vacuum system was activated to deal with any dust that might hamper the rescue effort.

The fire chief and the fire fighter entered the bin with their SCBA operating and attached a hoisting harness to the semiconscious man. When the low-air alarms on their SCBA sounded, the chief exchanged his air cylinder, removed his facepiece, and began to help the fire fighter with his unit. The chief, unable to change the fire fighter's cylinder, was beginning to look lethargic when the fire fighter told him to leave the bin. The fire fighter then started up the ladder himself, preceded by the grain company worker. Looking back down, the fire fighter realized the chief was having serious trouble breathing and had gone into convulsions. He climbed back down into the bin, replaced the chief's facepiece, and secured a rescue harness on him. He then started back up the ladder, guiding the chief as rescuers at the top of the bin pulled him out. The revived salvage company worker followed the fire fighter out of the bin, with help from rescuers using a rescue rope harness.

The fire fighter was taken to a local hospital, where he was treated and released. The injured salvage company worker was also taken to the local hospital, where he received emergency medical attention before he was airlifted to another hospital for treatment in a hyperbaric chamber. The fire chief was dead by the time he was removed from the bin, a victim of acute carbon monoxide poisoning. Blood samples drawn at autopsy revealed a carbon monoxide level of 50.4 percent.

OSHA issued fines of $458,500 against the grain and salvage companies for serious violations of its standards.

SPECIAL 10-YEAR ANALYSIS OF FIRE FIGHTER DEATHS WHILE RESPONDING TO, OR RETURNING FROM, ALARMS

From 1987 through 1996, 272 fire fighters died while responding to, or returning from, emergencies. Of these, 194 were killed while responding to alarms, and 78 died while they were returning, or just after they'd returned, from an emergency response. These deaths, which accounted for 26.0 percent of all fire fighter deaths over the period, bear closer examination because so many of them involve preventable factors.

It is interesting to note the differences between the causes of injuries incurred during a response and those that occurred while returning from an incident or shortly thereafter. More than half, or 57.2 percent, of the deaths that occurred while responding to an alarm were due to motor vehicle crashes, and another 29.9 percent were due to heart attacks. On the other hand, most, or 75.6 percent, of the 78 fire fighters who died after returning from alarms died of heart attacks. Another 20.5 percent of deaths were due to crashes.

Nine of the 10 who died as a result of falls from apparatus died between 1987 and 1991, five of them in 1987 alone. In the past five years, the only fire fighter to die in this manner while responding to, or returning from, an alarm was knocked off the back step of a pumper when it was hit by a private vehicle driven by another responding fire fighter. Requiring fire fighters to be seated and enclosed while traveling on apparatus appears to have paid off in reducing what used to be a significant part of the annual fire fighter death toll.

Of the four fire fighters killed over the past 10 years when they were hit by vehicles, one was struck by a responding police car as she waited by the side of the road for a ride to the scene. Another was directing traffic during a response. A third was crossing a highway to check on victims of a motor vehicle crash. And the fourth was crushed between two pieces of apparatus while preparing to respond to an incident.

Among the eight fire fighters whose deaths fall into the "Other" category, three were killed when their vehicles were struck by falling trees, one drowned when a bridge collapsed, one fell from a responding pickup truck, one fell from a fire station sliding pole, one fell down a flight of stairs, and one had heat stroke.

When we look at the fire fighters who died of heart attacks while responding to, or returning from, an alarm, we find—as usual—that those with existing medical problems account for the majority of the victims. Of the 117 heart attack victims, we were able to obtain medical documentation for 54. Of these 54, 33 had already had heart attacks or bypass surgery, or they had other existing heart problems. Fourteen others had severe, detectable arteriosclerotic heart disease. Another five had hypertension, one was diabetic, and one had bronchial asthma.

Almost half of the fire fighters who died while responding to, or returning from, alarms died as a result of motor vehicle crashes, and the vehicles most often involved were pumpers, tankers, and the fire fighters' own vehicles. Sixty fire fighters died in 60 crashes involving their own vehicles, 31 were killed in 27 tanker crashes, and 18 died in 15 crashes involving pumpers.

Thirty-four of the fire fighters killed in crashes involving their own vehicles died when they collided with other vehicles. Twenty collided with objects such as utility poles, trees, and bridge abutments. Four died when their vehicles overturned. And two were killed when their vehicles went off the road. Excessive speed, failure to stop at stop signs, failure to yield, and failure to wear seat belts were often cited as factors.

The 27 tanker crashes had a different distribution. In 22, the tankers overturned, killing 24 fire fighters. In two, the tankers went off the road, resulting in three deaths. And three tankers were involved in collisions, killing four fire fighters. Excessive speed, failure to negotiate curves (often due to excessive speed), failure to stop, and failure to wear seat belts were often cited as factors in these incidents.

Tankers are essential in rural fire fighting, but they are not always stable. Many are military vehicles or fuel tankers that have been converted for fire department use. As originally designed, military vehicles have a high center of gravity, and adding a tank increases their instability at higher speeds and on turns. In addition, the weight of the water can seriously tax their suspension, brakes, and tires.

Driver inexperience also played a role in many of the tanker crashes. Inexperienced drivers include not only young people, but also older drivers who are not often called upon to drive—under emergency conditions—a vehicle that handles very differently from a passenger car or truck.

Another 18 fire fighters died in 15 pumper crashes over the past 10 years. Nine of the pumpers overturned; four collided with other vehicles, killing five fire fighters; and two collided with objects, killing four fire fighters. The same factors tended to be cited in these incidents as in those described above.

Of the remaining vehicle crashes, seven involved aircraft, two involved ambulances, and one involved a National Guard truck. The seven aircraft accidents killed 15 fire fighters.

Among those killed in incidents that occurred while responding to, or returning from, alarms were 251 members of local fire departments. Of these, 226 were volunteer fire fighters and 25 were career fire fighters. Another 11 of the fire fighters killed while responding to, or returning from, alarms were contractors with state or federal agencies, 10 worked for state and federal forestry agencies, and 1 was a military fire fighter.

SUPPLEMENT 2

NTSB Special Investigation Report on Emergency Fire Apparatus

Editor's Note: This special investigation report, by the National Transportation Safety Board (NTSB), includes reports on eight separate accidents involving fire apparatus. It also includes supplementary reports on fire apparatus accidents, where lack of vehicle maintenance and driver training, or lack thereof, is cited. The Technical Committee on Occupational Safety felt that NTSB's recommendations should be included in the 1992 edition of NFPA 1500, and these requirements have been retained in the 1997 edition. As reported in Supplement 1, the NFPA Data Analysis Division's statistics show that responding to and returning from alarms continues to be the second largest category of fire fighter fatalities. The original report is available from National Transportation Safety Board, Public Inquiries Section, RE-51, 800 Independence Avenue, S.W., Washington, DC 20594.

INTRODUCTION

On May 10, 1990, a 1974 Hahn custom pumper fire engine operated by the Waterbury Fire Department (WFD), while responding to an emergency call in Waterbury, Connecticut, ran off the road and hit a large tree when the driver lost control on a steep downgrade. The fire engine carried five paid fire fighters and 500 gallons of water. Two fire fighters were fatally injured, one fire fighter sustained moderate injuries, and the driver and remaining fire fighter sustained only minor injuries. The pavement was wet from previous rain.

This accident and several others involving emergency fire apparatus[1] responding to alarms prompted the Safety Board to conduct a special investigation to determine the adequacy of fire apparatus maintenance and inspection, fire department operating procedures, and occupant seatbelt use. National Fire Protection Association (NFPA)[2] data indicate that between 1980 and 1989, 15 percent[3] of all fire fighters who died in the line of duty died as a result of accidents involving fire apparatus that were en route to alarms.[4] As part of this special investigation, the Safety Board examined eight separate fire apparatus accidents and conducted an informal survey of the 50 states and the District of Columbia to determine their requirements for inspecting fire apparatus.

MAINTENANCE AND INSPECTION

Accident Information

Waterbury, Connecticut. On May 10, 1990, at 11:19 a.m. eastern standard time, a 1974 Hahn custom pumper, Model HCP12-24, with two jumpseats[5] was dispatched from the WFD Highland Avenue firehouse to an alarm on Thomaston Avenue in Waterbury, Connecticut. *(See Figure S2-1.)* The driver stated that after the alarm sounded, he started the vehicle and observed that the brake system air pressure was 120 psi (within normal operating limits).

According to the driver, the apparatus was functioning normally while heading north on Highland Avenue. As the driver approached Chase Parkway, he slowed the vehicle by downshifting the automatic transmission from drive to drive 2, applied the brakes, and came to a stop at the intersection. Highland Avenue at this location is straight and level. The driver stated that the brakes

Figure S2-1 *Hahn custom pumper, model HCP-15 (similar to the accident vehicle).*

worked "okay" and that he had no trouble stopping. The driver then crossed Highland Avenue, successfully negotiated a sharp turn (with a radius of 355 feet), and proceeded down the 10 to 13 percent grade to the intersection of West Main Street. The driver stated that he slowed through the sharp turn by downshifting.

On the steep grade, he downshifted again and applied the brakes but "did not feel any braking." He then downshifted to drive 1 and applied the brakes and parking brake (spring brake), but the parking brake button kept "popping" back.[6] He stated that the only deceleration he could detect was from the transmission. When he reached the intersection of Highland Avenue and West Main Street, he made a right turn into the westbound lane of West Main Street. He saw traffic backed up from the light at a nearby intersection and attempted an immediate left turn into an apartment complex parking lot. The fire engine ran over a 7-inch curb, and the driver stated that he saw a tree and tried to steer away from it. The fire engine traveled about 38 feet on the grass and collided with a tree that had two trunks. *(See Figure S2-2.)*

As a result of the collision with the tree, the driver and fire fighter who had been seated in the left jumpseat received minor injuries. The fire fighter seated in the right front seat received moderate injuries. All of these fire fighters were restrained by lap belts. The fire fighter in the right jumpseat was fatally injured (the Safety Board could not determine whether this fire fighter was restrained by the available lap belt). The fire fighter standing behind the right jumpseat, who was unrestrained, was fatally injured. None of the occupants were ejected. The right front of the cab sustained most of the damage.

Tarrant County, Texas. About 2:34 p.m., on October 24, 1990, a Spillway Volunteer Fire Department (SVFD) fire fighter was dispatched in a tanker truck to transport 1000 gallons of water to other fire fighters at the scene of a housefire in rural Tarrant County, Texas. Before departing on the fire call, she had been babysitting the fire chief's 2-year-old daughter. She was unable to find another babysitter and took the infant with her. The 1963 International Loadstar 1600 fire truck was not equipped with seatbelts, and the infant was not restrained in a child safety seat.

The fire truck was eastbound on Farm-to-Market Road 1886 at a witness-estimated speed of 45 mph when the driver began negotiating a shallow left curve on a 6 percent downgrade. The right side tires of the fire truck dropped 5 inches off the right pavement edge, and the driver steered to the left and lost control of the road, dropped 10 feet, and crashed head-on into a dirt embankment. The fire truck exploded into flames at impact, and both occupants were killed.

Fire Apparatus Maintenance

Waterbury, Connecticut. WFD vehicle maintenance was performed by the WFD Bureau of Auto Repairs (BAR) located in the Waterbury Public Works service

Figure S2-2 *Accident vehicle at its final rest position. (Waterbury Republican American newspaper photograph; Don Cousey, staff photographer; Tom Kalbelka, photo lab)*

yard. The four employees at the BAR maintained all fire apparatus, fire-fighting equipment, fire station power generators, lawn mowers, nonemergency vehicles, and automobiles. The WFD had 42 motorized vehicles, including 21 fire apparatus. The WFD mechanics were required to pass a civil service mechanics test. They received on-the-job training and brief training seminars from truck dealers and distributors.

Generally, spare fire apparatus are used only when the first-line apparatus are out of service for maintenance or repair. In January 1990, the WFD purchased new equipment, and the accident fire apparatus was taken out of first-line service as engine 9 at the Northside firehouse on January 27, 1990. The accident fire apparatus eventually became the first-line spare at the firehouse on Highland Avenue. At the time of the accident, the WFD had three ladder trucks and five engines in spare service. They were under the same maintenance schedule as the regular first-line apparatus.

All the WFD fire apparatus had hour meters that recorded engine running time and were used to determine when vehicle service was needed. Under the WFD preventive maintenance program, a vehicle was to be serviced after 150 hours of operation. The 150-hour service check included changing the engine oil and filter, lubricating the chassis, checking all fluids, and inspecting all belts, hose, batteries, tires, exhaust system, fuel system, steering, suspension, and brakes. The service manual for the 1974 Hahn pumper, which was the accident vehicle, recommends service every 50 hours.

The master mechanic stated that the BAR also performs an annual service check on each vehicle that includes the items on the 150-hour service check; changing the fuel, automatic transmission, water, and air filters; and changing the pump transfer gear case and rear axle carrier case oil. Any rebuilding of components (brakes, transmission, etc.) is normally performed at this time. A service reminder (a 4-inch by 8-inch index card) is posted in the cab of the apparatus and states the hour meter reading for the next 150-hour service check and the date of the next annual service check. It is the responsibility of the personnel where the apparatus is stationed to notify the BAR when a vehicle is due for maintenance. Additionally, the WFD accident driver stated that shift duty drivers normally inspect their vehicles (pre-trip) at the beginning of a three-day duty shift; this inspection includes a check of all fluids and an examination of the tires for damage, low air pressure, and tread wear, but no road tests are performed.

Of the 12 request-for-repair forms filed on the accident vehicle between November 7, 1988, and May 3, 1990, 7 were requests to fix the brakes. Most of the forms had notes indicating that the brakes had been checked or adjusted. A request for repair dated May 3, 1990, stated that "the maxi brake doesn't hold on hills and the regular [brakes] have a hard time stopping the engine on emergency runs." No records or available information indicated that the brakes had been repaired. Earlier in the morning on the day of the accident, the crew took the accident vehicle to the BAR to exchange the 24-foot extension ladder. While there, the driver talked to the master mechanic about the brakes. The driver indicated that the master mechanic checked the air pressure and made several brake applications. He told the driver there were no mechanics in the shop at that time and that if the driver brought the engine back after lunch, someone would adjust the brakes. Shortly after the engine company returned to the fire station, it responded to the call that resulted in the accident.

The fire engine was equipped with an automatic transmission and air-mechanical service brakes. A mechanical examination of the vehicle following the accident indicated that the front axle brakes had no defects and that the push-rod adjustments were within operating limits. An accumulation of rust was observed in both the left and right rear axle brakes. Three of the four rear axle brakeshoes were not making contact with the drum upon application. The lower left and both the upper and lower right brakeshoes were frozen at the anchor pins. The rear axle brake chamber push-rod adjustments were within operating limits on the right side and at the maximum operating limit on the left side. The air chambers were misaligned, and the push rods had severe wear markings on the sides.[7]

If only one brakeshoe out of four makes contact with one of the two drums, the rear axle receives only 25 percent of the brake retarding force that it should. According to Safety Board calculations, which took into account the size of the air chamber (24 square inches on the front axle and 30 square inches on the rear axle) and which assumed an air pressure application of 100 psi, the rear axle brakes were in such poor condition that the apparatus had only 58 percent of its original braking capability. The driver indicated that the wet/dry switch[8] was in the wet position, thus providing only 50 percent of the braking capability of the front axle. (See Fire Department Operating Procedures.) The condition of the rear axle brakes, coupled with the use of the wet/dry switch in the wet position, reduced the original braking capability of the vehicle to about 36 percent.

The accumulated rust around the anchor pins of the WFD apparatus rear axle brakes indicated that they were in need of lubrication. According to the manufacturer's service manual, the brakeshoe pins should be cleaned and lubricated after every 500 hours of use. Based on the hour-meter recorded measurements, the accident vehicle's brakeshoe pins should have been serviced in November 1989. The rust and the frozen condition of the pins indicated that the service was not performed. The Safety Board concludes that the BAR did not adequately maintain the accident vehicle's brakes and did not follow the manufacturer's recommended service guidelines.

The WFD BAR policy was that fire apparatus should receive preventive maintenance after every 150 hours of operation, as measured by the engine hourmeters. A review of the service records for the accident vehicle shows that in September 1988 it received a 150-hour service check although it had been in service for 267 hours since its last check. In November 1989, 468 hours of service later, it received its next check. The Safety Board concludes that the BAR did not adhere to its own policy of servicing a vehicle after every 150 hours of service. The manufacturer's service intervals are intended to ensure that a vehicle performs as designed. Service intervals of 50 hours were recommended by the manufacturer's maintenance manual for the WFD accident vehicle. Most vehicle manufacturers recommend service based on either the amount of use or elapsed time, whichever comes first, because a vehicle can deteriorate even while it is idle. Lubricants can dry out, and rust and corrosion can develop, especially in the case of spare vehicles that may be used infrequently.

Tarrant County, Texas. The Tarrant County, Texas, SVFD had six vehicles (a tanker, two engines, a rescue vehicle, and two grass trucks). The SVFD did not have a formal maintenance program or record system. It did change the oil in its vehicles every 3 or 4 months and did take the vehicles to an outside shop for repair when they were not functioning properly.

The postcrash examination of the fire truck disclosed numerous deficiencies: The left front tire was underinflated; its rated inflation pressure was 95 psi; however, it was only inflated to 50 psi. The right rear dual tires were inflated to 45/44 psi; their rated inflation pressure was 85 psi. Further, the fire truck's steering components were excessively worn. The splined shaft attaching the pitman arm to the steering gear box was worn, and the ball socket joint where the steering arm attached to the drag link was excessively worn.

The fire truck's hydraulic brakes also had several deficiencies. SVFD personnel indicated that before the accident the fire truck would pull to the left during brake applications. An examination of the brakes revealed that the right front drum was rusted and the bottom shoe did not make contact with the drum.

As illustrated by the Waterbury, Connecticut, accident, some fire department maintenance programs do not ensure that fire apparatus are properly maintained. Further, as illustrated by the Tarrant County, Texas, accident some fire departments have no maintenance program. Because fire apparatus often stop suddenly, because they are frequently operated at higher speeds than are conventional vehicles, and because they are operated under hazardous conditions, it is essential that they be properly maintained. Therefore, the Safety Board believes that the U.S. Fire Administration (USFA)[9] of the Federal Emergency Management Agency and the International Association of Fire Chiefs (IAFC) should urge fire departments to establish vehicle maintenance programs that follow all of the manufacturers' service requirements and schedules.

Fire Apparatus Inspection

Connecticut State Inspection. Following the Waterbury accident, a mechanical inspection of the WFD fire apparatus was conducted by the Connecticut Department of Motor Vehicle (CDMV) Commercial Vehicle Safety Unit. The CDMV indicated that because of the condition of the brakes, the vehicle failed the safety criteria used in the commercial vehicle roadside inspection program developed by the Commercial Motor Carrier Safety Assistance Program (MCSAP) of the Federal Highway Administration (FHWA).[10] After the accident, the Waterbury City Maintenance Department examined the brakes of the WFD first-line fleet of 9 engines and 5 ladder trucks; 9 of the 14 (64 percent) were withdrawn from service to be repaired.

At the time of the Waterbury accident, the state did not require the inspection of emergency vehicles. After the accident, the CDMV initiated a voluntary non-fee inspection program for fire service vehicles. From July 1, 1990, to January 3, 1991, the CDMV inspected 559 fire apparatus from 64 cities and towns. During this period, 193, or 35 percent, of the fire apparatus failed the CDMV roadside inspection. Fifty percent of the deficiencies involved brakes, 18 percent involved steering systems, and the remaining deficiencies involved tires, suspension systems, and fuel leaks.

Texas State Inspection. The post-accident examination of the Tarrant County, Texas, fire apparatus disclosed numerous mechanical deficiencies, including underinflated tires, worn steering components, worn brake drums, and a rusted brake drum, all of which indicate inadequate maintenance. The apparatus had been inspected at an inspection station designated by the Texas Department of Public Safety (DPS) and had received an Annual Vehicle Inspection Certificate dated October 5, 1990, which was 19 days before the accident.[11] The requirements of the Texas inspection for this apparatus consisted of 22 elements that included emissions testing; examinations of the lights, horn, windshield wipers, and tires; and a brake test that required the vehicle to stop within 20 feet at a speed of 10 mph. This inspection did not include a visual or mechanical examination of the brakes.

State Vehicle Inspection Programs. The Safety Board conducted a limited survey of the 50 states and the District of Columbia to determine whether the states require vehicle inspections for fire emergency vehicles. Currently, 19 states require fire apparatus to be inspected periodically by the state or by designated fleet inspection stations.[12] (See Table S2-1.)

Table S2-1 States Requiring Periodic State Fire Apparatus Inspections

Arkansas	New York
California	North Carolina
Connecticut[1]	Oklahoma
District of Columbia	Pennsylvania
Hawaii	Rhode Island
Louisiana	South Carolina
Maine	Texas
Massachusetts	Utah
Mississippi	Vermont
New Hampshire	Washington[3]
New Mexico[2]	

[1]Voluntary program.
[2]Voluntary program.
[3]Fire apparatus inspection is required by the State Fire Marshal's Office.

Among the 18 highway safety program standards issued by the Department of Transportation were the periodic motor vehicle inspection (PMVI) standards. The Highway Safety Act of 1966 gave the Secretary of Transportation the authority to withhold highway construction funds if highway safety program standards were not met. By 1975, 31 states and the District of Columbia had periodic inspection programs. However, according to a report[13] by the U.S. General Accounting Office (GAS), the Highway Safety Act of 1976 removed the Secretary's authority to withhold highway construction funds and provided that state safety programs could be approved without meeting all of the 18 program standards. Ten states repealed the program as a result of the 1976 Act.[14]

The GAO report states that a 1989 National Highway Traffic Safety Administration (NHTSA) study[15] and other data show that periodic vehicle inspection programs reduce accident rates. The NHTSA study concluded that periodic inspection programs reduce the number of poorly maintained vehicles on the highways, but that available data do not conclusively demonstrate that inspection programs significantly reduce accident rates. The GAO took exception to this conclusion and reexamined the eight studies quoted in the NHTSA study. The GAO found that

> taken together, the studies discussed in NHTSA's report as well as several other studies identified by GAO indicated that inspection programs reduce accident rates. These studies included estimates of accident reduction ranging from less than 1 percent to as high as 27 percent. The actual magnitude of the reduction is unknown. GAO agrees with NHTSA that all of the studies had limitations either of scope, age, or methodological completeness. Thus, while the large majority of studies point to a safety benefit from inspection programs, they do not provide a reliable basis for judging how much effect the programs have on accident rates.[16]

As a result of the 1990 report, the GAO recommended that

> the Secretary of Transportation direct NHTSA to support state periodic motor vehicle inspection programs through such actions as (1) sponsoring research, (2) assisting inspection states to share their experiences and adapt to changing automotive technology, and (3) promoting public awareness of the need to properly maintain the safety-critical components of vehicles.

After the implementation of a MCSAP random roadside inspection program in Connecticut in 1986, the percentage of vehicles that had to be removed from service because of out-of-service violations declined,[17] indicating an improvement in the general condition of the commercial vehicles on the road. Fire apparatus are equipped with many of the same mechanical features as other trucks and can do fully as much damage in the event of an accident. However, most states do not have an oversight program for these vehicles that is comparable to the MCSAP inspections for heavy trucks. For example, although the Tarrant County, Texas, fire apparatus was inspected shortly before the accident, the vehicle was not taken out of service even though the apparatus was in poor condition. The Texas inspection did not provide the level of scrutiny that an inspection under MCSAP (mechanical) criteria would have provided. Additionally, the voluntary inspections of fire apparatus in Connecticut indicate that many of these vehicles are not maintained properly.

Currently, MCSAP programs do not include fire apparatus, and because of the random nature of MCSAP inspections, the Safety Board believes that it would be inappropriate to include them in MCSAP. However, the Safety Board believes that an improvement in the condition of fire apparatus could be expected if these vehicles were subjected to the level of inspections that commercial vehicles receive through MCSAP. Therefore, the Safety Board believes that states should require the inspection of fire apparatus and that these inspections should be performed by commercial vehicle inspectors in accordance with MCSAP (mechanical) criterion to ensure continuity in the depth and level of the inspections.

FIRE DEPARTMENT OPERATING PROCEDURES

Accident Information

About 6:50 p.m., on June 9, 1990, engine 381, a 1979 Oren pumper-tanker of the Long Green Volunteer Fire Company (LGVFC) in Baltimore County, Maryland, was traveling north on Manor Road responding to an emergency call when the driver lost control of the vehicle while turning at an intersection. The fire apparatus rotated 180 degrees and overturned in a ditch. The driver and four fire fighters received minor to no injuries. All of the fire fighters were restrained by seatbelts. The pavement was wet from a previous rain. The driver stated that as he entered the curve, he was traveling 25 to 30 miles per hour. He took his foot off the gas to slow the truck, and he "counted on the engaged engine retarder[18] to slow him down." He also stated, "The rear end went very fast, slipped around 180 degrees till I hit a ditch and flopped over." He indicated that the engine retarder was always left on and that none of the drivers turned it off.

The driver indicated that he had been driving fire apparatus for 26 years. He had participated in obstacle course driver training sponsored by the Baltimore County Fire Department. The LGVFC chief indicated that the company periodically received driver training from the Baltimore County Fire Department in which participants were taught to leave engine retarders on all the time. It was the LGVFC practice to have engine retarders on at all times. Additionally, the training officer of the Baltimore County Fire Department indicated that its drivers were taught to leave engine retarders on all the time.

Engine Retarders

The Jacobs Manufacturing Company, one of several manufacturers of engine retarders, warns drivers in its "Professional Driver Techniques and Owner's Manual" about the dangers of using retarders when they are driving on slippery or wet roads. The manual states that the driver should not use the retarder until he is sure that his truck is maintaining traction without its use. Then he can use the lower power settings on the retarder. Progressively higher power settings should not be used until it is established that the vehicle is maintaining traction in the lower settings. "If the tractor drive wheels lock or if there is a fishtail motion, immediately turn off the master switch and don't turn the Jake Brake [engine retarder] on until road conditions improve."

In the NHTSA (National Highway Traffic Safety Administration) booklet entitled "A Professional Truck Driver's Guide on the Use of Retarders,"[19] truck drivers are warned to turn engine retarders off when they are driving empty trucks or pulling empty trailers on wet pavement or when they are driving tractors without trailers.

The "Model Driver's Manual for Commercial Vehicle Driver Licensing"[20] also addresses engine retarders and states:

> Some vehicles have "retarders." Retarders help slow a vehicle, reducing the need for using your brakes. They reduce brake wear and give you another way to slow down. There are many types of retarders (exhaust, engine, hydraulic, electric). All retarders can be turned on or off by the driver. On some the retarding power can be adjusted. When turned "on" retarders apply their braking power (to the drive wheels only) whenever you let up on the accelerator pedal all the way.
>
> Caution: When your drive wheels have poor traction, the retarder may cause them to skid. Therefore you should turn the retarder off whenever the road is wet, icy or snow covered.

In 1982 and 1983, the NHTSA sponsored research that was done by the Transportation Research Institute of the University of Michigan.[21] The research explored the influence of retarder torque on directional control on slippery pavements. In summary, the study indicates that drivers of retarder-equipped vehicles should be informed that they may avoid potential control problems by turning off their retarders when they are operating either empty or lightly loaded vehicles on roads that are either icy or slippery. The experimental portion of the research was performed by a test driver who had experience in heavy-truck braking experiments on slippery surfaces. In the experiment, this driver could not recover from the rapid jackknifes that occurred on slippery surfaces when he was turning an empty vehicle while decelerating with the engine retarder.

In 1985 and 1986, the Safety Board investigated accidents in Texas and Colorado[22] in which heavy trucks lost directional control due to the misuse of engine retarders. The drivers of the trucks did not have manufacturers' operating manuals, and the motor carriers had not established operating procedures that were consistent with the manufacturers' warnings about the proper use of engine retarders.

As a result of these investigations, the Safety Board recommended that NHTSA:

> **H-89-38**
>
> Require the installation of a permanently affixed placard in the interior of new truck tractors equipped with an engine retarder to warn against using the retarder on slippery/wet surfaces when the vehicle is empty or lightly loaded. The placard should also warn against using the engine retarder to shift gears in these conditions.

The NHTSA responded that the warnings in the booklet "A Professional Truck Driver's Guide on the Use of Retarders" and in the commercial drivers license (CDL) "Model Driver's Manual" should reach the truck driving population and eliminate the need for placarding. The NHTSA was concerned about "driver-compartment clutter and information overload from an excessive number of lights, buzzers, and warnings." The NHTSA is investigating the "driver overload issue." Safety Recommendation (H-89-38) has been classified as "Open—Acceptable Action."

Also as a result of the Texas and Colorado accidents, the Safety Board issued recommendations to the Professional Truck Drivers Institute of America, Inc., the International Brotherhood of Teamsters, the American Trucking Associations, Inc., the manufacturers of engine retarders, and the Federal Highway Administration recommending that they inform their members of the potential hazards of misusing engine retarders and develop training on the proper use of engine retarders. *(See Appendix D to this supplement.)* However, no recommendations were issued to the fire service community.

Some of the newer fire apparatus are equipped with engine retarders and these vehicles have operating characteristics that are similar to those of heavy commercial trucks. The use of engine retarders on wet pavement can lead to loss of control. As the Baltimore County, Maryland, accident shows, some fire departments have policies that directly conflict with the written warnings issued by the manufacturers of engine retarders. Therefore, the Safety Board believes that the USFA and the IAFC should inform fire departments nationwide of the potential hazards of misusing engine retarders and encourage fire departments to establish operating procedures that are consistent with manufacturers' warnings about the proper use of engine retarders.

Limiting Valves

Following the Waterbury, Connecticut, accident, the front axle limiting valve was found in the "wet or "slippery-road" position. The driver stated that it had been raining on and off on the morning of the accident and that the streets were wet. He had set the valve to the "wet" position earlier that morning before driving the apparatus. It was WFD practice that when the roads were wet, the brake limiting valve was to be switched to the slippery road position.

Hahn "Maintenance-Operating Manual" states that "Putting the lever in the 'slippery road' position reduces pressure on the front brakes to half of that on the rear brakes. The front wheels will have less tendency to slide and steering control is maintained. Keep the lever in the 'dry road' position under all normal operating conditions." The "Model Driver's Manual for Commercial Vehicle Driver Licensing" states:

> Some older vehicles (made before 1975) have a front brake limiting valve and control in the cab. The control is usually marked "normal" and "slippery." When you put the control in the "slippery" position, the limiting valve cuts "normal" air pressure to the front brakes by half. Limiting valves were used to reduce the chance of the front wheels skidding on slippery surfaces. However, they actually reduce the stopping power of the vehicle. Front wheel braking is good under all conditions. Tests have shown front wheel skids from braking are not likely even on ice. Make sure the control is in the "normal" position to have normal stopping power.

According to a published NHTSA report,[23] a two-axle vehicle that weighs 27,300 pounds consistently performs better with the front axle limiting valve in the "dry road" position, even on a wet road surface. "Use of a limiting valve on this [type of] vehicle appears unwise; it degrades performance." This research program was completed in 1985.

Currently, the Safety Board is conducting a nationwide study of heavy-vehicle brake performance that evaluates nationwide data on inspections and accidents involving commercial vehicles. The results of the study will be used as a basis for making more definitive recommendations concerning the use of brake limiting valves on other types of highway vehicles. Many of the older fire service apparatus are equipped with dry road/slippery road brake limiting valve. Because fire apparatus often stop suddenly, because they are frequently operated at higher speeds than are conventional vehicles, and because they are operated under hazardous conditions, the Safety Board concludes that the use of manual brake limiting valves can diminish the apparatus stopping capability and, therefore, their use should be discontinued.

OCCUPANT SEATBELT USE

Accident Information

Catlett, Virginia. About 7:38 p.m. on September 28, 1989, wagon 7 of the Catlett Volunteer Fire Company was struck on its left side by a southbound National Railroad Passenger Corporation (AMTRAK) train. The accident occurred at a private-driveway grade crossing off Virginia Route 28 about 1 mile south of Catlett, Virginia.[24] The cab and chassis of the apparatus rotated counterclockwise 450 degrees during the collision and came to rest facing north about 80 feet southeast of the crossing. Most of the apparatus was destroyed; however, the passenger compartment of the canopy cab remained intact. The unrestrained driver and the other fire fighter seated in the cab were ejected and fatally injured, and two unrestrained fire fighters riding in the rear-facing canopied jumpseat behind the cab were ejected and sustained moderate to severe injuries. A fifth fire fighter riding in the rear-facing jumpseat remained within the apparatus following the collision. He received serious injuries.

Eugene, Oregon. About 6:09 a.m., on January 30, 1990, a Crow Valley Fire Protection District 1989 Pierce pumper fire engine responding to a house fire overturned while traversing a residential driveway which collapsed. The engine-pumper overturned 1.5 times down a 20-foot incline and came to rest on its roof. The apparatus was occupied by three fire fighters, who were restrained by seatbelts. All of the fire fighters remained within the apparatus during the overturn. Following the accident all of the fire fighters were treated for minor injuries and released from the hospital.

Los Angeles, California. On March 1, 1990, engine 91, a Seagrave firetruck of the Los Angeles City Fire Department, left the station house on a nonemergency run (no lights or siren) and was struck broadside at the intersection of Borden Avenue and Polk Street in the

Sylmar section of Los Angeles by an automobile that failed to stop for a red light.

The fire apparatus was hit on the right side behind the rear axle. The police estimated that the automobile's speed was "well in excess of 55 mph." As a result of the collision, the apparatus rotated approximately 90 degrees and overturned onto its roof. The driver and an officer were seated in the forward cab section, and the two fire fighters were seated facing rearward in the jumpseat in the enclosed rear cab section. The firetruck cab remained intact during the crash, and all of the fire fighters were wearing their seatbelts. The fire fighters received only minor injuries. The driver of the automobile was fatally injured.

Gallitzin Township, Pennsylvania. About 2:45 p.m., on May 17, 1990, the Cresson Volunteer Fire Company responded to an emergency call about a motor vehicle accident. As the 1968 Chevrolet fire truck was traveling northbound downhill on state Route 53, the driver lost control of the vehicle. The rear of the vehicle struck and rode up on a guardrail, and the vehicle overturned more than 360 degrees. The vehicle then struck a bridge abutment, traveled over the side of the bridge, and came to rest on its left side in a creek bed. Both occupants were ejected onto the roadway and were fatally injured.

The police report indicated that the occupants were not wearing seatbelts. Following the crash, the State Police Motor Carrier Inspection Division officer inspected the accident vehicle. The only problem noted was that the "female ends of both seatbelts were found tucked under the seat, rendering them unusable." The cab was intact after the accident.

Dallas, Texas. About 1:54 p.m., on August 5, 1990, Dallas Fire Department engine 9, a 1990 Quality fire truck with four occupants was responding to a medical emergency and was traveling south on South Beltline Road. The driver released the accelerator while he was traveling down a hill that curved to the left; the rear of the apparatus began to skid to the right. The apparatus skidded sideways down the road until the right front tires hit the soft dirt shoulder on the left side of the road and the apparatus rolled over and came to rest 30 feet from the road facing north. *(See Figure S2-3.)* It was drizzling rain, and the pavement was wet. The driver and officer in the cab and the two fire fighters in the jumpseat were wearing their seatbelts. Although the damage to the apparatus was extensive, there were no injuries.

National Fire Protection Association Standards

The NFPA is an independent, voluntary-membership, nonprofit organization. More than 200 NFPA committees develop voluntary standards and codes that serve as guidelines for the fire services in all phases of operations. These standards are updated every 3 to 5 years; however, they are not mandatory.

The 1987 NFPA Standard 1500, *Fire Department Occupational Safety and Health Program,* Chapter 4,

Figure S2-3 *Dallas, Texas, department engine 9. (Photograph courtesy of Dallas Fire Department)*

"Vehicles and Equipment," Section 3, Persons Riding on Fire Apparatus, states:

> 4-3.1 All persons riding on fire apparatus shall be seated and secured to the vehicle by seat belts or safety harnesses at any time the vehicle is in motion. Riding on tailsteps or in any other exposed positions shall be specifically prohibited. Standing while riding shall be specifically prohibited.

Fire Apparatus Occupant Seatbelt Use

In the Catlett, Virginia, accident four unrestrained fire fighters were ejected from the apparatus, and two of these fire fighters were fatally injured. Even though the fire apparatus was heavily damaged, the cab section remained intact. In the Gallitzin Township, Pennsylvania, accident, both unrestrained occupants were ejected. However, the apparatus passenger compartment remained intact. The NHTSA Fatal Accident Reporting System (FARS) 1988 data concerning fatal accidents indicate that 17.4 percent of the unrestrained passenger-car occupants were ejected from the vehicle; of those ejected, 73.5 percent were fatally injured. Although there is no similar data concerning occupant ejection as a result of accidents involving fire apparatus, it is clear that ejection from a vehicle during a collision is likely to cause a serious or fatal injury.

In contrast, several accidents in which fire apparatus overturned and the restrained occupants remained within the apparatus and were not injured illustrate the benefits of using seatbelts. In the Los Angeles, California, accident and in the Eugene, Oregon, accident, the vehicles overturned, yet the fire fighters, who had used their seatbelts, received only minor injuries. In the Dallas, Texas, accident, the fire apparatus rolled over and came to rest 30 feet from the road; however, the four fire fighters were uninjured. Accordingly, it is likely that had the occupants of the Catlett, Virginia, and Gallitzin Township, Pennsylvania, accident vehicles been restrained, they might not have been ejected and might have been less severely injured.

NFPA voluntary standard 1500 clearly states that all persons shall be seated and restrained while riding on fire apparatus, and most departments have policies requiring the use of seatbelts. Yet, fire fighters continue to be injured and killed because they are not restrained. Fire apparatus are frequently operated at higher speeds than conventional vehicles and, therefore, are prone to overturn and high-speed accidents. It is essential for fire fighters to wear available seatbelts to prevent ejection and injury. Although there are voluntary standards that encourage seatbelt use, there is no nationwide program to educate the fire-fighting community concerning the benefits of seatbelts. Thus, the Safety Board believes that the USFA in cooperation with the IAFC and the NFPA, should encourage fire departments to establish and enforce mandatory seatbelt policies and to develop programs that promote the use of seatbelts in fire apparatus.

CONCLUSIONS

1. The condition of the rear axle brakes coupled with the use of the wet/dry switch in the wet position reduced the original braking capability of the Waterbury, Connecticut, accident vehicle to about 36 percent.
2. The Waterbury Fire Department Bureau of Auto Repairs did not maintain the accident vehicle's brakes adequately and did not follow the manufacturer's recommended service guidelines.
3. The Waterbury Fire Department Bureau of Auto Repairs did not adhere to its own policy of servicing a vehicle after 150 hours of service.
4. The condition of fire apparatus can be improved if these vehicles are subjected to the level of inspections that commercial vehicles receive through MCSAP.
5. The use of manual brake limiting valves can diminish fire apparatus stopping capability.
6. The use of engine retarders on wet pavement can lead to loss of control.
7. Fire fighters are more likely to avoid ejection and injury if they are restrained.

RECOMMENDATIONS

As a result of this special investigation, the National Transportation Safety Board made the following recommendations:

To the U.S. Fire Administration of the Federal Emergency Management Agency:

- Urge fire departments to establish vehicle maintenance programs that follow all of the manufacturers service requirements and schedules. (Class II, Priority Action) (H-91-3)
- Inform fire departments nationwide of the potential hazards of misusing engine retarders, and encourage fire departments to establish operating procedures that are consistent with manufacturers warnings about the proper use of engine retarders. (Class II, Priority Action) (H-91-4)
- Notify fire departments of the hazards of using fire apparatus manual brake limiting valves, and urge them to discontinue the use of these devices. (Class II, Priority Action) (H-91-5)

- In cooperation with the National Fire Protection Association and the International Association of Fire Chiefs, encourage fire departments to establish and enforce mandatory seatbelt policies and to develop programs that promote the use of seatbelts in fire apparatus. (Class II, Priority Action) (H-91-6)

To the International Association of Fire Chiefs:

- Urge fire departments to establish vehicle maintenance programs that follow all of the manufacturers service requirements and schedules. (Class II, Priority Action) (H-91-7)
- Inform fire departments nationwide of the potential hazards of misusing engine retarders, and encourage fire departments to establish operating procedures that are consistent with manufacturers warnings about the proper use of engine retarders. (Class II, Priority Action) (H-91-8)
- Notify fire departments of the hazards of using fire apparatus manual brake limiting valves, and urge them to discontinue the use of these devices. (Class II, Priority Action) (H-91-9)
- Cooperate with the U.S. Fire Administration and the National Fire Protection Association to encourage fire departments to establish and enforce mandatory seatbelt policies and to develop programs that promote the use of seatbelts in fire apparatus. (Class II, Priority Action) (H-91-10)

To the National Fire Protection Association:

- Cooperate with the U.S. Fire Administration and the International Association of Fire Chiefs to encourage fire departments to establish and enforce mandatory seatbelt policies and to develop programs that promote the use of seatbelts in fire apparatus. (Class II, Priority Action) H-91-11)

To the Governors and legislative bodies of those States without fire apparatus inspection programs:

- Develop and implement a fire-apparatus inspection program that requires periodic inspections performed by commercial vehicle inspectors in accordance with the Federal Highway Administration Motor Carrier Assistance Program vehicle (mechanical) inspection criterion. (Class II, Priority Action) H-91-12)

By the National Transportation Safety Board
James L. Kolstad, Chairman
Susan M. Coughlin, Vice Chairman
Jim Burnett, Member
John K. Lauber, Member
Christopher A. Hart, Member
March 19, 1991

APPENDIX A: ACCIDENT DATA

The Safety Board examined published NFPA accident data from 1980 through 1989 (summarized in Table S2-2). In this 10-year period there were 1191 fire fighter fatalities; 262 fatalities, or 22 percent, occurred in apparatus or motor vehicle accidents. Of the 262, 179 (15 percent of the 1,191 fatalities) occurred in fire department vehicles, and 59 (5 percent of the 1,191 fatalities) occurred in personal vehicles.

Table S2-2 National Fire Protection Association Accident Data, 1980–1989

Year	Total Fire Fighter Fatalities	Career/ Volunteer	Apparatus or Motor Vehicle Accident	Fire Department Vehicle	Personal Vehicle
1980	134	67/67	21 (21%)	19	6
1981	123	64/59	20 (16%)	11	4
1982	117	49/68	23 (19%)	16	2
1983	106	58/48	21 (20%)	15	6
1984	116	47/69	32 (27%)	25	5
1985	119	57/62	23 (19%)	17	5
1986	113	60/53	27 (23%)	24	7
1987	124	52/72	33 (27%)	20	10
1988	129	48/81	33 (26%)	17	9
1989	110	46/64	21 (19%)	10	5
Total	1191		262 (22%)	179 (15%)	59 (5%)

APPENDIX B: WATERBURY, CONNECTICUT, ACCIDENT APPARATUS BRAKE CONDITION

Air Chamber Size	Slack Adjuster	Measured Push Rod Stroke (in.)	Recommended Maximum Stroke Before Readjustment (in.)
Front axle			
Left 24	Manual	$1^1/_8$	$1^3/_4$
Right 24	Manual	1	$1^3/_4$
Rear axle			
Left 30/30	Manual	2	2
Right 30/30	Manual	$1^3/_4$	2

APPENDIX C: INSPECTION REQUIREMENTS FOR FIRE APPARATUS

State	PMVI[a]	Commercial PMVI	Fire Apparatus
Alabama		b	
Alaska			
Arizona			
Arkansas	X	X	X
California		c	
Colorado			
Connecticut			d
Delaware	X		
District of Columbia	X	X	X
Florida		X	
Georgia		X	
Hawaii	X	X	X
Idaho			
Illinois		X	e
Indiana			
Iowa			
Kansas		X	
Kentucky			
Louisiana	X	X	X
Maine	X	X	X
Maryland		X	X
Massachusetts	X	X	X
Michigan		X	
Minnesota		X[f]	
Mississippi	X		X
Missouri	X		X
Montana			
Nebraska			
Nevada			
New Hampshire	X	X	X
New Jersey	X	X	X
New Mexico			X[g]
New York	X	X	X
North Carolina	X		X
North Dakota			
Ohio			
Oklahoma	X	X	X
Oregon			
Pennsylvania	X	X	X
Rhode Island	X	X	X
South Carolina	X		X
South Dakota			
Tennessee			
Texas	X	X	X
Utah	X	X	X
Virginia	X	X	X
Washington		X	d
West Virginia	X	X	e
Wisconsin			
Wyoming			

[a]Periodic motor vehicle inspection.
[b]PMVI for commercial vehicles is currently limited to liquid propane gas (LPG) carriers.
[c]Since 1989 California has required all commercial carriers to be inspected every 90 days.
[d]Voluntary program.
[e]Ambulances are required to be inspected. Fire apparatus are not.
[f]Minnesota started a PWI program for commercial vehicles in April 1991.
[g]Fire apparatus inspection is required by the State Fire Marshal's Office.

APPENDIX D: STATUS OF PREVIOUS RECOMMENDATIONS ABOUT ENGINE RETARDERS

As a result of the Texas and Colorado directional control accidents,* the Safety Board issued the following safety recommendations:

To the Professional Truck Drivers Institute of America, Inc:

- H-89-39. Inform your members of the potential hazards of misusing the engine retarder and urge your accreditation committee to require member schools to include training on the proper use of the engine retarder in their curricula. (Closed—Acceptable Action)

To the International Brotherhood of Teamsters:

- H-89-40. Inform your members of the potential hazards of misusing the engine retarder and ensure that drivers are adequately trained in the proper use of the engine and other types of retarders. (Open—Acceptable Action)
- H-89-41. Urge your members to comply with the advisory placards provided by the engine retarder manufacturers that warn against using the engine retarder on slippery/wet surfaces when the vehicle is empty or lightly loaded or that warn against using the engine retarder to shift gears in these conditions. (Open—Acceptable Action)

To the American Trucking Associations, Inc.:

- H-89-42. Inform your members of the potential hazards of misusing the engine retarder and urge them to formulate written policies for the operation of engine retarders and to ensure drivers are trained in their use. (Closed—Acceptable Action)
- H-89-43. Urge your members to install the advisory placards provided by the engine retarder manufacturers that warn against using the retarder on slippery/wet surfaces when the vehicle is empty or lightly loaded or that warn against using the engine retarder to shift gears in these conditions. (Closed—Acceptable Action)

To the manufacturers of engine retarders:

- H-89-44. Revise existing owner's manuals and placards to warn against the use of the engine retarder on slippery/wet surfaces when the vehicle is empty or lightly loaded, and call special attention to this warning in the owner's manuals for drivers operating a single-driver axle tractor. (Closed—Acceptable Action)

To the Federal Highway Administration:

- H-89-45. Include in the commercial driver's license testing procedures questions regarding the proper operation of engine retarder systems. (Closed—Reconsidered)

*Highway Field Report—"1981 GMC Astro Jackknife and Loss of Control, near Decatur, Texas," August 13, 1985 (NTSB-FTW-85-H-TR38), and Highway Field Report—"1981 Freightliner Jackknife and Overturn, near Mineral Wells, Texas," April 3, 1986 (NTSB-FTW-86-H-TR09).

REFERENCES

1. For the purposes of this report, "fire apparatus" refers to the heavy fire vehicles, such as pumpers/engines, ladder trucks, heavy squad units, 10,000 pounds and over, that transport people, and specialized equipment, such as foam/crash units used at airports.
2. The National Fire Protection Association (NFPA), organized in 1896, is an independent, voluntary membership, nonprofit organization that develops voluntary standards and codes which serve as guidelines for the fire services in all phases of operations.
3. One hundred and seventy-nine fire fighters.
4. See appendix A for further information concerning NFPA accident data.
5. This fire apparatus was a spare vehicle that was in use because the first-line apparatus was being serviced.
6. The parking brake for this fire apparatus was controlled by a push/pull control valve located on the apparatus instrument panel. The Hahn operating manual states: "To set the parking brake on the rear axle chambers, pull out the parking brake control. To release the parking brake, push control in."
7. See appendix B for further information concerning the condition of the brake.
8. Many vehicles use a manual limiting valve (commonly called a dry road/slippery road valve or wet/dry switch) that is controlled by a pneumatic switch in the cab. In the "dry road" position, the valve is a 1:1 valve. in the "slippery road" position, it reduces front brake pressure to 50 percent of control line pressure at all control line pressure levels.
9. The United States Fire Administration maintains offices and conducts programs in the following

areas: fire policy and coordination, fire fighter health and safety, fire data and analysis, and fire prevention and control. The Administration works closely with the Nation's fire service, with fire service organizations, with Federal, State, and local governments, and with the private sector in developing and implementing programs aimed at lowering the level of loss of life and property.

10. North American Uniform Service Criteria, Commercial Vehicle Safety Alliance, February 1990, *Out-of-Service Condition:* When any motor vehicle(s) by reason of its mechanical condition or loading, is determined to be so imminently hazardous as to likely cause an accident or breakdown, or when such condition(s) would likely contribute to loss of control of the vehicle(s) by the driver, said vehicle(s) shall be placed out of service. No motor carrier shall require nor shall any person operate any motor vehicle declared and marked "out-of-service" until all required repairs have been satisfactorily completed.
11. In July 1990, the DPS Motor Vehicle Inspection Unit cited the designated inspection station that had issued the certificate for issuing certificates of inspection without completing the required safety inspections.
12. See appendix C for further information concerning State motor vehicle and commercial vehicle inspection programs.
13. Motor Vehicle Safety, "NHTSA [National Highway Traffic Safety Administration] Should Resume Its Support of State Periodic Inspection Programs," Report to the Chairman, Subcommittee on Oversight and Investigations, House Committee on Energy and Commerce, United States General Accounting Office, (GAO/RCED-90-175), July 1990.
14. Those States that repealed PMVI programs after the 1976 legislation are listed with the dates of start and repeal: Colorado (1937-1981), New Mexico (1953-1977), Georgia (1965-1982), Wyoming (1967-1977), Florida (1968-1981), Idaho (1968-1976), Kentucky (1968-1978), South Dakota (1968-1979), Indiana (1969-1980), Nebraska (1969-1982).
15. "Study of the Effectiveness of State Motor Vehicle Inspection Programs," NHTSA, (Washington, D.C., August 1989).
16. GAO, executive summary, p. 5.
17. In 1986 7j0 percent of the heavy commercial vehicles inspected during CDMV MCSAP random roadside inspections failed or were put out of service because of safety violations; in 1990, 40 percent failed.
18. An engine retarder uses the engine itself to aid in slowing and controlling the vehicle. When activated, the engine retarder alters the operation of the engine's exhaust so that the engine works as a power-absorbing air compressor; however, this provides a retarding action only to the drive axle.
19. DOT HS 806 675, January 1985.
20. U.S. DOT, Federal Highway Administration Publication No. FHWA-MC-89-051, dated January 31, 1989.
21. "Retarders for Heavy Vehicles: Phase III Experimentation and Analysis; Performance, Brake Savings, and Vehicle Stability" (DOT HS 8006 672).
22. Highway Field Report—"1981 GMC Astro Jackknife and Loss of Control, near Decatur, Texas," August 13, 1985 (NTSB-FTW-85-H-TR38), and Highway Field Report—"1981 Freightliner Jackknife and Overturn, near Mineral Wells, Texas," April 3, 1986 (NTSB-FTW-86-H-TR09).
23. U.S. DOT, NHTSA DOT HS 806 738, Interim Report "NHTSA Heavy Duty Brake Research Program, Report No. 1—Stopping Capability of Air Brake Vehicles. Volume 1: Technical Report."
24. See docket HY-514-89 for further information concerning this accident.

SUPPLEMENT 3

Phoenix Fire Department Standard Operating Procedures: Rapid Intervention Crews

Editor's Note: The assembly and deployment of rapid intervention crews can be accomplished in a number of ways. This supplement contains a sample standard operating procedure (SOP) from the Phoenix Fire Department. It provides a template on how to increase the overall level of safety for fire department members operating at emergency incidents.

INTRODUCTION

The Phoenix Fire Department often responds to incidents that present a high risk to fire fighter safety. The SOP presented here identifies the requirements for and the operation of rapid intervention crews (RICs). Another related procedure is lost/trapped fire fighters basic survival. In some departments that are fully staffed, an additional company may be dispatched to enhance the first-due assignments. In other jurisdictions, crews may be assembled as personnel arrive on scene.

What is imperative is that at least one dedicated crew be available for rapid deployment in order to rescue trapped or lost members. The crew must be equipped with the necessary tools, equipment, first-aid supplies, and communication equipment to do their task, with speed and safety as their paramount concerns. The RTC procedure should integrate with procedures that are already in effect, such as the requirement for a back-up rescue team for hazardous materials entry. The objective of an RIC crew is to have a fully equipped rescue team on-site, in a ready state, for immediate rescue of injured or trapped fire fighters or civilians.

REQUIRED USE OF RICS

The SOP shall be implemented at all multiple alarm fires and other incidents where fire department members are subject to hazards that would be immediately dangerous to life and/or health in the event of an equipment failure, sudden change of conditions, or other possible mishaps.

Examples of special hazards include but are not limited to the following:

(a) Offensive fire operations
(b) Hazardous materials
(c) Trench rescue
(d) Confined space rescue
(e) Any other incident having significant risk

DISPATCH AND IMPLEMENTATION

Upon declaration of a working fire, an additional engine company will be dispatched and given the RIC designation. The assigned RIC unit will acknowledge response via radio [e.g., "RIC (unit ID) responding"]. The RIC unit should stage on-scene in a location to maximize their options and await instruction from command. During major operations, RICs will normally be assigned near the command post and the rehab operation. A minimum of one company will be assigned near the command post and the rehab operation. A minimum of one company will be required. Command may assign more than one company if necessary. Operations of a large or more complex nature may call for multiple RIC units to stand by at different entry points. After dispatch of an RIC company, command has the following options for use:

(a) Assign the company to RIC duties at the scene.
(b) Cancel the company en route after the declaration of fire under control *and* after personnel accountability reports (PARs) have been obtained from *all* crews.
(c) Assign the company to other duties, such as heat relief for working crews.
(d) Request another RIC if one is assigned to other duties.

All RIC crew members will assume a ready state, including full protective clothing and SCBA. For other types of incidents, the protective clothing and equipment will be appropriate for the hazards. The RIC team company officer will closely monitor the assigned tactical radio channel at all times.

Furthermore, this officer must maintain an accurate tactical worksheet of the position of all working companies. In some cases, the RIC may need to conduct a recon to maintain awareness of working companies. The team must be able to react immediately to sudden emergency events at the incident site. In all cases, the RIC must have the ability to rapidly deploy. In some situations, protective hoselines may need to be predeployed.

If RIC crew units are needed to respond to a sudden emergency in which the sector officer is incapacitated (physically or emotionally), the rescue team company officer will assume sector responsibilities for the area in which the emergency exists. Additional resources, including additional alarms, will be requested and sent to the rescue area as the emergency dictates.

If not needed as an RIC unit, command may assign this company as a heat relief unit, but not until it is certain that all crews are out of danger and PARs have been obtained. This unit could also take the place of the extra engine dispatched on 2 & 1 assignments when temperatures are above 105 degrees.

HIGH-RISE FIRES

For high-rise fires, RICs will be assigned to standby positions in the resource sector location or other appropriate location(s). A secondary standby location may be in the lobby sector location.

RIC–SCBA RESCUE KITS

Once assigned to RIC standby duties, the assigned company must obtain SCBA rescue kits from any battalion or command vehicle. Each kit should be checked for air supply and tools. Upon a report of a lost or trapped fire fighter, the kit (or more than one kit) must be taken to the rescue area.

RIC–SCBA Rescue Kit Contents. The items to be included in each R.I.C.–SCBA kit are as follows:

4 Flashlights
4 Pack straps
4 Door straps
4 Life lines with deployment bags
1 Bolt cutter (small, 12 in.)
1 Channel lock (multiadjustable pliers, 12 in.)
1 Phillips head screwdriver (6 in.)
1 Straight blade screwdriver (6 in.)
1 Folding knife (3–4-in. blade)
1 Wire cutter (snub-nose pliers with side cutter 7–10-in.)
4 Sprinkler wedges
1 SCBA bottle supply pigtail

COMMITMENT TO RESCUE OF A LOST OR TRAPPED FIRE FIGHTER

Upon report of a lost or trapped fire fighter(s), command should deploy the RIC(s) to the last reported location of the lost/trapped fire fighter(s). The RIC–SCBA kit(s) must be taken. The company officer of the RIC may be assigned a "rescue sector" designation. Appropriate rescue equipment and crews must be quickly assembled and organized.

S U P P L E M E N T 4

NFPA Fire Investigation Reports

Editor's Note: This supplement contains the abstracts of three NFPA Fire Investigation Reports: a carpet store fire in Branford, Connecticut, on November 28, 1996; a warehouse fire in Seattle, Washington, on January 5, 1995; and an auto parts store fire in Chesapeake, Virginia, on March 18, 1996. These three reports contain some common threads that include, but are not limited to, the lack of a personnel accountability system, the lack of or failure to use a formalized incident management system, and communication system problems. These common areas were identified by NFPA's fire investigators as contributing factors to fireground fatalities. NFPA's Occupational Safety Committee has used these reports to emphasize the need for those requirements in a department's occupational safety and health program. Copies of the full reports are available from NFPA Fire Investigations, 1 Batterymarch Park, Quincy, MA 02269-9101.

BRANFORD, CONNECTICUT, CARPET STORE FIRE: ONE FIRE FIGHTER FATALITY

At approximately 4:30 p.m. on Thursday, November 28, 1996, a fire occurred in a Branford, Connecticut, carpet store and warehouse. The fire started in the store's office area, damaged the ceiling assembly, and ignited the building's wood roof trusses. Seven fire fighters were making the initial attack when the roof collapsed. Five of seven fighters were able to find their way out of the building. The sixth fire fighter was unconscious and had to be rescued, and the seventh died before he could escape.

The building was 60 ft (18.3 m) wide and 120 ft (36.5 m) long. It had wood-frame exterior bearing walls in one section and masonry block exterior bearing walls in all other areas. Lightweight wood trusses carried the store's roof over a clear span of 60 ft (18.3 m). The building did not have any fire detection or suppression systems.

The Branford fire fighters responded to a report of smoke coming from the roof of a carpet store and found, upon arrival, light smoke showing near the roof eaves at the front of the building. On the basis of the observed conditions, the fire officers believed that the fire was located somewhere in the showroom area. Six fire fighters advanced two hoselines to the front of the building. Another Branford fire fighter entered the building without the knowledge of the incident commander and the officer in charge of interior operations, bringing the total number of fire fighters in the building to seven.

The fire fighters found fire in a corner of a showroom and attempted to extinguish that fire. At approximately the same time, the incident commander, who was outside of the building, and the interior officer realized that there was fire above the fire fighters. The interior officer ordered every one out of the building and the incident commander radioed the interior crews, also ordering them out. Before the fire fighters could leave the building, the roof collapsed. This was approximately 17 minutes after the fire fighters arrived on the scene.

Four fire fighters escaped out of the front of the building, and the officer and two fire fighters were trapped toward the center of the building. These fire fighters freed themselves from the debris and began spraying the burning rubble with a hoseline. The officer then told the two fire fighters that they would have to move to the rear of the building where two overhead doors were located. The officer and one fire fighter began moving toward the rear of the building and became separated from the other fire fighter.

Before reaching the door, the fire fighter who was with the officer ran out of air and collapsed. Unable to help the fire fighter, the officer continued on, found a door, and left the building. Once outside, the officer could not get assistance from other fire fighters, so he reentered the building. The fire officer found the collapsed fire fighter even though the fire fighter had not turned on his PASS (personal alert safety system) device. The officer dragged the fire fighter out of the building.

Once the incident commander learned that six fire fighters had escaped, he believed that everyone was out because he was not aware that a seventh fire fighter had entered the building. After a brief discussion of the events that had occurred, the officers determined that one fire fighter had, in fact, not escaped. The missing fire fighter was found approximately 20 ft (6 m) from the position where he was last seen by the officer. The cause of the fire fighter's death was listed as smoke inhalation.

On the basis of its investigation and analysis, the NFPA determined that the following factors contributed to the loss of the Branford fire fighter:

(a) The lack of knowledge that the roof of the Branford carpet store was constructed with lightweight wood trusses
(b) The ineffective use of an incident management system and no formal fire fighter accountability system
(c) The absence of a rapid intervention crew (RIC)
(d) The lack of automatic sprinkler protection

SEATTLE, WASHINGTON, WAREHOUSE FIRE: FOUR FIRE FIGHTER FATALITIES

A fire in a Seattle warehouse on January 5, 1995, resulted in the deaths of four members of the Seattle Fire Department. All four died when the floor between the upper and lower levels of the building collapsed. The fire, which was determined to have been set intentionally, began in the building's lower level directly below the area in which fire crews were conducting interior fire operations.

The building in which the fire occurred had been originally constructed in 1909 with a structural support system of heavy timber. Over the years, however, the warehouse was modified a number of times. One of these modifications was a cripple wall, constructed of material estimated to be 2 in. × 4 in. in dimension, that had been installed to support the joists of the floor assembly between the upper and lower levels. Unfortunately, this cripple wall was more susceptible to fire than the building's other structural support mechanisms, and when it failed it caused the floor to fail, creating the opening into which the four fire fighters fell.

As a result of NFPA's on-site investigation, which began the day after the collapse, and subsequent interviews, the following were identified as contributing factors in this incident:

(a) Confusion about the physical layout of the building, as well as the location of crews working in, above, and around the structure
(b) Lack of awareness on the fireground of the location of the fire and the various crews in relation to the fire
(c) Insufficient progress reports transmitted over the fireground frequency
(d) Lack of awareness of the length of time the building had been on fire and the passage of time after fire department notification
(e) Failure to take into account the fact that the building was a known arson target when formulating the fireground strategy
(f) Insufficient information to develop a risk/benefit evaluation of fireground operations

Over the past six years, the Seattle Fire Department has aggressively sought to enhance fire fighter safety by instituting a personnel accountability system that has become the model for many other fire departments around the country and by equipping personnel with protective equipment that meets current standards and portable radios that allow transmission of automatic, coded distress calls to the dispatch center. Despite these precautions, four fire fighters lost their lives. As this incident so tragically illustrates, a great many dangers must still be accounted for during fire-fighting operations.

CHESAPEAKE, VIRGINIA, AUTO PARTS STORE FIRE: TWO FIRE FIGHTER FATALITIES

At approximately 11:30 a.m. on Monday, March 18, 1996, fire fighters in Chesapeake, Virginia, responded to a fire in an auto parts store. No fire was visible from the exterior of the building when the fire fighters arrived. Two fire fighters entered the building and located a small fire at the rear of the store. The fire fighters extinguished the fire and began checking for fire extension. Approximately 20 minutes after their arrival, the roof of the building collapsed and the two fire fighters were trapped inside. Both fire fighters died of burns, with smoke inhalation being a contributory factor.

The building involved was approximately 12 years old. Two of the building's exterior bearing walls were constructed with unprotected steel frames and two were constructed with masonry block. Lightweight wood trusses with a clear span of 50 ft (15.2 m) supported the store's roof. Because the facility was an auto parts store, it contained a wide variety of combustible and noncombustible materials, flammable auto paints (liquid and aerosol), and other flammable and combustible liquids. Most packaging materials and some shelving materials were also combustible.

The fire occurred when a utility worker damaged the electrical service drop conductors on the outside of the store. Electrical arcing inside the store ignited fires that quickly involved the wood trusses supporting the roof and ignited a fire in the area of an electric hot water heater. Though some of the fire was visible to anyone in the occupied area of the building, much of the fire was hidden in the concealed space above the store's ceiling, and the fire was able to spread in that area.

The fire fighters who died in this fire probably did not know that the building was constructed with lightweight wood roof trusses. Approximately seven minutes after they had arrived on the scene, the crew inside the building radioed their battalion chief to report that they had found the fire. They asked for a second crew to come into the building and requested a pike pole. Approximately 13 minutes after this transmission, the roof collapsed, intensifying the fire and trapping the fire fighters inside the building. The trapped fire fighters radioed for assistance but, for an undetermined reason, the incident commander did not understand the transmission. Two other chief officers who were responding to the scene did hear the transmission and relayed the information to the on-scene commander. By the time the on-scene commander realized that fire fighters were possibly trapped inside the building, the fire had become too intense to attempt rescue operations.

On the basis of the NFPA's investigation and analysis of this fire, the following factors contributed significantly to the loss of the two Chesapeake fire fighters:

(a) The presence of lightweight wood roof trusses
(b) Fire officers and fire fighters unaware that the roof of the Chesapeake auto parts store was constructed with lightweight wood trusses
(c) The lack of a fire attack strategy that could minimize the risk to fire fighters while suppressing a fire involving lightweight wood trusses
(d) The lack of automatic sprinklers

SUPPLEMENT 5

Health, Fitness, and Wellness Resource Directory

Editor's Note: The directory of resources in this supplement represents the most up-to-date list available for fire department physicians and health and safety officers who are trying to develop or enhance their occupational safety and health programs. This list, which is in no way inclusive, is provided through the courtesy of the International Association of Fire Fighters (IAFF) and the International Association of Fire Chiefs (IAFC) and is included in this handbook for informational purposes only. All organizations and telephone numbers must be checked before giving them to a person in need.

AIDS/HIV

CDC National AIDS Hotline
1-800-342-2437

Spanish
1-800-344-7432

Service for the Deaf
1-800-243-7889

Project Inform HIV/AIDS Treatment Hotline
1-800-822-7422

Alcohol and Drug Abuse

Al-Anon Family Group Headquarters
1-800-356-9996

Alcohol and Drug Helpline
1-800-821-4357

American Council on Alcoholism
1-800-527-5344

The National Council on Alcoholism and Drug Dependency
1-800-622-2255

National Cocaine Hotline
1-800-262-2463

National Helplines
1-800-435-7111

Alzheimer's Disease

Alzheimer's Association
1-800-272-3900

Alzheimer's Disease Education and Referral Center
1-800-438-4380

Arthritis

Arthritis Foundation Information Line
1-800-283-7800

ADD/ADHD

Attention Deficit Disorder Association
1-800-487-2282

Cancer

American Cancer Society Response Line
1-800-227-2345

Cancer Information Service
1-800-422-6237

Y-ME National Breast Cancer Organization
1-800-221-2141

Child Abuse/Missing Children

Boys Town National Hotline
1-800-448-3000

ChildHelp/IOF Foresters National Child Abuse Hotline
1-800-422-4453

National Center for Missing and Exploited Children Hotline
1-800-843-5678

National Child Safety Council Childwatch
1-800-222-1464

National Clearinghouse on Child Abuse and Neglect Info
1-800-394-3366

National Council on Child Abuse and Family Violence
1-800-222-2000

National Runaway Switchboard
1-800-621-4000

Diabetes

American Diabetes Association
1-800-232-3472

Juvenile Diabetes Foundation Hotline
1-800-223-1138

Disabilities

American Rehabilitation Association
1-800-368-3513

National Center for Youth with Disabilities
1-800-626-2825

National Easter Seal Society
1-800-221-6827

National Information Center for Children and Youth with Disabilities
1-800-695-0285

National Information Clearinghouse for Children Deaf and Blind
1-800-438-9376

Fitness

Aerobics and Fitness Association of America
1-800-233-4886

American College of Sports Medicine
1-800-486-5643

Grief

Grief Recovery Helpline
1-800-445-4808

Headache/Head Injury

Brain Injury Association
1-800-444-6443

National Headache Foundation
1-800-843-2256

Hearing and Speech

American Speech-Language Hearing Association
1-800-638-8255

Dial A Hearing Screening Test
1-800-222-3277

Hear Now
1-800-648-4327

Hearing Aid Helpline
1-800-521-5247

John Tracy Clinic
1-800-522-4582

National Center for Stuttering
1-800-221-2483

Stuttering Foundation of America
1-800-992-9392

The LEAD LINE
1-800-352-8888

Hospital / Hospice Care

Hill-Burton Hospital Free Care
1-800-638-0742

Hospice Education Institute "Hospice Link"
1-800-331-1620

Impotence

The Geddings Osbon Foundation Impotence Resource Center
1-800-433-4215

Learning Disorders

The Orton Dyslexia Society
1-800-222-3123

Liver Diseases

American Liver Foundation Hepatitis / Liver Disease Hotline
1-800-223-0179

Lung Diseases

Asthma and Allergy Foundation of America
1-800-727-8462

Asthma Information Center
1-800-727-5400

Lung Line National Jewish Center for Immunology/Respiratory Medicine
1-800-222-5864

Mental Health

National Clearinghouse on Family Support and Children's Mental Health
1-800-628-1696

National Foundation for Depressive Illness
1-800-248-4344

National Institute of Mental Health Information Line
1-800-421-4211 and 1-800-647-2642

National Mental Health Association
1-800-969-6642

Nutrition

Consumer Nutrition Hotline
1-800-366-1655

Organ Donation

The Living Bank
1-800-528-2971

United Network for Organ Sharing
1-800-243-6667

Paralysis and Spinal Cord Injury

American Paralysis Association
1-800-225-0292

APA Spinal Cord Injury Hotline
1-800-526-3456

Parkinson's Disease

National Parkinson Foundation, Inc.
1-800-327-4545

Pregnancy / Miscarriage

Bradley Method of Natural Childbirth
1-800-423-2397

ASPO/Lamaze
1-800-368-4404

AAO National Problem Pregnancy Hotline
1-800-228-0332

Rare Disorders

American SIDS Institute
1-800-232-7437

Cleft Palate Foundation
1-800-242-5338

Crohn's and Colitis Foundation of America
1-800-932-2423

Cystic Fibrosis Foundation
1-800-344-4823

Epilepsy Foundation of America
1-800-332-1000

Lupus Foundation of America
1-800-558-0121

National Association for Sickle Cell Disease
1-800-421-8453

National Down Syndrome Congress
1-800-232-6372

National Down Syndrome Society
1-800-221-4602

National Multiple Sclerosis Society
1-800-344-4867

National Organization for Rare Disorders
1-800-999-6673

United Cerebral Palsy Association
1-800-872-5827

Safety

U.S. Consumer Product Safety Commission Hotline
1-800-638-2772

U.S. DOT Auto Safety Hotline
1-800-424-9393

National Lead Information Hotline
1-800-532-3394

Sexual Education

Planned Parenthood Federation of America, Inc.
1-800-230-7526

Sexually Transmitted Diseases

Centers for Disease Control National STD Hotline
1-800-227-8922

Stroke

American Heart Association Stroke Connection
1-800-553-6321

National Stroke Association
1-800-787-6537

Urological Disorders

American Association of Kidney Patients
1-800-749-2257

National Kidney Foundation
1-800-622-9010

The Simon Foundation for Continence
1-800-237-4666

Vision

American Council of the Blind
1-800-424-8666

Blind Children's Center
1-800-222-3566

The Lighthouse Center for Education
1-800-334-5497

National Association for Parents of the Visually Impaired
1-800-562-6265

Women

Endometriosis Association
1-800-992-3636

Women's Health America Group PMS Access/Menopause Natural Hormone Hotline
1-800-222-4767

SUPPLEMENT 6

Virginia Beach Fire Department Safety Officer Job Description

Editor's Note: The functional job description of safety officer provided by the Virginia Beach Fire Department is included here as an a example of how one department views the importance of this position. The requisite qualifications, training, and experience are important tools for the safety officer. Individual departments may decide that they wish to include more qualifications within their safety officer's position. The roles, responsibilities, and authority of this position are included in NFPA 1521, Standard for Fire Department Safety Officer, and the National Fire Academy in Emmitsburg, Maryland, provides a course entitled "Incident Safety Officer."

SUMMARY POSITION DESCRIPTION

The fire department safety officer is responsible for the management of the safety and health program. This position requires a significant degree of written and verbal communication skills, an ability to interact with industry professionals and government officials, an understanding of safety management principles and practices, and a knowledge of safety standards and regulations relative to the fire service.

The member is assigned to a 40-hour work week but will be required to respond as needed during off-duty hours. National Fire Protection Association (NFPA) 1521, *Standard for a Fire Department Safety Officer,* the most current edition, shall serve as a basis of information and compliance with this position.

Critical Element: Accident and Injury Analysis

Performance Standards. Reviews all accident and injury reports for accuracy and completeness. Compiles accident and injury statistics on a monthly basis for the district chiefs and the deputy chief plus provides an annual comprehensive report to the fire chief and administrative staff. Provides statistical data for the department, city, state, and national organizations.

Critical Element: Accident and Injury Investigations

Performance Standards. Conducts investigations relating to vehicular accidents, serious personnel injuries, and fatalities. The safety officer may request additional assistance if the situation dictates. This assistance may be from investigation experts from various organizations. Submits a detailed report to the deputy chief as to the cause of the accident or injury, determines preventability, and determines needed changes to department standard operating procedures.

Critical Element: City Safety Liaison

Performance Standards. Interacts with the city safety office to ensure that department safety issues are addressed. Ongoing safety issues include asbestos abatement and monitoring, bloodborne pathogens (infection control), hazard communication, hearing conservation, the Occupational Safety and Health Administration (OSHA) Accident and Injury Reporting.

Acts acts as a liaison with the Division of Risk Management regarding accident reports, workers' compensation claims, and any liability situations impacting the department.

Serves as an ex-officio member of the department's Occupational Health and Safety Committee, which mandates attendance and participation with this committee. Supplies information and provides assistance to the Occupational Safety and Health Committee on an as-needed basis.

Interacts with the city physician on members' health problems relating to communicable disease and to medical fitness for full duty, limited-duty personnel, and any other situation that requires medical evaluation of department members.

Critical Element: Hazard Communication

Performance Standards. Responsible for the department's compliance with 29 *CFR* 1910.1200, *Hazard Communication.* Provides necessary training programs as needed. Continuously evaluates the program regarding compliance, employee knowledge, submission and compilation of material safety data sheets (MSDSs), marking and labeling of containers, and contact with manufacturers if necessary.

Critical Element: Health and Fitness Program

Performance Standards. Supervises the department's health and fitness coordinator, who administers the health maintenance and fitness functions.

Critical Element: Incident Scene Safety

Performance Standards. As required by department policy, the safety officer is a vital part of the incident management process relating to fire fighter safety. The safety officer has the authority to immediately suspend any operation that jeopardizes the safety of department personnel. This authority is granted by the chief of the department.

The incident safety officer shall ensure that the health and welfare of department personnel is maintained through the rehabilitation process at the incident scene, especially during extended emergency operations.

Incident scene safety performance includes risk management, the monitoring of structure/container stability, proper and mandatory use of protective clothing and equipment by department personnel, accountability of personnel, rehabilitation of personnel, the addressing of any safety concerns of the incident commander, and investigation of damage to department equipment or injuries to department personnel at the scene.

Critical Element: Infection Control Officer

Performance Standards. Responsible for department compliance with the 29 *CFR* 1910.1030, *Bloodborne Pathogens,* and with NFPA 1581, *Fire Department Infection Control Program.* The primary responsibilities include training and education, hepatitis B vaccination, personnel protective equipment, record keeping, exposure control procedures and health maintenance, cleaning and decontamination procedures, facility safety issues, and program management.

If a significant or real exposure occurs, the safety officer may serve as department liaison to determine whether medical treatment will be needed. Ensures that proper documentation of health exposure is submitted by affected personnel. Serves as the department's liaison with the Infection Control Total Safety Management (TSM) team. Reviews and makes necessary changes to the department's and city's infection control policy on an annual basis.

Critical Element: Limited-Duty Program

Performance Standards. Responsible for supervising personnel assigned to limited duty due to injuries or illnesses, both occupationally and non-job related. Makes a determination of personnel assignment to limited duty. Ensures limited-duty assignments do not conflict with the attending physician's orders or would cause further aggravation or injury to personnel. Maintains adequate records to ensure compliance with the city policy governing limited-duty assignments. Serves as a liaison with Risk Management, Occupational Health, and any other parties involved with this process on an individual basis.

Critical Element: Program Manager Inspections

Performance Standards. Accountable for the program management of this process that involves the inspection of each shift of each station over an 18-month period. Coordinates the scheduling of these inspections with the shift division chief and the respective battalion chief.

This process involves the inspection of personnel protective clothing and equipment, station facilities, all department vehicles and apparatus assigned to the station, record keeping requirements of the company officer, driving evaluation, hydrant maintenance program, and proficiency testing. A detailed report is submitted to the deputy chief, each division chief, the battalion chief, and the company officer stating the results of the inspection.

Critical Element: Research and Development

Performance Standards. As an essential part of fire fighter safety, the equipment and protective clothing used by department personnel must be state of the art and meet any and all safety requirements. This process includes fire apparatus, protective clothing, protective equipment, and any other equipment that affects the safety of department personnel.

The safety officer supervises testing of trial clothing and equipment and is responsible for accumulating feedback for formal evaluation and recommendation. Develops bid specifications when appropriate for safety-related items. Responsible for evaluating compliance of clothing and equipment to state and national laws and standards. Maintains involvement in local, state, and national organizations, such as the National Fire Protection Association, to ensure that the department remains current with industry trends.

The safety officer is responsible for determining whether present equipment and clothing used by personnel is safe and can remove any clothing and/or equipment from service until replaced or tested.

Critical Element: Risk Management

Performance Standards. Responsible for the development of the department's written risk management program. The risk management program will be reviewed and revised annually. Risk management will be incorporated into all aspects of department operations.

Critical Element: Standard Operating Procedures

Performance Standards. Responsible for the development, implementation, and management of the department's safety standard operating procedures and risk management plan. The standard operating procedures shall be reviewed and updated annually.

Critical Element: Training and Education

Performance Standards. Delivers safety training and education programs to career and volunteer recruits and department personnel during station or company and officer in-service. Mandatory training will include such issues as infection control, hazards communication, hearing conservation, respiratory protection, and any other standards that affect department operations.

Critical Element: Vehicle and Building Maintenance

Performance Standards. Supervises the department's vehicle and building maintenance program on a daily basis, assuring compliance with department and city policy. The intent of the vehicle maintenance program is to sustain an operating fleet utilizing an aggressive preventive maintenance program. The vehicle maintenance program will maintain individual reports on each vehicle operated by the department to track maintenance costs and repairs.

The building maintenance program ensures all department facilities are adequately maintained relating to all applicable health, safety, fire, and building codes.

MINIMUM QUALIFICATIONS

Must possess a high school diploma or GED certificate. Must have graduated from Tidewater Regional Fire Academy (TRFA), having been certified as a state Level II Fire Fighter, driver/operator, and Virginia Emergency Medical Technician/D. Certifications as state Fire Officer I and Instructor III are to be maintained. The Fire Department Officer Candidate School must have been successfully completed.

Classified as fit for duty by Occupational Health as required by the current edition of NFPA 1582, *Standard for Medical Requirements for Fire Fighters*. Must pass the department's annual physical fitness test. Must possess a valid driver's license from the state in which the member resides. Conduct and character must meet the level expected of public safety personnel as outlined in the City of Virginia Beach Code of Ethics. Must have four consecutive years' experience as a paid fire fighter with the fire department.

SUPPLEMENT 7

Risk Management Planning

Editor's Note: The use of a risk management plan or process, both for emergency incident scene operations and other fire department activities, is an important tool in an occupational safety and health program. Planning can include city or town risk management personnel, insurance carriers, and other city or town departments. If the fire department participates in a city/town or county or state plan, it must ensure that a separate plan is developed and used for emergency incident operations. This supplement, which was prepared by Jonathan D. Kipp, outlines the steps in the development of a risk management plan and provides a sample risk management plan provided by the Virginia Beach Fire Department.

Jonathan Kipp is Loss Prevention Manager of Compensation Funds of New Hampshire. He is a principal member of the NFPA Technical Committee on Fire Service Occupational Safety and the NFPA Technical Committee on Fire Service Administrative Risk Management. Mr. Kipp was a contributing author to the first edition of this handbook and co-authored Emergency Incident Risk Management: A Safety and Health Perspective with Captain Murrey Loflin of the Virginia Beach Fire Department, published by Van Nostrand Reinhold (now John Wiley and Sons, Inc.) in 1996.

INTRODUCTION

Effective risk management can save your life. Ineffective risk management can cost you your life. These principles are true regardless of where you are or what you are doing.

It is impossible to live our lives in the absence of risk. Even if we never leave home and have no contact with the outside world, there are risks: starvation, a plan crashing on our house, falling and breaking a leg. When we do leave home, the risks are far more numerous and potentially dangerous: car crashes, violence, disease. The list is endless. It is how we manage these risks that determines our success, survival, and enjoyment of life.

Risk and the management of it are not foreign to us. In fact, they are such an integral part of our lives that we may never have consciously considered them. We've all heard, and probable used, terminology such as "it's not worth the risk," and "risky business." However, do we know what we actually mean when we say those words?

Many people believe that risk management is an administrative exercise. It is not. Rather, it is a decision-making process that each and every one of us uses continually in our everyday lives. It provides a systematic method for making choices. For example, before we step into the shower, most of us check the water temperature. Why? We don't want to risk being burned! We effectively manage that risk by checking the water temperature first. The key is to better understand the process that led us to check the temperature, and then to more deliberately apply it in our work lives as well.

NFPA 1500, *Standard on Fire Department Occupational Safety and Health Program,* first included language pertaining to risk management in the 1992 edition. The committee members believed that emergency service organizations (ESOs) needed guidance on the development of a comprehensive plan under which a safety program would logically fit. Since risk management as a discipline has been used successfully for years by other organizations, it seemed the appropriate vehicle for fire departments as well. In the 1997 edition of NFPA 1500 risk management is included in two chapters.

The standard includes language that requires the organization to develop and implement a plan for effectively managing its risks. Such a plan would be the umbrella under which the various other components of 1500 would fit. The section that addresses risk management for emergency operations is found in Chapter 6 of 1500. In a nutshell, the requirements of 1500:

- Stress the practicality of applying effective risk management techniques
- Define risk and the risk management process
- Highlight the risk management differences between an organization that responds to emergencies and one that doesn't
- Outline the different types of risk management that an emergency services organization can utilize
- Address risk management for emergency incidents, including the components of the risk management toolbox

The Risk Management Process

The effective management of risk is a process, not a static event or a document that resides in a binder. As such, it has various components and definitions associated with it. While the definitions vary, their meaning does not. A hazard is something that increases the chances of an accident occurring. Without a hazard, there is no risk. For example, in the assessment of risk in taking a shower, the obvious risk to be considered is the possibility of being burned by hot water (the hazard). Or, to put it another way, hot water can be hazardous to us. Without the hazard (hot water), there is no risk (of being burned).

Following the same logic, we use a risk management process to address our risk to the hazard. The process is composed of a series of logical steps, similar to a decision tree, that lead us to a course of action that, hopefully, will be as risk-free as possible.

Tolerance for Risk, or Risk Management in Reality

It is important to put risk management into the appropriate context. From the perspective of the organization (fire department), risks are numerous and varied. The organization, under the guidance of its leaders, attempts to put into place appropriate programs, policies, and procedures that will help to protect its resources (people, facilities, apparatus, equipment, etc.). However, each program, policy, and procedure depends on effective execution by an individual—and everybody is different.

On a personal level, each individual has a different tolerance for risk. Some of us will take more risks than others. That is why some people choose skydiving as a hobby, while others are more comfortable collecting stamps. Apply that premise to a group of fire fighters, and the same will be true: Some of the group will be more comfortable in a hazardous, or risky, situation than others. The organization's dilemma is to establish policies and procedures that will apply to everyone when each of us is different. There is no "risk tolerance" test that we can administer to definitively measure somebody's capabilities.

Therefore, it is vitally important that all fire fighters be trained as effectively as possible. Training, in conjunction with the appropriate personal protective equipment, policies, and procedures, will help to direct each fire fighter. Beyond those factors, however, others such as physical condition, judgment, and, ultimately, the individual's tolerance for risk at that very moment will determine what actions are taken.

An additional burden is time, or the lack of it. Decisions that will determine which actions are ultimately taken must be made quickly. Lives depend on it, and there is usually no second chance. Consider, for example, an off-duty fire fighter who is faced with a civilian in trouble—a rafter thrown from a raft and being carried away in a fast-running river. Immediate action is required. What does the fire fighter do? By training and experience, she knows to instantaneously size up the risks involved for both the rescuer and the victim (drowning, hypothermia, trauma for hitting rocks), measures them against the potential benefit (saving the civilian), calculates the odds of success (likelihood of reaching the victim, likelihood of the victim surviving), and decides what to do. Her choices can range from going to the nearest phone and dialing 911 (if she has concluded that the odds are not in her or the victim's favor and the risks greatly outweigh the benefits), to diving in and attempting to make the rescue (if she has concluded that the odds are in her favor and that she has a reasonable chance of reaching the victim, is a strong enough swimmer, has the appropriate rescue skills, and ultimately, feels up to it at that moment). There is no policy of guideline that can dictate which action should be chosen. There are just too many variables, many of them human factors that can only be calculated in the moment.

SUMMARY STEPS TO DEVELOPING A RISK MANAGEMENT PLAN

Step One

(a) Conduct a brief overview of the program concept with the fire department's administrative staff
(b) Review department's annual accident and injury data
(c) Randomly interview staff and personnel
(d) Formulate written report

Step Two

Understand the risk management process

Step Three

(a) Understand pre-emergency risk management

1. Policy and procedures
2. Training and education
3. Response
4. Personnel protective equipment
5. Incident management system
6. Health and safety officer

(b) Understand risk management plan

1. Identification
2. Frequency and severity
3. Priority
4. Control measures
5. Monitoring

Step Four

Provide written conclusions and recommendations to the fire chief, administrative staff, and Occupational Safety and Health Committee

SAMPLE PLAN: VIRGINIA BEACH FIRE DEPARTMENT 1997 RISK MANAGEMENT PLAN

Purpose

The Virginia Beach Fire Department has developed, implemented, and operates a risk management plan. The intent of this plan is as follows:

(a) To effectively serve our customers both internally and externally
(b) To reduce the severity of occupational risks encountered by our members that could have harmful consequences to service delivery

Scope

The Risk Management Plan is intended to comply with the requirements of NFPA 1500, *Standard for a Fire Department Occupational Safety and Health Program,* specifically with the following paragraphs:

- **2-2.1** The fire department shall adopt an official written risk management plan that addresses all fire department policies and procedures.
- **2-2.2** The risk management plan shall cover administration, facilities, training, vehicle operations, protective clothing and equipment, operations at emergency incidents, operations at nonemergency incidents, and other related activities.
- **2-2.3** The risk management plan shall include at least the following components:

  (a) *Risk identification.* Potential problems
  (b) *Risk evaluation.* Likelihood of occurrence of a given problem and severity of its consequences
  (c) *Prioritization of risks.* Prioritize risks based upon analysis factors
  (d) *Risk control techniques.* Solutions for elimination or mitigation of potential problems; implementation of best solution
  (e) *Risk management monitoring.* Evaluation of effectiveness of risk control techniques

Methodology

This plan employs a variety of strategies in order to meet the variety of objectives. The specific strategies are identified as follows:

(a) Records and reports on the frequency and severity of accidents, injuries, and occupational illnesses
(b) Reports received from the city's insurance carriers and workers' compensation
(c) Specific occurrences that identify the need for risk management
(d) National trends and reports that are applicable to the department
(e) Knowledge of the inherent risks that are encountered by fire departments and specific situations that are identified in Virginia Beach
(f) Additional areas identified by department members

Plan Organization

The plan organization utilizes the following tactics to strive toward compliance with the risk management plan:

(a) Identification of the risks that members encounter or may be expected to confront
(b) Identification of nonemergency risks including such functions as training, physical fitness, returning from an emergency incident, routine highway driving, station activities (vehicle maintenance, station maintenance, daily office functions, etc.)

(c) Identification of emergency risks including such fireground operations, EMS, hazardous materials incidents, and special operations; also including the emergency response of fire department vehicles

(d) Evaluation of the identified risks based upon the frequency and severity of these risks

(e) Development of an action plan for addressing each of the risks, in order of priority

(f) Selection of a means of controlling the risks

(g) Provisions for monitoring the effectiveness of the controls implemented

(h) A periodic review (annually) and required modifications to the plan

Responsibilities

This plan establishes a standard of safety for the daily operations of the department. The standard of safety establishes the parameters in which we conduct activities during emergency and nonemergency operations. The intent is for all members to operate within this standard of safety and not deviate from this process. We utilize a variety of control measures to ensure the safety and health of our members. These control measures include but are not limited to training, protective clothing and equipment, incident management, personnel accountability, and standard operating procedures. *(See Table S7-1.)*

The fire chief has responsibility for the implementation and operation of the department's risk management

Table S7-1 Virginia Beach Fire Department Control Measures

Identification	Frequency/Severity	Priority	Summary of Control Measures Ongoing or Action required
Incident scene safety	Medium/high	Medium	1. *A*—Revise and implement department incident management system 2. *A*—Revise current policy on mandatory use of full personal protective equipment including SCBA 3. *A*—Evaluate effectiveness of the department's personnel accountability system and make needed adjustments 4. *A*—Enforcement of department procedures on mandatory use of PPE 5. *A*—Implementation of high-rise incident procedures. 6. *A*—Better utilization of the post-incident analysis process, which includes a written report for all personnel of significant incidents
Compliance with VOSH	Low/high	High	1. *A*—Compliance with 29 *CFR* 1910.134 "Respiratory Protection Program" (2 In/2 Out) 2. *A*—Develop a department compliance program for all mandatory VOSH programs
Health and wellness	Low/high	High	1. *A*—Implement the health and wellness strategic plan to improve the health maintenance, fitness, and wellness 2. *A*—Upgrade health maintenance program to include physical stress tests for all personnel 3. *O*—Continue to monitor participation and success with a physical fitness program
Health exposures	Medium/high	High	1. *A*—Provide annual retraining on infection control procedures 2. *A*—Update the City's Exposure Control Plan and the Infection Control SOP 3. *A*—Implement city and department policy and procedures for an occupational exposure to tuberculosis 4. *A*—Monitor the asbestos exposure control plan for exposures during emergency incident operations 5. *O*—Continue mandatory training and education program for HAZWOPER

(continues)

Table S7-1 Continued

Identification	Frequency/Severity	Priority	Summary of Control Measures Ongoing or Action required
Facility safety	Medium/high	High	1. *A*—Conduct a fire, safety, and health inspection of all fire department facilities 2. *A*—Conduct an inventory of all fire department facilities in conjunction with risk management 3. *A*—Monitor the infection control compliance within all fire department facilities
Vehicle accidents	Medium/high	Medium	1. *A*—Enforcement of state motor vehicle laws and department procedures relating to emergency response 2. *O*—Monitor nonemergency vehicle operations 3. *O*—Monitor individual members' driving records
Tools and equipment	Low/medium	Medium	1. *A*—A review of the departments' 1996 Accident/Loss statistics indicate more accountability of lost/stolen/damaged equipment 2. *A*—Implement loss reduction procedures 3. *O*—Maintain department equipment inventory
Strains and sprains	High/medium	Medium	1. *A*—Based on 1996 incidents, continue to monitor frequency and severity of incidents 2. *O*—Evaluate function areas to determine location and frequency of occurrence
Cuts and bruises	Medium/medium	Medium	1. *A*—Require all supervisors to review use of protective clothing and equipment during emergency and nonemergency operations 2. *O*—Determine if protective clothing and equipment will reduce the number of incidents based on analysis
Safety and security	Medium/medium	Medium	1. *A*—Awareness training on fire training, resource management, and fire administration for all members to be conducted on a company-level basis 2. *A*—Inspection and evaluation of crime prevention by city police at all facilities 3. *A*—Develop written procedures as necessary
Environmental hazards	Medium/high	Medium	1. *O*—Department compliance with 29 *CFR* 1910.120 2. *O*—Written procedures for the hazardous materials team and environment inspectors regarding illegal dumping of hazardous waste and hazardous waste sites
Protective clothing and equipment	High/high	Medium	1. *A*—Enforcement of department's procedures for use of personal protective equipment 2. *O*—Revise department policy and procedures on mandatory usage 3. *A*—Retraining and education of personnel on chronic effects of inhalation of by-products of combustion 4. *A*—Provide monitoring process of carbon monoxide (CO) levels at fire scenes, especially during overhaul
Environmental stress	High/low	Medium	1. *A*—Revise current department policy relating to Emergency Incident Rehabilitation 2. *O*—Evaluate and implement procedures for "weather extremes"
Financial	Low/high	Low	1. *O*—Maintain liaison with risk management, office of budget management, and city attorney

plan. The department's health and safety officer has the responsibility of developing, managing, and annually revising the risk management plan. The health and safety officer has the assignment of making modifications to the risk management plan based upon the prompt demand and severity of need based upon the monitoring of the process.

All members of the department have responsibility for ensuring their health and safety based upon the requirements of the risk management plan and the department's occupational safety and health program.

Monitoring Risks

The risk management program will be monitored on an annual basis. Recommendations and revisions will be made based on the following criteria:

(a) Annual accident and injury data for the preceding year

(b) Significant incidents that have occurred during the past year

(c) Information and suggestions from the Division of Risk Management

(d) Information and suggestions from department staff and personnel

(e) Evaluation of the risk management program by an independent source every three (3) years. Recommendations will be sent to the fire chief, the health and safety officer, and the occupational safety and health committee.

SUPPLEMENT 8

Virginia Beach Fire Department Post-Incident Analysis Report

Editor's Note: In the past, some fire departments have used the process of post-incident critiques as a finger-pointing exercise to identify who did what wrong. It is hoped that a change in terminology from post-incident "critique" to post-incident "analysis" will help identify what went right, how training was used properly, what lessons were learned, and what can be done to improve training/operations in the future—without the finger pointing. Without a planned program or process in place, the exercise is usually frustrating and pointless. This supplement contains an example, provided by the Virginia Beach Fire Department, to assist those planning a defined process for post-incident analysis.

I. DATA

Address: 408 Canberry Court,
Lot 1531, Apartment Complex
Incident Number: 96-636202
Date: December 29, 1996
Unit: Safety 1—Captain Murrey E. Loflin
Time of Alarm: 1818
Time of Dispatch: 1819
Time Responding: 1826
Time of Arrival: 1843
Nature of Incident: Commercial Structure Fire

General Comments

I arrived at the apartment complex at 1843 hours after some difficulty. Vehicle traffic on Route 44 was at a complete standstill both eastbound and westbound. I had to maneuver through stopped traffic responding on Route 44 nearing the First Colonial Road exit. As I arrived at the complex entrance, E3 also arrived. I entered on Chase Point Circle, then to Canberry Court, and parked in front of E14. After donning my protective clothing, I went to Command, which was located further south on Canberry Court.

Listening to the radio traffic and visual observation of the fire from Route 44 and Canberry Court, it was obvious that the one structure on fire was a complete loss, plus an exposure problem of buildings on Side A and Side B/C. The initial alarm units had done a tremendous job of protecting the exposures and attacking the fire with master streams.

II. DESCRIBE ASSIGNMENTS GIVEN/ ACTIONS TAKEN IN CHRONOLOGICAL ORDER

A. Assignment Given by Division Chief M. R. Mathias

As I arrived at Command, I met face to face with District Chief M. R. Mathias. He advised me of the situation and wanted a complete walk around of the structure. I gave Battalion 1, Battalion Chief Hundley, my passport and prepared to conduct a complete walk around of the building.

I walked to Ladder 8 and talked briefly with MFF D. E. Ford, the operator of L8. The two members in the bucket were operating both of the ladder pipes on the main body of fire. I directed a fire fighter from E12 to move the $1^3/_4$-in. handline he was operating from Side

A to Side D. This was to extinguish fire on the second floor that was not accessible from L8. As I continued my walk around of the building, Engine 3 was located on the corner of Side B/C. They were protecting a building located on Side B of the fire building. There were crews from Engine 11 and Engine 14 operating handlines on Side B.

After this initial walk-around, my first concern was that the electrical service had not been secured. I tried to contact Command using emergency traffic in order to relay this information. I never got a response. I finally walked to Command and requested that Virginia Power respond. For the next 30 to 45 minutes, the fire was contained by master streams.

B. Assignment Given by Division Chief M. R. Mathias

I provided Command with a very brief diagram of the building that was involved. The master streams had knocked the majority of the fire down, and Command wanted to deploy crews with handlines to extinguish the remaining fire. Due to the amount of damage, it was questionable whether to allow crews in certain areas of the building. Ladder 11 was assigned to secure the power to the building which was located on Sides A and C.

Once the master streams were secured, crews were organized to enter the building. Due to a problem with freelancing, I notified Command and ordered the operation to be *halted*. The operation was reorganized and crews were deployed under the direction of Sectors. Crews extinguished a large amount of fire, but the fire started to burn on the third floor. The crews were pulled out of the building, and Ladder 8 was placed in service again. This process continued numerous times until the fire was completely extinguished.

C. Assignment Given by Division Chief M. R. Mathias

I worked with the Virginia Power personnel on scene to ensure that the power to the building was properly secured. This required Virginia Power personnel to enter various aboveground transformers in order to accomplish this task. Personnel from Ladder 11 had gone into the two electrical rooms prior to this and secured the power to the building.

Once the majority of fire was extinguished, I was asked to determine the possibility of deploying personnel on the upper floors of the structure. I went to the third floor of the building, where the fire was determined to have originated, with Investigator Boggs. Due to the collapse of the third and second floors, I made the decision not to allow any personnel into the structure for overhaul or any other type of operation.

III. OBSTACLES ENCOUNTERED/PROBLEMS NEEDING TO BE CORRECTED

- I tried to contact Command by requesting "emergency traffic" concerning the issue of securing the utilities but was not acknowledged. There was at times an excessive amount of radio traffic on the tactical channel. I tried to contact Command several times, but never received a response. Several times Operations answered, but I work directly for the incident commander, who in this case was District Chief M. R. Mathias. I found it difficult at times to have Operations and Command side by side.

  I strongly feel, based on problems encountered in other jurisdictions (i.e., Pittsburgh, Seattle, Chesapeake), that we need to develop a communications policy for the department. This would address emergency traffic and other information in the event of an emergency.
- Officers and fire fighters need to be more aware when master streams are operational, especially if they are using handlines in the same vicinity. One fire fighter was hit in the face by a stream from L8 and his glasses were broken. It should be one or the other, but not both.
- One of the issues relating to the accountability system, which I discussed with Chief Mathias at the incident, is that we need to explore the possibility of providing the officers in charge of sectors or divisions the accountability tags for their particular operation. Rather than all the tags being held at Command, the tags would go to the division officers and they would be responsible for them.
- Personnel from the training division will not be allowed on scene unless in full protective clothing. Live video is important, but their safety is more important.
- If Support 9 is needed, this request will come through Command, not EMS 5. We have to account for all personnel on scene, and this issue is starting to get out of hand.
- Though the rehab sector worked well, I feel that it was too close to Command. The noise, distractions, accountability are issues that I am concerned with. In a situation such as this, rehab needs to be established in a remote area not far from Command where personnel can rest and be treated.

- Pre-incident planning is a very effective risk management tool for emergency operations. As was discovered at this incident, the only item that E8 had was a site plan. It was at least two hours into the incident when Command was able to procure a copy of a diagram of the apartments and the numbering system. I think we need to give strong consideration to changing this process to include an apartment complex as a target hazard.
- As we experienced at the fire at Carper Housing in April, accessibility was an issue. One of the recommendations to come out of that PIA was to place a portable monitor on the tele-squirts. It would have been valuable to have a monitor to place on the ground between the fire building and the exposure on Side B/C.

IV. WHAT WORKED WELL

- This is the first time that I have completely stopped a fireground operation due to what I perceived as a safety problem. I contacted Chief Mathias and we met face to face to resolve the issue. Chief Mathias then instituted an operational plan to ensure the accountability of all members.
- The initial risk assessment by the first alarm assignments was perfect—to protect exposures and control the fire in the fire building. This was an excellent decision from the start, which reduced the risk to personnel on scene and set the tone for the remainder of the incident.
- The incident action plan was very effective. Chief Mathias instituted a plans officer, Battalion Chief Mauch, who proved to be a valuable asset to the operations of this incident.
- The accountability process worked once it was set up by Command. We need to ensure that the accountability process is established once Command is established by the first officer.
- One relatively minor injury occurred during this incident. Captain Hicks received a neck/back injury from a falling ceiling. He was transported to VBGH, treated, and released. He returned to duty the next shift. MFF R. L. Glover's glasses were broken when he was hit in the face with a master stream from L8.
- The rehab process was very effective in providing treatment and care for all personnel who were cycled through this process.

V. SUMMARY

The department was very fortunate regarding the time of day the fire occurred, the temperature, and the initial size-up made by the first arriving officers. This was a very effective operation considering the amount of fire that was encountered. I truly commend all personnel who were assigned to the first alarm.

SUPPLEMENT 9

Virginia Beach Fire Department Incident Checklists

Editor's Note: During emergency incident operations, the scene may become confusing, complicated, and fast moving. The following examples, provided by the Virginia Beach Fire Department, are checklists for the incident safety officer, fireground, EMS operations, hazardous materials, and special operations. Each incident scene presents a different set of challenges to the incident safety officer, who may rely on someone with specific technical expertise to provide assistance.

INCIDENT SAFETY OFFICER CHECKLIST

- Appropriate protective clothing and equipment for incident scene
- Checklist incorporated into the MPAS
- Face-to-face with the incident commander upon arrival
- Receive and understand the incident commander's incident action plan
- Develop and implement an incident safety plan
- Appropriate use of full protective clothing and equipment by all members
- Risk assessment/risk benefit analysis
  - Risk a lot to save a lot
  - Risk a little to save a little
  - Risk nothing to save nothing
- Personnel accountability system
- Rapid intervention crews
- Safety zones/collapse zones/hazardous areas
- Rehab/basic life support and transport capabilities
- Additional safety officer(s) required/operational safety officer
- Notes/comments
- PIA issues
- Positive issues

FIREGROUND CHECKLIST

- Protective clothing and equipment
  - Turnout gear
  - SCBA and facepiece
  - PASS on
- Fire conditions
  - Increasing
  - Decreasing
- Structural conditions/building construction indicators
- Incident safety plan—components
- Freelancing
- Operations
  - Offensive
  - Defensive
- Risk management forecasting
  - Roof operations
  - Entrance/egress
  - Utilities secured
  - Monitor air quality—overhaul
  - Rehab/welfare
  - Issues not covered

EMS INCIDENT CHECKLIST

- Risk management
- Scene safety/security
  - Law enforcement needed
  - Law enforcement on scene
- Protective hoseline(s)
- Infection control
  - Exposure control
  - PPE
  - Decon
- Use of an incident management system
- Traffic/highway safety
- Utilities secured
- Freelancing
- Appropriate level/use of protective clothing and equipment
- Rehab/basic life support and transport capabilities
- Critical incident stress management
- Landing zone (LZ) safety
- Issues not covered

HAZARDOUS MATERIALS SAFETY CHECKLIST

- Risk management
- Product identification and health hazards
- Components of the incident safety plan
- Risk assessment/risk benefit analysis
- Rapid intervention crews
- Adequate resources
  - Personnel
  - Specialized equipment
  - Knowledge—OSHA compliant program
- Appropriate protective equipment and clothing
- Rehab/medical evaluation
- Stability
  - Container
  - Trailer
  - Tank Car
  - Other
- Safety zones/evacuation
- Advanced life support and transport capabilities
- Complacency
- Extended operations
  - Food
  - Drink
  - Rest
  - Other
- Issues not covered

SPECIAL OPERATIONS SAFETY CHECKLIST

- Risk management
- All members briefed/understand incident action plan
- Components of the incident safety plan
  - Written documentation
  - Means of emergency egress
  - Map or diagram of defined safety zones
- Adequate resources
  - Personnel
  - Specialized equipment
  - Knowledge—OSHA compliant program
- Safety zones/collapse zones/hazardous zones
  - Crowd control/nonessential personnel removed
  - Shoring/trenching
- Protective clothing and equipment
  - Helmet/eyewear/gloves/boots/hearing protection
  - PASS
  - Weather concerns
- Building construction and type
- Secure utilities/hazardous materials
- Complacency
- Rehab/advanced life support and transport capabilities
- Complacency
- Extended operations
  - Food
  - Drink
  - Rest
  - Other
- Issues not covered—be specific

SUPPLEMENT 10

Incident Action Planning Process

Editor's Note: The incident action plan provides a sign-off for multiagency, multijurisdictional buy-in on how the scene will be managed, who will provide what resources, and under whose command the operation will be managed. The development of strategic goals for the operational period, usually 12 hours, and who will be doing what tactical objectives are also outlined in the plan. This plan may also include tactical benchmarks used to identify when certain tasks are accomplished in support of the overall strategic goals. This supplement provides an overview of the process and discusses various ICS forms, which are shown in Supplement 13.

The Incident Command System emphasizes orderly and systematic planning. The central tool for planning during a response to a major emergency is the incident action plan. The incident action plan is prepared by the planning section, with input from the appropriate sections and units of the incident management team. It should be written at the outset and revised continually throughout the response.

Incidents vary in their kind, complexity, size, and requirements for detailed and written plans. In an initial response for an incident that is readily controlled, a written plan is usually not necessary. Larger, more complex incidents will require an incident action plan to coordinate activities. The level of detail required in an incident action plan will vary according to size and complexity of the response. The incident commander may direct that a written incident action plan be developed for any incident.

A planning process has been developed as part of the Incident Command System to facilitate the development of an incident action plan in an orderly and systematic manner. The following explains the planning process required to develop an incident action plan. Following the planning steps will allow for the development of an incident action plan in a minimum amount of time.

It is important to remember that the incident management process is occurring on two tracks: those actions needed to manage the *current operational period*, and the planning tasks required to prepare for *the next operational period*.

GENERAL RESPONSIBILITIES

Command

- Provide general incident objectives and strategy
- Provide direction or overall management and strategy
- Ensure incident safety
- Approve the completed incident action plan by signature

Planning Section Chief

- Conduct the planning meeting
- Coordinate preparation of the incident action plan

Operations Section Chief

- Determine tactics to achieve command objectives
- Determine resource requirements
- Determine division boundaries
- Determine division/group work assignments
- Conduct operations shift briefing

Logistics Section Chief

- Establish/confirm the procedure for off-incident resource ordering
- Ensure that resource ordering procedures are communicated to appropriate agency dispatch centers
- Ensure that the logistics section can support the incident action plan
- Complete assigned portions of the written incident action plan

Finance Section Chief

- Provide cost assessment of incident objectives
- Ensure that the incident action plan is within the fiscal limits established by the incident commander

THE PLANNING CYCLE

The incident action planning cycle involves four major phases:

1. Set incident objectives and strategy
2. Prepare for the planning meeting
3. Conduct the planning meeting
4. Conduct the operations shift briefing

Phase 1: Set Incident Objectives and Strategy

Phase I is the responsibility of the incident commander. The incident objectives and strategy are not limited to a single operational period, but should consider the total incident situation.

The incident commander identifies the general strategy to be used to achieve the incident objectives and states major policy, legal, or fiscal constraints in accomplishing the objectives. The incident commander should also identify appropriate contingency considerations.

Setting or re-affirming goals and objectives at the beginning of each operational period is top priority of the incident commander and should observe the following guidelines:

(a) Objectives must be clearly stated and measurable, so that the incident management team can determine how much was accomplished during the current operational period.
(b) Objectives must be attainable, given the resources available during the operational period.
(c) Objectives must be broad and flexible enough so that the operations section chief can achieve them in the best tactical way possible.

Before finalizing the objectives, a draft should be discussed with the operations section chief. The operations section chief should understand the objectives and confirm that they are achievable and realistic.

After discussion, the draft objectives are documented on the incident objectives form, ICS 202 *(see Supplement 13, Form S13-2)*, and delivered to the command and general staff so that they will know what the strategy for the next operational period will be and can prepare for the planning meeting.

Phase 2: Prepare for Planning Meeting

Command Meeting. If the incident is being managed under a unified command, the incident commanders should meet prior to the tactics meeting to agree on a unified incident strategy and general objectives. Usually, only the incident commanders attend the command meeting, and they complete the following tasks as appropriate:

- Set jurisdiction or agency priorities
- Set jurisdiction or agency limitations, concerns, and restrictions
- Develop a collective set of incident objectives
- Establish and agree on acceptable priorities
- Adopt an overall strategy or strategies to achieve objectives
- Agree on basic organizational structure
- Designate the best qualified and acceptable operations section chief
- Agree on general staff personnel designations and planning, logistical, and financial arrangements and procedures
- Agree on the resource ordering process to be followed
- Agree on cost-sharing procedures
- Agree on informational matters
- Designate one IC to act as the unified command spokesperson

Tactics Meeting. The tactics meeting is facilitated by the planning section chief and allows command, operations, and planning an opportunity to fit tactics to objectives prior to the planning meeting. While strategy and tactics are sometimes revised as part of the planning meeting process, completing some of this work at the tactics meeting will facilitate an efficient planning meeting. If safety of tactical operations is of concern, the safety officer should be included in the tactics meeting.

The incident commander and the operations section chief discuss and agree on strategy, and the operations section chief details tactical assignments to ensure that those strategic goals will be met, including identification of the operations organizational assignments to the division or group level. The operations section chief defines geographic boundaries for divisions and branches; these boundaries will be plotted on the incident map for the planning meeting. Command and operations also determine the operational period for which the plan will be developed.

The planning section chief provides alternatives and contingency plans and describes their feasibility. Command and operations select appropriate contingency plans.

The results of this discussion are documented on the operational planning worksheet, ICS 215 *(see Supplement 13, Form S13-9)*, by the planning section.

Phase 3: Planning Meeting

Prior to the Meeting

- Planning should notify participants of time and place of meeting. In order to facilitate an orderly and brief exchange of information, only key personnel should attend the planning meeting.
- Planning should ensure that planning maps, forms, and resource and situation status displays are available and up to date.
- Operations should confirm the progress toward achieving objectives, the adequacy of resources, and the condition of personnel.
- Logistics should check on the status of outstanding resource orders and evaluate the adequacy of communications and medical support.
- Finance should complete cost reports and any cost/benefit analyses that have been assigned.

At the Meeting

- The planning section chief is responsible for conducting the planning meeting and ensuring that the flow of information is brief, complete, and to the point. Most of the groundwork for the plan should have been completed by all parties prior to the meeting.
- The meeting should proceed following the planning meeting agenda outlined in Table S13-1 and discussed in the following subsections.

Step 1, Give briefing on situation and resource status. The planning section chief and/or the resource and situation unit leaders provide a briefing on the situation as it currently exists. Information for this briefing may come from any or all of the following sources:

- Initial response IC
- Incident briefing form, ICS 201
- EOC staff briefing form
- Field observations
- Operations section
- Resource and situation reports

Table S13-1 Planning Meeting Agenda

Task	Primary Responsibility
Give briefing on situation/resource status	PSC
Set incident objectives and strategy	IC
Plot control lines and division boundaries	OPS
Specify tactics for each division or group	OPS
Specify resources needed by division or group	OPS/PSC
Specify facilities and reporting locations	OPS/PSC/LSC
Develop resource and personnel order	LSC
Consider communications/medical/traffic plan requirements	PSC/LSC
Consider safety issues	SO
Provide financial update	FSC
Consider interagency liaison issues	LO
Consider information issues	PIO
Finalize/approve/implement plan	IC/All

The information should include:

- Status of current tactical assignments
- Resource condition
- Resource shortages
- Major problems
- Projections that may impact the next operational period (weather changes, etc.)

Step 2, Set incident objectives and strategy. The incident commander confirms or modifies the objectives and strategy circulated in draft.

Step 3, Plot control lines and division boundaries. The operations section chief discusses the physical parameters of the incident, including traffic control points, hot and cold zones, and evacuation areas. Where appropriate, these will correspond to division assignments and be posted to the operational planning worksheet, ICS 215 (Form S13-9 in Supplement 13). Boundaries will also be plotted on the incident map.

Step 4, Specify tactics for each division or group. Using the operational planning worksheet, the operations section chief discusses the tactical assignment for each division and group. This should include specific, achievable tactical assignments and alternative or contingency plans. Divisions should be clearly tied to geographic reference points.

Step 5, Specify resources needed by division or group. The operations section chief, in cooperation with the planning section chief, specifies the resources needed for each division and group to achieve its tactical assignment. Planning will confirm whether or not the resource is assigned to the incident and available for the next shift.

Step 6, Specify facilities and reporting locations. Key facilities, staging areas, and important geographic locations such as drop-off points, safe zones, and congregation points are identified and placed on the map.

Step 7, Develop resource and personnel order. The difference between the resources needed and available in step 5 becomes the resource and personnel order for the next operational period. The logistics section chief compiles these orders and facilitates the procurement process with the supply unit.

Step 8, Consider communications, medical, and traffic plan requirements. The incident management team assesses the adequacy of communications, medical, and transportation/traffic support. If these requirements are deemed to be inadequate, additional plans should be developed and resource orders placed to ensure that the incident action plan can be supported when implemented.

Step 9, Consider safety issues. The safety officer discusses any accidents or injuries and recommends actions to avoid future mishaps (the safety officer may also be involved in step 4—assisting in identifying the safest tactical alternatives). The safety officer will develop a written safety message that will become part of the written incident action plan.

Step 10, Provide financial update. The finance section chief will provide a "cost to date" estimate for the incident, along with any special cost/benefit analyses that have been requested. In addition, the finance section chief may report on compensation and claims issues, such as the status of pending action against the organization, or follow up actions on accidents or injuries.

Step 11, Consider interagency liaison issues. The liaison officer will discuss issues related to cooperating and assisting agencies, including concerns of their management, restrictions on use, and so forth. This may include requests for release, management issues, and other concerns that may impact how external resources are used in the upcoming shift. The liaison officer may also have information about additional resources available through outside agencies.

Step 12, Information issues. The public information officer will provide an overview of press coverage to date. In addition, information staff may have information on the general perception of the media and the public toward the organization that may impact incident strategy and tactics. They may also need to coordinate interviews, visits to the field or the command post, or press conferences.

Step 13, Finalize, approve, and implement action plan. Information shared in the planning meeting is documented on the ICS incident action planning forms, ICS 202–206 *(see Supplement 13, Forms S13-2 through S13–6).* The planning section procures the IC's signature of approval, and the plan is duplicated for hand-off to the incident management team for implementation.

Phase 4: Operations Shift Briefing

The operations shift briefing is the meeting at which the supervisors of the operations section are briefed on their tactical assignments for the operational period. Facilitated by the operations section chief, the briefing is attended by the incident commander, the planning and logistics section chiefs, the safety officer, and other members of the command and general staff, as needed. The operations shift briefing may be conducted according to the following agenda:

1. Situation update
2. Review of plan
3. Discussion of logistical support details (e.g., transportation, communication, medical, food)
4. Review of safety message
5. Contingency planning

The review of plan in step 2 may include last-minute "pencil" changes to the plan and will include a discussion of each division or group assignment sheet, including potential contingency plans. Each division or group supervisor will have an opportunity to ask questions to clarify his or her assignment.

Some planning section staff have adapted the division/group assignment sheet, ICS 204 *(see Supplement 13, Form S13-4),* to document contingency plans. The form is copied in a different color than the rest of the incident action plan, so that it is clear that the contingency plan is not in current use but so it is readily available to operations resources in the event it must be implemented.

DAILY FLOW OF EVENTS

The general flow of events and timing for the planning cycle on an incident operating with a 12-hour operational period are shown in Figure S10.1. Times are approximate. The incident briefing form *(see Supplement 13, Form S13-1),* which is used by the initial incident commander, provides tools to prepare the following:

- A rough drawing of the structure/area
- A summary of the strategic goals and tactical objectives
- An organizational chart for tracking assignments
- A resource summary sheet

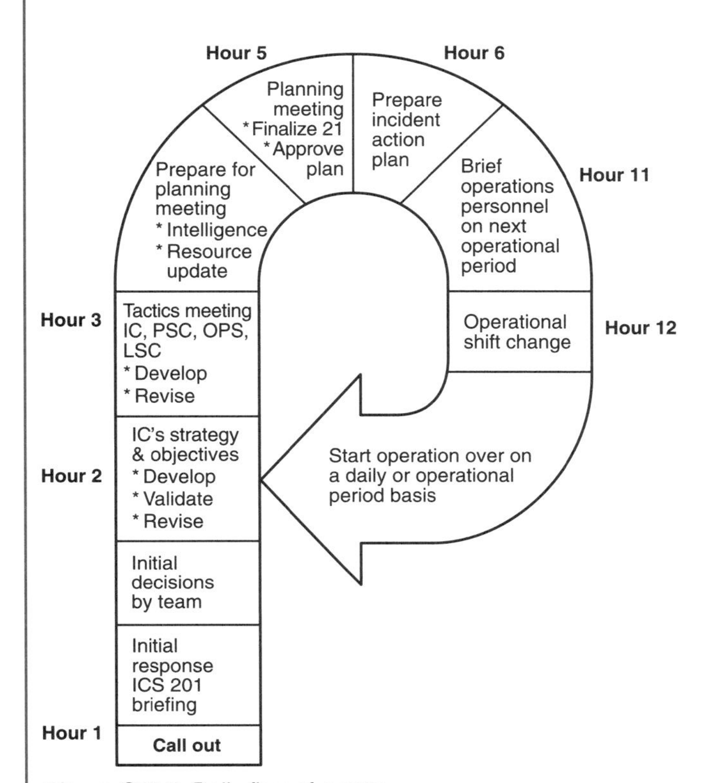

Figure S10.1 *Daily flow of events.*

In some departments or organizations the incident briefing and other forms may be filled out by someone assigned to the incident commander, such as an aide or a technician.

In other departments these forms may be called tactical worksheets and may be specific to certain types of incidents. See the EMS medical worksheet (Form S13-10) and the tactical worksheet (Form S13-11) in Supplement 13. These forms were provided by the Phoenix Fire Department.

As additional resources arrive on the scene and command is transferred, the initial incident commander uses these forms to describe what actions were taken, what resources are on-scene or en route, and what or who has filled assignments within the Incident Command System.

Once command is transferred, the incident commander begins with the incident objectives form *(see Supplement 13, Form S13-2)* and uses the other forms given in Supplement 13 as part of the written incident action plan objectives. The additional forms become part of the action planning process and are included as part of the incident documentation. This incident action plan should be updated as needed and always updated as part of each operational period.

The incident commander may have information similiar to that covered on these forms on one sheet—a mental checklist. Many departments refer to these forms as tactical worksheets, and they are designed for specific types of incidents, including hazardous materials and EMS, as well as fire suppression.

SUPPLEMENT 11

Communication Planning in the Incident Management System

Editor's Note: Communication planning becomes critical during multiagency, multijurisdictional operations. Knowing who is communicating on which frequency or channel provides for clearer understanding of orders given at the incident. With the advent of increased communication capabilities (cellular phones, fax transmissions, trunked radio systems), the following written plan is a valuable tool for use at the command post.

As discussed in the commentary to paragraph 2-2.2 of NFPA 1561, communications planning includes the following activities.

ATTEND PLANNING MEETING

The communications unit leader can provide specific information regarding communications capability that will have an impact on the development of the incident action plan. The communications unit leader's attendance at the initial briefing and the incident planning meetings is beneficial. It gives the unit leader specific knowledge of overall incident management strategy as well as the specific incident action plan for the next operational period. Such knowledge will assist in decision making regarding the number of frequencies needed, location of repeaters, determination of coverage patterns, potential distribution points for personal portable radios, cellular phones, and so forth.

OBTAIN DIVISION/GROUP ASSIGNMENT LISTS (ICS 204)

The division/group assignments are discussed at the planning meeting and formalized on the ICS 204 forms by the resource unit in the planning section. The 204 form indicates the number of personnel and resources assigned to the division or group and the supervisory contacts. This information indicates the number of communications resources that must be assigned to the division or group. The form also has a section to list specific communications assignments for the division or group. Filling out this portion of the form (or providing the information to the resource unit so that they can fill out the form) is the responsibility of the communications unit.

DETERMINE RADIO, PHONE, AND CELLULAR PHONE REQUIREMENTS

Using the ICS 204 form and the overall incident organization, determine the command, tactical, and support nets that will be needed.

- *Command*—Command and general staff, branch directors, division/group supervisors, and air operations personnel are assigned one channel and other required communications equipment.
- *Tactical*—Assignments are made to divisions or groups, with the most hazardous tactical operation receiving first priority. A separate tactical talk group for each division or group is provided, if possible. The minimum should be a separate tactical talk group for each branch. Tactical resources of one agency should be placed within the same division, group, or branch whenever possible to avoid problems of frequency incompatibility.

- *Support*—The division or group level in operations and other section personnel request resources and exchange status information. Additional support needs may also include "off-incident" contacts such as shelters, county and state emergency operations centers (EOCs), and major mutual aid providers. Support links may include amateur radio and cellular phone links if public safety nets are at a premium.

ESTABLISH REQUIRED RADIO NETS (COMMUNICATION PLAN—ICS 205)

List all frequencies and talk groups available to the incident. Establish talk group/frequency functional assignments, considering the numbers and types of radios needed and the number of nets required. Use the following guidelines:

- Command and support nets that tie the incident line organizations with command, general staff, and the EOC may require repeaters. Use only repeated frequencies for these purposes.
- If only one repeated frequency is available, it should be designated as command. Support requests from the line may be sent over the command net, or it may be necessary to establish cellular phone links to provide support services.
- Normally, operations personnel should be required to monitor no more than the command net and their assigned tactical talk group at any time. If the radios lack a scanning capability, these should be on separate radios.
- There is no requirement for routine monitoring of the support net by operations personnel.
- Depending on the geographic size of the incident, tactical frequencies for divisions may be simplex. Tactical frequencies for groups may need to be repeated.
- Assign a net to each division or group, addressing the needs of the most hazardous tactical operation first. If more than one division or group must share a net, consider short- vs. long-term communications needs (e.g., an evacuation group will ordinarily be on the air less time than the perimeter divisions), traffic load, and divisions or groups in the same branch in making assignments. Ensure that all volunteer, contract, and mutual aid resources are included in the plan.
- After all designated organizational units have been covered, determine the total number of radios any organizational unit will require.
- To assist in determining the potential communications load on a specific net, the total number of users may be classed in two categories, passive (i.e. those who will normally only be monitoring the frequency) and active (i.e., those who will be active transmitters on the channel).
- Document communication assignments on the communication plan—ICS 205.

PREPARE COMMUNICATIONS PORTION OF THE DIVISION/GROUP ASSIGNMENT LISTS (ICS 204)

The information described on the ICS 205 form is posted to the individual operational units on the division or group assignment lists according to the time lines established by the planning section. These forms become part of the written incident action plan.

MONITOR AND MAINTAIN THE SYSTEM

The communications unit leader should continue to monitor the system for overloaded frequencies or talk groups, operational units that have been disbanded or reassigned, marginal simplex channels, and so forth. The communications center and the planning meeting will continue to be valuable sources of information on the adequacy of the communications system.

SUPPLEMENT 12

NFPA Forms, Worksheets, and Checklists

Editor's Note: This supplement contains full-size, reproducible copies of the forms that are included in the Fire Service Occupational Safety and Health series of codes and standards that appear in this handbook. The forms are included in this supplement to provide users with a template for achieving compliance with the standards. Users may change or alter the forms to fit the needs of their own departments.

Form S12-1 Virginia Beach Fire Department Facilities Safety Checklist (NFPA 1500, Appendix A; NFPA 1521, Appendix B)

Form S12-2 Truckee Meadows (Reno, NV) Fire District Station Inspection Form (NFPA 1500, Appendix A; NFPA 1521, Appendix B)

Form S12-3 Fire Department Occupational Safety and Health Program Worksheet (NFPA 1500, Appendix B)

Form S12-4 Fire Department Infectious Exposure Form (NFPA 1581, Figure A-2-6.4)

Form S12-5 Physical Exam Summary (NFPA 1582, Appendix E-1)

Form S12-6 Medical Examination (NFPA 1582, Appendix E-2)

Virginia Beach Fire Department — Facilities Safety Checklist

This checklist will provide direction for company officers to conduct inspections of their particular facilities on a monthly basis. The information referenced here comes from various resource materials.

I. General

____ The required Virginia Occupational Safety and Health workplace poster shall be displayed in the station, as required, where all employees are likely to see it.

____ Emergency instructions and telephone numbers shall be available for the general public in the event of an emergency and fire personnel are out of quarters.

II. Housekeeping

____ All rooms, offices, hallways, storage rooms, and the apparatus floor shall be kept clean and orderly and in a sanitary condition.

____ All hallways and/or passageways shall be free from any type of protruding objects such as nails, splinters, and holes.

____ All waste containers shall be emptied regularly.

____ Waste containers shall be provided in the kitchen and/or eating areas. These containers shall have tight lids.

____ All areas of the station shall be adequately illuminated.

____ Stairways shall be in good condition with standard railings provided for every flight having four or more risers.

____ Portable ladders shall be adequate for their purpose, in good condition, and have secure footing.

____ Fixed ladders shall be equipped with side rails, cages, or special climbing devices.

____ Smoking shall not be permitted in designated no-smoking areas.

____ Containers of all cleaning agents shall be carefully labeled per the 1910.1200 standard of VOSH standards.

____ First-aid supplies shall be available and clearly identified as to location.

____ Shower curtains should provide adequate protection to prevent floors from becoming excessively wet and slippery.

____ Cooking appliances and eating utensils should be kept clean and in good working order.

III. Exits

____ All exits shall be visible and unobstructed.

____ All exits shall be marked with a readily visible sign that is illuminated.

____ Doors that might be mistaken for exits shall be marked "Not an Exit."

____ Exits and exit signs shall be free of decorations, draperies, and/or furnishings.

____ Primary exit routes shall be obvious, marked, and free of obstructions.

____ Exits should be wide enough for easy access.

IV. Walking and Working Surfaces

____ Floors shall be kept as clean and dry as possible.

____ Adequate lighting shall be provided in all working areas.

____ Fire fighters' routes to slide poles or to apparatus shall be completely free of projections, tripping hazards, loose objects, or other impediments.

____ Beds shall be located as to result in minimum interference during turnout of fire fighters.

____ Handrails shall be of sufficient strength and proper design for all stairways and floor openings.

____ All slide pole floor openings shall be provided with safety enclosures.

____ A safety mat shall be positioned at the bottom of the slide pole.

____ The slide pole shall be regularly inspected and maintained.

V. Apparatus Floor and Maintenance Areas

____ Ladders, pike poles, and other items projecting from the apparatus shall be clearly marked with bright colored flags, stripes, or other identification to warn against "head-bump" accidents.

____ Apparatus overhead doors shall be maintained in a safe, operating condition.

____ Apparatus doors shall have adequate space for proper clearance for vehicles.

____ Maintenance pits shall be adequately covered, sufficiently lighted, and ventilated.

____ Pit boundaries shall be clearly marked.

____ The pit floor shall be kept clean and as dry as possible.

____ Fire fighters shall use adequate eye protection when working with grinders, drills, saws, welding equipment, and other tools likely to present an eye hazard.

____ Eye protection shall be worn by personnel when working under vehicles.

Form 12-1 **NFPA (1 of 2)**

Virginia Beach Fire Department — Facilities Safety Checklist

____ In relation to the previous question, is eye protection provided, is it in good condition, and is it used?

____ Work rests on grinders shall be adjusted to within 1/8 in. (0.32 cm) to the grinding wheel.

____ Grinders and grinding wheels shall be adequately guarded. The safety guard shall cover the spindle end, nut, and the flange projections.

____ All power tools shall be provided with proper guarding for electrical, cutting, and moving parts.

____ Maintenance hand tools shall be safely stored when not being used. They shall be inspected periodically and maintained to assure their safe condition.

____ Unsafe conditions to check are as follows:

- ____ The tools shall be clean.
- ____ The handles/grips shall not be broken.
- ____ There shall be no worn, defective points/parts on the tool.
- ____ There shall be no parts missing.

____ Pulleys and belts shall be properly guarded.

____ Chain drives and sprockets shall be guarded.

____ Air cleaning nozzles shall not emit more than 30 psi deadened pressure. This information will be stamped on the nozzle.

____ A spotter shall be used when vehicles are backed up, especially as a vehicle is driven over a pit.

VI. Fire Prevention and Protection

____ Portable fire extinguishers shall be maintained in a fully operable condition and kept in designated places when not in use. They shall be inspected on a monthly basis.

____ Fire extinguishers shall be of the proper type for the expected hazards.

____ The fire extinguisher shall have a durable tag securely attached to show the maintenance or recharge date. Also, the initials or signature of the person who performed the inspection shall be on the tag.

____ The fire alarm system shall be tested on a quarterly basis, if the station is so equipped.

____ If the station is so equipped, the sprinkler system shall be serviced by a qualified person.

____ The minimum amount of clearance, 18 in. (45.7 cm), shall be maintained below the sprinkler heads.

____ Smoke detectors, which are in stations not equipped with a fire alarm system, shall be tested the first Tuesday of each month.

VII. Hazardous Materials

____ Cylinders of compressed gases shall be stored in an upright position away from combustible materials.

____ Flammable and combustible materials shall be stored in tanks or closed containers per NFPA 30, *Flammable and Combustible Liquids Code.*

____ Safety containers with self-closing lids shall be used for the storage of flammable liquids and soiled, oily rags.

____ Gasoline and diesel pumps shall be checked on a weekly basis for proper working order and the condition of the nozzles and hoses.

VIII. Electrical Wiring, Fixtures, and Controls

____ Electrical cords shall be strung so that they do not hang on pipes, nail hooks, and so forth.

____ Conduit shall be attached to all supports and tightly connected to junction and outlet boxes.

____ All electrical cords shall be checked for fraying.

____ All equipment shall be securely mounted to the surface on which it sits.

____ Flexible cords and cables shall not be used as a substitute for fixed wiring.

____ All extension cords shall be properly grounded and approved.

____ All electrical tools, whether department owned or personal property, shall be properly protected for damaged power cords, plugs, worn switches, defective ground circuits, or other faults that could render them unsafe for use.

____ Electrical switches and circuit breakers shall be marked to show their purpose.

IX. Other

____ Portable heaters used in stations shall be placed out of travel routes and away from combustibles, and if turned over, they shall turn themselves off.

____ Any situations that warrant a concern shall be brought to the attention of the health and safety officer.

X. Comments/Explanations

____

____

____

____

____

NFPA (2 of 2)

Form S12-1 *Continued*

Truckee Meadows (Reno, NV) Fire District — Station Inspection Form

Station ______________________ Date __________ Shift ______________________

Inspected by ______________________ Officer responsible for corrections ______________________

Answer all questions with yes or no. Explain any no answers. Comment on the bottom of the page.

General Work Environment

____ Are all work sites clean and orderly?

____ Are all work surfaces kept dry or are appropriate means taken to assure the surfaces are slip-resistant?

____ Are all combustibles stored properly?

____ Are all bathroom facilities clean and sanitary?

____ Is the kitchen clean and sanitary?

____ Is the day room clean?

____ Are the sleeping quarters clean?

____ Are there proper labels on all containers?

____ Are the apparatus room and shop area clean?

____ Is the outside of the station clean and cared for?

____ Are station log and all computer reports (INFERS, Training) up to date and correct?

Comments:

____

____

____

____

____

Environmental Controls

____ Are all electrical fixtures working?

____ Is the furnace working properly?

____ Are the furnace filters clean?

____ Are there any combustibles around the furnace or hot water heater?

____ Is the hood over the range clean?

____ Is the apparatus room exhaust system in use and working properly?

____ Is the air-conditioning or evaporative cooler clean and working properly?

____ Are all station exhaust fans working?

____ Are floor drains clean and draining properly?

____ Are all fire extinguishers up to date?

____ Are smoke detectors working?

____ Are material safety data sheets up to date?

____ Are extension cords used as permanent wiring?

____ Do all personnel have uniforms that meet NFPA 1975, *Standard on Station/Work Uniforms for Fire Fighters?*

____ Are station CO detectors in place and working properly?

Comments:

____

____

____

____

Apparatus

Apparatus Number ______________________

____ Are all apparatus tires safe?

____ Is there any broken or defective glass in any apparatus window?

____ Are all lights on apparatus working (i.e., red lights, working lights, headlights, taillights, marker lights, and so forth)?

____ Is apparatus clean?

____ Is all equipment on apparatus and working properly?

____ Are all apparatus checks and paperwork up to date and filled out properly? (SCBA check-off sheets)

____ Is apparatus ready to respond? (ask captain)

____ Is medical equipment clean and inspected?

____ Are all seat belts in place and working?

____ Are all safety gates in place and working?

____ Are all intercom headsets in place and working?

____ Are hand-held radios in place and working?

____ Is mobile radio working?

____ Are map books on apparatus and up to date?

____ Are building surveys on apparatus and up to date?

Comments:

____

____

____

____

NFPA (1 of 1)

Form S12-2

Form S12-3

NFPA 1500 Fire Department Occupational Safety and Health Program Worksheet

Fire Department: ______________________ Date: ______________

Person(s) Completing Worksheet

Name: ______________ Title: ______________ Name: ______________ Title: ______________

Name: ______________ Title: ______________ Name: ______________ Title: ______________

Standard Content	New in 1997 Ed.	Compliance	Partial Compliance	Compliance with Administrative Action	Expected Compliance Date	Compliance with Fiscal Action	Estimated $$	Targeted Compliance Date	Remarks or Modifications
Chapter 1 Administration									
1-4 Equivalency									
1-4.1 Equivalent levels of qualifications									
1-4.2 Training, education, competency, safety									
Chapter 2 Organization									
2-1 Fire Dept. Organizational Statement									
2-1.1 Written statement or policy									
2-1.2 Operational response criteria									
2-1.3 Statement available for inspection									
2-2 Risk Management Plan									
2-2.1 Written risk management plan									
2-2.2 Risk management plan coverage									
2-2.3 Risk management plan components									
2-3 Policy									
2-3.1 Written fire department occupational safety and health policy									
2-3.2 Occupational safety and health program audit									
2-4 Roles and Responsibilities									
2-4.1 Fire department responsibility									
2-4.1.1 Comply with laws									
2-4.1.2 Fire department rules, regulations, and SOPs									

NFPA (1 of 20)

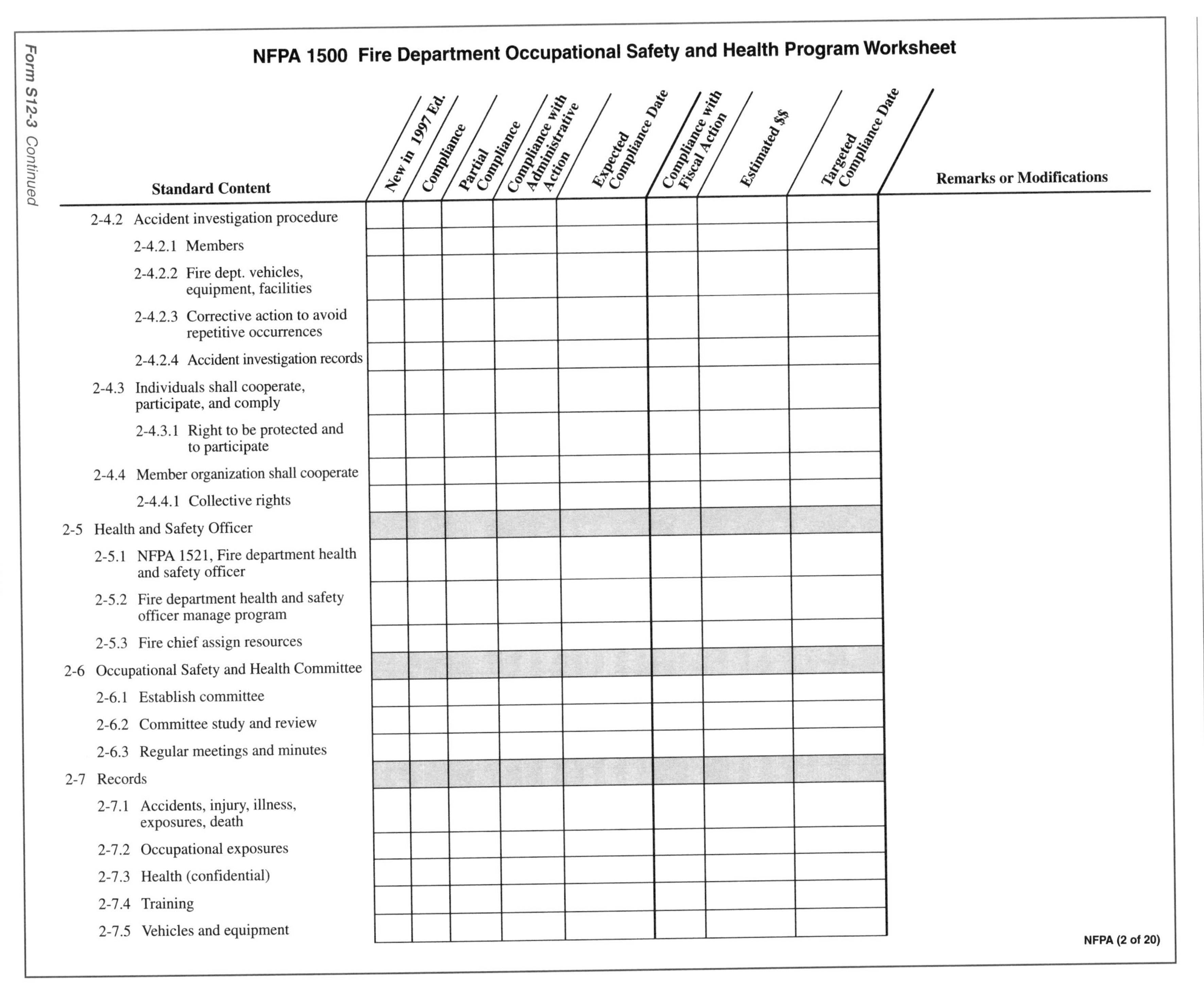

NFPA 1500 Fire Department Occupational Safety and Health Program Worksheet

Standard Content	New in 1997 Ed.	Compliance	Partial Compliance	Compliance with Administrative Action	Expected Compliance Date	Compliance with Fiscal Action	Estimated $$	Targeted Compliance Date	Remarks or Modifications
2-4.2 Accident investigation procedure									
2-4.2.1 Members									
2-4.2.2 Fire dept. vehicles, equipment, facilities									
2-4.2.3 Corrective action to avoid repetitive occurrences									
2-4.2.4 Accident investigation records									
2-4.3 Individuals shall cooperate, participate, and comply									
2-4.3.1 Right to be protected and to participate									
2-4.4 Member organization shall cooperate									
2-4.4.1 Collective rights									
2-5 Health and Safety Officer									
2-5.1 NFPA 1521, Fire department health and safety officer									
2-5.2 Fire department health and safety officer manage program									
2-5.3 Fire chief assign resources									
2-6 Occupational Safety and Health Committee									
2-6.1 Establish committee									
2-6.2 Committee study and review									
2-6.3 Regular meetings and minutes									
2-7 Records									
2-7.1 Accidents, injury, illness, exposures, death									
2-7.2 Occupational exposures									
2-7.3 Health (confidential)									
2-7.4 Training									
2-7.5 Vehicles and equipment									

NFPA (2 of 20)

Form S12-3 *Continued*

NFPA 1500 Fire Department Occupational Safety and Health Program Worksheet

Standard Content	New in 1997 Ed.	Compliance	Partial Compliance	Compliance with Administrative Action	Expected Compliance Date	Compliance with Fiscal Action	Estimated $$	Targeted Compliance Date	Remarks or Modifications
Chapter 3 Training and Education									
3-1 General Requirements									
3-1.1 Safety and health training									
3-1.2 Training on NFPA 1500									
3-1.2.1 Equivalent levels of training permitted	✓								
3-1.3 Training for duties and functions									
3-1.4 Training for every member									
3-1.5 Qualified persons instruct									
3-1.6 NFPA 1041, Instructor I									
3-1.7 Safe exit from emergency operations									
3-1.8 SOPs—anticipated emergency scene operations									
3-1.9 Training exercises									
3-1.10 Incident management system									
3-2 Training Requirements									
3-2.1 NFPA 1001, Fire Fighter I									
3-2.2 NFPA 1403, Live fire training									
3-2.3 NFPA 1002, Driver/operator									
3-2.4 NFPA 1003, Airport fire fighter									
3-2.5 NFPA 1021, Fire officer									
3-2.6 NFPA 1051, Wildland fire fighting									
3-2.7 AHJ emergency medical services	✓								
3-2.8 NFPA 1581, Infectious disease control	✓								
3-2.9 NFPA 472, Hazardous materials responders, all members trained to at least first responder operations level									
3-2.10 NFPA 1405, Responding to marine vessel fires from land-based companies	✓								

NFPA (3 of 20)

Form S12-3 Continued

Form S12-3 Continued

NFPA 1500 Fire Department Occupational Safety and Health Program Worksheet

Standard Content	New in 1997 Ed.	Compliance	Partial Compliance	Compliance with Administrative Action	Expected Compliance Date	Compliance with Fiscal Action	Estimated $$	Targeted Compliance Date	Remarks or Modifications
3-2.11 Minimum training for emergency operations									
3-2.11.1 All members aware of flammability and thermal stability of clothing	✓								
3-2.12 Members qualified and trained to use respiratory protection	✓								
3-2.13 Officers responsible for special training	✓								
3-2.14 NFPA 1406, Training for outside fires	✓								
3-2.15 Structural fire-fighting duties additionally									
3-2.16 Hazardous smoke-generating devices prohibited									
3-3 Frequency									
3-3.1 Training not less than twice a year									
3-3.2 Procedure, technology, or new hazard training									
3-3.3 Monthly training									
3-3.4 Structural fire fighting 10 monthly sessions, 24 hours annually									
3-3.5 Primary assigned—24 hours annually									
3-3.6 Occasional assigned—9 hours annually									
3-4 Special Operations									
3-4.1 Specific and advanced training									
3-4.2 SOPs—special operations									
3-4.3 NFPA 472, Hazardous materials responders									

NFPA (4 of 20)

NFPA 1500 Fire Department Occupational Safety and Health Program Worksheet

Standard Content	New in 1997 Ed.	Compliance	Partial Compliance	Compliance with Administrative Action	Expected Compliance Date	Compliance with Fiscal Action	Estimated $$	Targeted Compliance Date	Remarks or Modifications
Chapter 4 Vehicles, Equipment, and Drivers									
4-1 Fire Department Vehicles									
4-1.1 Safety and health are primary concerns									
4-1.2 NFPA 1901, Automotive fire apparatus									
4-1.3 NFPA 1906, Wildland fire apparatus									
4-1.4 Secure tools, equipment, and SCBA									
4-2 Drivers/Operators of Fire Department Apparatus									
4-2.1 Successful completion of approved driver training									
4-2.2 Valid driver's license									
4-2.3 Driver and officer are responsible									
4-2.4 All persons secured									
4-2.5 Nonemergency travel, obey all laws									
4-2.6 SOPs nonemergency and emergency travel									
4-2.7 Emergency travel—bring fire department vehicles to a complete stop									
4-2.7.1 Proceed only when safe									
4-2.8 Unguarded and guarded railroad track(s)									
4-2.9 SOPs—engine, transmission, and driveline retarders									
4-2.10 SOPs—manual brake limiting valves									
4-3 Persons Riding in Fire Apparatus									
4-3.1 Tailboards and standing prohibited									
4-3.1.1 Secured to vehicle while performing emergency medical care									
4-3.1.2 Hose loading operations									
4-3.1.3 Tiller training									

NFPA (5 of 20)

Form S12-3 Continued

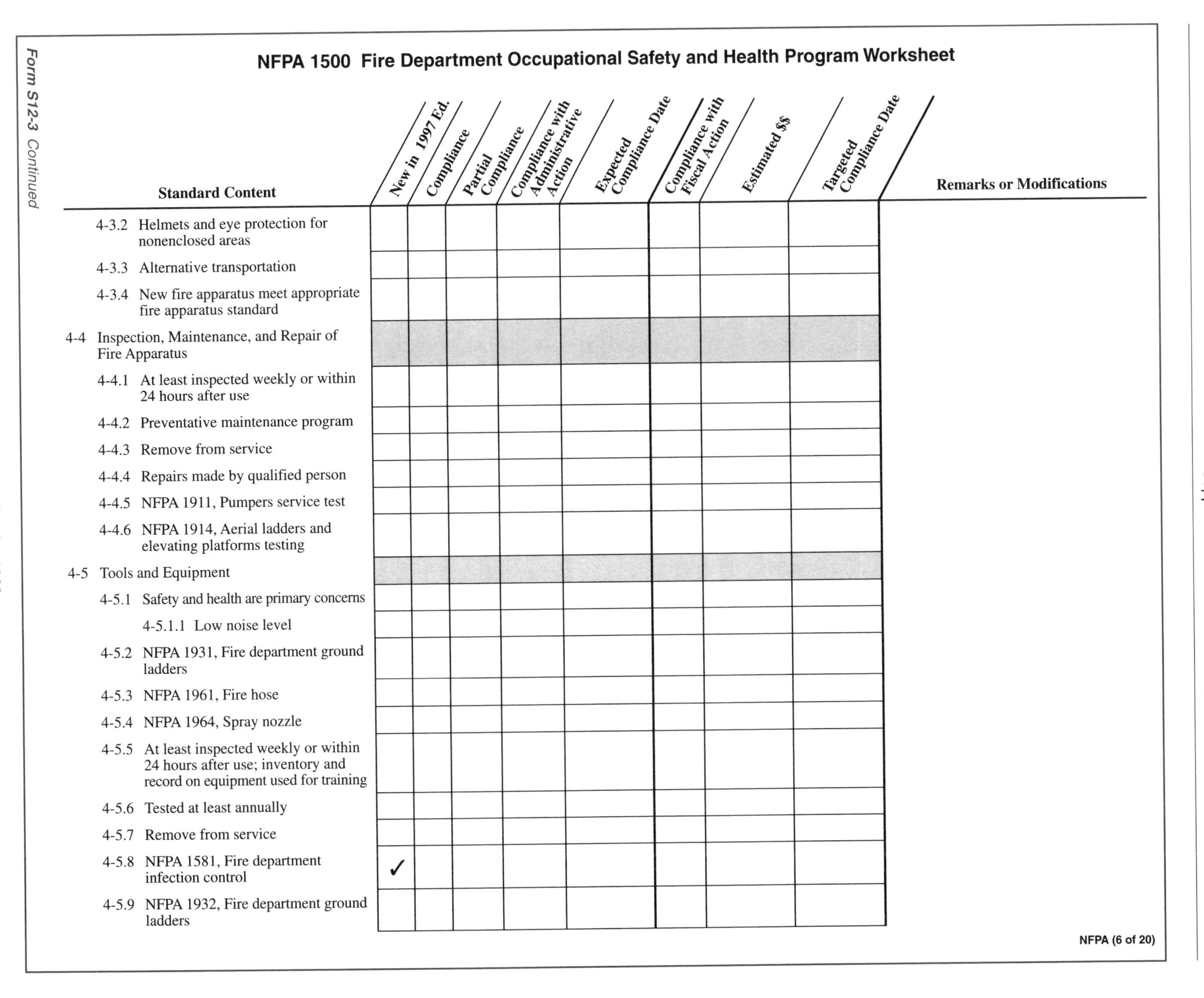

NFPA 1500 Fire Department Occupational Safety and Health Program Worksheet

Standard Content	New in 1997 Ed.	Compliance	Partial Compliance	Compliance with Administrative Action	Expected Compliance Date	Compliance with Fiscal Action	Estimated $$	Targeted Compliance Date	Remarks or Modifications
4-3.2 Helmets and eye protection for nonenclosed areas									
4-3.3 Alternative transportation									
4-3.4 New fire apparatus meet appropriate fire apparatus standard									
4-4 Inspection, Maintenance, and Repair of Fire Apparatus									
4-4.1 At least inspected weekly or within 24 hours after use									
4-4.2 Preventative maintenance program									
4-4.3 Remove from service									
4-4.4 Repairs made by qualified person									
4-4.5 NFPA 1911, Pumpers service test									
4-4.6 NFPA 1914, Aerial ladders and elevating platforms testing									
4-5 Tools and Equipment									
4-5.1 Safety and health are primary concerns									
4-5.1.1 Low noise level									
4-5.2 NFPA 1931, Fire department ground ladders									
4-5.3 NFPA 1961, Fire hose									
4-5.4 NFPA 1964, Spray nozzle									
4-5.5 At least inspected weekly or within 24 hours after use; inventory and record on equipment used for training									
4-5.6 Tested at least annually									
4-5.7 Remove from service									
4-5.8 NFPA 1581, Fire department infection control	✓								
4-5.9 NFPA 1932, Fire department ground ladders									

NFPA (6 of 20)

Form S12-3 *Continued*

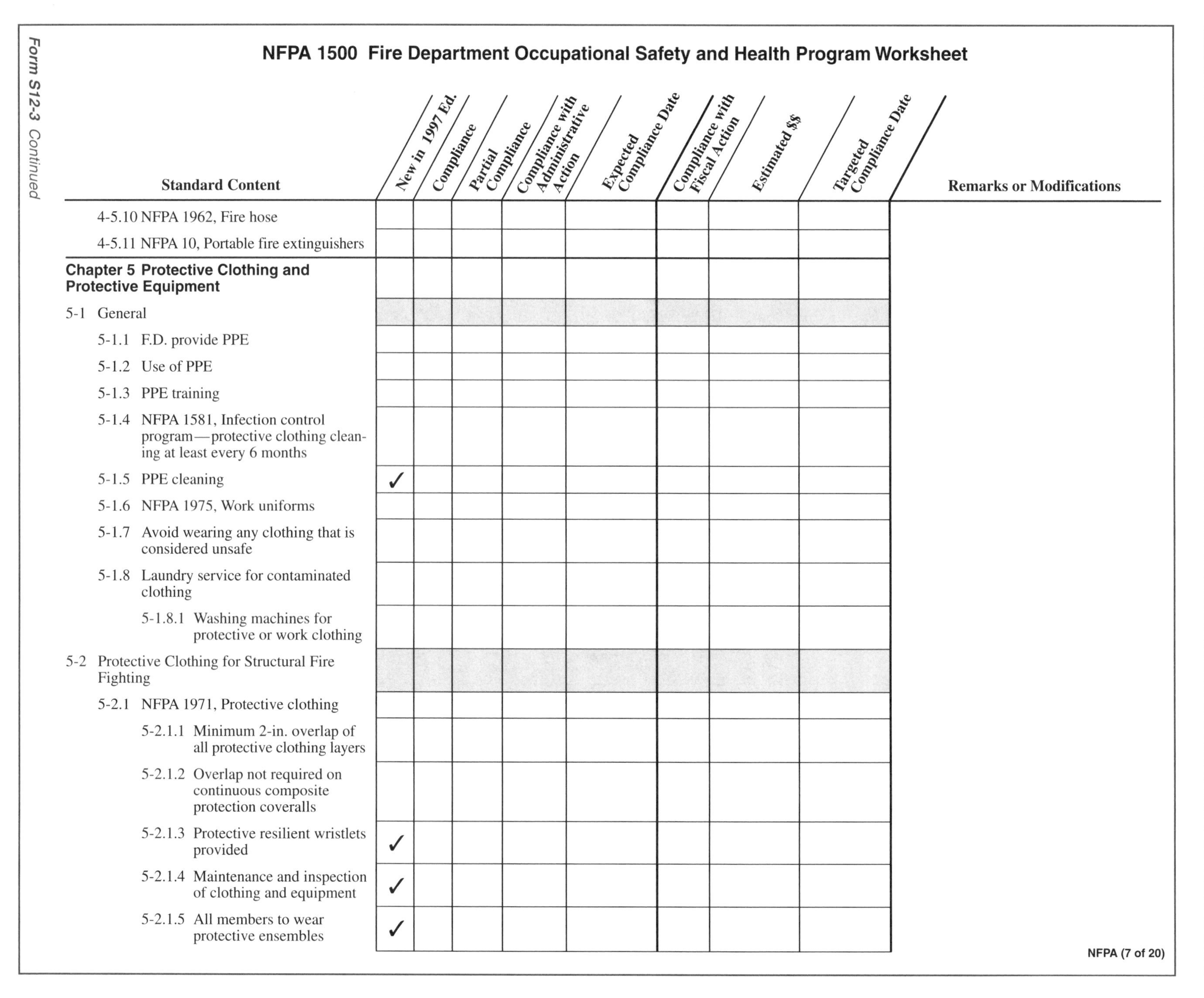

NFPA 1500 Fire Department Occupational Safety and Health Program Worksheet

Standard Content	New in 1997 Ed.	Compliance	Partial Compliance	Compliance with Administrative Action	Expected Compliance Date	Compliance with Fiscal Action	Estimated $$	Targeted Compliance Date	Remarks or Modifications
4-5.10 NFPA 1962, Fire hose									
4-5.11 NFPA 10, Portable fire extinguishers									
Chapter 5 Protective Clothing and Protective Equipment									
5-1 General									
5-1.1 F.D. provide PPE									
5-1.2 Use of PPE									
5-1.3 PPE training									
5-1.4 NFPA 1581, Infection control program—protective clothing cleaning at least every 6 months									
5-1.5 PPE cleaning	✓								
5-1.6 NFPA 1975, Work uniforms									
5-1.7 Avoid wearing any clothing that is considered unsafe									
5-1.8 Laundry service for contaminated clothing									
5-1.8.1 Washing machines for protective or work clothing									
5-2 Protective Clothing for Structural Fire Fighting									
5-2.1 NFPA 1971, Protective clothing									
5-2.1.1 Minimum 2-in. overlap of all protective clothing layers									
5-2.1.2 Overlap not required on continuous composite protection coveralls									
5-2.1.3 Protective resilient wristlets provided	✓								
5-2.1.4 Maintenance and inspection of clothing and equipment	✓								
5-2.1.5 All members to wear protective ensembles	✓								

NFPA (7 of 20)

Form S12-3 Continued

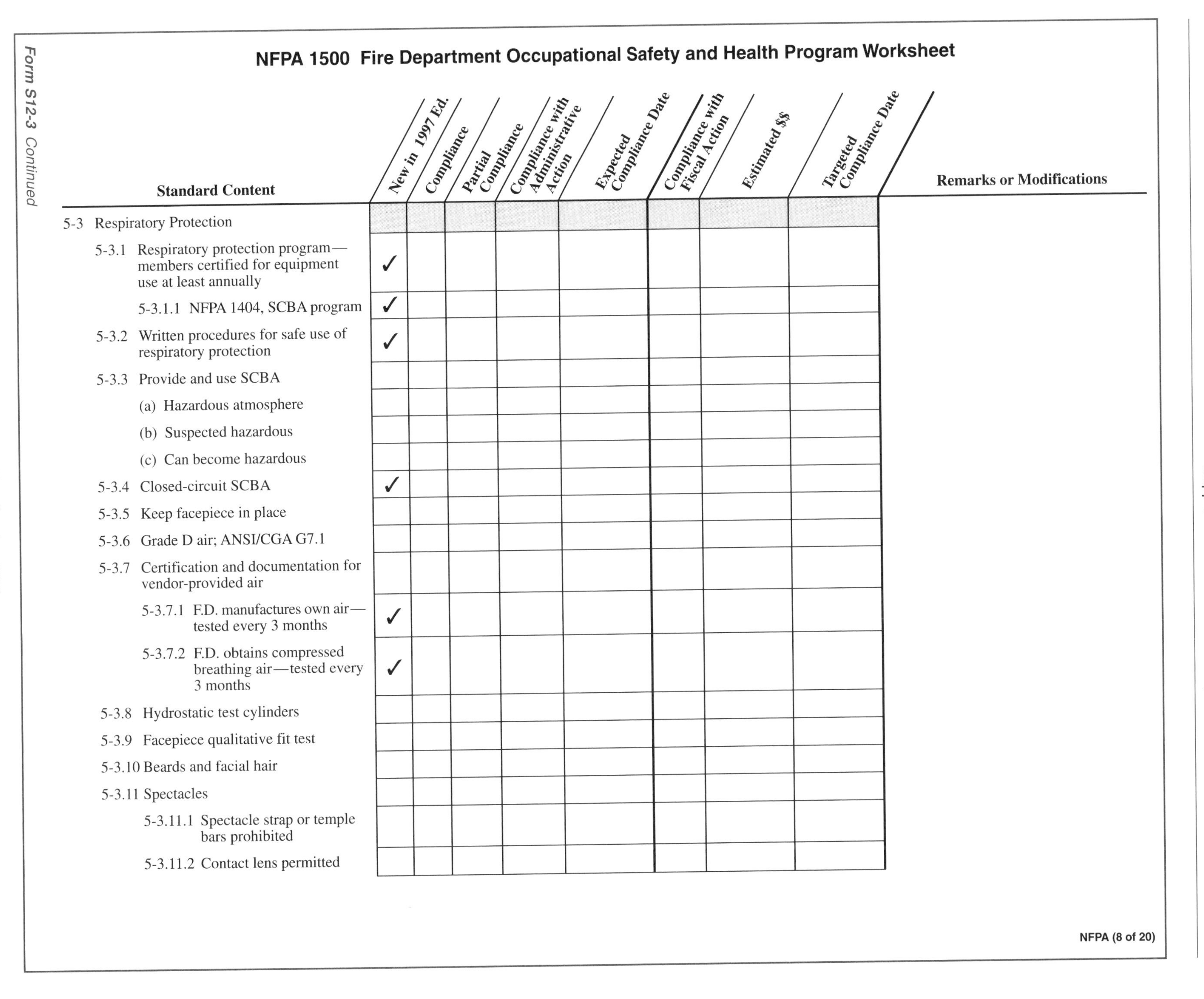

Form S12-3 *Continued*

NFPA 1500 Fire Department Occupational Safety and Health Program Worksheet

Standard Content	New in 1997 Ed.	Compliance	Partial Compliance	Compliance with Administrative Action	Expected Compliance Date	Compliance with Fiscal Action	Estimated $$	Targeted Compliance Date	Remarks or Modifications
5-3 Respiratory Protection									
5-3.1 Respiratory protection program—members certified for equipment use at least annually	✓								
5-3.1.1 NFPA 1404, SCBA program	✓								
5-3.2 Written procedures for safe use of respiratory protection	✓								
5-3.3 Provide and use SCBA									
(a) Hazardous atmosphere									
(b) Suspected hazardous									
(c) Can become hazardous									
5-3.4 Closed-circuit SCBA	✓								
5-3.5 Keep facepiece in place									
5-3.6 Grade D air; ANSI/CGA G7.1									
5-3.7 Certification and documentation for vendor-provided air									
5-3.7.1 F.D. manufactures own air—tested every 3 months	✓								
5-3.7.2 F.D. obtains compressed breathing air—tested every 3 months	✓								
5-3.8 Hydrostatic test cylinders									
5-3.9 Facepiece qualitative fit test									
5-3.10 Beards and facial hair									
5-3.11 Spectacles									
5-3.11.1 Spectacle strap or temple bars prohibited									
5-3.11.2 Contact lens permitted									

NFPA (8 of 20)

NFPA 1500 Fire Department Occupational Safety and Health Program Worksheet

Standard Content	New in 1997 Ed.	Compliance	Partial Compliance	Compliance with Administrative Action	Expected Compliance Date	Compliance with Fiscal Action	Estimated $$	Targeted Compliance Date	Remarks or Modifications
5-3.12 Facepiece/Face Seal									
5-3.12.1 Head covering breaking seal prohibited									
5-3.12.2 SCBA facepiece/head harness worn under protective hood									
5-3.12.3 SCBA facepiece/head harness worn under hazardous chemical protective clothing helmet									
5-3.12.4 Helmets shall not interfere with facepiece-to-face seal	✓								
5-4 Protective Clothing for Proximity Fire-Fighting Operations									
5-4.1 NFPA 1976, Proximity protective clothing									
5-4.1.1 Minimum 2-in. overlap of all proximity protective clothing layers									
5-4.1.2 Overlap not required on continuous full thermal and radiant heat protective coveralls									
5-4.2 NFPA 1971, Helmets and radiant reflective criteria									
5-4.3 NFPA 1971, Gloves and radiant reflective criteria									
5-4.4 NFPA 1971, Footwear and radiant reflective criteria									
5-4.5 NFPA 1971, Protective clothing—hoods and radiant reflective criteria									
5-4.6 Radiant reflective criteria over SCBA worn over the outside of proximity protective clothing									

NFPA (9 of 20)

Form S12-3 *Continued*

NFPA 1500 Fire Department Occupational Safety and Health Program Worksheet

Standard Content	New in 1997 Ed.	Compliance	Partial Compliance	Compliance with Administrative Action	Expected Compliance Date	Compliance with Fiscal Action	Estimated $$	Targeted Compliance Date	Remarks or Modifications
5-5 Protective Clothing for Emergency Medical Operations									
5-5.1 NFPA 1999, Emergency medical protective clothing									
5-5.2 Members shall not initiate patient care before emergency medical gloves are in place									
5-5.2.1 Fire fighters likely to be exposed to airborne infectious disease provided with NIOSH-approved Type C respirators	✓								
5-5.3 Members shall use emergency medical body and face protection									
5-5.4 NFPA 1581, Infection control program protective clothing cleaning									
5-5.5 NFPA 1971, Gloves during operations where sharp or rough edges likely to be encountered	✓								
5-6 Chemical-Protective Clothing for Hazardous Chemical Emergency Operations									
5-6.1 Vapor-protective garments									
5-6.1.1 NFPA 1991, Vapor-protective suits									
5-6.1.2 Garment appropriate for specific hazardous chemical emergency									
5-6.1.3 SCBA during hazardous chemical emergencies	✓								
5-6.1.4 Use only in vapor hazard atmospheres									
5-6.1.5 Use for protection from liquid splash or solid chemicals and particulates protection permitted									

NFPA (10 of 20)

Form S12-3 Continued

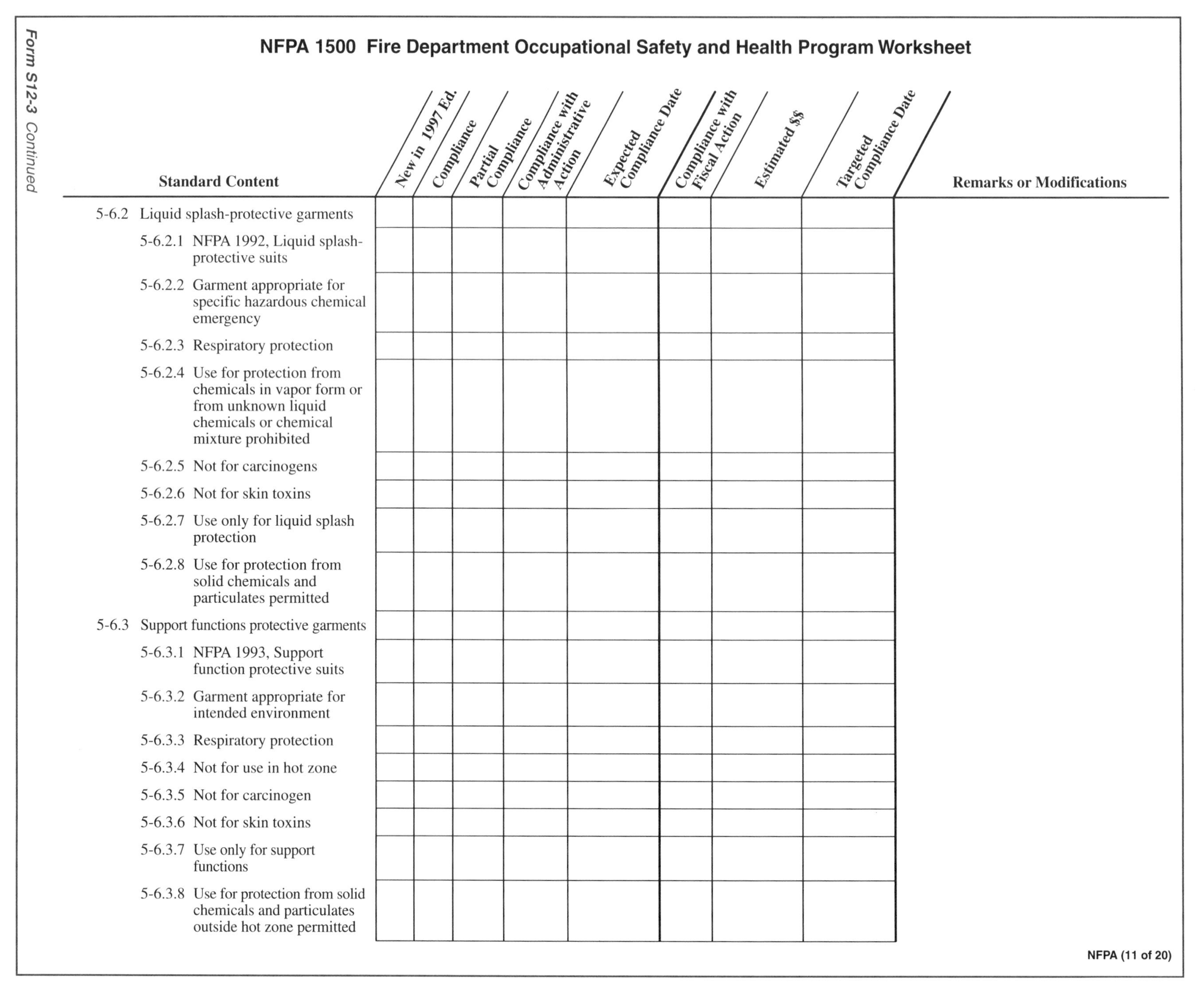

NFPA 1500 Fire Department Occupational Safety and Health Program Worksheet

Standard Content	New in 1997 Ed.	Compliance	Partial Compliance	Compliance with Administrative Action	Expected Compliance Date	Compliance with Fiscal Action	Estimated $$	Targeted Compliance Date	Remarks or Modifications
5-6.2 Liquid splash-protective garments									
5-6.2.1 NFPA 1992, Liquid splash-protective suits									
5-6.2.2 Garment appropriate for specific hazardous chemical emergency									
5-6.2.3 Respiratory protection									
5-6.2.4 Use for protection from chemicals in vapor form or from unknown liquid chemicals or chemical mixture prohibited									
5-6.2.5 Not for carcinogens									
5-6.2.6 Not for skin toxins									
5-6.2.7 Use only for liquid splash protection									
5-6.2.8 Use for protection from solid chemicals and particulates permitted									
5-6.3 Support functions protective garments									
5-6.3.1 NFPA 1993, Support function protective suits									
5-6.3.2 Garment appropriate for intended environment									
5-6.3.3 Respiratory protection									
5-6.3.4 Not for use in hot zone									
5-6.3.5 Not for carcinogen									
5-6.3.6 Not for skin toxins									
5-6.3.7 Use only for support functions									
5-6.3.8 Use for protection from solid chemicals and particulates outside hot zone permitted									

NFPA (11 of 20)

Form S12-3 *Continued*

NFPA 1500 Fire Department Occupational Safety and Health Program Worksheet

Standard Content	New in 1997 Ed.	Compliance	Partial Compliance	Compliance with Administrative Action	Expected Compliance Date	Compliance with Fiscal Action	Estimated $$	Targeted Compliance Date	Remarks or Modifications
5-6.4 Inspection, maintenance, and disposal of chemical-protective clothing									
5-6.4.1 Manufacturer's recommendations									
5-6.4.2 Dispose of contaminated garments									
5-7 Protective Clothing and Equipment for Wildland Fire Fighting									
5-7.1 Operating guidelines	✓								
5-7.2 NFPA 1977, Protective clothing	✓								
5-7.3 Overlap of clothing at waist, ankles, and wrists	✓								
5-7.4 NFPA 1977, Protective helmet	✓								
5-7.5 NFPA 1977, Protective gloves	✓								
5-7.6 NFPA 1977, Protective footwear	✓								
5-7.7 Members provided with approved fire shelter	✓								
5-7.7.1 Members trained in proper deployment of fire shelter at least annually	✓								
5-7.8 Members provided with 2 quarts of water; process established for replenishment of water supplies	✓								
5-7.9 Members provided with laminated pocket card with safety orders and "watch-out" situations	✓								
5-8 Personal Alert Safety System (PASS)									
5-8.1 NFPA 1982, PASS for hazardous area									
5-8.2 Tested at least weekly and prior to each use									
5-9 Life Safety Ropes and System Components									
5-9.1 NFPA 1983, Life safety rope, harness, and hardware									

NFPA (12 of 20)

Form S12-3 *Continued*

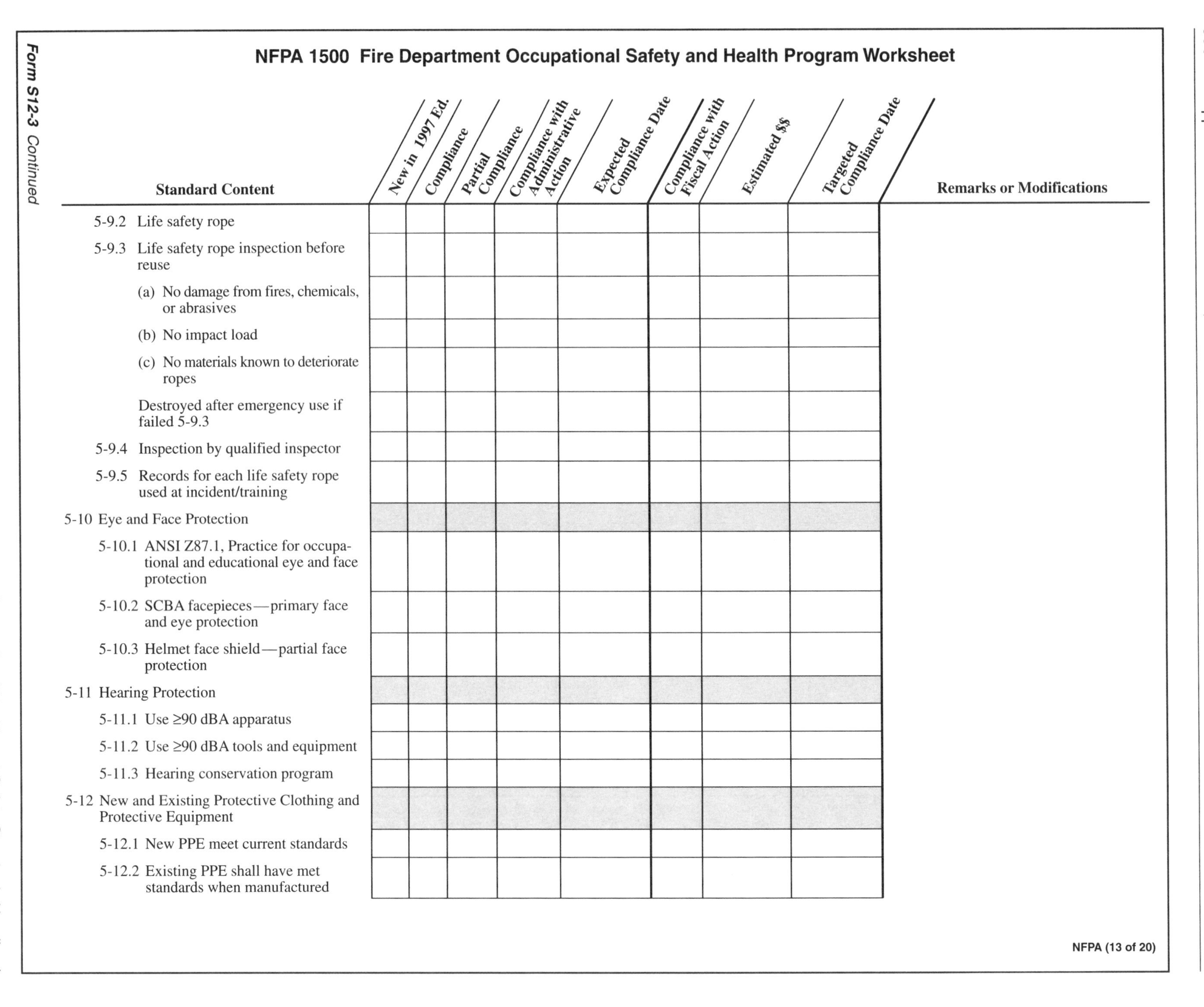

NFPA 1500 Fire Department Occupational Safety and Health Program Worksheet

Standard Content	New in 1997 Ed.	Compliance	Partial Compliance	Compliance with Administrative Action	Expected Compliance Date	Compliance with Fiscal Action	Estimated $$	Targeted Compliance Date	Remarks or Modifications
5-9.2 Life safety rope									
5-9.3 Life safety rope inspection before reuse									
(a) No damage from fires, chemicals, or abrasives									
(b) No impact load									
(c) No materials known to deteriorate ropes									
Destroyed after emergency use if failed 5-9.3									
5-9.4 Inspection by qualified inspector									
5-9.5 Records for each life safety rope used at incident/training									
5-10 Eye and Face Protection									
5-10.1 ANSI Z87.1, Practice for occupational and educational eye and face protection									
5-10.2 SCBA facepieces—primary face and eye protection									
5-10.3 Helmet face shield—partial face protection									
5-11 Hearing Protection									
5-11.1 Use ≥90 dBA apparatus									
5-11.2 Use ≥90 dBA tools and equipment									
5-11.3 Hearing conservation program									
5-12 New and Existing Protective Clothing and Protective Equipment									
5-12.1 New PPE meet current standards									
5-12.2 Existing PPE shall have met standards when manufactured									

NFPA (13 of 20)

Form S12-3 Continued

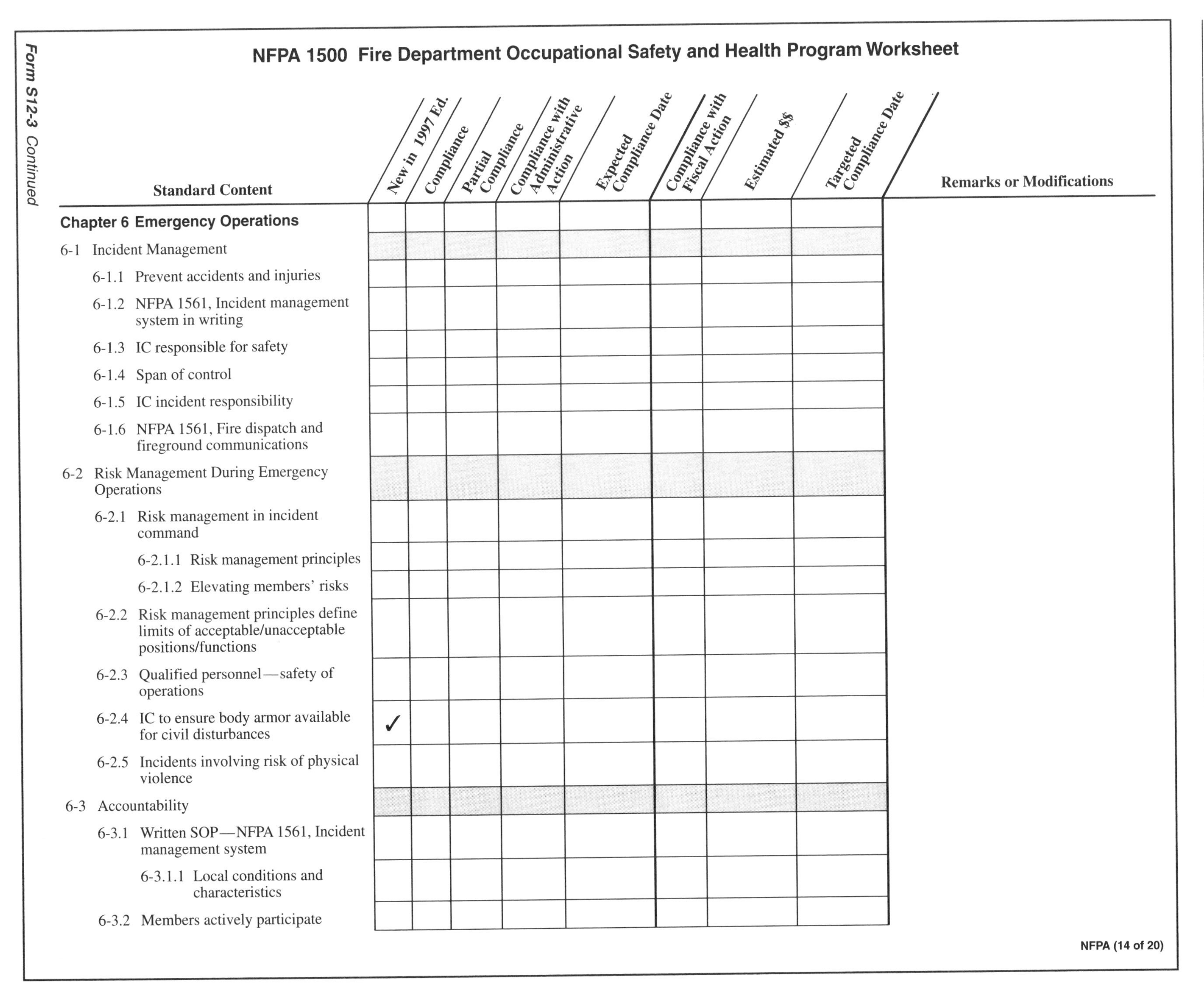

NFPA 1500 Fire Department Occupational Safety and Health Program Worksheet

Standard Content	New in 1997 Ed.	Compliance	Partial Compliance	Compliance with Administrative Action	Expected Compliance Date	Compliance with Fiscal Action	Estimated $$	Targeted Compliance Date	Remarks or Modifications
Chapter 6 Emergency Operations									
6-1 Incident Management									
6-1.1 Prevent accidents and injuries									
6-1.2 NFPA 1561, Incident management system in writing									
6-1.3 IC responsible for safety									
6-1.4 Span of control									
6-1.5 IC incident responsibility									
6-1.6 NFPA 1561, Fire dispatch and fireground communications									
6-2 Risk Management During Emergency Operations									
6-2.1 Risk management in incident command									
6-2.1.1 Risk management principles									
6-2.1.2 Elevating members' risks									
6-2.2 Risk management principles define limits of acceptable/unacceptable positions/functions									
6-2.3 Qualified personnel—safety of operations									
6-2.4 IC to ensure body armor available for civil disturbances	✓								
6-2.5 Incidents involving risk of physical violence									
6-3 Accountability									
6-3.1 Written SOP—NFPA 1561, Incident management system									
6-3.1.1 Local conditions and characteristics									
6-3.2 Members actively participate									

NFPA (14 of 20)

Form S12-3 Continued

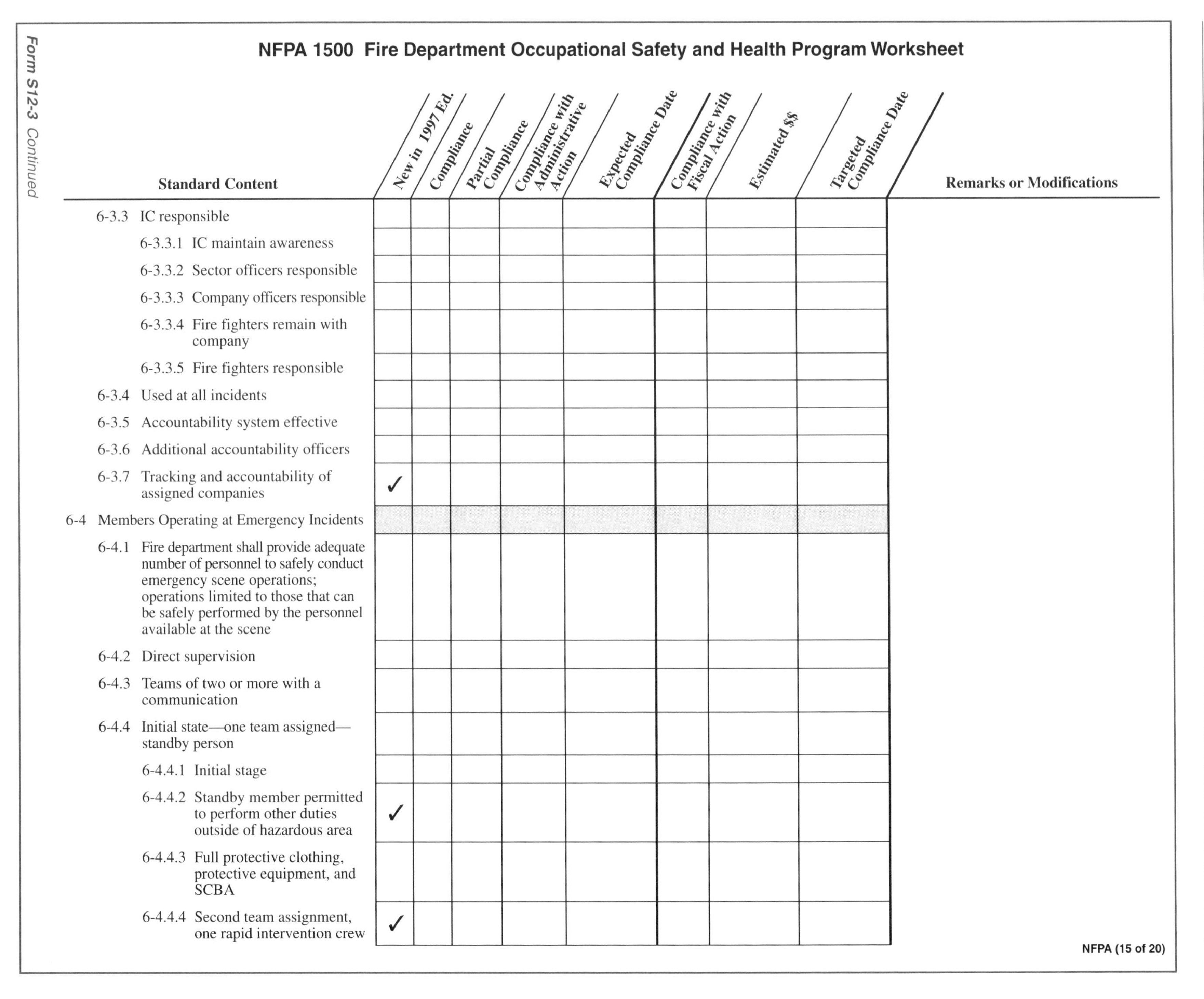

NFPA 1500 Fire Department Occupational Safety and Health Program Worksheet

Standard Content	New in 1997 Ed.	Compliance	Partial Compliance	Compliance with Administrative Action	Expected Compliance Date	Compliance with Fiscal Action	Estimated $$	Targeted Compliance Date	Remarks or Modifications
6-3.3 IC responsible									
6-3.3.1 IC maintain awareness									
6-3.3.2 Sector officers responsible									
6-3.3.3 Company officers responsible									
6-3.3.4 Fire fighters remain with company									
6-3.3.5 Fire fighters responsible									
6-3.4 Used at all incidents									
6-3.5 Accountability system effective									
6-3.6 Additional accountability officers									
6-3.7 Tracking and accountability of assigned companies	✓								
6-4 Members Operating at Emergency Incidents									
6-4.1 Fire department shall provide adequate number of personnel to safely conduct emergency scene operations; operations limited to those that can be safely performed by the personnel available at the scene									
6-4.2 Direct supervision									
6-4.3 Teams of two or more with a communication									
6-4.4 Initial state—one team assigned—standby person									
6-4.4.1 Initial stage									
6-4.4.2 Standby member permitted to perform other duties outside of hazardous area	✓								
6-4.4.3 Full protective clothing, protective equipment, and SCBA									
6-4.4.4 Second team assignment, one rapid intervention crew	✓								

NFPA (15 of 20)

Form S12-3 *Continued*

NFPA 1500 Fire Department Occupational Safety and Health Program Worksheet

Standard Content	New in 1997 Ed.	Compliance	Partial Compliance	Compliance with Administrative Action	Expected Compliance Date	Compliance with Fiscal Action	Estimated $$	Targeted Compliance Date	Remarks or Modifications
6-4.4.5 In imminent life-threatening situation, action to prevent loss of life permitted with less than four personnel	✓								
6-4.5 Highest level of emergency medical care for special operations—basic life support minimum									
6-4.5.1 NFPA 473— EMS for hazardous materials operations									
6-4.5.2 Basic life support for other emergency operations									
6-4.6 Secured to aerial device									
6-4.7 Fluorescent retroreflective material—MV traffic									
6-4.7.1 Apparatus utilized as shield									
6-4.7.2 Warning devices for oncoming traffic									
6-5 Rapid Intervention for Rescue of Members									
6-5.1 Rescue of members									
6-5.2 Rapid intervention crew									
6-5.3 Composure and structure									
6-5.4 Crew(s) status—early stages of incident									
6-5.5 Crew(s) status—expanded incident									
6-5.6 Special operations rapid intervention crews(s)									
6-6 Rehabilitation During Emergency Operations									
6-6.1 SOP for rehabilitation of members	✓								
6-6.2 IC provide rest and rehab									
6-6.3 On-scene rehabilitation to include basic life support	✓								
6-6.4 Each member responsible to communicate rest and rehab needs	✓								

NFPA (16 of 20)

Form S12-3 *Continued*

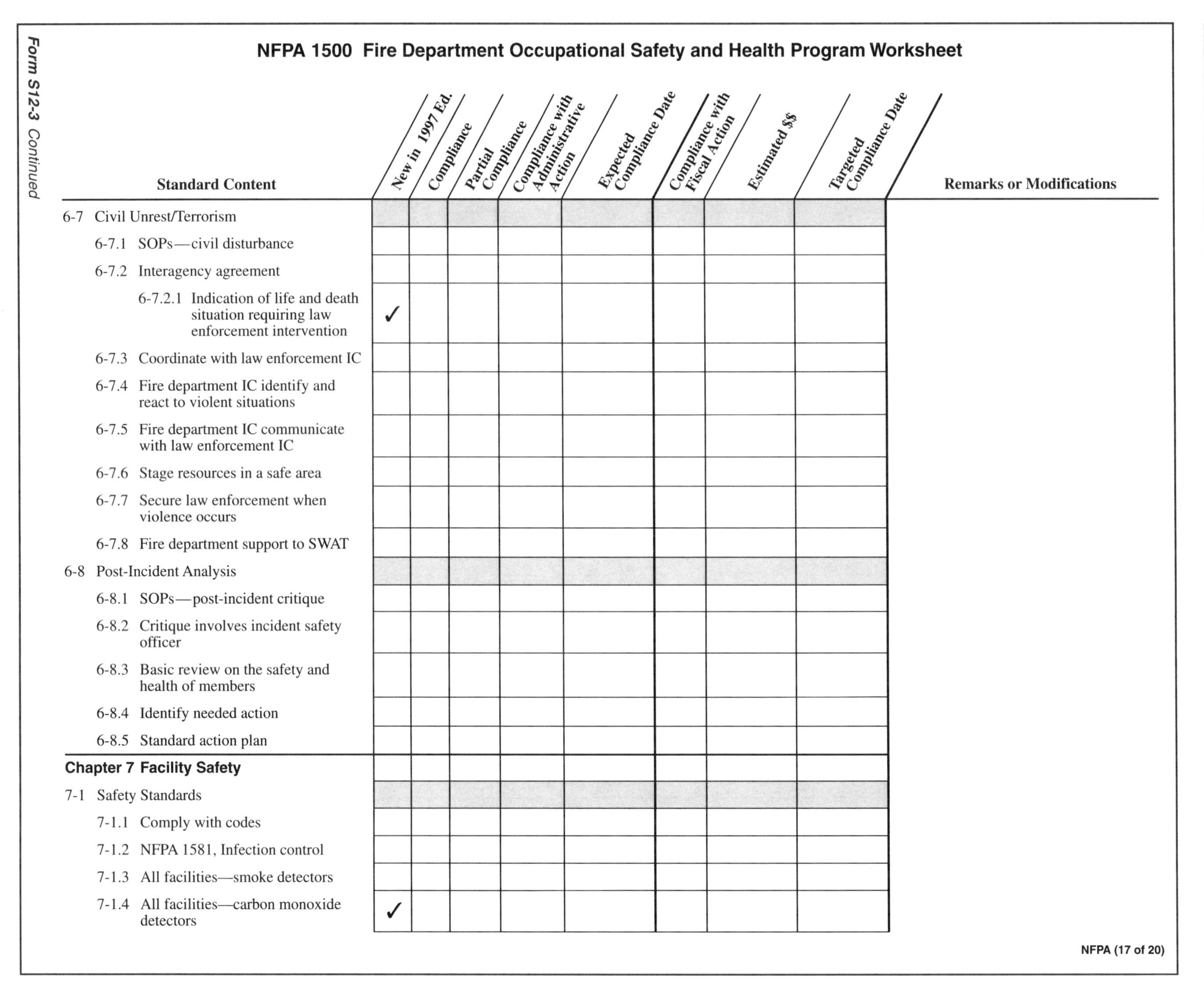

NFPA 1500 Fire Department Occupational Safety and Health Program Worksheet

Standard Content	New in 1997 Ed.	Compliance	Partial Compliance	Compliance with Administrative Action	Expected Compliance Date	Compliance with Fiscal Action	Estimated $$	Targeted Compliance Date	Remarks or Modifications
6-7 Civil Unrest/Terrorism									
6-7.1 SOPs—civil disturbance									
6-7.2 Interagency agreement									
6-7.2.1 Indication of life and death situation requiring law enforcement intervention	✓								
6-7.3 Coordinate with law enforcement IC									
6-7.4 Fire department IC identify and react to violent situations									
6-7.5 Fire department IC communicate with law enforcement IC									
6-7.6 Stage resources in a safe area									
6-7.7 Secure law enforcement when violence occurs									
6-7.8 Fire department support to SWAT									
6-8 Post-Incident Analysis									
6-8.1 SOPs—post-incident critique									
6-8.2 Critique involves incident safety officer									
6-8.3 Basic review on the safety and health of members									
6-8.4 Identify needed action									
6-8.5 Standard action plan									
Chapter 7 Facility Safety									
7-1 Safety Standards									
7-1.1 Comply with codes									
7-1.2 NFPA 1581, Infection control									
7-1.3 All facilities—smoke detectors									
7-1.4 All facilities—carbon monoxide detectors	✓								

NFPA (17 of 20)

***Form S12-3** Continued*

Form S12-3 *Continued*

NFPA 1500 Fire Department Occupational Safety and Health Program Worksheet

Standard Content	New in 1997 Ed.	Compliance	Partial Compliance	Compliance with Administrative Action	Expected Compliance Date	Compliance with Fiscal Action	Estimated $$	Targeted Compliance Date	Remarks or Modifications
7-1.5 New/existing facilities comply with *Life Safety Code*									
7-1.6 Prevent exhaust exposure									
7-1.7 Smoke-free areas									
7-2 Inspections									
7-2.1 Annual code inspection									
7-2.2 Monthly safety inspection									
7-3 Maintenance and repairs									
7-3.1 Established maintenance system									
Chapter 8 Medical and Physical									
8-1 Medical Requirements									
8-1.1 Medical evaluation and certification before becoming a member									
8-1.2 NFPA 1582, Medical requirements									
8-1.3 Periodic medical evaluation									
8-1.4 No cost to candidate, current fire fighter, or member									
8-1.5 Under the influence of alcohol or drugs									
8-2 Physical Performance Requirements									
8-2.1 Fire department develop requirements									
8-2.2 Certification for use of respiratory protection conducted annually	✓								
8-2.3 Candidates certified by fire dept.									
8-2.4 Current fire fighters annually certified by fire department									
8-2.5 Physical performance rehabilitation									

NFPA (18 of 20)

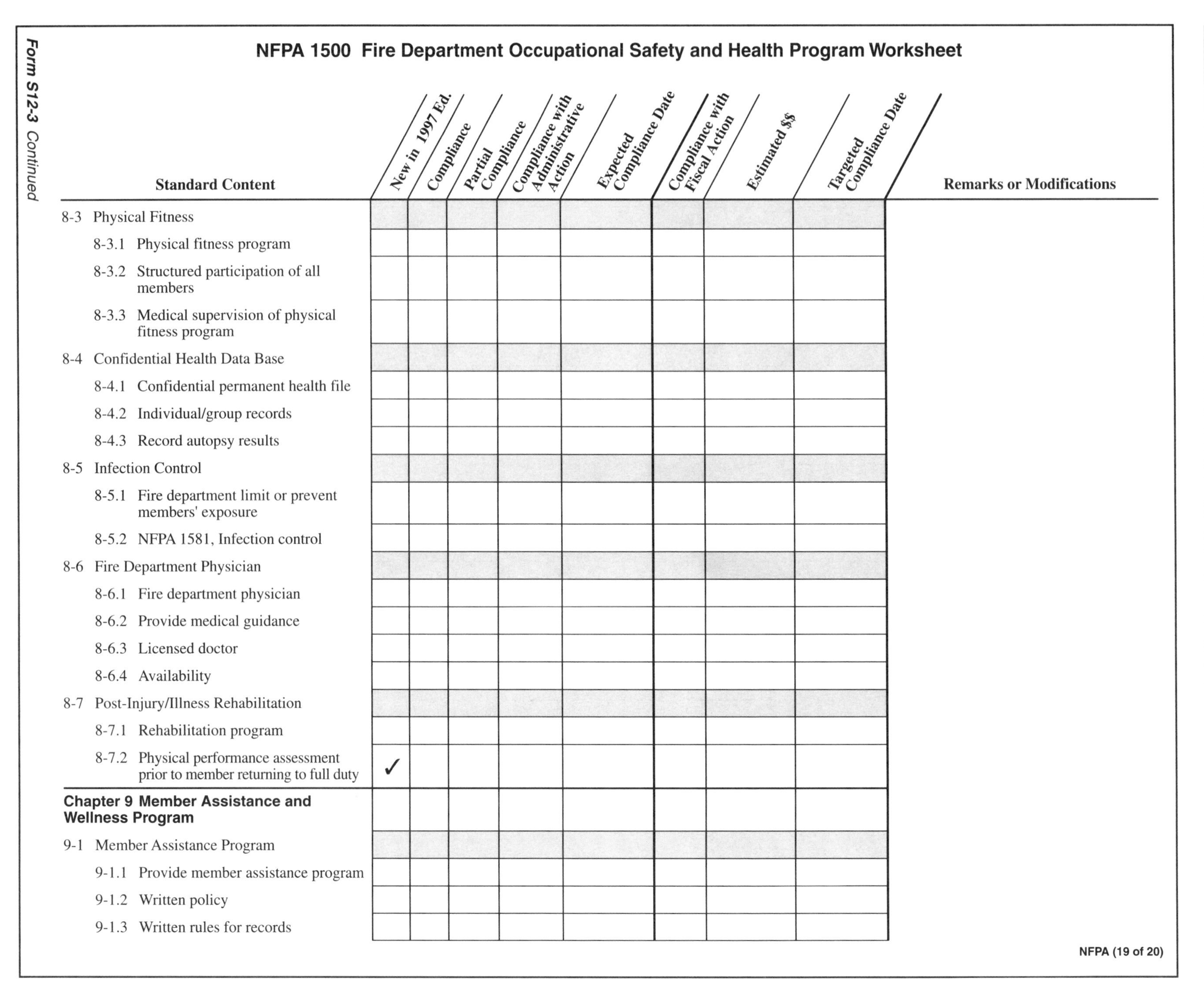

NFPA 1500 Fire Department Occupational Safety and Health Program Worksheet

Standard Content	New in 1997 Ed.	Compliance	Partial Compliance	Compliance with Administrative Action	Expected Compliance Date	Compliance with Fiscal Action	Estimated $$	Targeted Compliance Date	Remarks or Modifications
8-3 Physical Fitness									
8-3.1 Physical fitness program									
8-3.2 Structured participation of all members									
8-3.3 Medical supervision of physical fitness program									
8-4 Confidential Health Data Base									
8-4.1 Confidential permanent health file									
8-4.2 Individual/group records									
8-4.3 Record autopsy results									
8-5 Infection Control									
8-5.1 Fire department limit or prevent members' exposure									
8-5.2 NFPA 1581, Infection control									
8-6 Fire Department Physician									
8-6.1 Fire department physician									
8-6.2 Provide medical guidance									
8-6.3 Licensed doctor									
8-6.4 Availability									
8-7 Post-Injury/Illness Rehabilitation									
8-7.1 Rehabilitation program									
8-7.2 Physical performance assessment prior to member returning to full duty	✓								
Chapter 9 Member Assistance and Wellness Program									
9-1 Member Assistance Program									
9-1.1 Provide member assistance program									
9-1.2 Written policy									
9-1.3 Written rules for records									

NFPA (19 of 20)

Form S12-3 Continued

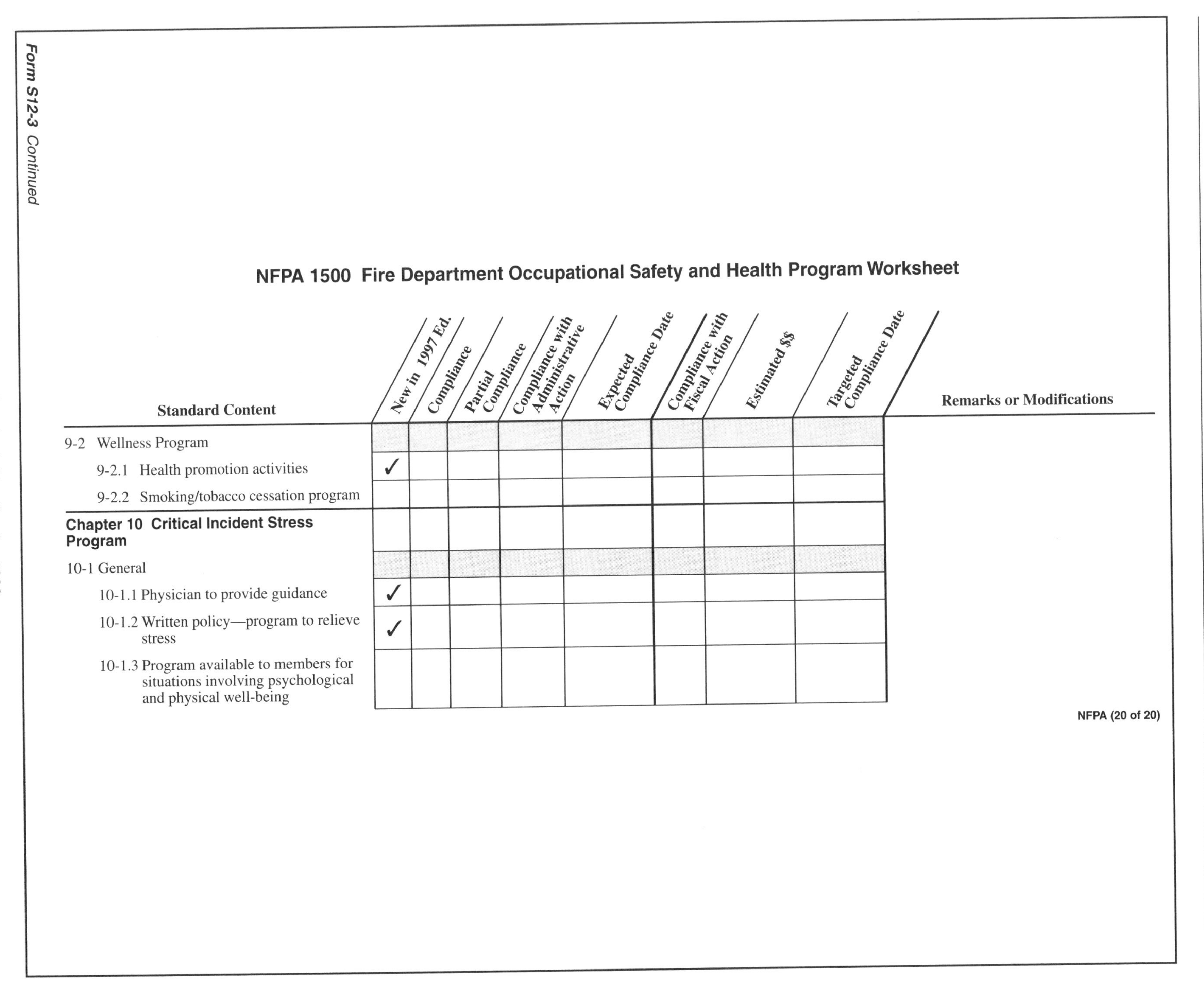

NFPA 1500 Fire Department Occupational Safety and Health Program Worksheet

Standard Content	New in 1997 Ed.	Compliance	Partial Compliance	Compliance with Administrative Action	Expected Compliance Date	Compliance with Fiscal Action	Estimated $$	Targeted Compliance Date	Remarks or Modifications
9-2 Wellness Program									
9-2.1 Health promotion activities	✓								
9-2.2 Smoking/tobacco cessation program									
Chapter 10 Critical Incident Stress Program									
10-1 General									
10-1.1 Physician to provide guidance	✓								
10-1.2 Written policy—program to relieve stress	✓								
10-1.3 Program available to members for situations involving psychological and physical well-being									

NFPA (20 of 20)

Form S12-3 *Continued*

Fire Department — Infectious Exposure Form

Exposed Member's Name: ______________________ Rank: ______________

Soc. Sec. #: ______________________

Field Inc. #: __________ Shift: __________ Company: __________ District: __________

Name of Patient: ______________________ Sex: __________

Age: __________ Address: ______________________

Suspected or Confirmed Disease: ______________________

Transported to: ______________________

Transported by: ______________________

Date of Exposure: ______________ Time of Exposure: ______________

Type of Incident (auto accident, trauma): ______________________

What were you exposed to?

Blood ________ Tears ________ Feces ________ Urine ________ Saliva ________

Vomitus ________ Sputum ________ Sweat ________ Other ________

What part(s) of your body became exposed? Be specific: ______________________

____

____

Did you have any open cuts, sores, or rashes that became exposed? Be specific: ______________

____

____

How did exposure occur? Be specific: ______________________

____

____

Did you seek medical attention? ______ yes ______ no

Where? ______________________ Date: __________

Contacted Infection Control Officer: Date: ______________ Time: __________

Supervisor's Signature: ______________________ Date: __________

Member's Signature: ______________________ Date: __________

NFPA (1 of 1)

Form S12-4

Employer:

Employee's Name:	Position Title:
Date of Exam:	Examining Physician:

Components Performed	Within Normal Limits	Abnormal, Able to Perform Job Tasks	Abnormal, Unable to Perform Job Tasks	Significant Changes Noted from Previous Exam (if applicable)
☐ Physical exam				
☐ Audiogram				
☐ Pulminary function				
☐ Treadmill stress				
☐ EKG-12 lead				
☐ Chest X-ray				
☐ Mammogram				
☐ Pelvic/Pap				
☐ Laboratory tests				
☐ Other				

Explanation of Abnormal Results/Significant Changes:

☐ Medically cleared to perform job tasks

☐ Denied medical clearance for current job tasks

NFPA (1 of 2)

Form S12-5

H of P.I.: Mr./Mrs. ______________________________ is a _________ y.o. Fire Fighter Police Officer with the ____________________ department. The purpose of this annual physical is to establish fitness for the continuation of those duties. He/She has enjoyed good health. Mr./Mrs. ___________________ voiced the following questions:

Medical History
- ____ D.M.
- ____ HTN
- ____ CVD
- ____ Asthma

Surgical History
- ____ Orthopedic
- ____ ENT
- ____ Optho
- ____ Other

Medications

Allergies

Exercise

Social History
- ____ Smoke
- ____ PPD
- ____ Quit
- ____ PkYr
- ____ Alcohol
- ____ Amount
- ____ Frequency

ROS

GI
- ____ Hematochezia
- ____ Stool caliber
- ____ Bowel habits

G.U.
- ____ Stones
- ____ Hematuria

CV
- ____ Chest pain
- ____ SOB

Resp
- ____ Cough
- ____ Wheezes
- ____ SOB

FH
- ____ DM
- ____ HTN
- ____ CVD

Physical

Insert physical here

Audio
- ____ HFHL
- ____ Speech range

Vision
- ____ Near
- ____ Far
- ____ Corrected

Stool OB
- ____ Positive
- ____ Negative

UA
- ____ Blood
- ____ Protein
- ____ Glucose

EKG/TMT
- ____ HR
- ____ Target
- ____ Interp
- ____ Stage achieved

Pulm

FVC ______

% Pred _____

FEVI ______

% Pred _____

Blood

H/H ______

WBC _____

Glu ______

Chol ______

HDL _____

Ratio _____

Risk ______

LFTs

SGOT ____

SGPT ____

GGT _____

Other _____

NFPA (2 of 2)

Form S12-5 *Continued*

1. Name (Last)	(First)	(Middle)	2. Sex	3. Date of Examination

4. Plant or Division	5. Soc. Sec. or Employee No.	6. Occupation	7. Date Last Examination

8. Reason for Present Examination
☐ Pre-placement ☐ D.O.T. ☐ Surveillance ☐ Immigration ☐ F.I.T.

9. Temp.	10. Pulse	11. Blood Pressure	12. Height Ft In.	13. Weight	14. Titmus Snelling

15. Vision	Uncorrected			Corrected			16. Color Vision (use code)*
Distant	RE 20/	Both	LE 20/	RE 20/	Both	LE 20/	
Near	RE 20/	Both	LE 20/	RE 20/	Both	LE 20/	17. Peripheral

Clinical Evaluation

	Area Examined	* Use Code	Remarks (Describe all "Code 1s" in detail)
18.	Head and neck		
19.	Thyroid		
	Lymph nodes		
20.	Eyes		
	Fundi		
21.	Ears		
22.	Nose and sinuses		
23.	Mouth and throat		
24.	Teeth		
25.	Chest and lungs		
	Breast		
26.	Heart		
27.	Abdomen		
28.	Inguinal, e.g., hernia		
29.	Genitalia		

* Code: 0 — within normal limits 1 — significantly abnormal X — not examined

NFPA (1 of 12)

Form S12-6

30.	Pelvis		
31.	Anus and rectum		
	Prostate		
	Proctoscopic		
32.	Spine		
33.	Skin		
34.	Arms		
	Hands		
35.	Legs		
	Feet		
36.	Peripheral-Vascular		
37.	Neurologic		
38.	Emotional status		
39.	Other		

40. Urine dip:	Glucose:	Albumin:	S.G.:
	Heme:	Leukocyte-Esterase:	Other:

41. Flex	42. Step test	43. Body fat	44. PFT	45. Audio

46. Chest X-ray (use 0, 1, or X)	47. EKG (use 0, 1, or X) and specify test used	48. Hemocult

49. Back eval.	50. Tetanus	51. PPD	52. Stress test

* Code: 0 — within normal limits 1 — significantly abnormal X — not examined

NFPA (2 of 12)

Form S12-6 *Continued*

53. Other X-ray or laboratory findings

54. Physician's summary, remarks, and diagnoses, including recommendations made to patient (include code numbers for diagnoses and conditions found)

55. Recommendations/Restrictions

☐

☐

☐

56. R.N. signature

57. Physician's signature

58. Patient's signature

59. Work qualification:	60. Contact person:	61. Date:	62. Initial:

* Code: 0 — within normal limits 1 — significantly abnormal X — not examined

NFPA (3 of 12)

Form S12-6 *Continued*

Health History	Yes	No	If "Yes," Give Details.
Have You Had Any Surgeries/Operations:			
On your back, arm, leg, or knee?	☐	☐	
To treat a hernia?	☐	☐	
Varicose veins?	☐	☐	
Other operations?	☐	☐	
Have you ever been hospitalized?	☐	☐	
Allergy — Have You Ever Had or Do You Currently Have:			
Serious allergy?	☐	☐	
Bad reaction to any medication?	☐	☐	
Advised not to take any medication (e.g., aspirin)?	☐	☐	
Skin — Have You Ever Had or Do You Currently Have:			
Hives/eczema or rash?	☐	☐	
Chronic skin problems (i.e., cuts slow to heal)?	☐	☐	
Excessive skin dryness?	☐	☐	
Problems with "easy bruising"?	☐	☐	
Chemical or jewelry rash/sensitivity?	☐	☐	
Neuro — Have You Ever Had or Do You Currently Have:			
A psychiatric or emotional problem?	☐	☐	
Numbness/weakness/paralysis?	☐	☐	
Dizziness or fainting spells?	☐	☐	
Severe/frequent or migraine headaches?	☐	☐	
Head injury, concussion, or skull fracture?	☐	☐	
Neurological disorders?	☐	☐	
Seizures or blackouts?	☐	☐	
Stroke?	☐	☐	
Eye — Have You Ever Had or Do You Currently Have:			
Hearing loss?	☐	☐	
Frequent ear infections?	☐	☐	

NFPA (4 of 12)

Form S12-6 *Continued*

Health History	Yes	No	If "Yes," Give Details.
Ringing in ears?	☐	☐	
Other ear problems?	☐	☐	
Glaucoma or cataracts?	☐	☐	
Red eyes?	☐	☐	
Eye injury/vision loss?	☐	☐	
Other eye problems (i.e., strain from VDT use)?	☐	☐	
Glasses/contacts?	☐	☐	
Date of last vision screen?	☐	☐	

Head/Neck — Have You Ever Had or Do You Currently Have:

	Yes	No	If "Yes," Give Details.
Date of last dental exam:	☐	☐	
Recent problems with teeth/dentures?	☐	☐	
Frequent mouth ulcers/infections?	☐	☐	
Sinus or hay fever?	☐	☐	
Frequent sore throats?	☐	☐	
Frequent nose bleeds?	☐	☐	
Trouble with thyroid (i.e., taking thyroid medication)?	☐	☐	
Problem requiring radiation treatment to the neck area?	☐	☐	

Lungs — Have You Ever Had or Do You Currently Have:

	Yes	No	If "Yes," Give Details.
Asthma or wheezing?	☐	☐	
Coughed up any blood?	☐	☐	
Shortness of breath without apparent reason?	☐	☐	
TB or a positive skin test for TB?	☐	☐	
Pneumonia or pleurisy?	☐	☐	
Do you cough every day, especially in the morning?	☐	☐	
Pain or tightness in chest?	☐	☐	
More than three episodes of bronchitis in one year?	☐	☐	
Ever smoked tobacco in any form?	☐	☐	How long: yrs. Packs per day: When quit:
Had a chest X-ray?	☐	☐	Last time:

NFPA (5 of 12)

Form S12-6 *Continued*

Health History	Yes	No	If "Yes," Give Details.
Heart — Have You Ever Had or Do You Currently Have:			
Rheumatic fever or heart murmur?	☐	☐	
Heart disease?	☐	☐	
Treated for heart condition?	☐	☐	
Unusually cold or bluish-colored hands or feet?	☐	☐	
High blood pressure. If "Yes" how is it treated?	☐	☐	❏ Medicine ❏ Diet ❏ Exercise
Do you have a history of elevated cholesterol?	☐	☐	
Anemia or any blood disease?	☐	☐	
Phlebitis, varicose veins, or blood clots/ poor circulation?	☐	☐	
Chest pain with activity?	☐	☐	
GI — Have You Ever Had or Do You Currently Have:			
Ulcers?	☐	☐	
Hiatal hernia?	☐	☐	
Indigestion, pain, or unusual burning in stomach?	☐	☐	
Vomiting of blood?	☐	☐	
Bloody/tarry bowel movements?	☐	☐	
Colitis or nervous stomach?	☐	☐	
Yellow jaundice or hepatitis?	☐	☐	
Problems with your pancreas?	☐	☐	
Gallbladder disease?	☐	☐	
Kidneys — Have You Ever Had or Do You Currently Have:			
Bladder or kidney infections?	☐	☐	
Kidney stones?	☐	☐	
Burning or discomfort on urination, or frequent urination?	☐	☐	
Hernia?	☐	☐	
Blood in urine?	☐	☐	

NFPA (6 of 12)

Form S12-6 Continued

Health History	Yes	No	If "Yes," Give Details.
Miscellaneous — Have You Ever Had or Do You Currently Have:			
Diabetes or sugar in your blood or urine?	☐	☐	
Cancer of any kind?	☐	☐	
Muscle-Skeletal — Have You Ever Had or Do You Currently Have:			
Arthritis, rheumatism, neck, back, or spine injury or disease?	☐	☐	
Been treated for a back problem?	☐	☐	
Recurrent stiffness or back pain?	☐	☐	
Bursitis, tendonitis?	☐	☐	
Recurrent pulled muscles or sprains?	☐	☐	
Hand or wrist injury or problem?	☐	☐	
Hip or knee injury or problem?	☐	☐	
Ankle or foot injury or problem?	☐	☐	
Frostbite?	☐	☐	
Job requiring heavy lifting or standing, or sitting for long periods of time?	☐	☐	
Any broken bones?	☐	☐	
For Females Only — Have You Ever Had or Do You Currently Have:			
Menstrual irregularities?	☐	☐	
Recurrent problems of the female organs?	☐	☐	
Breast masses or lumps?	☐	☐	
Do you practice monthly breast self-exam?	☐	☐	
Have you ever had a mammogram?	☐	☐	
Date of last pap smear:	☐	☐	
For Males Only — Have You Ever Had or Do You Currently Have:			
Prostate or testicular problems?	☐	☐	
Breast tenderness, swelling, or lumps?	☐	☐	
Do you practice monthly testicular self-exam?	☐	☐	

NFPA (7 of 12)

Form S12-6 *Continued*

Health History

General Lifestyle I.

Check the Answer That Best Describes You

General health	❑ Poor	❑ Fair	❑ Good	❑ Excellent
% Seatbelt use	❑ 0–24%	❑ 25–49%	❑ 50–74%	❑ 75–100%
Daily stress	❑ Low	❑ Moderate	❑ High	
Average hours sleep	❑ 6 hours or less	❑ 7–8 hours	❑ 8 hours or more	
Average meals daily	❑ 1 meal	❑ 2 meals	❑ 3 or more	
Number of eggs per week	❑ 0–1	❑ 2	❑ 3 or more	
Average number red meat meals per week	❑ 0–1	❑ 2–3	❑ 3 or more	
Average number of alcoholic beverages/beers per week	❑ 0–5	❑ 6–14	❑ 15 or more	

	Yes	No	If "Yes," Give Details.
Do you exercise three times per week? 30–40 minutes each time? Identify types of exercise.	☐	☐	
Are you more than 30% above your ideal weight?	☐	☐	
Have you received a tetanus booster in the last 10 years?	☐	☐	
Have you been immunized against hepatitis B?	☐	☐	Year immunized:
Do you take any prescription medication?	☐	☐	
Do you take nonprescription medication (or over the counter) drug on a regular basis?	☐	☐	

General Lifestyle II.

Do you participate in a workplace wellness/ help promotion program?	☐	☐	
Which of the following would you like to see offered and would you participate in?			
Cholesterol screen	☐	☐	
Blood pressure screen	☐	☐	
Weight loss	☐	☐	
Nutrition program	☐	☐	
Stress management	☐	☐	
Smoking cessation	☐	☐	
CPR	☐	☐	

NFPA (8 of 12)

Form S12-6 *Continued*

Health History	**Yes**	**No**	**If "Yes," Give Details.**
Blood drive	☐	☐	
Health risk appraisal	☐	☐	
Self-directed exercise	☐	☐	
Health education program	☐	☐	
Women's health	☐	☐	
Work History I. **Have you ever:**			
Been restricted in your work or given "light duty" because of your health or injury?	☐	☐	
Left a job because of health problems?	☐	☐	
Been injured on the job and treated by a doctor?	☐	☐	
Received compensation for an industrial injury or illness?	☐	☐	
Are you receiving any health care treatment (e.g., physician therapy, chiropractic, acupuncture, medical, etc.)?	☐	☐	
Been hospitalized in the last five years?	☐	☐	
Have you had any illness or injury that we have not asked you about?	☐	☐	
Work History II:			
Do you have hobbies such as furniture refinishing, painting, hunting, shooting, or model building?	☐	☐	
Do you moonlight or have a second job?	☐	☐	
Work History III. **Exposures — Have You Ever Worked Around a:**			
Chemical plant?	☐	☐	
Coke oven?	☐	☐	
Construction?	☐	☐	
Cotton, flax, or hemp mill?	☐	☐	
Electronics plant?	☐	☐	
Farm?	☐	☐	
Foundry?	☐	☐	

NFPA (9 of 12)

Form S12-6 *Continued*

Health History	**Yes**	**No**	**If "Yes," Give Details.**
Hazardous waste industry?	☐	☐	
Hospital?	☐	☐	
Lumber mill?	☐	☐	
Metal production?	☐	☐	
Mine?	☐	☐	
Nuclear industry?	☐	☐	
Paper mill?	☐	☐	
Pharmaceutical?	☐	☐	
Plastic production?	☐	☐	
Pottery mill?	☐	☐	
Refinery?	☐	☐	
Rubber processing plant?	☐	☐	
Sand pit or quarry?	☐	☐	
Service station?	☐	☐	
Shipyard?	☐	☐	
Smelter?	☐	☐	
Have You Ever Worked With or Been Exposed To:			
Aldrin?	☐	☐	
Arsenic?	☐	☐	
Asbestos?	☐	☐	
Benzene?	☐	☐	
Benzidine?	☐	☐	
Beryllium?	☐	☐	
BIS chlormethyl ether?	☐	☐	
Cadmium?	☐	☐	
Carbon disulfide?	☐	☐	
Carbon tetrachloride?	☐	☐	
Chlorine?	☐	☐	
Chlorodane?	☐	☐	
Chloroform?	☐	☐	

NFPA (10 of 12)

Form S12-6 *Continued*

Health History	Yes	No	If "Yes," Give Details.
Chloroprene?	☐	☐	______
Chromates?	☐	☐	______
Chromic acid mist?	☐	☐	______
Cutting oils?	☐	☐	______
DDT?	☐	☐	______
Dieldrin?	☐	☐	______
Dioxin?	☐	☐	______
Dust, coal?	☐	☐	______
Dust, sandblasting?	☐	☐	______
Dust, other?	☐	☐	______
Ethyl dibromide?	☐	☐	______
Ethylene oxide?	☐	☐	______
Extreme heat or cold?	☐	☐	______
Heptachlor?	☐	☐	______
Hexachlorobenzene?	☐	☐	______
Isocyanates (TDI, MDI)?	☐	☐	______
Loud or continuous noise?	☐	☐	______
Mercury?	☐	☐	______
Methylene chloride?	☐	☐	______
Microwaves, lasers?	☐	☐	______
Nickel?	☐	☐	______
PCBs?	☐	☐	______
Pesticides, herbicides?	☐	☐	______
Phenois?	☐	☐	______
Phosgene?	☐	☐	______
Plastics?	☐	☐	______
Radioactive materials?	☐	☐	______
Roofing materials?	☐	☐	______
Rubber?	☐	☐	______
Silica?	☐	☐	______

NFPA (11 of 12)

Form S12-6 *Continued*

Health History	Yes	No	If "Yes," Give Details.
Solvents/degreasers?	☐	☐	______
Soots and tars?	☐	☐	______
Spray painting?	☐	☐	______
TRI/PER chloroethylene?	☐	☐	______
Vinyl chloride?	☐	☐	______

List Any Toxins/Chemicals/Biological Hazards You Might Currently Be Exposed To: ______

______

______

______

Work History IV.
Jobs — Start with the Most Recent:

Date (Year to Year)	Company	Position	Any Work Hazards
______	______	______	______
______	______	______	______
______	______	______	______
______	______	______	______
______	______	______	______
______	______	______	______
______	______	______	______

I certify that the above information is true and complete to the best of my knowledge. I hereby give ______ ______ permission to release work-related information to the proper authorities of my employer or the company for which I am a job applicant.

Date: ______ Signature: ______

Examiner: ______

NFPA (12 of 12)

***Form S12-6** Continued*

SUPPLEMENT 13

Sample Incident Management System Forms

Editor's Note: This supplement contains full-size, reproducible copies of sample incident action planning forms that are routinely used in the Incident Command System. The editor believes that proper documentation demands that standard forms be used for all incidents so that all the appropriate information is documented. Forms S13-1 through S13-9 are adapted from the National Inter-Agency Incident Management System's (NIIMS) 1983 publication Incident Command System, which is available from Fire Protection Publications, Oklahoma State University at Stillwater. Forms S13-10 through S13-12 were provided by the Phoenix Fire Department.

Form S13-1 ICS 201, Incident Briefing

Form S13-2 ICS 202, Incident Objectives

Form S13-3 ICS 203, Organization Assignment List

Form S13-4 ICS 204, Division Assignment List

Form S13-5 ICS 205, Communications Plan

Form S13-6 ICS 206, Medical Plan

Form S13-7 ICS 207, Incident Organization Chart

Form S13-8 ICS 209, Incident Status Summary

Form S13-9 ICS 215, Operational Planning Worksheet

Form S13-10 EMS Medical Worksheet

Form S13-11 Tactical Worksheet

Form S13-12 Post-Incident Review Worksheet

INCIDENT BRIEFING (ICS 201)	1. INCIDENT NAME	2. DATE PREPARED	3. TIME PREPARED

4. MAP SKETCH

ICS 201 Page 1	8. PREPARED BY (NAME AND POSITION)

Form S13-1

7. SUMMARY OF CURRENT ACTIONS

ICS 201
Page 2

Form S13-1 *Continued*

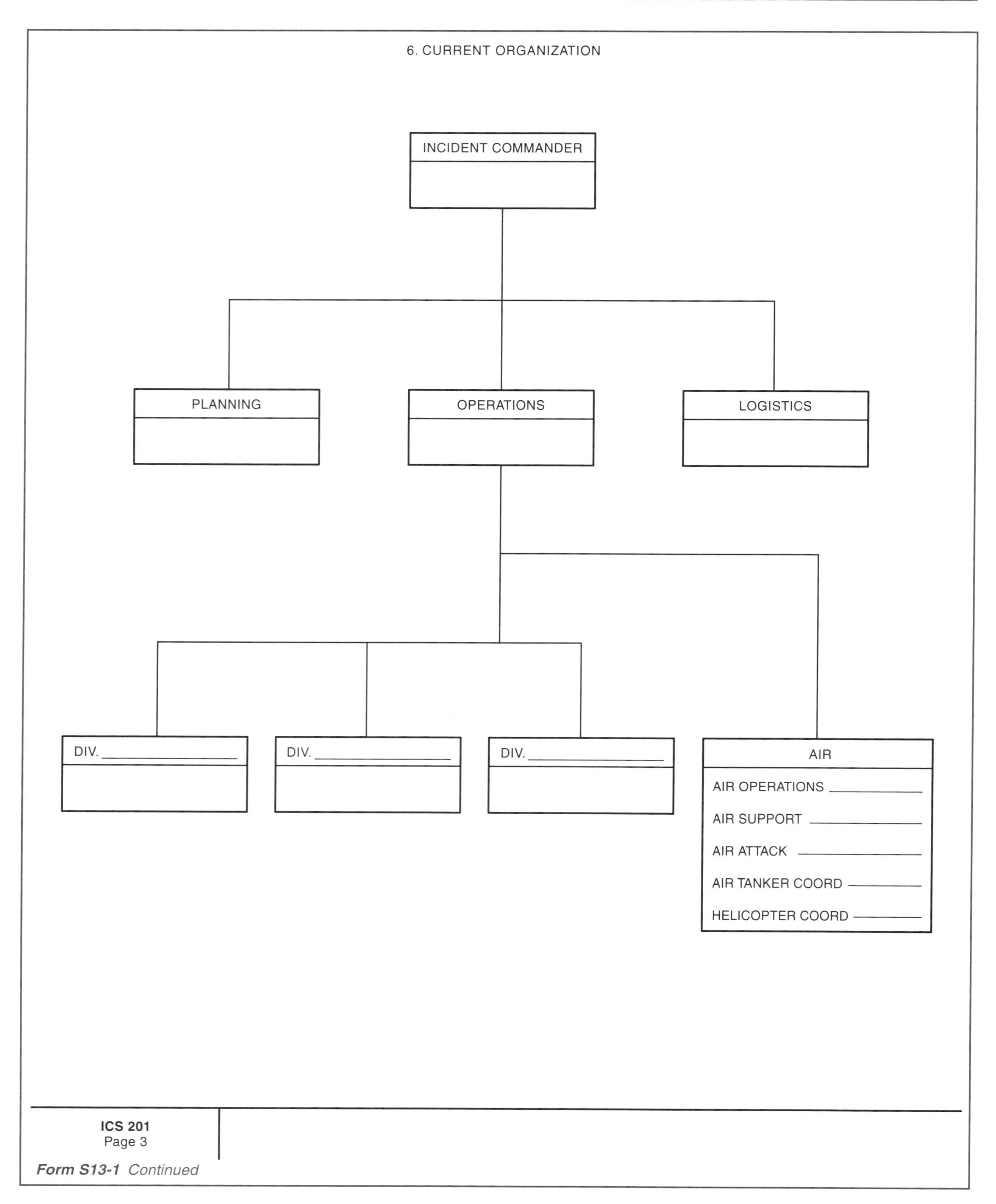

Form S13-1 *Continued*

5. RESOURCES SUMMARY

RESOURCES ORDERED	RESOURCE IDENTIFICATION	ETA	ON SCENE ✓	LOCATION / ASSIGNMENT

ICS 201
Page 4

Form S13-1 *Continued*

INCIDENT OBJECTIVES (ICS 202)	1. INCIDENT NAME	2. DATE PREPARED	3. TIME PREPARED
4. OPERATIONAL PERIOD (DATE/TIME)			
5. GENERAL CONTROL OBJECTIVES FOR THE INCIDENT (INCLUDE ALTERNATIVES)			
6. WEATHER FORECAST FOR OPERATIONAL PERIOD			
7. GENERAL/SAFETY MESSAGE			

8. ATTACHMENTS (✓ IF ATTACHED)

- ☐ ORGANIZATION LIST (ICS 203)
- ☐ DIVISION ASSIGNMENT LISTS (ICS 204)
- ☐ COMMUNICATIONS PLAN (ICS 205)
- ☐ MEDICAL PLAN (ICS 206)
- ☐ INCIDENT MAP
- ☐ TRAFFIC PLAN
- ☐ ____________
- ☐ ____________
- ☐ ____________

ICS 202	9. PREPARED BY (PLANNING SECTION CHIEF)	10. APPROVED BY (INCIDENT COMMANDER)

Form S13-2

ORGANIZATION ASSIGNMENT LIST (ICS 203)

1. INCIDENT NAME	2. DATE PREPARED	3. TIME PREPARED

4. OPERATIONAL PERIOD (DATE/TIME)

POSITION	NAME
5. INCIDENT COMMANDER AND STAFF	
INCIDENT COMMANDER	
DEPUTY	
SAFETY OFFICER	
INFORMATION OFFICER	
LIAISON OFFICER	

6. AGENCY REPRESENTATION

AGENCY	NAME

POSITION	NAME
7. PLANNING SECTION	
CHIEF	
DEPUTY	
RESOURCES UNIT	
SITUATION UNIT	
DOCUMENTATION UNIT	
DEMOBILIZATION UNIT	
TECHNICAL SPECIALISTS	
8. LOGISTICS SECTION	
CHIEF	
DEPUTY	
a. SUPPORT BRANCH	
DIRECTOR	
SUPPLY UNIT	
FACILITIES UNIT	
GROUND SUPPORT UNIT	
b. SERVICE BRANCH	
DIRECTOR	
COMMUNICATIONS UNIT	
MEDICAL UNIT	
FOOD UNIT	
9. OPERATIONS SECTION	
CHIEF	
DEPUTY	
a. BRANCH I – DIVISIONS/GROUPS	
BRANCH DIRECTOR	
DEPUTY	
DIVISION/GROUP	
DIVISION/GROUP	
DIVISION/GROUP	
DIVISION/GROUP	
DIVISION/GROUP	
b. BRANCH II – DIVISIONS/GROUPS	
BRANCH DIRECTOR	
DEPUTY	
DIVISION/GROUP	
DIVISION/GROUP	
DIVISION/GROUP	
DIVISION/GROUP	
DIVISION/GROUP	
c. BRANCH III – DIVISIONS/GROUPS	
BRANCH DIRECTOR	
DEPUTY	
DIVISION/GROUP	
DIVISION/GROUP	
DIVISION/GROUP	
DIVISION/GROUP	
DIVISION/GROUP	
d. AIR OPERATIONS BRANCH	
AIR OPERATIONS BR. DIR.	
AIR ATTACK SUPERVISOR	
AIR SUPPORT SUPERVISOR	
HELICOPTER COORDINATOR	
AIR TANKER COORDINATOR	
10. FINANCE SECTION	
CHIEF	
DEPUTY	
TIME UNIT	
PROCUREMENT UNIT	
COMPENSATION/CLAIMS UNIT	
COST UNIT	

ICS 203	PREPARED BY (RESOURCES UNIT)

Form S13-3

1. BRANCH	2. DIVISION/GROUP	**DIVISION ASSIGNMENT LIST** (ICS 204)
3. INCIDENT NAME		4. OPERATIONAL PERIOD DATE ______ TIME ______

5. OPERATIONS PERSONNEL

OPERATIONS CHIEF ______ DIVISION/GROUP SUPERVISOR ______

BRANCH DIRECTOR ______ AIR ATTACK SUPERVISOR ______

6. RESOURCES ASSIGNED THIS PERIOD

STRIKE TEAM/TASK FORCE/ RESOURCE DESIGNATOR	LEADER	NUMBER PERSONS	TRANS. NEEDED	DROP OFF PT./TIME	PICK UP PT./TIME

7. CONTROL OPERATIONS

8. SPECIAL INSTRUCTIONS

9. DIVISION/GROUP COMMUNICATION SUMMARY

FUNCTION		FREQ.	SYSTEM	CHAN.	FUNCTION		FREQ.	SYSTEM	CHAN.
COMMAND	LOCAL				SUPPORT	LOCAL			
	REPEAT					REPEAT			
DIV./GROUP TACTICAL					GROUND TO AIR				

PREPARED BY (RESOURCE UNIT LDR.)	APPROVED BY (PLANNING SECT. CH.)	DATE	TIME

Form S13-4

COMMUNICATIONS PLAN (ICS 205)	1. INCIDENT NAME	2. DATE/TIME PREPARED	3. OPERATIONAL PERIOD TO

4. COMMUNICATIONS RESOURCE ALLOCATION

SYSTEM/CACHE	TALK GROUP/ FREQUENCY	FUNCTION	KNOW POSITION CHANNEL/PHONE #	ASSIGNMENT	REMARKS

PREPARED BY (COMMUNICATIONS UNIT LEADER)

Form S13-5

MEDICAL PLAN (ICS 206)	1. INCIDENT NAME	2. DATE PREPARED	3. TIME PREPARED	4. OPERATIONAL PERIOD

5. INCIDENT MEDICAL AID STATIONS

MEDICAL AID STATIONS	LOCATION	PARAMEDICS	
		YES	NO

6. TRANSPORTATION

A. AMBULANCE SERVICES

NAME	ADDRESS	PHONE	PARAMEDICS	
			YES	NO

B. INCIDENT AMBULANCES

NAME	LOCATION	PARAMEDICS	
		YES	NO

7. HOSPITALS

NAME	ADDRESS	TRAVEL TIME		PHONE	HELIPAD		BURN CENTER	
		YES	NO		YES	NO	YES	NO

8. MEDICAL EMERGENCY PROCEDURES

ICS 206	9. PREPARED BY (MEDICAL UNIT LEADER)	10. REVIEWED BY (SAFETY OFFICER)

Form S13-6

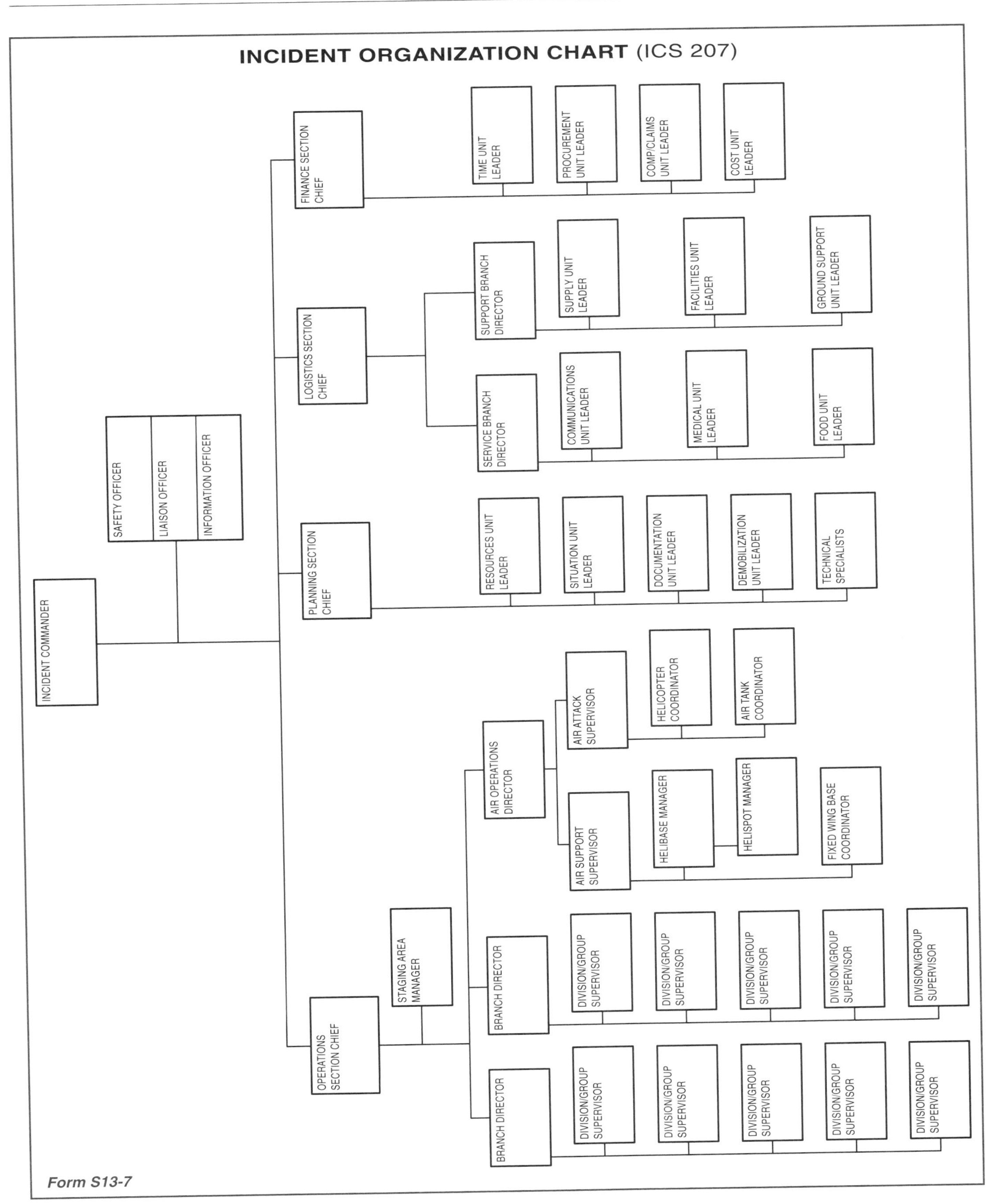
INCIDENT ORGANIZATION CHART (ICS 207)
INCIDENT COMMANDER
SAFETY OFFICER
LIAISON OFFICER
INFORMATION OFFICER
FINANCE SECTION CHIEF
TIME UNIT LEADER
PROCUREMENT UNIT LEADER
COMP/CLAIMS UNIT LEADER
COST UNIT LEADER
LOGISTICS SECTION CHIEF
SUPPORT BRANCH DIRECTOR
SUPPLY UNIT LEADER
FACILITIES UNIT LEADER
GROUND SUPPORT UNIT LEADER
SERVICE BRANCH DIRECTOR
COMMUNICATIONS UNIT LEADER
MEDICAL UNIT LEADER
FOOD UNIT LEADER
PLANNING SECTION CHIEF
RESOURCES UNIT LEADER
SITUATION UNIT LEADER
DOCUMENTATION UNIT LEADER
DEMOBILIZATION UNIT LEADER
TECHNICAL SPECIALISTS
AIR OPERATIONS DIRECTOR
AIR ATTACK SUPERVISOR
HELICOPTER COORDINATOR
AIR TANK COORDINATOR
AIR SUPPORT SUPERVISOR
HELIBASE MANAGER
HELISPOT MANAGER
FIXED WING BASE COORDINATOR
OPERATIONS SECTION CHIEF
STAGING AREA MANAGER
BRANCH DIRECTOR
DIVISION/GROUP SUPERVISOR
DIVISION/GROUP SUPERVISOR
DIVISION/GROUP SUPERVISOR
DIVISION/GROUP SUPERVISOR
DIVISION/GROUP SUPERVISOR
BRANCH DIRECTOR
DIVISION/GROUP SUPERVISOR
DIVISION/GROUP SUPERVISOR
DIVISION/GROUP SUPERVISOR
DIVISION/GROUP SUPERVISOR
DIVISION/GROUP SUPERVISOR

Form S13-7

INCIDENT STATUS SUMMARY (ICS 209)

1. INCIDENT NAME
2. INCIDENT NO.
3. INCIDENT COMMANDER
4. JURISDICTION
5. COUNTY

6. TYPE INCIDENT
7. LOCATION
8. STARTED (DATE/TIME)

9. CAUSE
10. AREA INVOLVED
11. PERCENT CONTAINED
12. EXPECTED CONTAINMENT Date ________ Time ________
13. PERCENT CONTROLLED
14. EXPECTED CONTROL Date ________ Time ________

15. CURRENT THREAT
16. CONTROL PROBLEMS

17. EST. LOSS
18. EST. SAVINGS
19. INJURIES ____________ DEATHS ____________
20. LINE BUILT
21. LINE TO BUILD

22. CURRENT WEATHER
WS | TEMP
WD | RH

23. PREDICTED WEATHER NEXT PERIOD
WS | TEMP
WD | RH

24. INCIDENT COSTS— PREVIOUS DAY
25. TOTAL COST TO DATE

26. AGENCIES / 27. RESOURCES																							TOTALS	
KIND OF RESOURCES	**INC**	**ST**	**INC**	**ST**	**INC**	**ST**	**INC**	**ST**	**INC**	**ST**	**INC**	**ST**	**INC**	**ST**	**INC**	**ST**	**INC**	**ST**	**INC**	**ST**	**INC**	**ST**	**INC**	**ST**
ENGINES																								
DOZERS																								
CREWS																								
HELICOPTERS																								
AIR TANKERS																								
TRUCK COS.																								
RESCUE/MED.																								
WATER TENDERS																								
OVERHEAD PERSONNEL																								
TOTAL PERSONNEL																								

28. COOPERATING AGENCIES

29. REMARKS

30. PREPARED BY
31. APPROVED BY
32. DATE ________ TIME ________
33. INITIAL ☐ UPDATE ☐ FINAL ☐
34. SENT TO DATE ______ TIME ______ BY ________

Form S13-8

Form S13-9

OPERATIONAL PLANNING WORKSHEET (ICS 215)

1. INCIDENT NAME	2. DATE PREPARED	3. OPERATIONAL PERIOD (DATE/TIME)
	TIME PREPARED	

4. DIVISION/ GROUP OR OTHER LOCATION	5. WORK ASSIGNMENTS		6. RESOURCES BY TYPE (SHOWN STRIKE TEAM AS ST) — ENGINES				WATER TENDERS		HAND CREWS		DOZERS			HELICOPTERS				AIR TANKERS			OTHER	7. REPORTING LOCATION	8. REQUESTED ARRIVAL TIME
			1	2	3	4	1	2	1	2	1	2	3	1	2	3	4	1	2	3			
		REQ.																					
		HAVE																					
		NEED																					
		REQ.																					
		HAVE																					
		NEED																					
		REQ.																					
		HAVE																					
		NEED																					
		REQ.																					
		HAVE																					
		NEED																					
		REQ.																					
		HAVE																					
		NEED																					
		REQ.																					
		HAVE																					
		NEED																					
		REQ.																					
		HAVE																					
		NEED																					
		REQ.																					
		HAVE																					
		NEED																					
		REQ.																					
		HAVE																					
		NEED																					
		REQ.																					
		HAVE																					
		NEED																					
	9. TOTAL RESOURCES REQ.	SINGLE RESOURCES / STRIKE TEAMS																				PREPARED BY (NAME AND POSITION)	
	TOTAL RESOURCES ON HAND																						
ICS 215	TOTAL RESOURCES NEEDED																						

CITY OF PHOENIX, ARIZONA
FIRE DEPARTMENT

EMS MEDICAL WORKSHEET

☐ 2 + 1 MEDICAL
☐ FIRST ALARM MEDICAL

INCIDENT NO. ____________

ADDRESS ______________________________ TIME ____________

INCIDENT TYPE ____________________

[1] [2] [3] [4] [5] [6] [7] [ ]

☐ INITIAL REPORT
☐ INITIATE COMMAND
☐ PERSONNEL PROTECTION
☐ TRIAGE
☐ EXTRICATION ☐ ALL CLEAR
☐ TREATMENT
☐ TRANSPORTATION
☐ TRAFFIC/CROWD CONTROL
☐ HOSPITAL NOTIFICATION
☐ SCENE STABILIZED
☐ PROGRESS REPORTS
☐ ____________________

COMMAND

FIRE DEPT		
EP		
EP		
EP		
E		
E		
L		
L		
R		
R		
BC		

RESCUE		
1		
2		
3		
4		

HELICOPTER		
1		
2		

EXTRICATION	TREATMENT	TRANSPORTATION	

PRIORITY 1	PRIORITY 2	PRIORITY 3	PRIORITY 4

PT # ______ PRIORITY ____________ UNIT(S) TREATING ____________ UNIT TRANSPORTING ____________ HOSPITAL ____________ INJURY ____________ NAME ____________ ADDRESS ____________ SEX ____________ AGE ____________	PT # ______ PRIORITY ____________ UNIT(S) TREATING ____________ UNIT TRANSPORTING ____________ HOSPITAL ____________ INJURY ____________ NAME ____________ ADDRESS ____________ SEX ____________ AGE ____________
PT # ______ PRIORITY ____________ UNIT(S) TREATING ____________ UNIT TRANSPORTING ____________ HOSPITAL ____________ INJURY ____________ NAME ____________ ADDRESS ____________ SEX ____________ AGE ____________	PT # ______ PRIORITY ____________ UNIT(S) TREATING ____________ UNIT TRANSPORTING ____________ HOSPITAL ____________ INJURY ____________ NAME ____________ ADDRESS ____________ SEX ____________ AGE ____________
PT # ______ PRIORITY ____________ UNIT(S) TREATING ____________ UNIT TRANSPORTING ____________ HOSPITAL ____________ INJURY ____________ NAME ____________ ADDRESS ____________ SEX ____________ AGE ____________	PT # ______ PRIORITY ____________ UNIT(S) TREATING ____________ UNIT TRANSPORTING ____________ HOSPITAL ____________ INJURY ____________ NAME ____________ ADDRESS ____________ SEX ____________ AGE ____________

92-45.2D Rev. 4/94
61582505824-CP

Form S13-10

TACTICAL WORKSHEET

Address: ______________________

Occupancy: ______________________

Incident No. ______________

Dispatch Time ______________

Wind Direction

____

Radio Channel ______________

Elapsed Time

5 10 15 20 25 30 PAR

Level II Staging Loc.

____

Personnel Accountability
(PAR)

All Clear
Under Control
Off-To-Def
30 Min.
Hazardous Event
Missing Fire Fighter
No "PAR" Upgrade Assign.

Benchmarks

Tactical

- ☐ Strategy / Offense-Defense
- ☐ Action Plan
- ☐ Fire Attack
- ☐ Search & Rescue
- ☐ **All Clear (PAR)**
- ☐ **Fire Control (PAR)**
- ☐ Water Supply
- ☐ Pumped Water
- ☐ Property Conservation
- ☐ **Loss Stopped**
- ☐ Ventilation
- ☐ Exposures
- ☐ Rapid Intervention Crew (RIC)

Functional

- ☐ Accountability
- ☐ Command Location
- ☐ Evacuation
- ☐ Logistics
- ☐ Gas
- ☐ Electrical
- ☐ Recon
- ☐ Investigator
- ☐ Police
- ☐ Outside Agency
- ☐ Occupant Services
- ☐ Red Cross
- ☐ **Secondary All Clear**

Branch

Command

Branch

92-121D Rev. 10/96
61582506681-CP

Form S13-11

POST-INCIDENT REVIEW WORKSHEET

Units / Disp.	From Quarters?	Turnouts / When?	Account. / Locations	Staged Per S.O.P.s / Assignment

Inc. # ______________
Date ______________

Strategy (Offensive or Defensive) (Marginal* *rescue only*) **RIC Team** ______________

Initial ____________ 10 min. ____________ 20 min. ____________ 30 min. ____________

Command Mode (Command-Fast Attack-Nothing Showing)? ______________________ Crew Assign. ______________________

On-scene Report: ____

Incident Command Roll Call

Initial IC ____________ IC#2 ____________ IC#3 ____________ IC#4 ____________ SO ____________ SA ____________

Incident Action Plan: ____

Water Supply: Initial (1st Eng.?) ________________ 2nd Supply ________________ Pumped ________________

Benchmarks: All Clear *(PAR)* ___________ Fire Control *(PAR)* ___________ Loss Stopped___________ 30 min *(PAR)* ___________

Progress Reports: (yes or no) ___________ (Change Plan?) ______________________

Ventilation: Who? _________ PPV _________ Vertical _________ Other _________ **Utilities Secured:** ____________

Reason? ____

Effectiveness ____

Property Conservation: Who? _________ Occ. Serv. _________ Salvage _________ Overhaul _________ Red Cross _________

Customer Response ____

Structural/Fire Evaluation: ____

Rehabilitation/RIC Activities: ____

Accidents, Injuries/Near Misses: ____

Comments: ____

____

____

____

____

Fire Fighter Safety, Loss Control, and Customer Service are ongoing throughout the incident.

92-121D Rev 10/96
61582506681-CP

Form S13-12

Index

-D-

-E-

-I-

-K-

-L-

-M-